Standard Catalogue of British Coins

# COINS OF
# ENGLAND

## AND
## THE UNITED KINGDOM

**40th Edition**

**SPINK**
LONDON

A Catalogue of the Coins of Great Britain
and Ireland
*first published 1929*

Standard Catalogue of British Coins
Coins of England and the United Kingdom
*40th edition, 2005*

© Spink & Son Ltd, 2004
69 Southampton Row, Bloomsbury
London WC1B 4ET

Typeset by Design to Print UK Ltd,
The Studio, Forge House, Lower Road, Forest Row, East Sussex RH18 5HE
Printed in Great Britain by
Cromwell Press
Trowbridge
Wiltshire

ISBN 1 902040 59 7

# CONTENTS

# CONTENTS

# PREFACE

It was with some degree of surprise that we realised that this edition was to be both the 40th edition of this catalogue and the 75th anniversary of its first publication in 1929. This led us to look at copies of old editions going back to the original in 1929 to see how the catalogue has changed and developed over the years.

The very first edition in 1929 was issued as a paper cover booklet with a cover price of 6d. and was entitled *Catalogue of the Coins of Great Britain and Ireland*. It later became the *Standard Catalogue of the Coins of Great Britain and Ireland* in 1945 which was written by Herbert Allen Seaby between air raids, whilst in Air Raid Precautions Control Room in North London. So popular was this edition that it ran to three impressions, reprinted in 1947 and 1949.

These early editions were basically pricelists of coins held in stock at the time of going to press, but also with prices offered for sought after items. One example being the 1936 edition which offered no less than £200 at the time for a specimen of the gold penny of Edward the Confessor (S.1178), an amount approximately equivalent in today's monetary terms to £11,000; a huge sum of money at the time for a coin, considering what that amount of money would have bought in 1936.

Editions were surprisingly regular from 1929 up to the outbreak of war in 1939, there being a new edition approximately every two years, resuming on a bi-annual basis with the publication of the 1945 edition.

It was in 1962 that the Scottish, Irish, Anglo-Gallic and coins of the Islands were taken out of the catalogue and published separately and the catalogue became known as the *Standard Catalogue of British Coins*, volume 1. England and the United Kingdom that is, excluding Scottish, Irish and the Island Coinages. Its editor then was Peter Seaby and this 1962 edition became the first edition of the new series which was then published annually through to 1976. It was this 1962 edition which first saw the introduction of photographic illustrations in place of the beautiful line-drawings which had previously been used.

It is amusing to note that in the introduction to the 1952 edition it was mentioned that 'generally speaking the prices of hammered gold have been lowered' and in the Market Trends in our 2004 edition we stated 'Hammered gold continues to be a robust market, the average price having risen 18% (2002 15%) in twelve months.... our opinion is that hammered gold is now at a far more realistic level than it was five years ago but is by no means overpriced.' As with everything, trends change and prices rise and fall accordingly, dictated to by supply and demand and also individual taste.

Looking back over the last seven years since Spink took over this title from Seaby, it is incredible to note the improvement of the catalogue. Now at nearly 550 pages, packed with information it is difficult to see how to improve the catalogue significantly. It is however our intention in time to produce a full colour edition, which involves the enormous undertaking of replacing every single photograph in the catalogue.

We are certain though that this new 40th edition will again remain the standard and most up-to-date reference and that you will find this edition extremely beneficial whatever your requirements are. Be it from valuing your collection, identifying coins which you have found or helping you make a start on this fascinating, rewarding and educating hobby.

Our website www.spink.com continues to be a useful resource for collectors, with details of our regular auctions and items listed for sale at fixed prices. Also featured is a large selection of books for sale, covering all aspects of coin collecting from the beginner's level to the specialist.

We receive many comments each year on our catalogue, mostly complimentary, but we do still appreciate all the information supplied by collectors and specialists which continually helps to improve and sometimes correct the information herein. So if you have any comments on Spink's *Coins of England* please address them to: **The Editor, *Coins of England,* Spink & Son Ltd., 69 Southampton Row, Bloomsbury, London WC1B 4ET.**

Last, but not least, thanks are again due to the contributing specialists in their respective areas, May Sinclair, Steve Hill, Paul Hill and Geoff Kitchen.

Philip Skingley
Editor, Coins of England

# INTRODUCTION

## Arrangement

The arrangement of this catalogue is not completely uniform, but generally it is divided into metals (gold, silver, copper, etc) under each reign, then into coinages, denominations and varieties. In the Celtic section the uninscribed coins are listed before the dynastic coins; under Charles II all the hammered coins precede the milled coinage; the reign of George III is divided into coins issued up to 1816 and the new coinage from 1816 to the end of the reign; and under Elizabeth II the decimal issues are separated from the pre-decimal (£.s.d.) coinages.

Every major coin type is listed though not every variety. We have endeavoured to give rather more coverage to the varieties of relatively common coins, such as the pennies of Edward I, II and III, than to the very much rarer coins of, for instance, King Offa of Mercia.

## Values

The values given represent the range of retail prices at which coins are being offered for sale at the time of going to press and **not** the price which a dealer will pay for those coins. These prices are based on our knowledge of the numismatic market, the current demand for particular coins, recent auction sale prices and, in those cases where certain coins have not appeared for sale for some years, our estimation of what they would be likely to sell at today, bearing in mind their rarity and appeal in relation to somewhat similar coins where a current value is known. Values are given for two grades of preservation from the Celtic period onwards and three to four grades of preservation for coins of the 17th to the 20th century.

Collectors normally require coins in the best condition they can afford and, except in the case of a really rare coin, a piece that is considerably worn is not wanted and has little value. The values given in the catalogue are for the exact state of preservation stated at the head of each column and bearing in mind that a score of identical coins in varying states of wear could be lined up in descending order from mint condition (FDC, *fleur de coin*), through very fine (VF) to *poor* state. It will be realized that only in certain instances will the values given apply to particular coins. A 'fine' (F) coin may be worth anything between one quarter and a half of the price quoted for a 'very fine' (VF); on the other hand, a piece in really mint condition will be valued substantially higher than the price quoted for 'extremely fine' (EF). The designation BV has been adopted for coins whose value on the market has yet to exceed its bullion value. Purchasing sovereigns, catalogued as BV, will attract a dealers' premium.

We emphasize again that the purpose of this catalogue is to give a general value for a particular class of coin in a specified state of preservation, and also to give the collector an idea of the range and value of coins in the English series. The value of any particular piece depends on three things:

Its exact design, legend, mintmark or date.

Its exact state of preservation; this is of prime importance.

The demand for it in the market at any given time.

Some minor varieties are much scarcer than others and, as the number of coins issued varies considerably from year to year, coins of certain dates and mintmarks are rarer and of more value than other pieces of similar type. The prices given for any type are for the commonest variety, mintmark or date of that type.

## The Scope

Coin collecting, numismatics, is a fascinating hobby. It requires very little physical exertion and only as much mental effort as one wishes or is able to put into it at any time. There is vast scope and boundless ramifications and byways encompassing not only things historical and geographical, but also touching on economics, metallurgy, heraldry, literature, the fine arts, politics, military history and many other disciplines. This catalogue is solely concerned with British coinage from its earliest times right up to date. From the start the beginner should appreciate that the coinage of our own nation may be seen as a small but very important part of the whole story of world currency.

The first coins, made of electrum, a natural alloy of gold and silver, were issued in western Asia Minor (Lydia) in the later seventh century B.C. Over the next century or so coinage of gold and silver spread across the Aegean to mainland Greece, southwards to the eastern Mediterranean lands and eventually westward to the Greek colonies in southern Italy, Sicily (Magna Graecia) and beyond. The coins of the Greeks are noted for their beautiful, sometimes exquisite craftsmanship, with many of the coin types depicting the patron deities of their cities. Coins of Philip II of Macedon (359-336 B.C.), father of Alexander the Great, circulated amongst the Celtic peoples of the Danubian Basin and were widely copied through central Europe and by the Gauls in France. Gold Gaulish staters were reaching Britain around the beginning of the first century B.C. and the earliest gold to be struck in the island must have been produced shortly afterwards. Although their types and designs copy the Apollo head and racing charioteer of Philip II's gold coins, they are stylistically much removed from the original representation and very individually Celtic in concept.

The coins of the Romans cover some seven centuries and include an enormous number of different types that were current throughout a major part of the civilized world from Spain to Syria and from the Rhine in the north to the Sudan in the south. The Roman province of Britain was part of this vast empire for four hundred years from AD 43 until the early fifth century. Innumerable Roman coins have been recovered from sites in this country, most being made of brass or bronze. Many of these are quite inexpensive and very collectable. In recent years many hoards of gold and silver coins have been found, usually by use of metal detectors.

Following the revival of commerce after the Dark Ages, coinage in Western Europe was virtually restricted to silver until the thirteenth century, though gold was still being minted in Byzantium and in the Islamic world. In the Middle Ages many European cities had their own distinctive coinage and money was issued not only by the kings but also by nobles, bishops and abbots. From the time of the later Crusades gold returned to the West, and the artistic developments of the Renaissance in the fifteenth century brought improved portraiture and new minting techniques.

Large silver crown-size thalers were first minted at Joachimsthal in Bohemia early in the sixteenth century. The substantial shipments of silver coming to Europe from the mines of Spanish America over the next couple of centuries led to a fine series of larger coins being issued by the European states and cities. The larger size allowed greater artistic freedom in the designs and the portraits on the coins.

Both Germany and Italy became unified nation states during the later nineteenth century, thereby substantially reducing the number of mints and coin types. Balancing the reduction in European minting authorities were the new coins that were issued by the independent states of South and Central America. Since the 1950s many new nations have established their independence and their coinage provides a large field for the collector of modern coins.

It can be seen that the scope for the collector is truly vast, but besides the general run of official coinage there is also the large series of token coins—small change unofficially produced to supplement the inadequate supply of authorized currency. These tokens were issued by merchants, innkeepers and manufacturers in many towns and villages in the seventeenth, eighteenth and nineteenth centuries and many collectors specialize in their local issues.

Some coins have designs of a commemorative nature; an example being the Royal Wedding crown of 1981, but there are also large numbers of commemorative medals which, though never intended for use as coinage, are sometimes confused with coins because they are metal objects of a similar shape and sometimes a similar size to coins. This is another interesting field for collectors as these medals often have excellent portraits of famous men or women, or they may commemorate important events or scientific discoveries. Other metallic objects of coin-like appearance that can be confusing for the beginner are reckoning counters, advertising tickets, various other tickets and passes, and items such as brass coin weights.

## Minting processes

From the time of the earliest Greek coins in the late seventh century BC to about the middle of the sixteenth century AD, coins were made by hand. The method of manufacture was simple. The obverse and reverse designs were engraved or punched into the prepared ends of two bars of bronze or iron, shaped or tapered to the diameter of the required coin. The obverse die, known as the *pile,* was usually spiked so that it could be anchored firmly into a block of wood or metal. The reverse die, the *trussel,* was held by hand or grasped by tongs.

The coin was struck by placing a metal blank between the two dies and striking the trussel with a hammer. Thus, all coinage struck by this method is known as 'hammered'. Some dies are known to have been hinged so there would be an exact register between the upper and lower die. Usually a 'pair of dies' consisted of one obverse die (normally the more difficult to make because it had the finer detail, such as the ruler's portrait) and two reverse dies. This was because the shaft of iron bearing the reverse design eventually split under the constant hammering; two reverse dies were usually needed to last out the life of the obverse die.

Some time toward the middle of the sixteenth century, experiments, first in Germany and later in France, resulted in the manufacture of coins by machinery.

The term 'milled', which is applied to all machine-made coins, comes from the type of machinery used – the mill and screw press. With this machinery the obverse die was fixed as the lower die and the reverse die brought down into contact with the blank by heavy vertical pressure applied by a screw or worm-drive connected to a cross bar with heavy weights at each end. These weights usually had long leather thongs attached which allowed a more powerful force to be applied by the operators who revolved the arms of the press. New blanks were placed on the lower die and the struck coins were removed by hand. The screw press brought more pressure to bear on the blanks and this pressure was evenly applied, producing a far better and sharper coin.

Various attempts were made during the reigns of Elizabeth I and Charles I to introduce this type of machinery with its vastly superior products. Unfortunately problems associated with the manufacture of blanks to a uniform weight greatly reduced the rate of striking and the hand manufacture of coins continued until the Restoration in 1660, when Charles II brought to London from Holland the Roettiers brothers and their improved screw press.

The first English coins made for circulation by this new method were the silver crowns of 1662, which bore an inscription on the edge, DECVS ET TVTAMEN, 'an ornament and a safeguard', a reference to the fact that the new coins could not be clipped, a crime made easy by the thin and often badly struck hammered coins.

The mill and screw press was used until new steam-powered machinery made by Boulton and Watt was installed in the new mint on Tower Hill in London. This machinery had been used most successfully by Boulton to strike the large 'cartwheel' two- and one-penny pieces of 1797 and other coins, including 'overstriking' Spanish *eight-reale* pieces into Bank of England 'dollars' since the old Mint presses were not able to exert sufficient power to do this. This new machinery was first used at the Mint to strike the 'new coinage' halfcrowns of 1816, and it operated at a far greater speed than the old type of mill and screw presses and achieved a greater sharpness of design.

The very latest coining presses now operating at the Royal Mint at Llantrisant in South Wales, are capable of striking at a rate of up to 800 coins a minute.

## Condition

One of the more difficult problems for the beginner is to assess accurately the condition of a coin. A common fault among collectors is to overgrade and, consequently, to overvalue their coins.

Most dealers will gladly spare a few minutes to help new collectors. Many dealers issue price lists with illustrations, enabling collectors to see exactly what the coins look like and how they have been graded.

Coins cannot always be graded according to precise rules. Hammered coins often look weak or worn on the high parts of the portrait and the tops of the letters; this can be due to weak striking or worn dies and is not always attributable to wear through long use in circulation. Milled coins usually leave the Mint sharply struck so that genuine wear is easier to detect. However a x5 or x10 magnifying glass is essential, especially when grading coins of Edward VII and George V where the relief is very low on the portraits and some skill is required to distinguish between an uncirculated coin and one in EF condition.

The condition or grade of preservation of a coin is usually of greater importance than its rarity. By this we mean that a common coin in superb condition is often more desirable and more highly priced than a rarity in poor condition. Coins that have been pierced or mounted as a piece of jewellery generally have little interest to collectors.

One must also be on the lookout for coins that have been 'plugged', i.e. that have been pierced at some time and have had the hole filled in, sometimes with the missing design or letters re-engraved.

Badly cleaned coins will often display a complexity of fine interlaced lines and such coins have a greatly reduced value. It is also known for coins to be tooled or re-engraved on the high parts of the hair, in order to 'increase' the grade of coin and its value. In general it is better to have a slightly more worn coin than a better example with such damage.

## Cleaning coins

Speaking generally, *do not* clean coins. More coins are ruined by injudicious cleaning than through any other cause, and a badly cleaned coin loses much of its value. A nicely toned piece is usually considered desirable. Really dirty gold and silver can, however, be carefully washed in soap and water. Copper coins should never be cleaned or washed, they may be lightly brushed with a brush that is not too harsh.

## Buying and selling coins

Exchanging coins with other collectors, searching around the antique shops, telling your relatives and friends that you are interested in coins, or even trying to find your own with a metal detector, are all ways of adding to your collection. However, the time will come when the serious collector needs to acquire specific coins or requires advice on the authenticity or value of a coin.

At this point an expert is needed, and the services of a reputable coin dealer are necessary. There are now a large number of coin dealers in the UK, many of whom belong to the B.N.T.A. (The British Numismatic Trade Association) or the I.A.P.N. (The International Association of Professional Numismatists) and a glance through the 'yellow pages' under 'coin dealer' or 'numismatist' will often provide local information. Many dealers publish their own lists of coins. Studying these lists is a good way for a collector to learn about coins and to classify and catalogue their own collections.

*The Standard Catalogue of Coins of England and the UK* has been published since 1929. It serves as a price guide for all coin collectors. Spink also publish books on many aspects of English, Greek, Roman and Byzantine coins and on British tokens which serve as a valuable source of information for coin collectors. Our books are available directly from Spink or through reputable booksellers. Many branches of W. H. Smith, and other High Street booksellers, stock copies of *The Standard Catalogue*.

## Numismatic Clubs and Societies

There are well over one hundred numismatic societies and clubs in the British Isles. For details of how to contact them see page 509. Joining one is the best way to meet fellow enthusiasts, learn about your coins and other series and acquire coins in a friendly and informative way.

## Useful suggestions

*Security and insurance.* The careful collector should not keep valuable coins at home unless they are insured and have adequate protection. Local police and insurance companies will give advice on what precautions may be necessary.

Most insurance companies will accept a valuation based on *The Standard Catalogue*. It is usually possible to have the amount added to a householder's contents policy but particularly valuable individual coins may have to be separately listed. A 'Fire, Burglary and Theft' policy will cover loss only from the insured's address, but an 'All Risks' policy will usually cover accidental damage and loss anywhere within the U.K.

For coins deposited with a bank or placed in a safe-deposit box a lower insurance premium is usually payable.

*Keeping a record.* All collectors are advised to have an up-to-date record of their collection and, if possible, photographs of the more important and more easily identifiable coins. This should be kept in a separate place from the collection so that a list and photographs can be given to the police should loss occur. Note the price paid, from whom purchased, the date of acquisition and the condition of the coin.

*Storage and handling.* New collectors should get into the habit of handling coins by the edge. This is especially important as far as highly polished proof coins are concerned.

Collectors may initially keep their coins in paper or plastic envelopes housed in boxes, albums or special containers. Many collectors will eventually wish to own a hardwood coin cabinet in which the collection can be properly arranged and displayed. If a home-made cabinet is being constructed avoid using oak and cedar wood; mahogany, walnut and rosewood are ideal. It is important that coins are not kept in a humid atmosphere; especial care must be taken with copper and bronze coins which are very susceptible to damp or condensation which may result in a green verdigris forming on them.

### From beginner to numismatist
The new collector can best advance to becoming an experienced numismatist by examining as many coins as possible, noting their distinctive features and by learning to use the many books of reference that are available. It will be an advantage to join a local numismatic society, as this will provide an opportunity for meeting other enthusiasts and obtaining advice from more experienced collectors. Most societies have a varied programme of lectures, exhibitions and occasional auctions of members' duplicates.

Those who become members of one or both of the national societies, the Royal Numismatic Society and the British Numismatic Society, receive an annual journal containing authoritative papers and have access to the societies' library and programme of lectures.

Many museums have coin collections available for study, although they may not always be displayed, and a number of museum curators are qualified numismatists.

# ABBREVIATIONS

| | | | |
|---|---|---|---|
| Archb. | Archbishop | laur. | laureate |
| Æ | bronze | *mm.* | *mintmark* |
| AR | silver | mon. | monogram |
| A/ | gold | *O., obv.* | obverse |
| Bp. | Bishop | p. | new penny, pence |
| BV | bullion value | pl | plume |
| cuir. | cuirassed | quat. | quatrefoil |
| d. | penny, pence | qtr. | quarter |
| diad. | diademed | rad. | radiate |
| dr. | draped | R., *rev.* | reverse |
| ex. | exergue | r. | right |
| grs. | grains | s. | shillings |
| hd. | head | trun. | truncation |
| i.c. | inner circle | var. | variety |
| illus. | illustration | wt. | weight |
| l. | left | | |

The market in British coins continues to be a strong one, with widespread price rises again being a feature of this catalogue. The average price for a coin in VF condition has risen by 7.5% (2004 15%) in the last year, and rises outnumber falls by 60% to 10% (2004 90% to 2%). Attractive type coins in the more popular series are now realizing three times the prices that they would have commanded five years ago. In a healthy development, however, there have been few of the startling new records set in 2003, and this year has been more one of consolidation than of dramatic advance. A considerable quantity of material has been offered and this has enabled the market to confirm that the gains of the last five years are not due to temporary conditions but that they represent a solid basis for future growth.

The most important development is that the market is now confident that coins are now more likely to appreciate or to hold their value than to fall. The British coin market is not, and has never been, a monolithic entity which moves as a single bloc. At any one time the chances of supply and demand means that some series, denominations, metals or types of coin will be more in demand than others, and some will be consolidating or falling in price while others are advancing. The fact that 10% of the VF catalogue entries have fallen this year, albeit slightly, confirms this point. The expectation though is now that on average a British coin will hold its value or appreciate. Once this expectation is established, the expenditure, whether of £500 or £50,000, on purchasing a coin is no longer seen as an outright risk.

Two factors underpin this confidence. The first is that this is now the established trend, and trends are, in the absence of an external shock, more likely to continue than to end. For much of the 1980s and 1990s it could plausibly have been argued that the collecting of British coins, as a serious endeavour, was a thing of the past. The decline in the collecting instinct, difficulty of storage and display, and the move towards museum rather than private ownership had brought a proud tradition to an end. This has proved not to be the case. The beauty, rarity and historical fascination of the series has won through and re-ignited the desire to obtain a representative or even an important collection. Britain is one of the most successful economies in the world today, with a GDP per head higher than any other EU country apart from Luxemburg and the potential demand for good British coins remains enormous in comparison to the supply. Thus, a good F Charles I gold triple unite, an honest but not spectacular piece, was pushed to £9,400 in Spink Auction 168. The same coin sold for £3,340 when last offered by Glendining's, in February 1999. In January 2004 a finer example, almost EF but not one of the best, fetched £20,500 in a UBS auction in Basel, nearly twice the price that would have been realised the year before.

The other factor is that good British coins, despite the recent advance in price levels, remain cheap both in historic terms and by comparison to other classes of asset. An overheated market, the dot-com boom of 2000 or, to a degree, the current housing market, is often revealed by the new reasons, the famous 'paradigm shift' put forward to explain unprecedented valuations. No such reasons are required to account for the strength of the British coin market, indeed the traditional inducements to buy – 'you may never see another' etc, are conspicuous by their absence. Often the collector is keener to buy than the dealer is to sell. The most dramatic gulf in asset values remains that between the prices placed on houses and those for historic coins. These are different types of asset, but they are ones which can be compared over many years and houses now command a ten-fold premium over the price of British coins compared to the last true market high in 1974. Yet it is extraordinary that the rarest and most important coin in the British series would not realise the price of a one bedroom flat in most London boroughs, though it is unlikely that this anomaly will continue for much longer.

Every market has a risk, and the risk to the continuing prosperity of the British coin market remains its heavy dependence on auctions. Auctioneers, like estate agents, prosper in good times but take no financial interest when buyers fail to turn up or markets turn choppy. Confidence is much dependent on the knowledge that an asset remains liquid, that a coin, even if recently purchased, can be readily sold for a price not completely unrelated to its cost. An illiquid asset loses a considerable part of its attraction and value. In recent years the Spink Numismatic Circular has become increasingly popular among collectors for offering a broad range of material at fixed prices, 4,500 items with a list total of £2.2 million in the last twelve months, and providing an alternative for the many who do not find auctions the most satisfying medium through which to add to or dispose of their collections.

The 2003/4 season, with the notable exception of the Marshall collection[1], lacked the range of big name sales which were such a feature of 2002/3. Despite this, both the value of British coins offered, and their number sold, rose by more than ten percent, and ample fresh material became available to maintain the interest of collectors and to test the firmness of the price advances of recent years.

Turning the focus to individual categories within the English series, Celtic coins are the smallest sector of the British market, and remain a difficult one, for they are chronologically detached from the main series by nearly six hundred years of Roman and Dark Age rule. This year, an attempt has been made to market Celtic coins as part of the pan-European market for Ancient coins rather than part of the British series. This approach has always had strengths and weaknesses. The advantage is that prices for artistic, high quality large denominations are much higher in the Ancient market. The disadvantage is that there are relatively few such coins in the Celtic series and that the small denominations, and the minor varieties, in which it abounds are rather less sought after, and are indeed in the lower grades virtually unwanted. The result has been a few strong prices, noticeably in Triton VII where a picked selection of attractive coins including a lovely Cunobeline Biga Stater, sold almost en bloc to an Italian dealer, but also unusually high unsold percentages. On average, prices for Celtic coins in top condition have advanced slightly, in VF condition have remained stable, and in F condition have fallen by about 5%.

The Saxon and Norman series, in contrast, continues to recover strongly from its low of five years ago and good coins, undamaged and without the surface corrosion associated with many ground finds, are much sought after. The Marshall collection contained a small group of Saxon and Norman pieces, including an EF flower type penny of Edward the Elder by the moneyer Buga, S.1079, and an unusually fine example of the strange Stephen 'martlets' type penny struck by the moneyer Walkelin at Derby, S.1298. The last flower type penny, an almost identical coin in the Stack collection in 1999, sold for £2,970. The Marshall piece in 2004 sold for £11,000. The Stephen martlets penny also comfortably eclipsed the £4,450 realized by Lockett/Conte example in 2001, and sold for £7,820.

The strongest section of this market is the commonest, the standard late Saxon and early Norman pennies of kings such as Eadgar, Aethelred II, Edward the Confessor and William I. These used to be plentiful, and almost disregarded, but have almost disappeared from dealer's trays, a sure sign of demand and attractive toned examples can now sell for £500. These coins have the added interest of a place of mintage and collecting mints, for more than twenty years a peripheral interest, is again attracting attention. At the last peak in this market, in the 1970s, a rare mint was as expensive as a rare type coin and this history may be repeated. An Edward the Confessor penny of Bedwyn, good VF, sold in the 2002 Conte sale for £720. Another of the same type, sold in June 2004, but in lower condition, was much sought after at £940, at least twice the grade-adjusted price.

---

[1] Spink Auction 167, a very attractive run of British coins, purchased with an eye for quality largely from the Spink Numismatic Circular in the 1940s.

Many coins represented by Standard Catalogue numbers in the Saxon and Norman series are, if not absolutely unique, extremely rare on the market and pricing remains a matter of informed guesswork. Of particular interest is the market reaction to a new source of supply, such as hoards or metal detector finds. The general rule is that, where a coin is commended only by its rarity, and other pieces of the same ruler/denomination/mint are available, any significant increase in supply will cause the price to fall. In contrast if the type is a pleasing and historical one then a larger supply may increase its marketability and value. Early Anglo-Saxon 'Witmen' and 'Two Emperors' thrymsas have recently become much commoner, thanks to finds, while other thrymsa types remain rare. It is possible, as a result, either that all thrymsas will depreciate, now that the denomination per se is no longer difficult to obtain, that the commoner types will fall relative to those that remain rare, or that all thrymsas will benefit from increased collectability. Auction records suggest the second scenario is correct. 'Witmen' thrymsas, at bottom rather dull coins, are now falling in price, while the other types of thrymsa are sufficiently differentiated that their prices are continuing to rise. In contrast the recent appearance of possibly a dozen new pennies of Stephen type IV, S.1301, has had a marked effect. Much more attractive coins of Stephen are available and now this variety is no longer a great rarity, it has registered a considerable fall, from £3,000 to £2,000, in VF catalogue value.

One of the most interesting numismatic offerings of the year was the first portion of the Jeffrey Mass collection of short cross pennies, Henry II to Henry III, sold in March 2004. Long a niche market with a devoted, if budget conscious, following, this sale took short cross pennies into the main stream of collecting. This trend was greatly aided by the fact that Professor Mass had, just before his death, completed the superb sylloge volume, SCBI 56, of his collection. This sale has provided revised catalogue prices for many of the rarer mints and varieties, but was dominated by a single buyer who, as is often the case, while expending more than half the total realised, was unsuccessful on many of the better pieces. The bargain of the sale was the most expensive coin, a superb Canterbury penny of the very curious and rare Henry III type 6x, which sold for just over £1,000, the first short cross penny ever to reach this benchmark.

Hammered gold continues to be a robust market, average VF prices having risen 10% (2003 15%) during the year and, as noted above, many coins in this series now realise three times the prices of five years ago. An interesting feature of this market is that a number of established collectors, who may not have purchased gold coins in the past, have taken the view that a few good pieces would make an attractive and complementary addition to their existing collections. The medieval gold market has been tested in the last year or so by the large hoard of nobles, predominantly of Edward III and Richard II, but including at least six heavy nobles of Henry IV, which has turned up on the Continent. Henry IV heavy nobles were struck immediately before the reduction in weight standard in 1412, and consequently few have survived, a fact reflected by the £12,000 VF catalogue price for the 'normal' London issue. Usually it would be difficult to absorb six new examples of such a rarity, but all have sold and the VF catalogue price has risen slightly to £12,500.

A new class of buyer has recently emerged for hammered gold coins of exceptional quality. For many years, the traditional price for an extremely fine example was double that for a very fine gold coin, since hammered gold is often finely struck and attractive even in the lesser grade. The last year has seen fierce competition for the very best coins which has driven the extremely fine price well above this level. Spink Auction 168 realized £6,400 for a superb Henry VI York noble (S.1804, 2004 VF catalogue £1,650). Allan Davisson Auction 20 achieved £4,250 for an exceptional Edward IV Angel (S.2091, VF catalogue £1,000 - the same coin sold for £900 in 2001), and again Spink Auction 168 realized £10,350 for a magnificent Mary Angel (S.2490, VF catalogue £2,400). These are choice and desirable pieces, and it seems likely that the premium for the relatively few surviving coins in this very high grade is not going to diminish.

Medieval hammered silver, from Edward III to Henry VII, is an historically interesting, if difficult series, for the types fossilized and hardly evolved for one hundred and fifty years. Tthere are more catalogue entries in this section, some 570, than would now be justified if the Standard Catalogue were to be completely revised. As a result, many of the less obvious varieties have moved little in price for some time, and in lower grade have fallen, while the much smaller number of basic type coins have forged ahead. For the first time this year, no medieval groat lists at under £100 in VF condition (2004 Henry VI annulet issue groat, S.1836, £85), and the basic Henry V groat, S.1765, common (264 in the Reigate Hoard), but now difficult to obtain, has risen 25% to £375. The average coin in this series has risen by 2.5% in VF, but fallen by 5% in F.

Tudor portrait silver has been a strong market for several years and this trend, not surprisingly, has continued. The finest coin to be sold during the year, the magnificent portrait testoon of Henry VIII in the Marshall collection, realized £34,500, four times the previous record for the denomination. Like the Edward VI crown, sold for £41,400 in the Slaney sale in 2003, such a price disturbs the price levels for similar coins in the lesser grade. Since the Slaney sale, over fifty Edward VI crowns (S.2478) have been offered, and the price in good VF initially spiked sharply upwards but is now subsiding again. This year the VF catalogue price for an Edward VI crown has advanced by a very modest £100 to £1,750. The catalogue price for the Henry VIII testoon (S.2364) has risen sharply, from £650 to £850 in F, and from £2,500 to £4,000 in VF. The reason being that these are scarce coins, struck in reasonable metal which are quite presentable even in F condition. In contrast the baser testoons (S.2365) have advanced by much less, 20% in VF and hardly at all in F, since they tend to be poorly struck with little eye appeal in the lower grades. Exceptional prices continue to be realized for Elizabeth I sixpences with strong portraits, it is not unusual to see £750 for this very common coin in approaching EF condition. This is the price for a 'one-off' purchase of an Elizabeth I portrait, and few will collect the series by date at this level.

Stuart silver coins, particularly Charles I provincial issues, have also performed solidly, rising on average by 12.5% in VF and by nearly 10% in F. Curiously Charles I provincial has been strongest at the commonest level, the coins of the York mint and the plentiful small denominations of the Aberystwyth mint. It is partly that these coins remain reasonably freely available and feature in most auctions, but the Marshall collection contained a useful representative selection of the rarer mints and these sold for what, by modern standards, were relatively modest prices. It is certainly not true that every coin at auction fetches a high price. There are often bargains in even the most important sale and the most imposing dealer's list.

Milled coins, particularly early milled silver, have been one of the most active sections of the market in the last year, with a very considerable quantity of high quality material available, and strong two way business. We have recorded a remarkable 133 gold five guinea pieces offered in the last twelve months alone. Catalogue prices for milled coins in all metals, with the exception of twentieth century, have risen in the higher grades, EF and UNC, by 10% on average, and have remained stable in F and VF. There has always been some overlap of collector interest between the later hammered and the early milled coinage, up to George II, and with the broadening of collector interests, this has become more pronounced. The result is that prices in these series are synchronised to a greater extent than at some periods in the past. The high prices for hammered gold in the last three years has encouraged growth in demand for comparable milled gold, which had begun to look cheap by comparison and in the last year prices for high quality milled gold has largely caught up. Price levels for the very best milled coins are, in comparison to ordinary examples, now quite as rarefied as those for their hammered equivalents. The £22,000 paid in the Marshall sale for the best known Charles II 1681 elephant and castle halfcrown is but a dramatic example, but it is still important to realize that these levels only apply to the very best and that values fall away steeply for pieces that are not quite so fine.

The market for British coins is, and we have reason to expect will continue to be, a strong and healthy one, which offers many opportunities for assembling a pleasing and rewarding collection. Accurate grading, however, remains a key skill and confidence in this regard accounts in part for the substantial premium given for those coins which have passed muster by the great collectors of the past. The incentive for a dealer or auctioneer to 'stretch' grades in a rising market is substantial, whether conscious or not, and the opportunity for a collector to examine and handle top quality coins, either from a major private collection or in the best museum holdings, will always prove to be worthwhile.

# SOME NUMISMATIC TERMS EXPLAINED

| | |
|---|---|
| Obverse | That side of the coin which normally shows the monarch's head or name. |
| Reverse | The side opposite to the obverse, the 'Tails'. |
| Blank | The coin as a blank piece of metal, i.e. before it is struck. |
| Flan | The whole piece of metal after striking. |
| Type | The main, central design. |
| Legend | The inscription. Coins lacking a legend are called 'mute' or anepigraphic. |
| Field | That flat part of the coin between the main design and the inscription or edge. |
| Exergue | That part of the coin below the main design, usually separated by a horizontal line, and normally occupied by the date. |
| Die | The block of metal, with design cut into it, which actually impresses the coin blank with the design. |
| Die variety | Coin showing slight variation of design. |
| Mule | A coin with the current type on one side and the previous (and usually obsolete) type on the other side, or a piece struck from two dies that are not normally used together. |
| Graining or reeding | The crenellations around the edge of the coin, commonly known as 'milling'. |
| Proof | Carefully struck coin from special dies with a mirror-like or matt surface. (In this country 'Proof' is *not* a term used to describe the state of preservation, but the method of striking.) |
| Hammered | Refers to the old craft method of striking a coin between dies hammered by hand. |
| Milled | Coins struck by dies worked in a coining press. The presses were hand powered from 1560-1800, powered by steam from 1790 and by electricity from 1895. |

The Celtic or Ancient British issues are amongst the most interesting and varied of all British coins. They are our earliest coins and are the product of a society that left no historical sources of its own. It is therefore often difficult to be specific about for whom, when or where they were produced. Despite only being used for approximately a hundred and fifty years they do provide a rich variety of designs and types in gold, silver and bronze. Collectors looking for a theme to concentrate on may find the coins of one tribe, an individual ruler or a particular phase in the coinage interesting.

## Grading Celtic Coins

The majority of Celtic coins were struck by hand, sometimes resulting in a loss of definition through weak striking. In addition, the design on the dies was often bigger than the blank flan employed, resulting in the loss of some of the design. Coins with full legends are generally more valuable than examples with incomplete legends. Bronze coins in good condition (VF or better) and especially toned examples attract a premium. Factors that detract from a coin's value are chips, scratches and verdigris on bronze coins. It is important to take into account these factors as well as the amount of wear on a coin when assessing its grade.

|  | Cunobelin Bronze Unit | Epatticus Silver Unit | Cunobelin Gold Stater |
|---|---|---|---|
| Fine | | | |
| Very Fine | | | |

## Plated Coins

Plated gold staters, quarter staters and silver units are recorded for many known types. They vary considerably in the quality of their production and are usually priced at around a quarter of the substantive types value. Their exact purpose or relation to the type they copy is not fully understood.

## References and Select Bibliography.

M    Mack, R.P. (1975) 3rd edition, The Coinage of Ancient Britain.
V    Van Arsdell, R.D. (1989), Celtic Coinage of Britain.
BMC   Hobbs, R. (1996), British Iron Age Coins in the British Museum.

de Jersey, P. (1996), Celtic Coinage in Britain. *A good general introduction to the series.*
Nash, D. (1987), Coinage in the Celtic World. *Sets the coinage in its social context.*

The layout of the following list is derived from the standard works by Mack, Van Arsdell and the British Museum Catalogue by Richard Hobbs. References are made to these works where possible, in the case of the last work it should be noted that the British Museum collection is not exhaustive, and therefore should not be used to assess the rarity of a coin. More detailed information than that given here can be gained from these works.

# IMPORTED COINAGE

The earliest coins to circulate in Britain were made in northern Gaul (Belgica) and imported into the south-east of England from around 150 B.C. onwards. They were principally the product of two tribal groups in this region, the Ambiani and Suessiones. In Britain these types are known as Gallo-Belgic A to F. The first type Gallo-Belgic A is ultimately derived from the Macedonian gold staters (M) of Philip II (359-336 B.C.)

The reasons why they were imported are not fully understood. However, the context for their importation is one of close social, political and economic ties between Britain and Gaul. Within this cross-channel relationship they undoubtedly had various functions, such as payment for military service or mercenaries, in exchanges between the elite of each society: in cementing alliances for example, or as gifts in a system of exchange.

*Numbers in brackets following each entry refer to numbers employed in previous editions of this catalogue.*

## GALLO-BELGIC ISSUES

### GOLD

| M | 2 | 3 | 5 | 7 |

|  |  | F | VF |
|--|--|----|----|
|  |  | £ | £ |

**From *c.*150 B.C. – *c.*50 B.C.**

| | | F | VF |
|--|--|----|----|
| 1 | **Stater.** Gallo-Belgic A. (Ambiani). Good copy of Macedonian stater, large flan. Laureate head of Apollo r. R. Horse r. *M. 1; V. 10. (1)* | 550 | 2250 |
| 2 | Similar, but head and horse l. *M. 3; V. 12. (1)* | 425 | 1350 |
| 3 | B. (Ambiani). Somewhat similar to 1, but small flan and 'defaced' *obv.* die. R. Horse r. *M. 5; V. 30. (3)* | 300 | 900 |
| 4 | — Similar, but with lyre between horse's legs. *M. 7; V. 33. (3)* | 375 | 1250 |
| 5 | C. (Ambiani), *Stater.* Disintegrated Apollo head. R. horse. *M. 26; V. 44. (5)* | 275 | 750 |
| 6 | **Quarter Stater.** Gallo-Belgic A. Similar to 1. *M. 2; V.15. (2)* | 250 | 650 |
| 7 | — Similar to 2. *M. 4; V. 20. (2)* | 225 | 575 |
| 8 | B. Similar to 3. *M. 6; V. 35. (4)* | 175 | 450 |
| 9 | — Similar. R. Two horses l. with lyre between legs. *M. 8; V. 37. (4)* | 135 | 350 |
| 10 | D. Portions of Apollo head R. A mixture of stars, crescents, pellets, zig-zag lines; often referred to as 'Geometric' types,(See also British 'O', S. 46.). *M. 37, 39, 41, 41a, 42; V. 65/7/9/146. (6)* | 65 | 125 |

**From *c*.50 B.C.**

11

|  | | F £ | VF £ |
|---|---|---|---|
| 11 | **Stater.** Gallo-Belgic E. (Ambiani). Blank obv. R. Disjointed curved horse r., pellet below, zig-zag in exergue. *M. 27; V. 52, 54. (7)* | 125 | 250 |
| 12 | F. (Suessiones). Devolved Apollo head r. R. Disjointed horse r. With triple-tail. *M. 34a; V. 85. (8)* | 275 | 750 |
| 13 | Xc. Blank except for VE monogram at edge of coin, R. S below horse r. *M. 82; V. 87-1. (9)* | 225 | 600 |

## BILLON

**Armorican (Channel Islands and N.W. Gaul, *c*.75-50 B.C.)**

14                                              15

| 14 | **Stater.** Class I. Head r. R. Horse, boar below, remains of driver with Victory above, lash ends in or two loops, or 'gate'. *(12)* | 35 | 120 |
|---|---|---|---|
| 15 | — Class II. Head r. R. Horse, boar below, remains of Victory only, lash ends in small cross of four pellets. *(13)* | 30 | 100 |
| 16 | — Class III. Head r., anchor-shaped nose. R. Somewhat similar to Class I. *(14)* | 30 | 100 |
| 17 | — Class IV. Head r. R. Horse with reins, lyre shape below, driver holds vertical pole, lash ends in three prongs. *(15)* | 35 | 110 |
| 18 | — Class V. Head r. R. Similar to last, lash ends in long cross with four pellets. *(16)* | 40 | 135 |
| 19 | — Class VI. Head r. R. Horse, boar below, lash ends in 'ladder' *(17)* | 45 | 150 |
| 20 | **Quarter Stater.** Similar types to above. *(18)* | 45 | 140 |

20

# CELTIC COINS STRUCK IN BRITAIN

Coin production in Britain began at the very end of the second century B.C. with the cast potin coinage of Kent (Nos 62-64). Inspired by Gaulish issues and ultimately derived from the potin coins of Massalia (Marseilles) in southern Gaul, the precise function and period of use of this coinage is not fully understood. The domestic production of gold coins started around 70 B.C., these issues are traditionally known as British A-P and are derived from imported Gallo-Belgic issues. Broadly contemporary with these issues are quarter staters, silver units, and bronze units. Recent work by John Sills has further enhanced our understanding of this crucial early period with the identification of two new British staters (Insular Belgic C or Kentish A and the Ingoldisthorpe type) and their related quarters and a Westerham quarter stater. The Insular Belgic C or Kentish A type derived from Gallo-Belgic C now becomes the first British stater.

## EARLY UNINSCRIBED COINAGE

### GOLD

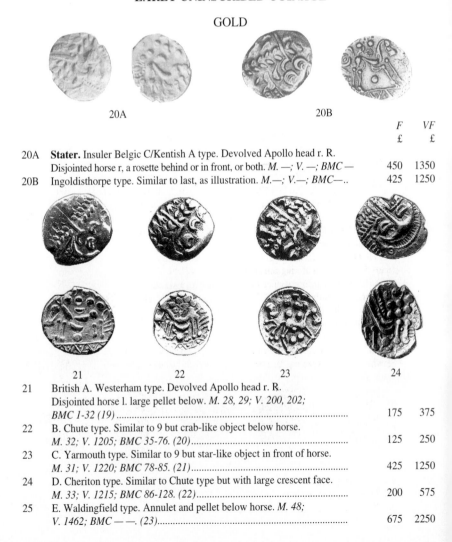

20A      20B

| | | F | VF |
|---|---|---|---|
| | | £ | £ |
| 20A | **Stater.** Insuler Belgic C/Kentish A type. Devolved Apollo head r. R. Disjointed horse r, a rosette behind or in front, or both. *M. —; V. —; BMC —* | 450 | 1350 |
| 20B | Ingoldisthorpe type. Similar to last, as illustration. *M.—; V.—; BMC—*.. | 425 | 1250 |

21      22      23      24

| 21 | British A. Westerham type. Devolved Apollo head r. R. Disjointed horse l. large pellet below. *M. 28, 29; V. 200, 202; BMC 1-32 (19)* | 175 | 375 |
|---|---|---|---|
| 22 | B. Chute type. Similar to 9 but crab-like object below horse. *M. 32; V. 1205; BMC 35-76. (20)* | 125 | 250 |
| 23 | C. Yarmouth type. Similar to 9 but star-like object in front of horse. *M. 31; V. 1220; BMC 78-85. (21)* | 425 | 1250 |
| 24 | D. Cheriton type. Similar to Chute type but with large crescent face. *M. 33; V. 1215; BMC 86-128. (22)* | 200 | 575 |
| 25 | E. Waldingfield type. Annulet and pellet below horse. *M. 48; V. 1462; BMC — —. (23)* | 675 | 2250 |

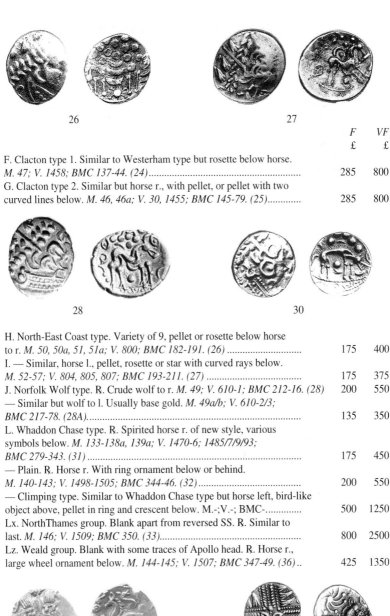

26 27

|  | | F<br>£ | VF<br>£ |
|---|---|---|---|

26 F. Clacton type 1. Similar to Westerham type but rosette below horse.
*M. 47; V. 1458; BMC 137-44. (24)*...................................................... 285 800

27 G. Clacton type 2. Similar but horse r., with pellet, or pellet with two
curved lines below. *M. 46, 46a; V. 30, 1455; BMC 145-79. (25)*.............. 285 800

28 30

28 H. North-East Coast type. Variety of 9, pellet or rosette below horse
to r. *M. 50, 50a, 51, 51a; V. 800; BMC 182-191. (26)* ............................... 175 400

29 I. — Similar, horse l., pellet, rosette or star with curved rays below.
*M. 52-57; V. 804, 805, 807; BMC 193-211. (27)* .................................... 175 375

30 J. Norfolk Wolf type. R. Crude wolf to r. *M. 49; V. 610-1; BMC 212-16. (28)* 200 550

31 — Similar but wolf to l. Usually base gold. *M. 49a/b; V. 610-2/3;
BMC 217-78. (28A)*........................................................................................ 135 350

32 L. Whaddon Chase type. R. Spirited horse r. of new style, various
symbols below. *M. 133-138a, 139a; V. 1470-6; 1485/7/9/93;
BMC 279-343. (31)* ......................................................................................... 175 450

33 — Plain. R. Horse r. With ring ornament below or behind.
*M. 140-143; V. 1498-1505; BMC 344-46. (32)*......................................... 200 550

33A — Climping type. Similar to Whaddon Chase type but horse left, bird-like
object above, pellet in ring and crescent below. M.-;V.-; BMC-............. 500 1250

34 Lx. North Thames group. Blank apart from reversed SS. R. Similar to
last. *M. 146; V. 1509; BMC 350. (33)*...................................................... 800 2500

35 Lz. Weald group. Blank with some traces of Apollo head. R. Horse r.,
large wheel ornament below. *M. 144-145; V. 1507; BMC 347-49. (36)* .. 425 1350

33A 36

36 Ma. Wonersh type. Crossed wreath design with crescents back to back
in centre. R. Spiral above horse, wheel below. *M. 148; V. 1520;
BMC 351-56. (37)* ......................................................................................... 350 1000

37                               38

|  | | F £ | VF £ |
|---|---|---|---|
| 37 | Mb. Savernake Forest type. Similar but *obv.* plain or almost blank. M. 62; V. 1526; BMC 361-64 | 175 | 475 |
| 38 | Qa. British 'Remic' type. Crude laureate head. ℞. Triple-tailed horse, wheel below. M. 58, 60, 61; V. 210-124; BMC 445-58. (41) | 200 | 550 |
| 39 | Qb. — Similar, but *obv.* blank. M. 59; V. 216; BMC 461-76. (42) | 150 | 350 |
| 39A | **Quarter Stater.** Insuler Belgic C/Kentish A type. Similar to Gallo-Belgic D, but with rosette in field on obverse. M. —; V.—; BMC— | 200 | 675 |
| 39B | Ingoldisthorpe type. Similar to last but with sperm-like objects in field. M.—; V.—; BMC— | 225 | 700 |
| 39C | British A. Westerham type. Similar to last but of cruder style, or with L-shapes in field on rev. M.—; V.—; BMC— | 175 | 525 |
| 40 | British D. Cheriton type. Similar to Stater, large crescent face. ℞. Cross motif with pellets. M. —; V. 143 var; BMC 129-136 | 165 | 475 |
| 41 | F/G. Clacton type. Plain, traces of pattern. ℞. Ornamental cross with pellets. M. 35; V. 1460; BMC 180-1. (43A) | 150 | 450 |
| 42 | H. Crescent design and pellets. ℞. Horse r. M. —; V. —; BMC 192 | 135 | 375 |
| 43 | Lx. N.Thames group. Floral pattern on wreath. ℞. Horse l. or r. M. 76; V. 234; BMC 365-370. (44) | 140 | 425 |

43            44            45

| 44 | Ly. N.Kent group. Blank. ℞. Horse l. or r. M. 78; V. 158; BMC 371-3. (45) | 125 | 300 |
|---|---|---|---|
| 45 | Lz. Weald group. Spiral design on wreath. ℞. Horse l. or r. M. 77; V. 250; BMC 548-50. (46) | 110 | 300 |

46            47            48

| 46 | O. Geometric type. Unintelligible patterns (some blank on obv.). M. 40, 43-45; V. 143, 1225/27/29; BMC 410-32. (49) | 75 | 150 |
|---|---|---|---|
| 47 | P.Trophy type. Blank. ℞. Trophy design. M. 36, 38; V. 145-7; BMC 435-44. (50) | 125 | 300 |
| 48 | Qc.British 'Remic' type. Head or wreath pattern. ℞. Triple-tailed horse, l. or r. M. 63-67; 69-75; V. 220-32, 36, 42-6, 56; BMC 478-546. (51) | 125 | 300 |
| 49 | Xd. Head l. of good style, horned serpent behind ear. ℞. Horse l. M. 79; V. 78; BMC 571-575. (11) | 250 | 675 |

## SILVER

**Units** (unless otherwise stated)

50 52

|  |  | F £ | VF £ |
|---|---|---|---|
| 50 | Lx. Head l.or r. R. Horse l. or r. *M. 280, 435, 436, 438, 441; V. 80, 1546, 1549, 1555; BMC 376-382. (53)* | 65 | 210 |
| 51 | — Head l. R. Stag r. with long horns. *M. 437; V. 1552; BMC 383-7. (54)* | 100 | 375 |
| 52 | — **Half Unit.** Two horses or two beasts. *M. 272, 442, 443, 445; V. 474, 1626, 1643, 1948; BMC 389-400. (55)* | 95 | 325 |
| 53 | Lz. Danebury group. Head r. with hair of long curves. R. Horse l., flower above. *M. 88; V. 262; BMC 580-82* | 85 | 275 |

54 54A

| 54 | — Helmeted head r. R. Horse r. wheel below. *M. 89; V. 264; BMC 583 -592. (58)* | 100 | 350 |
|---|---|---|---|
| 54A | Cruciform pattern with ornaments in angles. R. Horse l., ear of corn between legs, crescents and pellets above, *M.—; V.—; BMC—* | 95 | 325 |
| 55 | — **Quarter Unit.** As last. *M. 90; V. 268; BMC 642-43. (59)* | 45 | 150 |
| 56 | — Head r. R. Horse r. star above, wheel below. *M. –; V. 280; BMC 595-601* | 80 | 250 |
| 57 | — Head l., pellet in ring in front. R. Horse l. or r. *M. –; V. 284; BMC 610-630* | 60 | 175 |
| 58 | — Serpent looking back. R. Horse l. *M. –; V. 286; BMC 631-33* | 90 | 250 |
| 59 | — **Quarter Unit.** Cross pattern. R. Two-tailed horse. *M. 119; V. 482; BMC 654-56. (56C). (Formerly attributed to Verica)* | 40 | 135 |

## BRONZE

| 60 | **Unit.** Lx. Winged horse l. R. Winged horse l. *M. 446; V. 1629; BMC 401 (78)* | 85 | 350 |
|---|---|---|---|
| 61 | Chichester Cock type. Head r. R. Head r. surmounted by cock. *M. –; V. — BMC 657-59* | 75 | 275 |

## POTIN
### (Cast Copper/Tin alloy)

62

|  | | F | VF |
|--|--|---|----|
|  | | £ | £ |

62   **Unit.** Thurrock type.Head l. R. Bull butting l. or r. *M. —; V. 1402-42;*
     *BMC 660-666. (84A)* ............................................................................. 35   120

| 63 | 64 |

63   Class I type. Crude head. R. Lines representing bull *(Allen types A-L.)*
     *M. 9-22a; V. 104, 106, 108, 112, 114, 115, 117, 119, 120, 122, 123, 125,*
     *127, 129, 131, 133; BMC 667-714. (83)* ...................................................... 30   80
64   Class II type. Smaller flan, large central pellet. *(Allen types M-P.)*
     *M. 23-25; V. 135-39; BMC 715-23. (84)* .................................................... 25   75

# CELTIC DYNASTIC AND LATER UNINSCRIBED COINAGE

From Julius Caesar's expeditions to Britain in 55/54 B.C. and his conquest of Gaul in 52 B.C. to the Claudian invasion in 43 A.D., southern Britain was increasingly drawn into the orbit of the Roman world. This process is reflected not only in the coins but also in what we know about their issuers and the tribes they ruled. Latin legends begin to appear for the first time and increasingly accompany objects and designs drawn from the classical world. A lot of what we know about the Celtic tribes and their rulers, beyond just their names on coins, is drawn from contemporary and slightly later Roman historical sources. A great deal however is still uncertain and almost all attributions to either tribes or historically attested individuals have to be seen as tentative.

The coin producing tribes of Britain can be divided into two groups, those of the core and those of the periphery. The tribes of the core, the Atrebates/Regni, Trinovantes/Catuvellauni and Cantii, by virtue of their geographical location controlled contact with the Roman world. Unlike the tribes of the periphery they widely employed Latin legends, classical designs and used bronze coinage in addition to gold and silver.

Following the Roman invasion of 43 A.D. it is likely that some coinage continued to be produced for a short time. However in 61 A.D. with the death of King Prasutagus and the suppression of the Boudiccan revolt that followed, it is likely that Celtic coinage came to an end.

TRIBAL/MINT MAP

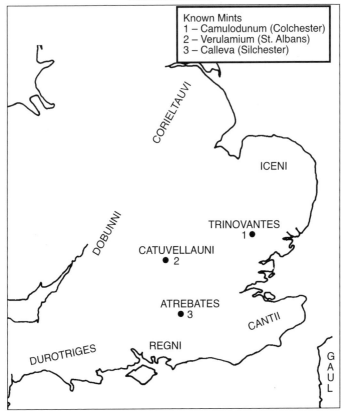

Known Mints
1 – Camulodunum (Colchester)
2 – Verulamium (St. Albans)
3 – Calleva (Silchester)

# ATREBATES AND REGNI

The joint tribal area of these two groups corresponds roughly with Berkshire and Sussex and parts of northern and eastern Hampshire. The Atrebatic portion being in the north of this region with its main centre at Calleva (Silchester). The Regni occupying the southern part of the region centred around Chichester.

## COMMIUS
### (Mid to Late 1st Century B.C.)

The first inscribed staters to appear in Britain, closely resemble British Q staters (no.38) and are inscribed 'COMMIOS'. Staters and silver units with an inscribed 'E' are also thought to be related. Traditionally this Commius was thought to be the Gaulish chieftain who Caesar refers to in De Bello Gallico, as firstly serving him in his expeditions to Britain and finally fleeing to Britain c.50 B.C. This attribution does however present chronological problems, and the appearance of a few early staters reading 'COM COMMIOS' suggests that the Commius who issued coins is more likely to have been the son of Caesar's Commius.

### GOLD

65

|  | F | VF |
|---|---|---|
|  | £ | £ |
| 65   **Stater.** Devolved Apollo head r. R. COMMIOS around triple tailed horse r., wheel below. *M. 92; V. 350; BMC 724-29. (85)* | 325 | 925 |

66

67

| 66   Similar, but 'E' symbol above horse instead of legend. *M. —;V. 352. BMC 730* | 350 | 950 |
|---|---|---|
| 67   **Quarter Stater.** Blank except for digamma. R. Horse l. *M. 83; V. 353-5; BMC —. (10)* | 125 | 300 |

### SILVER

69

| 69   **Unit.** Head l. R. Horse l. Mostly with 'E' symbol above. *M. —;V. 355; BMC 731-58. (57)* | 45 | 150 |
|---|---|---|

70

|  | F | VF |
|--|--|--|
|  | £ | £ |

70    **Minim.** Similar to Unit. *M. —; V. 358-5; BMC 759-60* ..........................    40    125

## TINCOMARUS or TINCOMMIUS
### (Late 1st Century B.C. – Early 1st Century A.D.)

Successor to Commius and on his coins styled as 'COM.F' (son of Commius). Early coins of the reign like his predecessors are very obiviously Celtic in their style. However later coins exhibit an increasing tendancy towards Roman designs. Indeed Tincommius is recorded as a supliant king of the Roman emperor Augustus (Res Gestae, xxxii), finally fleeing to Rome in the early 1st century A.D. The discovery of the Alton Hoard in 1996 brought to light gold staters with the new legend TINCOMARVS.

## GOLD

71                                                    73

71    **Stater.** *Celtic style.* Devolved Apollo head r. R. TINC COMM. F.
      around horse. *M. 93; V. 362; BMC —. (86)* ...............................................    425    1350
72    Similar but legend reads TINCOMARVS. *M. 94; V. 363;*
      *BMC 761-765. (86)* ...................................................................................    325    850
73    **Quarter Stater.** Spiral with pellet centre. R. Horse r. T above. *M. 81;*
      *V. 366; BMC 781-797. (46)* .....................................................................    100    225

74                                                    75

74    TINCOM, zig-zag ornament below. R. Horse l. *M. 95; V. 365;*
      *BMC 798-810. (87)* ...................................................................................    135    375
75    **Stater.** *Classical style.* TINC(O) on a sunk tablet. R. Horseman with
      javelin r. often with CF in field. *M. 96-98; V. 375-76; BMC 765-769. (88)*    275    750

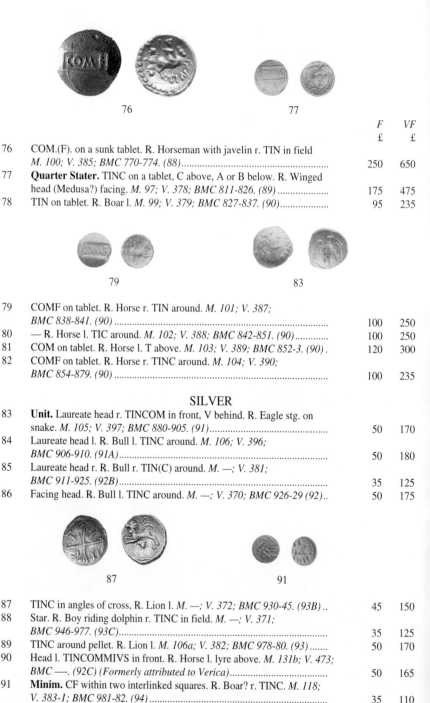

76                                              77

|    |                                                                                                      | F £ | VF £ |
|----|------------------------------------------------------------------------------------------------------|-----|------|
| 76 | COM.(F). on a sunk tablet. R. Horseman with javelin r. TIN in field M. 100; V. 385; BMC 770-774. (88) | 250 | 650  |
| 77 | **Quarter Stater.** TINC on a tablet, C above, A or B below. R. Winged head (Medusa?) facing. M. 97; V. 378; BMC 811-826. (89) | 175 | 475 |
| 78 | TIN on tablet. R. Boar l. M. 99; V. 379; BMC 827-837. (90) | 95 | 235 |

79                                      83

| 79 | COMF on tablet. R. Horse r. TIN around. M. 101; V. 387; BMC 838-841. (90) | 100 | 250 |
|----|------------------------------------------------------------------------------|-----|------|
| 80 | — R. Horse l. TIC around. M. 102; V. 388; BMC 842-851. (90) | 100 | 250 |
| 81 | COM on tablet. R. Horse l. T above. M. 103; V. 389; BMC 852-3. (90) | 120 | 300 |
| 82 | COMF on tablet. R. Horse r. TINC around. M. 104; V. 390; BMC 854-879. (90) | 100 | 235 |

## SILVER

| 83 | **Unit.** Laureate head r. TINCOM in front, V behind. R. Eagle stg. on snake. M. 105; V. 397; BMC 880-905. (91) | 50 | 170 |
|----|-----------------------------------------------------------------------------------------------------------------|----|-----|
| 84 | Laureate head l. R. Bull l. TINC around. M. 106; V. 396; BMC 906-910. (91A) | 50 | 180 |
| 85 | Laureate head r. R. Bull r. TIN(C) around. M. —; V. 381; BMC 911-925. (92B) | 35 | 125 |
| 86 | Facing head. R. Bull l. TINC around. M. —; V. 370; BMC 926-29 (92) | 50 | 175 |

87                                      91

| 87 | TINC in angles of cross, R. Lion l. M. —; V. 372; BMC 930-45. (93B) | 45 | 150 |
|----|---------------------------------------------------------------------|----|-----|
| 88 | Star. R. Boy riding dolphin r. TINC in field. M. —; V. 371; BMC 946-977. (93C) | 35 | 125 |
| 89 | TINC around pellet. R. Lion l. M. 106a; V. 382; BMC 978-80. (93) | 50 | 170 |
| 90 | Head l. TINCOMMIVS in front. R. Horse l. lyre above. M. 131b; V. 473; BMC —. (92C) (Formerly attributed to Verica) | 50 | 165 |
| 91 | **Minim.** CF within two interlinked squares. R. Boar? r. TINC. M. 118; V. 383-1; BMC 981-82. (94) | 35 | 110 |
| 92 | As above but CO. R. Bull r. TI. M. —; V. 383-5; BMC — | 35 | 125 |

|    |    |    | F<br>£ | VF<br>£ |
|----|----|----|--------|---------|

93　C inside box, box above and below. R. Bull r. TIN. *M. —; V. 383-7;*
　　*BMC 983* ............................................................................................　40　135

94　Cross, T? in angles. R. uncertain object. *M. 120; V. 483; BMC 984-85.*
　　*(Formerly attributed to Verica)* .............................................................　35　125

## EPPILLUS
### (Later 1st Century B.C. – Early 1st Century A.D.)

His reign is likely to have coincided with that of Tincommius's, who also claimed to be a son of
Commius. Two coinages appear in his name, one for Kent and one minted at Calleva (Silchester,
Hants.) in the northern part of the territory of the Atrebates and Regni. The coins of Calleva conform
to the southern denominational structure of gold and silver with fractions of each, whilst the Kentish
series is distinctly tri-metallic, replacing the silver minim with bronze. A joint coinage was issued by
Eppillus and Verica. It is not understood if Eppillus held both territories simultaneously.

## COINAGE STRUCK AT CALLEVA
### GOLD

95　**Stater.** Devolved Apollo head r. R. EPPI COMMI F around horse.
　　*M. —; V. 405; BMC —*............................................................................　975　3250

96

96　**Quarter Stater.** CALLEV, star above and below. R. Hound r. EPPI.
　　*M. 107; V. 407-08; BMC 986-1005. (95)* ................................................　100　235

97　　　　　　　　　　　　　　　　　　　98

97　COMM F EPPILV, around crescent. R. Horse r. *M. —; V. 409;*
　　*BMC 1006-1009. (95A)*............................................................................　110　300

98　EPPI COMF in two lines. R. Winged horse r. *M. 302; V. 435;*
　　*BMC 1010-15. (129)* ...............................................................................　100　250

### SILVER

99　　　　　　　　　　　　　　　　　100

99　**Unit.** Crescent REX CALLE above and below. R. Eagle r. EPP. *M. 108;*
　　*V .415. BMC 1016-1060. (96)*....................................................................　40　135

100　Bearded hd. r. in wreath. R. Boar r. EPPI(L) F CO(M). *M. —; V. 416;*
　　*BMC 1061-87. (96A)*................................................................................　40　145

|     |                                                                                                          | F £ | VF £ |
|-----|----------------------------------------------------------------------------------------------------------|-----|------|
| 101 | Bearded hd. in pellet border. R̟. Lion r. EPP COMF. *M. 305; V. 417; BMC 1088-1115. (131)* ................ | 40  | 130  |
| 102 | **Minim.** Floral cross. R̟. Eagle r. EPPI. *M. —; V. 420; BMC 1116-17* ..... | 40  | 135  |
| 103 | Spiral and pellets. R̟. Ram r. EPP. *M. —; V. 421; BMC 1118-20. (96C)* . | 40  | 150  |
| 104 | Bulls head facing. R̟. Ram r. EPP. *M. —; V. 422; BMC 1121-24. (96D)* . | 45  | 160  |
| 105 | Wreath pattern. R̟. Boar r. EPP. *M. —; V. 423; BMC —* ......................... | 50  | 175  |
| 106 | Crescent cross. R̟. Hand holding trident. *M. —; V. 487; BMC —. (111C)* | 50  | 175  |

## KENTISH TYPES
### GOLD

| 107 | **Stater.** COMF within wreath. R̟. Horseman l. EPPILLVS above. *M. 300; V. 430; BMC 1125-26. (127)* ............................................. | 975 | 3250 |

108                                    107

| 108 | Victory holding wreath l., within wreath. R̟. Horseman r. holding carnyx, F EPPI COM below. *M. 301; V. 431; BMC 1127-28. (128)* ........ | 1250 | 4250 |
| 109 | **Quarter Stater.** Crossed wreaths, EPPI in angles. R̟. Horse l. *M. 303; V. 436; BMC 1129. (130)* ................................................................ | 275 | 800 |
| 110 | COMF in pellet border. R̟. Horse r. EPPI. *M. 304; V. 437; BMC 1130-31. (130)* ................................................................... | 250 | 650 |

### SILVER

| 111 | **Unit.** Head l. EPPIL in field. R̟. Horseman holding carnyx, EPPILL. *M. 306; V. 441; BMC 1132. (131)* ................................................. | 165 | 525 |

### BRONZE

| 112 | **Unit.** Bow cross, EPPI COMF around. R̟. Eagle facing. *M. 309; V. 450; BMC 1137-38. (134)* ................................................................. | 60 | 275 |
| 113 | Bull r., EPPI COF around. R̟. eagle facing. *M. 310; V. 451; BMC 1139-41. (134)* ................................................................. | 60 | 275 |
| 114 | Head l., EPPI in front. R̟. Victory l. holding wreath and standard. *M. 311; V. 452; BMC 1142. (133)* ................................................. | 70 | 325 |
| 115 | Bearded hd. r., EPPI CF. R̟. Biga r. CF. *M. 312; V. 453; BMC —* ........... | 75 | 375 |

## JOINT TYPES OF EPPILUS AND VERICA
### SILVER

|  |  |  | F £ | VF £ |
|---|---|---|---|---|

116   **Unit.** Head l. CO VIR in front. R. Victory, EP. *M. 307; V. 442;*
     *BMC 1133-34. (132)* .................................................................  250   750

117

117   Head r. VIR CO in front. R. Capricorn l. EPPI COMF. *M. 308/a; V. 443;*
     *BMC 1135-36. (132)* .................................................................  150   475

## VERICA
### (c.10.-c.40 A.D.)

The exact details of Verica's succession and relationship to Eppillus and Tincommius are not fully understood. However by c.10 A.D. it seems likely that Verica was the sole ruler of the southern region. His close contact with Rome, both political and economic, seen in the increasing use of classical designs on his coins, culminated in his flight to Rome in c.42 A.D. to seek assistance from Claudius.

### GOLD

118   **Stater.** COM:F on tablet. R. Horseman r. holding spear, VIR below.
     *M. 109; V. 460; BMC 1143-44. (97)* .........................................  250   675
119   COM.F. on tablet, pellet in ring ornament above and below. R.
     Similar to last. *M. 121; 461; BMC 1146-53. (97)* ....................................  250   675

120                                    121

120   COM.F on tablet. R. Horseman r. holding spear, VIR above, REX below.
     *M. 121 var; V. 500; BMC 1155-58. (98)* ...................................  175   475
121   Vine-leaf dividing VI RI. R. Horseman r. with shield and spear. COF in
     field. *M. 125; V. 520-1; BMC 1159-73. (99)* ...........................................  225   600
122   Similar, reads VE RI. *M. 125; V. 520-5/7; BMC 1174-76. (99)* ...............  225   625
123   **Quarter Stater.** COMF on tablet. R. Horse l. VIR. *M. 111; V. 465;*
     *BMC 1177-78. (100)* .................................................................  110   275

124

124   COMF on tablet, pellet in ring ornament above and below R. Horse
     r. VI. *M. 112; V. 466; BMC 1179-1206. (100)* .........................................  100   210

|     |                                                                                  | F    | VF  |
|-----|----------------------------------------------------------------------------------|------|-----|
|     |                                                                                  | £    | £   |
| 125 | COMF on tablet, pellet border. Ŗ. Horse r. VI above. *M. 113; V. 467;*            |      |     |
|     | *BMC 1207-16. (100)* ..........................................................   | 100  | 210 |

126                                              128

| 126 | COM FILI. in two lines, scroll in between. Ŗ. Horse r. VIR(I) above.              |      |     |
|     | *M. 114; V. 468; BMC 1217-22. (100)* ...............................              | 110  | 250 |
| 127 | VERI COMF, crescent above, star below. Ŗ. Horse r. REX below.                     |      |     |
|     | *M. 122; V. 501; BMC 1223-36. (101)* ...............................              | 110  | 250 |
| 128 | VERI beneath vine-leaf. Ŗ. Horseman r. with sword and shield,                     |      |     |
|     | FRX in field. *M. 124; V. 525; BMC 1237-38. (102)* ...............                | 175  | 625 |
| 129 | COM, horseman r. Ŗ. Seated figure, VERICA around. *M. 126; V. 526;*              |      |     |
|     | *BMC 1239. (103)* ...............................................................   | 250  | 850 |
| 130 | Similar to last. Ŗ. Laureate bust r., VIRI in front. *M. 127; V. 527;*            |      |     |
|     | *BMC 1240. (103)* ...............................................................   | 250  | 825 |

## SILVER

| 131 | **Unit.** COMF, crescent and or pellet in ring above and below. Ŗ. Boar r.        |      |     |
|     | VI(RI) below. *M. 115; V. 470/72; BMC 1241-1331. (104)* .................          | 35   | 145 |

132                                              133

| 132 | VERICA COMMI F around pellet in ring. Ŗ. Lion r. REX below.                       |      |     |
|     | *M. 123; V. 505; BMC 1332-1359. (105)* ...............................             | 40   | 150 |
| 133 | COMMI F, horseman with shield r. Ŗ. VERI CA, mounted warrior with                 |      |     |
|     | spear r. *M. 128; V. 530; BMC 1360-92. (106)* ...........................          | 40   | 150 |

134                                              137

| 134 | Two cornucopiae, COMMI F. Ŗ. Figure seated r. VERICA. *M. 129;*                   |      |     |
|     | *V. 531; BMC 1393-1419. (107)* ...............................................     | 35   | 130 |
| 135 | Bust r. VIRI. Ŗ. Figure seated l. *M. 130; V. 532; BMC 1420. (108)* .......        | 85   | 325 |
| 136 | Naked figure l. Ŗ. Laureate bust r., COMMI F. *M. 131; V. 533;*                   |      |     |
|     | *BMC 1421-49. (108)* ...........................................................   | 35   | 130 |
| 137 | VERICA REX, bull r. Ŗ. Figure stg. l., COMMI F. *M. —; V. 506;*                   |      |     |
|     | *BMC 1450-84. (108B)* .........................................................     | 35   | 135 |
| 138 | COMF, in tablet and scroll. Ŗ. Eagle facing, VI RI. *M. —; V. 471;*               |      |     |
|     | *BMC 1485-1505. (104A)* .......................................................     | 35   | 135 |

| | | F £ | VF £ |
|---|---|---|---|
| 139 | VIRIC across field,ornaments above and below. R̄. Pegasus r., star design below. *M. —; V. —; BMC —. (104B)* | 75 | 275 |
| 140 | Head r. Verica. R. COMMI F., eagle l. *M. 131A; V. 534; BMC —. (108A)* | 85 | 350 |
| 141 | **Minim.** COF in tablet, R̄. Facing head (Medusa?), VE below. *M. —; V. 384; BMC 1506.(94A). (Formerly attributed to Tincommius)* | 45 | 160 |
| 142 | Head r. R̄. Horse r., VIRICO. *M. 116; V. 480; BMC —. (109)* | 40 | 150 |
| 143 | Pellet and ring pattern. R̄. Lion r. VIR. *M. 120a/c; V. 484; BMC 1514-17. (109)* | 35 | 120 |
| 144 | VIRIC reversed. R̄. Boar r. *M. —; V. 485; BMC 1518* | 35 | 120 |
| 145 | Cross. R̄. Trident. *M. —; V. 486-1; BMC —* | 45 | 160 |
| 146 | Uncertain. R̄. Boar r. *M. 120b; V. 510-1; BMC —. (109)* | 30 | 110 |
| 147 | Crescent cross. R̄. Boar r. *M. —; V. 510-5; BMC 1521-23. (109)* | 40 | 135 |
| 148 | VIR VAR in tablets. R̄. Winged horse r. CO. *M. 120d; V. 511; BMC 1507-12. (109)* | 35 | 135 |

149          150

| | | | |
|---|---|---|---|
| 149 | Vine-leaf, CFO. R̄. Horse r. VERI CA. *M. —; V. 550; BMC 1524-25* | 35 | 135 |
| 150 | CF in torc. R̄. Head r. VERIC. *M. 132; V. 551; BMC 1526-33. (111A)* | 30 | 125 |
| 151 | Altar, CF, R̄. Bulls head facing, VERICA. *M. 120e; V. 552; BMC 1534-37. (109)* | 45 | 175 |
| 152 | Temple, CF. R̄. Bull r, VER REX. *M. —; V. 553; BMC 1538-41* | 30 | 110 |

153          154

| | | | |
|---|---|---|---|
| 153 | Cornucopia, VER COM. R. Lion r. *M. —; V. 554; BMC 1542* | 35 | 135 |
| 154 | Two cornucopiae. R̄. Eagle l. *M. —; V. 555; BMC 1543-58* | 30 | 100 |
| 155 | Floral pattern, CF. R̄. Lion r. *M.—; V. 556; BMC 1559-63. (111E)* | 35 | 135 |
| 156 | Sphinx r., CF, R̄. dog curled up, VERI. *M. —; V. 557; BMC 1564-68. (109B)* | 30 | 120 |
| 157 | VERI. R̄. Urn, COMMI F. *M. —; V. 559; BMC —* | 40 | 150 |
| 158 | A in star. R̄. Bird r. *M. 316; V. 561; BMC 1569-71* | 45 | 160 |
| 159 | Urn, Rex. R̄. Eagle r., VERRICA COMMI F. *M. —; V. 563; BMC 1572-78. (109C)* | 30 | 110 |
| 160 | VIR inside tablet. R̄. Boars head r. *M. 117; V. 564; BMC 1579-81. (109A)* | 30 | 120 |
| 161 | Cross. R̄. bull l. *M. —; V. —; BMC 1582* | 35 | 140 |
| 162 | Boars head r., CF, R̄. Eagle, VE. *M. —; V. —; BMC 1583-86* | 30 | 110 |

163

| | | | |
|---|---|---|---|
| 163 | Head r, COMM IF., R̄. Sphinx, R VE. *M. —; V. —; BMC 1587-89* | 35 | 140 |

| | F | VF |
|---|---|---|
| | £ | £ |
| 164 A in tablet. R. Boar r. VI CO. *M. —; V. —; BMC 1590* ........................... | 45 | 160 |

*The two following coins are possibly issues of Epatticus.*

| 165 Bull r. R. Eagle with snake l. *M. —; V. 512; BMC 2366-70*..................... | 35 | 140 |
| 166 Bust r. R. dog r. *M. —; V. 558; BMC 2371-74* ........................................ | 40 | 150 |

# CANTII

The Cantii, who gave their name to Kent, occupied a similar area to that of the modern county. Caesar considered this the most civilised part of Britain and the early production of potin units in Kent can be seen as indicative of this. A number of Kentish rulers for whom we have coins, appear to be dynasts from the two neighbouring kingdoms, who were involved in struggles to acquire territory. Eppillus (see Atrebates and Regni) produced coins specifically for circulation in Kent and like those of Cunobelin they circulated widely.

## EARLY UNINSCRIBED
### GOLD

| 167 **Stater.** Ly. Blank. R. Horse l. numerous ring ornaments in field. *M. 293; V. 142; BMC 2472. (34)* ............................................................. | 325 | 1050 |
| 168 Blank. R. Horse r. numerous ornaments in field. *M. 294; V. 157; BMC— (34)* ............................................................................................... | 325 | 1050 |

169

| 169 Lz. Blank. R. Horse l., box with cross hatching below. *M. 84, 292; V. 150, 144; BMC 2466-68. (35)* ............................................................... | 400 | 1350 |

170        171

| 170 **Quarter Stater.** Ly. Blank. R. Horse r., pentagram below. *M. 285; V. 163; BMC 2473-74. (45)* .................................................................... | 100 | 225 |
| 171 Blank. R. Horse r., 'V' shape above. *M. 284; V. 170; BMC 2475-77. (45)* | 100 | 210 |
| 172 Lz. Blank. R. Horse l., 'V' shape above. *M. 85; V. 151; BMC 2469-70. (47)* | 100 | 225 |

### SILVER

| 173 **Unit.** Curved star. R. Horse r. Pentagram below. *M. 272a; V. 164; BMC—. (56)* .............................................................................................. | 135 | 425 |
| 174 Serpent torc. R. Horse r., box with cross hatching below. *cf Mossop 8; BMC 2478* ........................................................................................... | 165 | 600 |
| 175 **Half Unit.** Spiral of three arms. R. Horse l. *M. —; V. —; BMC 2479*...... | 55 | 250 |

## BRONZE

|     |                                                                                   | F<br>£ | VF<br>£ |
|-----|-----------------------------------------------------------------------------------|------|-------|
| 176 | **Unit.** Various animal types, Ɍ. Various animal types. *M. 295-96,*<br>*316a-d; V. 154/167; BMC 2480-91. (80/141-44)* .................................... | 50 | 250 |

## DUBNOVELLAUNUS
(Late 1st Century B.C.)

Likely to be the same Dubnovellaunus recorded on coins in Essex (see Trinovantes / Catuvellauni).
The two coinages share the same denominational structure and have some stylistic similarities. It has
been suggested that Dubnovellaunus is the British king of that name mentioned along with
Tincommius as a client king in the Res Gestae of the Roman emperor Augustus.

## GOLD

177

|     |                                                                                          |     |     |
|-----|------------------------------------------------------------------------------------------|-----|-----|
| 177 | **Stater.** Blank. Ɍ. Horse r., bucranium above, serpent like object below,<br>DUBNOV[ELLAUNUS] or similar around. *M. 282; V. 169;*<br>*BMC 2492-96. (118)* ............................................................................... | 225 | 575 |
| 178 | — Ɍ. Horse r., but without bucranium and with wheel below.<br>*M. 283; V. 176; BMC 2497-98. (118)* ....................................................... | 275 | 850 |

## SILVER

|     |                                                                                          |     |     |
|-----|------------------------------------------------------------------------------------------|-----|-----|
| 179 | **Unit.** Winged animal r. R. Horse l., DVBNO. *M. 286; V. 171;*<br>*BMC 2499-2501. (119)* ............................................................................ | 125 | 375 |

180

|     |                                                                                          |     |     |
|-----|------------------------------------------------------------------------------------------|-----|-----|
| 180 | Winged animal l. Ɍ. Seated fig. l., holding hammer, DVBNO.<br>*M. 287; V. 178; BMC 2502-03. (119)* ....................................................... | 135 | 475 |

## BRONZE

|     |                                                                                          |     |     |
|-----|------------------------------------------------------------------------------------------|-----|-----|
| 181 | **Unit.** Horse r. Ɍ. Lion l., DVBN. *M. 290; V. 166; BMC 2504-06. (122).* | 75 | 325 |
| 182 | Boar l., DVBNO. Ɍ. Horseman r. *M. 291; V. 181; BMC 2507-08. (121).* | 75 | 325 |
| 183 | Boar r., DVBNO. Ɍ. Eagle facing. *M. 289; V. 180; BMC 2509-10. (121)* | 70 | 300 |

## VOSENOS
( Late 1st Century B.C./ Early 1st Century A.D.)
Little is known of this ruler who issued coins in a characteristically Kentish style similar to those of Dubnovellaunus.

## GOLD

|     |                                                                                                                 | F £  | VF £ |
| --- | --------------------------------------------------------------------------------------------------------------- | ---- | ---- |
| 184 | **Stater.** Blank. R. Horse l., bucranium above, serpent like object below., [VOSE]NOS. *M. 297; V. 184; BMC 2511-12. (123)* | 1250 | 3500 |

185

| 185 | **Quarter Stater.** Blank. R. Horse r., VOSI below. *M. 298; V. 185; BMC 2514-15. (124)* | 425 | 1250 |
| --- | --- | --- | --- |

## SILVER
| 186 | **Unit.** Horse and griffin. R. Horse r., retrograde legend. *M. 299a; V. 186; BMC —. (125)* | 175 | 600 |
| --- | --- | --- | --- |

## "SA" or "SAM"
(Late 1st Century B.C./ Early 1st Century A.D.)
An historically unattested individual whose coins are stylistically associated with those of Dubnovellaunus and Vosenos. His coins have been predominantly found in north Kent

## SILVER
| 187 | **Unit.** Head l., R. Horse l., SA below. *M. —; V. —; BMC —* | 200 | 675 |
| --- | --- | --- | --- |

## BRONZE
| 187A | **Unit.** Boar l., R. Horse l., SA below. *M. 299; V. 187; BMC 2516-19. (126)* | 110 | 425 |
| --- | --- | --- | --- |

187B

| 187B | Horse l., SAM below. R. Horse l., SAM below. *M. —; V. —; BMC —* | 125 | 450 |
| --- | --- | --- | --- |

## AMMINUS
(Early 1st Century A.D.)

Issued a coinage stylistically distinct from other Kentish types and with strong affinities to those of Cunobelin. Indeed it has been suggested that he is the Adminius recorded by Suetonius, as a son of Cunobelin. The enigmatic legend DVN or DVNO may be an unknown mint site.

## SILVER

188

|  | F £ | VF £ |
|---|---|---|
| 188  **Unit.** Plant, AMMINUS around. R. Winged horse r., DVN. *M. 313; V. 192; BMC 2522-23. (136)* | 100 | 400 |

189

|  | | |
|---|---|---|
| 189  (Last year 190). A in wreath. R. Capricorn r., S AM. *M. 314; V. 194; BMC 2520-21. (137)* | 100 | 400 |

## BRONZE

190

|  | | |
|---|---|---|
| 190  (Last year 189). AM in wreath. R. Horse r., DVNO. *M. —; V. 193; BMC ——* | 95 | 375 |
| 191  **Unit.** Head r. R. Hippocamp r., AM. *M. 315; V. 195; BMC 2524. (139).* | 95 | 400 |

# TRINOVANTES AND CATUVELLAUNI

Occupying the broad area of Essex, southern Suffolk, Bedfordshire, Buckinghamshire, Hertfordshire, parts of Oxfordshire, Cambridgeshire and Northamptonshire, they are likely to have been two separate tribes for most of their history. The Trinovantes were originally located in the eastern half of this area, with their main centre at Camulodunum (Colchester). The original Catuvellauni heartland was further west, with their main centre at Verulamium (St.Albans). The whole area eventually came under the control of Cunobelin at the end of the period.

## TRINOVANTES

### ADDEDOMAROS
(Late 1st Century B.C.)

Unknown to history, he appears to have been a contemporary of Tasciovanus. The design of his staters is based on the Whaddon Chase type (No.32) which circulated widely in this region.

## GOLD

200

|     |                                                                                                                    | F<br>£ | VF<br>£ |
|-----|--------------------------------------------------------------------------------------------------------------------|--------|---------|
| 200 | **Stater.** Crossed wreath. R. Horse r., wheel below, AθθDIIDOM above. *M. 266; V. 1605; BMC 2390-94. (148)* | 250 | 600 |

201                                      202

|     |                                                                                                                    | F<br>£ | VF<br>£ |
|-----|--------------------------------------------------------------------------------------------------------------------|--------|---------|
| 201 | Six armed spiral. R. Horse r., cornucopia below, AθθDIIDOM above. *M. 267; V. 1620; BMC 2396-2404. (148)* | 200 | 475 |
| 202 | Two opposed crescents. R. Horse r., branch below, spiral or wheel above, AθθDIIDOM. *M. 268; V. 1635; BMC 2405-2415. (149)* | 275 | 650 |
| 203 | **Quarter Stater.** Circular flower pattern. R. Horse r. *M. 271; V. 1608; BMC 2416. (44)* | 150 | 375 |
| 204 | Cross shaped flower pattern. R. Horse r. *M. 270; V. 1623; BMC 2417-21. (44)* | 135 | 300 |
| 205 | Two opposed crescents. R. Horse r., AθθDIIDOM around. *M. 269; V. 1638; BMC 2422-24. (150)* | 165 | 475 |

## BRONZE

|     |                                                                                                                    | F<br>£ | VF<br>£ |
|-----|--------------------------------------------------------------------------------------------------------------------|--------|---------|
| 206 | **Unit.** Head l. R. Horse l. *M. 274; V. 1615/46 BMC 2450-60. (77)* | 35 | 120 |

## DUBNOVELLAUNUS
(Late 1st Century B.C./ Early 1st Century A.D.)

Dubnovellaunus is likely to have been the successor to Addedomaros, with whom his coins are stylistically related. It is not clear if he was the same Dubnovellaunus who also issued coins in Kent (see Cantii) or if he is the same Dumnobeallaunos mentioned in the Res Gestae of the emperor Augustus c.AD14.

### GOLD

207                                        208

|   | | F £ | VF £ |
|---|---|---|---|
| 207 | **Stater.** Two crescents on wreath. R. Horse l., leaf below, pellet in ring, DVBNOVAIIAVNOS above. *M. 275; V. 1650; BMC 2425-40. (152)*.... | 275 | 800 |
| 208 | **Quarter Stater.** Similar. *M. 276; V. 1660; BMC 2442. (153)*................ | 135 | 375 |

### SILVER

| 209 | Unit. Head l., DVBNO. R. Winged horse r., lattice box below. *M. 288; V. 165; BMC 2443-44. (120)* ...................................... | 150 | 475 |
|---|---|---|---|
| 210 | Head l., legend ?, R. Horse l. DVB[NOV]. *M. 278; V. 1667; BMC 2445. (154)*.............................................................................. | 110 | 325 |

### BRONZE

| 211 | **Unit.** Head l., R. Horse l., DVBNO above. *M. 281; V. 1669; BMC 2446-48. (154)* ................................................ | 60 | 200 |
|---|---|---|---|
| 212 | Head r., R. Horse l. *M. 277; V. 1665; BMC 2461-65. (154)*.................... | 50 | 175 |

## DIRAS
(Late 1st Century B.C./ Early 1st Century A.D.)

An historically unattested ruler, responsible for a gold stater related stylistically to Dubnovellaunus's.

### GOLD

| 213 | **Stater.** Blank. R. Horse r., DIRAS? above, yoke like object above. *M. 279; V. 162; BMC 2449. (151)* .......................................... | 1250 | 3500 |
|---|---|---|---|

## CATUVELLAUNI

### TASCIOVANUS

(Late 1st Century B.C./ Early 1st Century A.D.)

The early gold coins of Tasciovanus, like those of his contemporary Addedomaros, are based on the Whaddon Chase stater. Verulamium (St.Albans) appears to have been his principal mint, appearing as VER or VERL on the coinage. Staters and quarter staters inscribed CAM (Camulodunum/Colchester) are known and perhaps suggest brief or weak control of the territory to the east. The later coins of Tasciovanus use increasingly Romanised designs. The adoption of the title RICON, perhaps a Celtic equivalent to the Latin REX (King), can be seen as a parallel move to that of his contemporary Tincommius to the south.

## GOLD

214　　　　　　　　　　217

|  |  | F £ | VF £ |
|---|---|---|---|
| 214 | **Stater.** Crescents in wreath. ℞. TASCIAV and bucranium over horse r. M. 149; V. 1680; BMC 1591-1603. (157) | 325 | 925 |
| 215 | — ℞. Similar reads TAXCIAV. M. 150; V. 1682; BMC 1604-05. (157). | 350 | 1000 |
| 216 | — ℞. Similar reads TASCIOVAN above, CAM below. M. 186/a; V. 1684; BMC 1606-07. (160) | 575 | 1650 |
| 217 | — ℞. Horseman r. helmeted and with carnyx, TASC in field. M. 154-55/57; V. 1730-32; BMC 1608-1613. (158) | 275 | 750 |
| 218 | Crescents in wreath, with V or VER in design. ℞. Similar to last. M. 156-57; V. 1734-35; BMC 1623-24. (158) | 325 | 950 |

219　　　　　　　　　　221

| 219 | TASCIO(V) RICON in panel. ℞. Horseman l., wearing armour and holding sword and shield. M. 184; V. 1780; BMC 1628-36. (161) | 525 | 1350 |
|---|---|---|---|
| 220 | **Quarter Stater.** Floral design. ℞. Horse r. M. —; V. —; BMC 1638-39. | 175 | 500 |
| 221 | Crossed Wreath. ℞. Horse l. M. 151; V. 1688; BMC 1651-53. (44) | 110 | 250 |
| 222 | — ℞. Horse r., CAM. M. 187; V. 1694; BMC 1640. (164) | 150 | 425 |
| 223 | Similar, TASCI in wreath. ℞. Horse r., TASC. M. 153; V. 1692; BMC 1641. (163) | 110 | 250 |

224 226

| | F £ | VF £ |
|---|---|---|
| 224 Similar, VERO in wreath. R. Horse l., TAS. *M. 152; V. 1690;* *BMC 1642-43. (163)* ............... | 100 | 225 |
| 225 TASCIO on tablet. R. Horse l. *M. 195; V. 1848; BMC 1646. (166)* ........ | 150 | 425 |
| 226 TASC on tablet. R. Horse l. *M. 185; V. 1786; BMC 1647-50. (165)* ....... | 100 | 225 |

## SILVER

| | F £ | VF £ |
|---|---|---|
| 227 **Unit.** Head l. R. Horse r. *M. —; V. 1698; BMC 1654*............... | 65 | 200 |
| 228 Cross and box. R. Horse r., VER in front. *M. —; V. —; BMC 1655* ........ | 70 | 225 |
| 229 Cross and crescent. R. Horse l., TASCI. *M. —; V. —; BMC 1665-57* ..... | 65 | 200 |
| 230 Bearded head l. R. Horseman r., TASCIO. *M. 158; V. 1745;* *BMC 1667-68. (167)* ............... | 85 | 300 |
| 231 Winged horse l., TAS. R. Griffin r., within circle of pellets. *M. 159;* *V. 1790; BMC 1660. (168)*............... | 75 | 275 |
| 232 Eagle stg. l., TASCIA. R. Griffin r. *M. 160; V. 1792; BMC 1658-59. (169)* | 85 | 300 |
| 233 VER in beaded circle. R. Horse r., TASCIA. *M. 161; V. 1699;* *BMC 1670-73. (170)* ............... | 75 | 275 |
| 234 — R. Naked horseman. *M. 162; V. 1747; BMC 1674-76. (171)* ............... | 85 | 300 |

235 238 242

| | F £ | VF £ |
|---|---|---|
| 235 Laureate hd. r., TASCIA. R. Bull l. *M. 163; V. 1794; BMC 1681-82. (172)* | 75 | 275 |
| 236 Cross and box, VERL. R. Boar r. TAS. *M. 164; V. 1796;* *BMC 1661-62. (173)* ............... | 85 | 300 |
| 237 TASC in panel. R. Winged horse l. *M. 165; V. 1798; BMC 1664-65. (174)* | 65 | 200 |
| 238 — R. Horseman l., carrying long shield. *M. 166; V. 1800;* *BMC 1677-79. (174)* ............... | 60 | 185 |
| 239 Two crescents. R. Winged griffin, VIR. *M. —; V. —; BMC 1666* .......... | 100 | 350 |
| 240 Head r., TAS?. R. Horseman r. *M. —; V. —; BMC 1669* ...................... | 85 | 300 |

## BRONZE

241

| | F £ | VF £ |
|---|---|---|
| 241 **Double Unit.** Head r., TASCIA, VA. R. Horseman r. *M. 178; V. 1818;* *BMC 1685-87. (190)* ............... | 175 | 650 |

|     |                                                                                                                                              | F<br>£ | VF<br>£ |
|-----|----------------------------------------------------------------------------------------------------------------------------------------------|--------|---------|
| 242 | **Unit.** Two heads in profile, one bearded. R. Ram l., TASC. *M. 167; V. 1705; BMC 1711-13. (178)* ............................................... | 60     | 225     |
| 243 | Bearded head r. VER(L). R. Horse l., VIIR or VER. *M. 168; V. 1707; BMC 1714-21. (179)* ............................................................ | 50     | 200     |
| 244 | Bearded head r. R. Horse l., TAS. *M. 169; V. 1709; BMC 1722-23. (179)*                                                                       | 60     | 225     |
| 245 | Head r., TASC. R. Winged horse l., VER. *M. 170; V. 1711; BMC 1688-89. (180)* .................................................................... | 50     | 200     |
| 246 | — R. Horseman r., holding carnyx, VIR. *M. 171; V. 1750; BMC 1724-27. (182)* ...................................................................... | 50     | 200     |

247

|     |                                                                                                                                              | F<br>£ | VF<br>£ |
|-----|----------------------------------------------------------------------------------------------------------------------------------------------|--------|---------|
| 247 | VERLAMIO between rays of star. R. Bull l. *M. 172; V. 1808; BMC 1745-51. (183)* .................................................................... | 45     | 185     |
| 248 | Similar without legend. R. Bull r. *M. 174; V. 1810; BMC 1752-55. (185)*                                                                      | 60     | 225     |
| 249 | Similar. R. Horse l., TASCI. *M. 175; V. 1812; BMC 1709-10. (186)* ......                                                                     | 60     | 225     |
| 250 | Head r., TASCIO. R. Lion r., TA SCI. *M. 176; V. 1814; BMC 1736-38. (188)* .......................................................................... | 45     | 185     |
| 251 | Head r. R. Figure std. l., VER below. *M. 177; V. 1816; BMC 1739-44. (189)* .......................................................................... | 60     | 225     |
| 252 | Cross and Crescents. R. Boar r., VER. *M. 179; V. 1713; BMC 1702-05. (191)* ...................................................................... | 50     | 200     |
| 253 | Laureate head r. R. Horse l., VIR. *M. 180; V. 1820; BMC 1706-08. (192)*                                                                      | 50     | 200     |
| 254 | Raised band across centre, VER or VERL below. R. Horse grazing r. *M. 183a; V. 1717; BMC —. (193)* ................................................ | 90     | 350     |
| 255 | **Fractional Unit.** Animal r. R. Sphinx l. *M. 181; V. 1824; BMC 1760-61. (198)* .................................................................... | 45     | 200     |
| 256 | Head l., VER. R. Goat r. *M. 182; V. 1715; BMC 1765-68. (199)* ...........                                                                    | 35     | 150     |
| 257 | Head r. R. Boar r, *M. 183; V. 1826; BMC 1762-64. (199)* ......................                                                               | 35     | 150     |
| 258 | Head l. R. Animal with curved tail. *M. 183b, c; V. 1822; BMC 1759. (200)* ............................................................................ | 35     | 160     |

## ASSOCIATES OF TASCIOVANUS

(Early 1st Century A.D.)

Towards the end of his reign, a number of joint issues bearing his name and the name of either Sego or Dias appear. In addition coins similar in style to those of Tasciovanus appear with either the name Andoco or Rues. It has been suggested that these issues belong to a period of struggle following the death of Tasciovanus and are all rival contestants for the throne. Another theory is that they are associates or sub-kings of Tasciovanus responsible for areas within the wider territory.

## SEGO

### GOLD

259

|  |  | F £ | VF £ |
|---|---|---|---|
| 259 | **Stater.** TASCIO in tablet, annulets above. R. Horseman with carnyx r., SEGO. *M. 194; V. 1845; BMC 1625-27. (162)* | 1250 | 3250 |

### SILVER

260

| 260 | **Unit.** SEGO on panel. R. Horseman r. *M. 196; V. 1851; BMC 1684. (176)* | 325 | 900 |
|---|---|---|---|

### BRONZE

| 261 | **Unit.** Star shaped pattern. R. Winged sphinx l., SEGO. *M. 173; V. 1855; BMC 1690. (184)* | 150 | 525 |
|---|---|---|---|

## ANDOCO

### GOLD

262

| 262 | **Stater.** Crescents in wreath. R. Bucranium over horse r., AND below. *M. 197; V. 1860; BMC 2011-14. (202)* | 425 | 1200 |
|---|---|---|---|

| | F | VF |
|---|---|---|
| | £ | £ |

263 **Quarter Stater.** Crossed wreaths, ANDO in angles. Ɍ. Horse l. *M. 198; V. 1863; BMC 2015-17. (203)* ................................................................ 125 350

## SILVER

264

264 **Unit.** Bearded head l. Ɍ. Winged horse l., ANDOC. *M. 199; V. 1868; BMC 2018. (204)*...................................................................................... 125 375

## BRONZE

265

265 **Unit.** Head r., ANDOCO. Ɍ. Horse r., ANDOCO. *M. 200; V. 1871; BMC 2019-20. (205)* ............................................................................. 65 250
266 Head r., TAS ANDO. Ɍ. Horse r. *M. 175a; V. 1873; BMC —. (187)* ...... 85 350

## DIAS
### SILVER

267          268

267 **Unit.** Saltire over cross within square. Ɍ. Boar r., TASC DIAS. *M. —; V. —; BMC 1663. (173A)*................................................................ 135 425
268 DIAS CO, in star. Ɍ. Horse l., VIR. *M. 188; V. 1877; BMC 1683. (177).* 125 375

## BRONZE

269

269 **Unit.** Bearded head r., DIAS TASC. Ɍ. Centaur r., playing pan pipes. *M. 192; V. 1882; BMC 1728-35. (197)*...................................................... 125 450

## RUES
### BRONZE

|  |  | F | VF |
|---|---|---|---|
|  |  | £ | £ |
| 270 | **Unit.** Lion r., RVII. R. Eagle. *M. 189; V. 1890; BMC 1691. (194)*.......... | 85 | 350 |
| 271 | — R. Similar reads RVE. *M. 189; V. 1890-3; BMC 1692. (194)*............. | 80 | 325 |

272                                         273

| 272 | Bearded head r., RVIIS. R. Horseman r., VIR. *M. 190; V. 1892;* |  |  |
|---|---|---|---|
|  | *BMC 1698-1701. (195)*......................................................................... | 85 | 350 |
| 273 | RVIIS on tablet. R. Winged sphinx l. *M. 191; V. 1895;* |  |  |
|  | *BMC 1693-97. (196)* ....................................................................... | 90 | 375 |
| 274 | **Fractional Unit.** Annulet within square with curved sides. R. Eagle l., |  |  |
|  | RVII. *M. 193; V. 1903; BMC 1756-58. (201)*......................................... | 75 | 325 |

## CUNOBELIN
### (Early 1st Century A.D. to *c.*40 A.D.)

Styled as son of Tasciovanus on some of his coins, Cunobelin appears to have ruled over the unified territories of the Trinovantes and Catuvellauni, with additional territory in Kent. His aggressive policy of expansion that involved members of family eventually lead to Roman concern over the extent of his power. Following his death just prior to 43 AD, the emperor Claudius took the decision to invade Britain.

During his long reign an extensive issue of gold, silver and bronze coins used ever increasingly Romanised designs. It has been estimated from a study of known dies that around one million of his gold corn ear staters were produced. His main centre and mint was at Camulodunum (Colchester) appearing as the mint signature CAMV. The names SOLIDV and AGR appear on a few coins associated with Cunobelin and are likely to represent personal names.

### GOLD

280                                         281

| 280 | **Stater.** Biga type. CAMVL on panel. R. Two horses l., wheel below, |  |  |
|---|---|---|---|
|  | CVNOBELIN. *M. 201; V. 1910; BMC 1769-71. (207)*............................ | 625 | 1750 |
| 281 | Linear type. Corn ear dividing CA MV. R. Horse r., branch above., |  |  |
|  | CVN. *M. 210; V. 1925; BMC 1772-76. (208)* ........................................ | 210 | 500 |
| 282 | — Similar, privy mark 'x' above a letter in *obv.* legend. *M. 210a;* |  |  |
|  | *VA 1925-3/5; BMC 1777-81. (208)*.......................................................... | 300 | 825 |

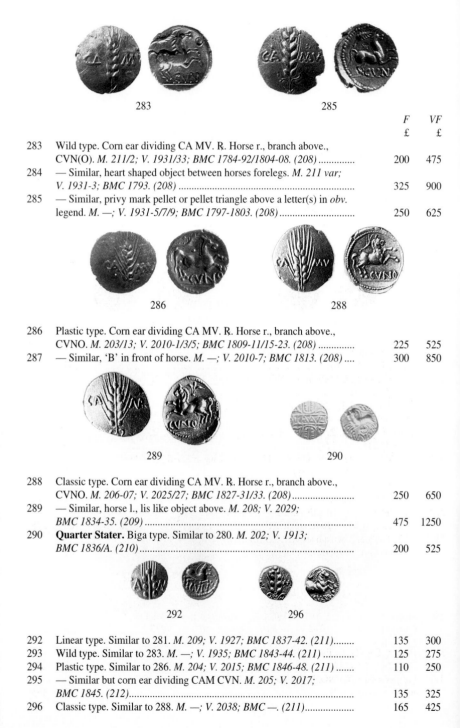

283                                        285

|  | F £ | VF £ |
|---|---|---|
| 283 Wild type. Corn ear dividing CA MV. ℞. Horse r., branch above., CVN(O). *M. 211/2; V. 1931/33; BMC 1784-92/1804-08. (208)* | 200 | 475 |
| 284 — Similar, heart shaped object between horses forelegs. *M. 211 var; V. 1931-3; BMC 1793. (208)* | 325 | 900 |
| 285 — Similar, privy mark pellet or pellet triangle above a letter(s) in *obv.* legend. *M. —; V. 1931-5/7/9; BMC 1797-1803. (208)* | 250 | 625 |

286                                        288

| 286 Plastic type. Corn ear dividing CA MV. ℞. Horse r., branch above., CVNO. *M. 203/13; V. 2010-1/3/5; BMC 1809-11/15-23. (208)* | 225 | 525 |
|---|---|---|
| 287 — Similar, 'B' in front of horse. *M. —; V. 2010-7; BMC 1813. (208)* | 300 | 850 |

289                                        290

| 288 Classic type. Corn ear dividing CA MV. ℞. Horse r., branch above., CVNO. *M. 206-07; V. 2025/27; BMC 1827-31/33. (208)* | 250 | 650 |
|---|---|---|
| 289 — Similar, horse l., lis like object above. *M. 208; V. 2029; BMC 1834-35. (209)* | 475 | 1250 |
| 290 **Quarter Stater.** Biga type. Similar to 280. *M. 202; V. 1913; BMC 1836/A. (210)* | 200 | 525 |

292                                        296

| 292 Linear type. Similar to 281. *M. 209; V. 1927; BMC 1837-42. (211)* | 135 | 300 |
|---|---|---|
| 293 Wild type. Similar to 283. *M. —; V. 1935; BMC 1843-44. (211)* | 125 | 275 |
| 294 Plastic type. Similar to 286. *M. 204; V. 2015; BMC 1846-48. (211)* | 110 | 250 |
| 295 — Similar but corn ear dividing CAM CVN. *M. 205; V. 2017; BMC 1845. (212)* | 135 | 325 |
| 296 Classic type. Similar to 288. *M. —; V. 2038; BMC —. (211)* | 165 | 425 |

## SILVER

299

|  | | F £ | VF £ |
|---|---|---|---|
| 299 | **Unit.** Two bull headed serpents, inter twined. R̶. Horse l., CVNO. *M. 214; V. 1947; BMC 1856. (213)* ........................................................ | 125 | 475 |
| 300 | Curled serpent inside wheel. R̶. Winged horse l., CVN. *M. —; V. —; BMC 1857* ............................................................................................... | 125 | 475 |
| 301 | CVN on panel R̶. Horse l., (C)M. *M. 255; V. 1949; BMC 1858-59. (228)* | 75 | 250 |
| 302 | CVNO BELI on two panels. R̶. CVN below horseman r. *M. 216/7; V. 1951/53; BMC 1862. (215)*.................................................................... | 85 | 300 |
| 303 | Head l., CAMVL. R̶. CVNO beneath Victory std. r. *M. 215; V. 2045; BMV 1863-65. (214)* .............................................................................. | 85 | 300 |

304                                      305

|  | | F £ | VF £ |
|---|---|---|---|
| 304 | Two leaves dividing CVN. R̶. Horseman r., CAM. *M. 218; V. 2047; BMC 1866-67. (216)* ....................................................................... | 100 | 375 |
| 305 | Flower dividing CAMV. R̶. CVNO below horse r. *M. 219; V. 2049; BMC1867A. (217)* .............................................................................. | 100 | 400 |
| 306 | CVNO on panel. R̶. CAMV on panel below griffin. *M. 234; V. 2051; BMC 1868-69. (218)* .............................................................................. | 95 | 350 |
| 307 | CAMVL on panel. R̶. CVNO below centaur l. carrying palm. *M. 234a; V. 1918; BMC —. (219)* ............................................................................ | 110 | 425 |
| 308 | CAMVL on panel. R̶. Figure seated l. holding wine amphora, CVNOBE. *M. —; V. —; BMC —. (219A)* ............................................................. | 75 | 250 |
| 309 | Plant, CVNOBELINVS. R̶. Figure stg. r. holding club and thunderbolt dividing CA MV. *M. —; V .—; BMC 1897. (219B)* ................................. | 110 | 425 |
| 310 | Laur. hd. r., CVNOBELINVS. R̶. Winged horse springing l., CAMV below. *M. —; V. —; BMC —. (219C)*.................................................... | 100 | 375 |
| 311 | CVNO on panel, wreath around. R̶. Winged horse r., TASC F. *M. 235; V. 2053; BMC 1870. (220)*........................................................................ | 100 | 375 |

312                                      313

|  | | F £ | VF £ |
|---|---|---|---|
| 312 | Head r., CVNOBELINI. R̶. Horse r., TASCIO. *M. 236; V. 2055; BMC 1871-73. (221)* ...................................................................................... | 75 | 250 |
| 313 | Winged bust r., CVNO. R̶. Sphinx std. l., TASCIO. *M. 237; V. 2057; BMC 1874-78. (222)* ...................................................................................... | 55 | 185 |

314                    316

| | F £ | VF £ |
|---|---|---|
| 314 Draped female fig. r., TASCIIOVAN. ℞. Figure std. r. playing lyre, tree behind. *M. 238; V. 2059; BMC 1879-82. (223)* | 85 | 300 |
| 315 Figure stg. l., holding club and lionskin., CVNO. ℞. Female rider r., TASCIOVA. *M. 239; V. 2061; BMC 1884-85. (224)* | 75 | 250 |
| 316 Female head r., CVNOBELINVS. ℞. Victory r., TASCIO(VAN). *M. —; V. —; BMC 1883. (224A)* | 75 | 250 |
| 317 Fig. r. carrying dead animal, CVNOBELINVS. ℞. Fig. stg. holding bow, dog at side, TASCIIOVANI. *M. 240; V. 2063; BMC 1886-88. (225)* | 85 | 300 |
| 318 CVNO on panel, horn above, dolphin below. ℞. Fig. stg. r. altar behind. *M. 241/41a; V. 2065; BMC 1889-90. (226)* | 100 | 375 |

319

| | | |
|---|---|---|
| 319 CVN on panel. ℞. Fig. holding club walking r., CVN. *M. 254; V. 2067; BMC 1891-92. (227)* | 95 | 350 |
| 320 CVN in wreath. ℞. CAM, dog? trampling on serpent r. *M. 256; V. 2069; BMC 1893. (229)* | 120 | 450 |
| 321 Winged horse l., CVN. ℞. Std. fig. r. *M. 258; V. 2071; BMC 1896. (230)* | 100 | 375 |
| 322 CVNO in angles of cross. ℞. Capricorn r., CVNO. *M. —; V. —; BMC 1898* | 100 | 375 |

## BRONZE

| | | |
|---|---|---|
| 323 Head l., CVNO. ℞. Boar l., branch above. *M. 220; V. 1969; BMC—. (232)* | 60 | 225 |
| 324 CVNOB ELINI in two panels. ℞. Victory std. l., TASC. *M. 221; V. 1971; BMC 1921-27. (233)* | 40 | 165 |
| 325 Winged horse l., CAM. ℞. Winged Victory stg l., CVN. *M. 222; V. 1973; BMC 1938-43. (234)* | 45 | 175 |

326

| | | |
|---|---|---|
| 326 Bearded head facing ℞. Boar l., CVN. *M.223; V.1963; BMC 1904-05. (235)* | 45 | 185 |
| 327 Ram-headed animal coiled up in double ornamental circle. ℞. Animal l., CAM. *M. 224; V. 1965; BMC —. (236)* | 50 | 200 |
| 328 Griffin r., CAMV. ℞. Horse r., CVN. *M. 225; V. 2081; BMC 1909-12. (237)* | 45 | 175 |

| | F | VF |
| --- | --- | --- |
| | £ | £ |

329 Bearded head l., CAMV. ℞. CVN or CVNO below horse l. *M. 226, 229; V. 2085/2131; BMC 1900-01. (238)* ............................................................ 40 165

330 Laureate head r., CVNO. ℞. CVN below bull butting l. *M. 227; V. 2083; BMC 1902-03. (239)* ................................................................................ 50 200

331 Crude head r., CVN. ℞. Figure stg. l., CVN. *M. 228; V. 2135; BMC —. (240)* ................................................................................................ 55 225

332

332 CAMVL / ODVNO in two panels. ℞. CVNO beneath sphinx crouching l. *M. 230; V. 1977; BMC 1928-30. (241)* .................................................. 45 175

333 Winged horse l., CAMV. ℞. Victory stg. r. divides CV NO. *M. 231; V. 1979; BMC 1931-34. (242)* ................................................................ 45 175

334 Victory walking r. ℞. CVN below, horseman r. *M. 232; V. 1981; BMC 1935. (243)* ........................................................................................ 55 225

335 Head l., CAM. ℞. CVNO below eagle. *M. 233; V. 2087; BMC —. (244)* 55 225

336                     337

336 Head l., CVNOBELINI. ℞. Centaur r., TASCIOVANI.F. *M. 242; V. 2089; BMC 1968-71. (245)* ................................................................ 35 150

337 Helmeted bust r. ℞. TASCIIOVANII above, sow stg. r., F below. *M. 243; V. 2091; BMC 1956-60. (246)* ........................................................ 35 150

338 Horseman galloping r. holding dart and shield, CVNOB. ℞. Warrior stg. l., TASCIIOVANTIS. *M. 244; V. 2093; BMC 1961-67. (247)* ................ 35 140

339

339 Helmeted bust l., CVOBELINVS REX. ℞. TASC FIL below boar l., std. on haunches. *M. 245; V. 1983; BMC 1952-55. (248)* ........................ 50 200

340 Bare head r., CVNOBELINVS REX. ℞. TASC below bull butting r. *M. 246; V. 2095; BMC 1944-51. (249)* .................................................... 40 160

341 Bare head l., CVNO. ℞. TASC below bull stg. r. *M. 247; V. 1985; BMC —. (250)* ................................................................................................ 50 200

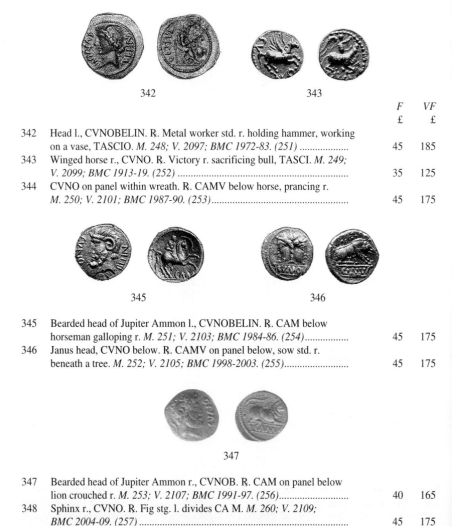

342                                         343

|  | F £ | VF £ |
|---|---|---|
| 342 Head l., CVNOBELIN. ℞. Metal worker std. r. holding hammer, working on a vase, TASCIO. *M. 248; V. 2097; BMC 1972-83. (251)* | 45 | 185 |
| 343 Winged horse r., CVNO. ℞. Victory r. sacrificing bull, TASCI. *M. 249; V. 2099; BMC 1913-19. (252)* | 35 | 125 |
| 344 CVNO on panel within wreath. ℞. CAMV below horse, prancing r. *M. 250; V. 2101; BMC 1987-90. (253)* | 45 | 175 |

345                                         346

| 345 Bearded head of Jupiter Ammon l., CVNOBELIN. ℞. CAM below horseman galloping r. *M. 251; V. 2103; BMC 1984-86. (254)* | 45 | 175 |
|---|---|---|
| 346 Janus head, CVNO below. ℞. CAMV on panel below, sow std. r. beneath a tree. *M. 252; V. 2105; BMC 1998-2003. (255)* | 45 | 175 |

347

| 347 Bearded head of Jupiter Ammon r., CVNOB. ℞. CAM on panel below lion crouched r. *M. 253; V. 2107; BMC 1991-97. (256)* | 40 | 165 |
|---|---|---|
| 348 Sphinx r., CVNO. ℞. Fig stg. l. divides CA M. *M. 260; V. 2109; BMC 2004-09. (257)* | 45 | 175 |
| 349 Horse r. ℞. CVN below horseman r. *M. 261; V. 1987; BMC 1936-47. (258)* | 50 | 200 |
| 350 Animal l. looking back. ℞. CVN below horse l. *M. 233a; V. 1967; BMC—. (259)* | 50 | 200 |
| 350A Ship, CVN below. ℞. Fig. r. dividing S E. *M. —; V. 1989; BMC 2010.* | 150 | 650 |

## "SOLIDV"

### SILVER

351

| | F<br>£ | VF<br>£ |
|---|---|---|
| 351 **Unit.** SOLIDV in centre of looped circle. R, Stg. fig. l., CVNO.<br>*M. 259; V. 2073; BMC 1894-95. (231)*..................................................... | 325 | 950 |

## "AGR"

### GOLD

| | | |
|---|---|---|
| 352 Quarter Stater. Corn ear dividing CAM CVN. R. Horse r., branch<br>above., AGR below *M. —; V. —; BMC 1854*.......................................... | 375 | 1000 |

353

| | | |
|---|---|---|
| 353 — R. Horse r., branch above., cross and A below. *M. —; V. —;*<br>*BMC 1855* ............................................................................................... | 350 | 975 |

### SILVER

| | | |
|---|---|---|
| 354 **Unit.** AGR inside wreath. R. Female dog r., AGR below. *M. —; V. —;*<br>*BMC 1899*................................................................................................ | 300 | 900 |

## EPATICCUS
### (1st Half 1st Century A.D.)

Epaticcus, styled as a son of Tasciovanus on his coins, was most probably a brother of Cunobelin. The corn ear employed on his staters is similar to that of his brother's produced at Colchester. His coins appear in northern Atrebatic territory and conform to the area's denominational structure. It seems likely that Epaticcus's coinage reflects an incursion into Atrebatic territory by the Trinovantian/Catuvellaunian dynasty.

### GOLD

355

| | | |
|---|---|---|
| 355 **Stater.** Corn ear dividing TAS CIF. R. Horseman r., with spear and<br>shield. EPATI. *M. 262; V. 575; BMC 2021-23. (112)*............................... | 675 | 1850 |

## SILVER

356　　　　　　　　　　　　357

| | | F<br>£ | VF<br>£ |
|---|---|---|---|
| 356 | **Unit.** Head of Hercules r., EPAT(I). Ɍ. Eagle stg. on snake.<br>*M. 263/a; V. 580; BMC 2024-2268/2270-76. (113)* ................................ | 25 | 80 |
| 357 | Victory seated r. TASCIOV. Ɍ. Boar r., EPAT. *M. 263; V. 581;*<br>*BMC 2294-2328. (114)* .............................................................................. | 30 | 125 |

358

| 358 | Bearded head l., TASCIO. Ɍ. EPATI below lion r. *M. —; V. 582;*<br>*BMC 2329* ................................................................................................ | 125 | 400 |
|---|---|---|---|
| 359 | EPATI inside panel. Ɍ. Lion r. *M. —; V. 583; BMC 2330. (114A)* .......... | 125 | 375 |

360　　　　　　　　　　　361

| 360 | **Minim.** EPATI. Ɍ. Boars head r., TA. *M. 264; V. 585; BMC 2331-46.*<br>*(115)* ........................................................................................................ | 30 | 100 |
|---|---|---|---|
| 361 | TA inside star. Ɍ. Winged horse r., EPA below. *M. —; V. 560;*<br>*BMC 2351-57. (116)* ................................................................................ | 30 | 100 |
| 362 | Helmeted head r. Ɍ. Horse r., E below. *M. —; V. —; BMC 2358-63* ....... | 35 | 125 |
| 363 | EPATI. Ɍ. Winged horse r., cross below. *M. —; V .—; BMC 2365* ......... | 50 | 165 |

## CARATACUS
### (1st Half 1st Century A.D.)

Coins inscribed CARA have been traditionally associated with the historically attested son of Cunobelin, Caratacus the leader of British resistance against Rome. His coins appear in the same area as those of Epaticcus and he may have been his successor.

## SILVER

364　　　　　　　　　　　364A

| 364 | **Unit.** Head of Hercules r., CARA. Ɍ. Eagle stg. on snake. *M. 265;*<br>*V. 593; BMC 2376-84. (117)* ..................................................................... | 100 | 350 |
|---|---|---|---|
| 364A | **Minim.** CARA around pellet in ring. Ɍ. Winged horse r. *M. —; V. 595;*<br>*BMC 2385-89. (117A)* ............................................................................. | 85 | 225 |

# DUROTRIGES

(Mid 1st Century B.C. to Mid 1st Century A.D.)

The Durotriges inhabited West Hampshire, Dorset and adjoining parts of Somerset and Wiltshire. Their coinage is one of the most distinctive in Britain due to its rapid debasement. The disappearance of precious metals from the coinage should perhaps be linked to the declining trade between the south-west and western Gaul, following the Roman conquest of the Gaul. Hengistbury Head is the probable mint site of the cast bronzes. Coins inscribed CRAB have been traditionally associated with the tribe.

## UNINSCRIBED

### SILVER

|     |                                                                                                                              | F<br>£ | VF<br>£ |
|-----|------------------------------------------------------------------------------------------------------------------------------|--------|---------|
| 365 | **Stater.** White Gold type. Derived from Westerham stater (no. 21).<br>M. 317; V. 1235, 52, 54, 55; BMC 2525-2731. (60)      | 95     | 275     |

366                                   368

|     |                                                                                                                                                                  | F<br>£ | VF<br>£ |
|-----|------------------------------------------------------------------------------------------------------------------------------------------------------------------|--------|---------|
| 366 | Silver type. Similar. M. 317; V. 1235, 52, 54, 55; BMC 2525-2731. (60)                                                                                           | 40     | 110     |
| 367 | Billon type. Similar. M. 317; V. 1235, 52, 54, 55; BMC 2525-2731. (60)                                                                                           | 25     | 75      |
| 368 | **Quarter Stater.** Geometric type. Crescent design. R. Zig-zag pattern.<br>M. 319; V. 1242/29; BMC 2734-79. (61). Quality of metal varies, obv.<br>almost blank on later issues | 30     | 95      |

369

|     |                                                                                                                           | F<br>£ | VF<br>£ |
|-----|---------------------------------------------------------------------------------------------------------------------------|--------|---------|
| 369 | Starfish type. Spiral. R. Zig-zag pattern. M. 320; V. 1270; BMC 2780-81<br>(61A)                                          | 45     | 175     |
| 370 | Hampshire Thin Flan type. Crude head of lines and pellets. R.<br>Stylised horse l. M. 321; V. 1280; BMC 2782-87. (62)     | 55     | 200     |

### BRONZE

|     |                                                                                                      | F<br>£ | VF<br>£ |
|-----|------------------------------------------------------------------------------------------------------|--------|---------|
| 371 | **Stater.** Struck Bronze type. Similar to No.365-67. M. 318; V. 1290;<br>BMC 2790-2859. (81)         | 20     | 50      |

372

| | F | VF |
| | £ | £ |

372   Cast Bronze type. Many varities, as illustration. *M. 322-70;*
*V. 1322-70; BMC 2860-2936. (82)* ........................................................... 35 125

## "CRAB"

### SILVER

373

373   **Unit.** CRAB in angles of cross. ℞. Eagle. *M. 371; V. 1285;*
*BMC 2788. (145)* ...................................................................................... 325 900
373A  **Minim.** CRAB on tablet. ℞. Star shape. *M. 372; V. 1286; BMC 2789.*
*(146)* ...................................................................................................... 175 575

## DOBUNNI
### (Mid 1st Century B.C. to Mid 1st Century A.D.)
Dobunnic territory stretched over Gloucestershire, Hereford and Worcester and into parts of Somerset, Wiltshire and Gwent. The earliest Dobunnic coins are developed from the British Q stater, and have the distinctive tree-like motif of the tribe on the obverse. The inscribed coinage is difficult to arrange chronologically and it may be that some of the rulers named held different parts of the territory simultaneously.

## UNINSCRIBED
### GOLD
374   **Stater.** Plain except for tree-like object. ℞. Three tailed horse r.,
wheel below. *M. 374; V. 1005; BMC 2937-40. (43)* ............................... 275 800
375   **Quarter Stater.** Plain with traces of wreath pattern. ℞. Horse r.
*M. 68; V. 1010-3; BMC 2942-46. (52)* ................................................... 135 300
376   Wreath pattern. ℞. Horse l., pellet in ring motifs in field. *M. 74; V. 1015;*
*BMC 2949. (51)* ...................................................................................... 145 325

## SILVER

377 378

|  | | F<br>£ | VF<br>£ |
|---|---|---|---|
| 377 | **Unit.** Allen types A-F/I-J. Regular series. Head r. ℞. Triple-tailed horse l. or r. *M. 374a, b/75/76, 378a-384; V. 1020/45/49/74/78/95/1135/1137; BMC 2950-3011. (63-64). Style becomes progressively more abstract, from-* | 25 | 90 |
| 378 | Allen types L-O. Irregular series. Similar to last. *M. 377-384d; V. 1170-85; BMC 3012-22. (63-64)* | 35 | 135 |

## INSCRIBED
The following types are not arranged chronologically.

## ANTED
### GOLD
| 379 | **Stater.** Dobunnic emblem. ℞. ANTED or ANTEDRIG over triple tailed horse r., wheel below. *M. 385-86; V. 1062-69; BMC 3023-3031. (260)* | 375 | 1050 |
|---|---|---|---|

### SILVER
| 380 | **Unit.** Crude head r. ℞. ANTED over horse. *M. 387; V. 1082; BMC 3032-38. (261)* | 60 | 165 |
|---|---|---|---|

## EISV
### GOLD

381

| 381 | **Stater.** Dobunnic emblem. ℞. EISV or EISVRIG over triple tailed horse r., wheel below. *M. 388; V. 1105; BMC 3039-42. (262)* | 475 | 1350 |
|---|---|---|---|

### SILVER

382

| 382 | **Unit.** Crude head r. ℞. Horse l., EISV. *M. 389; V. 1110; BMC 3043-55. (263)* | 45 | 135 |
|---|---|---|---|

## INAM or INARA

### GOLD

| | | F £ | VF £ |
|---|---|---|---|
| 383 | **Stater.** Dobunnic emblem. R̃. INAM or INARA over triple tailed horse r., wheel below. *M. 390; V. 1140; BMC 3056. (264)*...................... | 825 | 2500 |

## CATTI

### GOLD

384

| | | | |
|---|---|---|---|
| 384 | **Stater.** Dobunnic emblem. R̃. CATTI over triple tailed horse r., wheel below. *M. 391; V. 1130; BMC 3057-60. (265)*......................................... | 325 | 950 |

## COMUX

### GOLD

| | | | |
|---|---|---|---|
| 385 | **Stater.** Dobunnic emblem. R̃. COMVX retrograde, over triple tailed horse r., wheel below. *M. 392; V. 1092; BMC 3061-63. (266)* ............... | 750 | 2250 |

## CORIO

### GOLD

386                    387

| | | | |
|---|---|---|---|
| 386 | **Stater.** Dobunnic emblem. R̃. CORIO over triple tailed horse r., wheel below. *M. 393; V. 1035; BMC 3064-3133. (267)*.................................... | 350 | 975 |
| 387 | **Quarter Stater.** COR in centre. R̃. Horse r., without legend. *M. 394; V. 1039; BMC 3134. (268)*......................................................................... | 475 | 1250 |

# BODVOC

## GOLD

388                                              389

|  | | F | VF |
|---|---|---|---|
|  | | £ | £ |

388  **Stater.** BODVOC across field. R. Horse r., without legend. *M. 395;*
 *V. 1052; BMC 3135-42. (269)* ...............................................................  650  1750

## SILVER

389  **Unit.** Head l., BODVOC. R. Horse r., without legend. *M. 396; V. 1057;*
 *BMC 3143-45. (270)* ...........................................................................  110  350

# CORIELTAUVI

The Corieltauvi, formerly known as the Coritani, occupied Lincolnshire and adjoining parts of
Yorkshire, Northamptonshire, Leicestershire and Nottinghamshire. The earliest staters, the South
Ferriby type, are developed from Gallo-Belgic C staters, and are associated with the silver
Boar/Horse types. The distinctive dish shaped scyphate coinages have no parallels in Britain and
stand apart from the main series. The later inscribed issues present a complex system of inscriptions.
It has been suggested that some of the later inscriptions refer to pairs of names, possibly joint rulers
or moneyers and rulers.

## EARLY UNINSCRIBED
(Mid to Late 1st Century B.C.)

## GOLD

390                                              393

390  **Stater.** South Ferriby type. Crude laureate head. R. Disjointed horse l.,
 rosette or star below, anchor shape and pellets above. *M. 449-50;*
 *V. 809-815/19; BMC 3146-3179. (30)* .....................................................  135  300
391  Wheel type. Similar, but wheel below horse. *M. 449c; V. 817; BMC 3180*  325  900
392  Kite type. Similar to 390, but diamond shape containing pellets above,
 spiral below horse. *M. 447; V. 825; BMC 3181-84. (29)* ........................  200  525
393  Domino type. Similar to last, but with rectangle containing pellets.
 *M. 448; V. 829; BMC 3185-86. (29)* .........................................................  175  450

394                                       395

|     |     | F<br>£ | VF<br>£ |
|-----|-----|--------|---------|

394   Trefoil type. Trefoil with central rosette of seven pellets. R. Similar to
      390. *M. 450a; V. 821; BMC —. (30A)* ..................................................... 1350  4500
395   North Lincolnshire Scyphate type. Stylised boar r. or l. R. Large S
      symbol with pellets and rings in field. *M. —; V. —; BMC 3187-93* ......... 275   700
*\* chipped or cracked specimens are often encountered and are worth less*

## SILVER

396

396   **Unit.** Boar/Horse type I.Boar r., large pellet and ring motif above,
      reversed S below. R. Horse l. or r., pellet in ring above. *M. 405-06,
      451; V. 855-60, 864, 867; BMC 3194-3214. (66)* .................................... 60   175
397   Boar Horse type II. Vestiges of boar on obv. R. Horse l. or r. *M. 410,
      452-53; V. 875-877; BMC 3214-27. (68)* ................................................ 45   125

398                          399

398   Boar Horse type III. Blank. R. Horse l.or r. *M. 453-54; V. 884-77;
      BMC 3228-35. (69)* ................................................................................ 35   95
399   **Fractional Unit.** Similar to 396-97. *M. 406a, 451a; V. 862/66;
      BMC 3236-3250. (67)* ............................................................................ 35   110
400   Similar to 398. *M. —; V. 877-81; BMC 3251-55. (70/71)* ........................ 20   70
401   Pattern/Horse. Flower pattern. R. Horse l. *M. —; V. —; BMC 3256-57*... 65   225

## INSCRIBED

(Early to Mid 1st Century A.D.)
The following types are not arranged chronologically.

## AVN COST

### GOLD

|  |  | F | VF |
|---|---|---|---|
|  |  | £ | £ |
| 402 | **Stater.** Crude wreath design. R̶. Disjointed horse l., AVN COST. *M. 457;* *V. 910; BMC 3258. (286)* ........................................................... | 475 | 1350 |

### SILVER

403

| 403 | **Unit.** Remains of wreath or blank. R̶. AVN COST, horse l. *M. 458;* *V. 914; BMC 3261-66. (287)* ........................................................ | 40 | 100 |
|---|---|---|---|
| 404 | **Fractional Unit.** Similar. *M. —; l V. 918; BMC 3267-68. (288)* ............. | 35 | 90 |

## ESVP RASV

### GOLD

| 405 | **Stater.** Crude wreath design. R̶. Disjointed horse l., IISVP RASV. *M. 456b; V. 920; BMC 3269. (289)* ............................................................. | 375 | 975 |
|---|---|---|---|

### SILVER

| 406 | **Unit.** Similar. *M. 456c; V. 924; BMC 3272-73. (290)* ............................... | 90 | 300 |
|---|---|---|---|

## VEP

### GOLD

| 407 | **Stater.** Blank or with traces of wreath. R̶. Disjointed horse l., VEP. *M. —; V. 905; BMC 3274-75. (296)* .......................................................... | 375 | 950 |
|---|---|---|---|

### SILVER

| 408 | **Unit.** Blank or with traces of wreath. R̶. VEP, horse r. *M. —; V. 963;* *BMC 3277-82. (297)* ................................................................................ | 60 | 165 |
|---|---|---|---|
| 409 | **Half Unit.** Similar. *M. 464b; V. 967; BMC 3283-3295. (298)* ................. | 35 | 100 |

## VEP CORF

### GOLD

410

| | | F | VF |
|---|---|---|---|
| | | £ | £ |
| 410 | **Stater.** Crude wreath design. R̟. Disjointed horse l., VEP CORF. *M. 459, 460; V. 930/40/60; BMC 3296-3304. (291)* | 350 | 850 |

### SILVER

| 411 | **Unit.** Similar. *M. 460b/464; V. 934/50; BMC 3305-14. (292)* | 40 | 120 |

412

| 412 | Similar but VEPOC (M)ES, pellet in ring below horse. *M. —; V. 955; BMC —. (294)* | 60 | 175 |
| 413 | **Half Unit.** Similar. *M. 464a; V. 938/58; BMC 3316-24. (293/95)* | 35 | 100 |

## DVMNO TIGIR SENO

### GOLD

414

| 414 | **Stater.** DVMN(OC) across wreath. R̟. Horse l., TIGIR SENO. *M. 461; V. 972; BMC 3325-27. (299)* | 625 | 1650 |

### SILVER

415

| 415 | **Unit.** DVMNOC in two lines. R̟. Horse r., TIGIR SENO. *M. 462; V. 974; BMC 3328-29. (300)* | 200 | 600 |

# VOLISIOS DVMNOCOVEROS

## GOLD

416

| | | F £ | VF £ |
|---|---|---|---|
| 416 | **Stater.** VOLISIOS between three lines in wreath. ℞. Horse r. or l., DVMNOCOVEROS. *M. 463/a; V. 978-80; BMC 3330-3336. (301)*....... | 375 | 950 |

## SILVER

| | | | |
|---|---|---|---|
| 417 | **Unit.** Similar. ℞. Horse r., DVMNOCO. *M. 463a; V. 980; BMC 3339. (302)*.................. | 165 | 475 |
| 418 | **Half Unit.** Similar. *M. 465; V. 984; BMC 3340-41. (303)*...................... | 70 | 225 |

# VOLISIOS DVMNOVELLAUNOS

## GOLD

| | | | |
|---|---|---|---|
| 419 | **Stater.** VOLISIOS between three lines in wreath. ℞. Horse r. or l., DVMNOVELAVNOS. *M. 466; V .988; BMC 3342-43. (304)*............... | 675 | 2000 |

## SILVER

| | | | |
|---|---|---|---|
| 420 | **Half Unit.** As last but DVMNOVE. *M. 467; V. 992; BMC 3344-46. (305).* | 150 | 475 |

# VOLISIOS CARTIVEL

## SILVER

| | | | |
|---|---|---|---|
| 421 | **Half Unit.** VOLISIOS between three lines in wreath. ℞. Horse r., CARTILEV. *M. 468; V. 994; BMC 3347-48. (306)*................................. | 225 | 650 |

# IAT ISO E

## SILVER

| | | | |
|---|---|---|---|
| 422 | **Unit.** IAT ISO (retrograde)on tablet, rosettes above and below. ℞. Horse r., E above. *M. 416; V. 998; BMC 3349-51. (284)*........................ | 175 | 525 |

# CAT

## SILVER

| | | | |
|---|---|---|---|
| 422A | **Unit.** Boar r., pellet ring above, CAT above. ℞. Horse r. *M. —; V. —; BMC 3352* ............................................................................................. | 250 | 700 |

## LAT ISON

### GOLD

423

|     | F   | VF  |
| --- | --- | --- |
|     | £   | £   |

423   **Stater.** LAT ISO(N) in two lines retrograde. Ꝛ. Horse r., ISO in box
     above, N below. *M. —; V. —; BMC —. Only recorded as an AE/AV*
     *plated core, as illustrated.*........................................................................     *Extremely rare*

# ICENI

The Iceni, centered on Norfolk but also occupying neighbouring parts of Suffolk and
Cambridgeshire, are well attested in the post conquest period as the tribe who under Boudicca
revolted against Roman rule. Their earliest coins are likely to have been the British J staters, Norfolk
Wolf type (no.30/31), replaced around the mid first century B.C. by the Snettisham, Freckenham and
Irstead type gold staters and quarter staters. Contemporary with these are silver Boar/Horse and
Face/Horse units and fractions. The introduction of legends around the beginning of the millennia
led to the adoption of a new obverse design of back to back crescents. The continuation of the
coinage after the Roman invasion is attested by the coins of King Prasutagus. Some of the
Face/Horse units (no.434) have been attributed to Queen Boudicca.

### EARLY UNINSCRIBED
(Mid to Late 1st Century B.C.)
### GOLD

424                                                                   425

424   **Stater.** Snettisham type. Blank or with traces of pellet cross. Ꝛ. Horse
     r., serpent like pellet in ring motif above. *M. —; V .—; BMC 3353-59*....   275    800
425   Similar. Blank or with 3 short curved lines. Ꝛ. Horse r., symbol above
     more degraded. *M. —; V. —; BMC 3360-83* ............................................   250    675

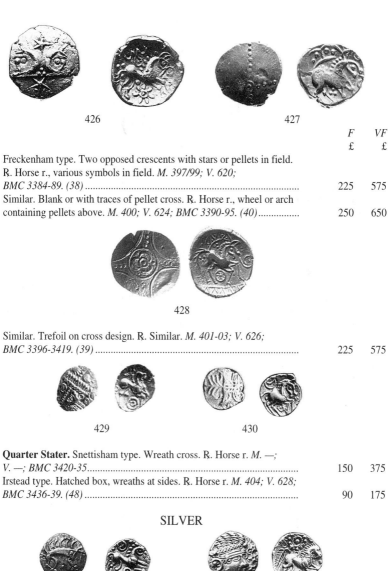

426    427

|   |   | F £ | VF £ |
|---|---|---|---|

426    Freckenham type. Two opposed crescents with stars or pellets in field.
       R. Horse r., various symbols in field. *M. 397/99; V. 620;*
       *BMC 3384-89. (38)* ................................................................................    225    575
427    Similar. Blank or with traces of pellet cross. R. Horse r., wheel or arch
       containing pellets above. *M. 400; V. 624; BMC 3390-95. (40)* ...............    250    650

428

428    Similar. Trefoil on cross design. R. Similar. *M. 401-03; V. 626;*
       *BMC 3396-3419. (39)* ............................................................................    225    575

429    430

429    **Quarter Stater.** Snettisham type. Wreath cross. R. Horse r. *M. —;*
       *V. —; BMC 3420-35* ..............................................................................    150    375
430    Irstead type. Hatched box, wreaths at sides. R. Horse r. *M. 404; V. 628;*
       *BMC 3436-39. (48)* ................................................................................    90    175

## SILVER

431    432

431    **Unit.** Boar / Horse type. Boar r. R. Horse r. *M. 407-09; V. 655-59;*
       *BMC 3440-3512. (72)* .............................................................................    25    70
432    Bury type. Head l. or r. R. Horse l. or r. *M. —; V. —; BMC 3524-35* ......    70    200

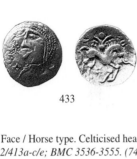

433                          433

|   |   | F | VF |
|---|---|---|----|
|   |   | £ | £ |

433   Early Face / Horse type. Celticised head l. or r. R. Horse l. or r.
      *M. 412/413a-c/e; BMC 3536-3555. (74)* ................................................ 90   300

434                          435

434   Face / Horse Regular type. Head r. R. Horse r. *M. 413/d; V. 790-94;
      BMC 3556-3759. (74). Attributed to Queen Boudicca by
      R.D. van Arsdell* ...................................................................................... 45   150
435   Early Pattern / Horse type. Cross of two opposed crescents. R. Horse
      l. or r. *M. 414-15; V. 675-79; BMC 3763-74. (75)* ................................... 30   90

436

436   ECEN symbol type. Two opposed crescents. R. Horse r. *M. 429;
      V. 752; BMC 4297-4325* ............................................................................ 20   55
437   **Half Unit.** Boar / Horse type. Similar to 431. *M. 411; V. 661;
      BMC 3513-20. (73)* ..................................................................................... 20   55
438   **Fractional Unit.** Early Pattern / Horse type. Similar to 435. *M. 417/a;
      V. 681-83; BMC 3775-89. (76/A)* ................................................................ 20   60

# INSCRIBED

(Early to Mid 1st Century A.D.)
The following types are not arranged chronologically.

# CAN DVRO

## SILVER

439

439   **Unit.** Boar. R. Horse r., CAN(S) above, DVRO below. *M. 434; V. 663;
      BMC 3521-23. (271)* ..................................................................................... 90   275

# ANTED

## GOLD

440

|       |       | F<br>£ | VF<br>£ |
|-------|-------|--------|---------|
| 440 | **Stater.** Triple crescent design. ℞. Horse r., ANTED monongram below.<br>M. 418; V. 705; BMC 3790. (272) ............................................................... | 525 | 1350 |

## SILVER

441

| 441 | **Unit.** Two opposed crescents. ℞. Horse r., ANTED. M. 419-21;<br>V. 710-11/15; BMC 3791-4025. (273) ...................................................... | 25 | 65 |
| 442 | **Fractional Unit.** Similar to last. M. 422; V. 720; BMC 4028-31. (274).. | 25 | 75 |

# ECEN

## GOLD

443

| 443 | **Stater.** Triple crescent design. ℞. Horse r., ECEN below. M. —; V. 725;<br>BMC 4032. .......................................................................................... | 975 | 3250 |

## SILVER

| 443A | **Unit.** Two opposed crescents. ℞, Horse r., ECEN. M. 424; V. 730;<br>BMC 4033-4215. (275) ............................................................................. | 25 | 60 |
| 443B | **Half Unit.** Similar to last. M. 431; V. 736; BMC 4216-17. (276) ............ | 20 | 60 |

## EDN

### SILVER

|  | F £ | VF £ |
|---|---|---|
| 444 **Unit.** Two opposed crescents. Ɍ, Horse r., ED, E, EI or EDN. *M. 423, 425b; V. 734/40; BMC 4219-81. (277)* | 20 | 60 |

## ECE

### GOLD

| 444A **Stater** Triple crescent design R. Horse r., ECE *M. — ; V. — ;* | 1000 | 3500 |

### SILVER

445

| 445 **Unit.** Two opposed crescents. Ɍ, Horse r., ECE. *M. 425-28; V. 761-66; BMC 4348-4538. (278-80)* | 25 | 60 |

## SAENU

### SILVER

| 446 **Unit.** Two opposed crescents. Ɍ. Horse r., SAENV. *M. 433; V. 770; BMC 4540-57. (281)* | 40 | 110 |

## AESU

### SILVER

447

| 447 **Unit.** Two opposed crescents. Ɍ. Horse r., AESV. *M. 432; V. 775; BMC 4558-72. (282)* | 40 | 110 |

## ALE SCA

### SILVER

| 448 **Unit.** Boar r., ALE. Ɍ. Horse r., SCA. *M. 469; V. 996; BMC 4576* | 125 | 375 |

## AEDIC SIA

### SILVER

| | | F £ | VF £ |
|---|---|---|---|
| 449 | **Unit.** AEDIC in two lines. R. Horse r., SIA? below. *M.—; V.—; BMC 4581* .......................................................................................... | 250 | 650 |

## PRASUTAGUS

### SILVER

450

| | | | |
|---|---|---|---|
| 450 | **Unit.** Romanised head l., SUB RII PRASTO. R. Rearing horse r., ESICO FECIT. *M. 434a; V. 780; BMC 4577-80. (283)*............................ | 575 | 1650 |

*This legend translates as "Under King Prasto, Esico made me", giving the name of both King and moneyer.*

The systematic conquest of Britain by the Romans began in A.D. 43 when the Emperor Claudius (41-54), anxious to enhance his military reputation, authorized an invasion in which he personally participated, albeit in a purely symbolic role. The initial military contact between the two cultures had taken place almost a century before when Julius Caesar, during the course of his conquest of Celtic Gaul, led expeditions to the island in 55 and 54 B.C. Although no actual Roman occupation of Britain resulted from Caesar's reconnoitring campaigns, commercial intercourse was certainly accelerated, as evidenced by the 'Romanization' of the British Celtic coinage in the final decades of its production.

The Claudian conquest, commencing in A.D. 43, brought about a complete change in the nature of the currency circulating in Britain and ushered in a period lasting more than three and a half centuries during which Roman coinage was the only official medium of exchange. Local copies of the money brought with them by the four legions of the invasion army began to appear at a very early stage, the most popular type for imitation being the well-known Claudian copper as with reverse type fighting Minerva. Some of these copies are well-executed and of a style not much inferior to the prototype, suggesting that their local minting may have been officially sanctioned by the Roman government in order to make good a shortage of currency in the newly-conquered territory. Other examples are of much poorer style and execution and are frequently well below the normal weight of a Claudian as (usually between 10 and 11 grams). These copies must have been issued unofficially and provide evidence of the huge demand for this type of currency in a population which had never before experienced the benefits of having base metal coins available for small everyday transactions.

In the decades that followed, the boundaries of the Roman province of Britannia were continually pushed further north and west until, under the celebrated Flavian governor Gnaeus Julius Agricola, the Roman army even penetrated to northern Scotland (A.D. 83/4). A few years later, under Trajan, the northern frontier was established along the Tyne-Solway line, a barrier made permanent by the construction of Hadrian's Wall following the emperor's visit to the province in 122. For a brief period in the mid-2nd century the frontier was temporarily advanced to the Forth-Clyde line with the building of the Antonine Wall, though this seems to have been abandoned early in the reign of Marcus Aurelius (ca. 163) when the Hadrianic barrier was re-commissioned and became the permanent frontier. The security thus provided to the now-peaceful province in the south facilitated urban expansion and the development of commerce. The new prosperity brought a flood of Roman coinage into the island-province and it was no longer necessary for shortages to be made good by large scale local imitation.

Until the mid-3rd century the production of Roman coinage remained the prerogative of the mint in the capital, with only occasional issues from provincial centres to serve short-term local needs. But with the deepening political and economic crisis in the third quarter of the century there was a dramatic decentralization of minting operations, with permanent establishments being set up in many important cities in the western as well as the eastern provinces. Britain, however, still remained without an official mint at this time and in the dark days of the 270s, when the separatist Gallic Empire to which Britain belonged was close to collapse, large scale production of imitative antoniniani (commonly called 'barbarous radiates') occurred in the province. The integrity and prestige of the Empire was, to some extent, restored by a rapid succession of Illyrian 'soldier emperors', until the situation was finally stabilized by Diocletian (A.D. 284-305) who established the tetrarchy system under which governmental responsibility was shared by four rulers. By the end of the 3rd century Britain had been reorganized into a civil diocese of four provinces: it had already been subdivided into Britannia Superior and Britannia Inferior almost a hundred years before, under Septimius Severus or Caracalla.

It was left to the colourful and enigmatic usurper Carausius (A.D. 287-293) to establish mints in Britain. It was, of course, vital for him to do so as his dominion was mostly confined to the island-province. Londinium (London) was his principal mint, with a secondary establishment at a place usually signing itself 'C' (probably Camulodunum, modern Colchester). After the downfall of Carausius' murderer and successor Allectus (293-296) Britain was restored to the central government, an event commemorated by the celebrated gold medallion of Constantius I showing the Caesar riding alongside the Thames approaching the gateway of the city of Londinium. At this point the mysterious 'C' mint disappears from the picture. Londinium, on the other hand, retained its status as an official mint under Diocletian's tetrarchy and its successors down to A.D. 325, when it was closed by Constantine the Great who regarded it as superfluous to his needs. In nearly four decades of existence as a Roman mint Londinium had produced a varied and extensive coinage in the names of almost all the emperors, empresses and Caesars of the period. It was destined never again to be active during Roman times, unless the extremely rare gold and silver issues of the late 4th century usurper Magnus Maximus, signed AVG, AVGOB and AVGPS, are correctly attributed to Londinium under its late Roman name of Augusta.

The termination of Roman rule in the British provinces is traditionally dated to A.D. 410 when the emperor Honorius, in response to an appeal for aid from his British subjects, told them to arrange for their own defence as best they might ('Rescript of Honorius'). In reality, the end probably came quite gradually. As the machinery of government ground to a halt and the soldiers stopped receiving their pay there would have been a steady drift of population away from the semi-ruinous cities and military installations to the countryside, where they could better provide for themselves through farming. Under these conditions the need for coinage would have been drastically reduced, as a primitive economy based on barter would largely have replaced the complex monetary economy of the late Roman period. In any case the supply of coinage from the Continent would now have dried up. The few monetary transactions which still took place were made with worn-out coins from earlier periods augmented by local imitations, production of which in Britain had resumed in the mid-4th century. Such was the pitiful end of the long tradition of Roman coinage in the remote island-province of Britannia. More than two centuries of 'Dark Ages' were to elapse before England's new rulers, the Anglo-Saxons, commenced the issue of gold thrymsas, the designs of many of which were based on late Roman types.

As Rome's Imperial coinage provided the currency needs of this country over a period of almost four centuries no representative collection of British coins is complete without some examples of these important issues. The following listing is divided into four categories: 1. Regular Roman issues, all of which would have been legal tender in Britain after A.D. 43; 2. Issues with types referring specifically to the province of Britannia, usually in commemoration of military campaigns in the north; 3. Official Roman coinage struck in Britain; 4. Imitations of Roman coins produced in Britain, all but possibly some of the earliest being of unofficial origin. The reference 'R.R.C.' is to the listing of the type in Michael Crawford's *Roman Republican Coinage* (Cambridge, 1974); and 'R.I.C.' to *The Roman Imperial Coinage* (London, 1923-1994, in ten volumes).

For more detailed collectors' information on Roman coinage, including a more comprehensive listing of types, the reader is referred to *Roman Coins and their Values Volumes 1 and 2* by David R. Sear. The forthcoming volume 3 will cover A.D. 235—491. A complete catalogue of silver issues may be found in the 5 volumes of *Roman Silver Coins* (H.A. Seaby and C.E. King) which provides a quick and convenient reference and is especially aimed at the collector. Gilbert Askew's *The Coinage of Roman Britain* (2nd edition) concentrates on those issues which are particularly associated with the Roman province of Britannia, but does not provide valuations. More recent works on this subject include R. Reece's *Coinage in Roman Britain* and *The Coinage of Roman Britain,* and also David R. Sear's *The History and Coinage of the Roman Imperators, 49—27 BC* which is devoted to the vital two decades of transition from Republic to Empire.

The standard works on the coinages of the Roman Republic and the Roman Empire have already been mentioned *(Roman Republican Coinage and Roman Imperial Coinage).* These monumental publications are essential to the advanced collector and student and their importance cannot be overstated. The British Museum Catalogues (3 volumes of Republican, 6 volumes of Imperial) are also vital. They contain superb interpretive material in their introductions and are very fully illustrated. A similar work is Anne S. Robertson's *Roman Imperial Coins in the Hunter Coin Cabinet,* in 5 volumes (volume 4 is especially important for the later 3rd century coinage). For more general reading we may recommend J.P.C. Kent and M. & A. Hirmer's *Roman Coins,* undoubtedly the most lavishly illustrated book on the subject; C.H.V. Sutherland's *Roman Coins;* and R.A.G. Carson's *Coins of the Roman Empire.* Finally, for a most useful single-volume work on interpretation and background information, we would suggest A *Dictionary of Ancient Roman Coins* by John Melville Jones.

# 1. REGULAR ROMAN ISSUES

A token selection of the types of Roman coins which might be found on Romano-British archaeological sites. Many of the rarer emperors and empresses have been omitted and the types listed often represent only one of hundreds of variant forms which might be encountered.

|  |  | F £ | VF £ |
|---|---|---|---|
| 451 | **THE REPUBLIC: P. Aelius Paetus** (moneyer), 138 B.C. Æ *denarius.* Helmeted hd. of Roma r. Rev. The Dioscuri galloping r. R.R.C. 233/1 ... | 20 | 60 |
| | *Although dating from long before the Roman conquest many Republican coins circulated well into the Imperial period and found their way to Britain where they are often represented in early hoards.* | | |
| 452 | **L. Thorius Balbus** (moneyer), 105 B.C. Æ denarius. Hd. of Juno Sospita r., clad in goat's skin. Rev. Bull charging r. *R.R.C. 316/1.* | 25 | 60 |
| 453 | **Q. Antonius Balbus** (moneyer), 83-82 B.C. Æ *denarius.* Laur. hd. of Jupiter r. Rev. Victory in quadriga r. *R.R.C. 364/1.* | 25 | 60 |

454      456

| 454 | **C. Calpurnius Piso** (moneyer), 67 B.C. Æ *denarius.* Laur. hd. of Apollo r. Rev. Horseman galloping r., holding palm-branch. *R.R.C. 408/1a. .....* | 30 | 70 |
|---|---|---|---|
| 455 | **Mn. Acilius Glabrio** (moneyer), 49 B.C. Æ *denarius.* Laur. hd. of Salus r. Rev. Valetudo stg. l., holding snake and resting on column. *R.R.C. 442/1.* | 20 | 60 |
| 456 | **Julius Caesar** (dictator), visited Britain 55 and 54 B.C., died 44 B.C. Æ *denarius.* CAESAR. Elephant r. Rev. Priestly emblems. *R.R.C. 443/1....* | 75 | 175 |
| 456A | — Wreathed hd. of Caesar r. Rev. P. SEPVLLIVS MACER. Venus stg. l., holding Victory and sceptre. *R.R.C. 480/9.* | 300 | 800 |
| 457 | **Mark Antony** (triumvir), died 30 B.C. Æ *denarius.* Galley r. Rev. LEG. II. Legionary eagle between two standards. *R.R.C. 544/14.* | 50 | 125 |

458      459

| 458 | **Octavian** (triumvir), named Augustus 27 B.C. Æ *denarius.* Bare hd. of Octavian r. Rev. IMP. CAESAR. Trophy set on prow. *R.I.C. 265a. ........* | 90 | 200 |
|---|---|---|---|
| 459 | **THE EMPIRE: Augustus,** 27 B.C.-A.D. 14. Æ *denarius.* Rev. C. L. CAESARES AVGVSTI F COS DESIG PRINC IVVENT. The emperor's grandsons, Gaius and Lucius, stg. facing, with spears and shields. *R.I.C. 207.* | 55 | 130 |
| | *Almost all the coins in the Roman Imperial series have a head or bust of the emperor, empress or prince as their obverse type. Therefore, in most instances only the reverses will be described in the following listings.* | | |

| | | F | VF |
|---|---|---|---|
| | | £ | £ |
| 460 | Æ as. ROM. ET AVG. The altar of Lugdunum. *R.I.C. 230.* | 50 | 125 |
| 460A | Æ quadrans. Obv. Anvil. Rev. Moneyers' inscription around large S. C. *R.I.C. 443.* | 15 | 35 |
| 461 | **Augustus and Agrippa,** general and designated heir of Augustus, died 12 B.C. Æ *dupondius.* Obv. Their hds. back to back. Rev. COL. NEM. Crocodile r., chained to palm-branch. *R.I.C. 159.* | 55 | 140 |
| | *See also no. 468.* | | |
| 462 | **Divus Augustus,** deified A.D. 14. Æ as. PROVIDENT S. C. Large altar. *R.I.C. 81.* | 60 | 150 |
| 463 | **Tiberius,** A.D. 14-37. *N aureus.* PONTIF MAXIM. Livia (?) seated r., holding sceptre and branch. *R.I.C. 29.* | 400 | 1000 |

464                    467

| 464 | ÆR denarius. Similar. *R.I.C. 30.* | 80 | 175 |
|---|---|---|---|
| | *This type is commonly referred to as the 'Tribute Penny' of the Bible (Matthew 22, 17-21).* | | |
| 464A | Æ as. Inscription around large S. C. *R.I.C. 44.* | 55 | 140 |
| 465 | **Livia,** wife of Augustus, mother of Tiberius. Æ *dupondius.* Obv. Veiled bust of Livia as Pietas r. Rev. Inscription of Drusus Caesar around large S. C. *R.I.C. 43.* | 150 | 375 |
| 466 | **Drusus,** son of Tiberius. Æ *as.* Inscription around large S. C. *R.I.C. 45.* | 65 | 175 |
| 467 | **Caligula,** A.D. 37-41. Æ *as.* VESTA S. C. Vesta seated l. *R.I.C. 38.* | 85 | 240 |

468

| 468 | **Agrippa,** grandfather of Caligula, died 12 B.C. Æ *as.* S. C. Neptune stg. l., holding dolphin and trident. *R.I.C. 58.* | 60 | 170 |
|---|---|---|---|
| | *See also no. 461 and under Category 4.* | | |
| 469 | **Germanicus,** father of Caligula, brother of Claudius, died A.D. 19. Æ *as.* Inscription of Caligula around large S. C. *R.I.C. 35.* | 75 | 175 |
| 470 | **Agrippina Senior,** mother of Caligula, died A.D. 33. Æ *sestertius.* S.P.Q.R. MEMORIAE AGRIPPINAE. Carpentum drawn l. by two mules. *R.I.C. 55.* | 250 | 850 |

471                                                              474

|  | F £ | VF £ |
|---|---|---|

471    **Claudius,** A.D. 41-54, initiated the conquest of Britain by his invasion in
       A.D. 43. Æ *as.* LIBERTAS AVGVSTA S. C. Libertas stg. r., holding pileus.
       *R.I.C. 113.* ....................................................................................................... 65    175

471A   Æ *quadrans.* Obv. Hand holding scales. Rev. Inscription around large
       S. C. *R.I.C. 85.* ............................................................................................... 15    35
       *See also under Categories 2 and 4.*

472    **Nero Claudius Drusus,** father of Claudius, died 9 B.C. Æ *sestertius.*
       TI. CLAVDIVS CAESAR AVG. P. M. TR .P. IMP. P. P. S. C. Claudius seated
       l. on curule chair amidst arms. *R.I.C. 109.* ............................................... 130    450
       *See also under Category 4.*

473    **Antonia,** mother of Claudius, died A.D. 37. Æ *dupondius.* TI. CLAVDIVS
       CAESAR AVG P.M. TR. P. IMP. S. C. Claudius stg. l., holding simpulum.
       *R.I.C. 92.* ....................................................................................................... 100    275
       *See also under Category 4.*

474    **Nero,** 54-68, emperor at the time of Queen Boudicca's rebellion in Britain.
       *N aureus.* SALVS. Salus seated l. *R.I.C. 66.* ............................................. 500    1200

475    Æ *denarius.* IVPPITER CVSTOS. Jupiter seated l. *R.I.C. 53.* ................ 85    275

476    Æ *sestertius.* ROMA S. C. Roma seated l., holding Victory and parazonium.
       *R.I.C. 274.* ....................................................................................................... 140    450

476A   Æ as. S. C. Victory hovering l., holding shield inscribed S. P. Q. R. *R.I.C. 312.* 60    160

477    **Galba,** 68-69. Æ *denarius.* S.P.Q.R. / OB / C.S. within oak-wreath. *R.I.C. 167.* 100    275

478    **Otho,** 69. Æ *denarius.* SECVRITAS P. R. Securitas stg. l. *R.I.C. 10.* ...... 200    550

479    **Vitellius,** 69. Æ denarius. CONCORDIA P. R. Concordia seated l. *R.I.C. 90.* 100    250

480    **Vespasian,** 69-79, commanded Legio II in the Claudian invasion of Britain
       (43) and appointed Agricola to governorship of the province in 77/8. *N aureus.*
       ANNONA AVG. Annona seated l. *R.I.C. 131a* ............................................. 500    1,200

481

481    Æ *denarius.* VICTORIA AVGVSTI. Victory advancing r., crowning standard.
       *R.I.C. 52.* ....................................................................................................... 25    75

481A   Æ *dupondius.* FELICITAS PVBLICA S. C. Felicitas stg. l. *R.I.C. 554...* 40    110

482    **Titus,** 79-81 (Caesar 69-79). Æ *denarius.* TR. P. IX. IMP. XV. COS. VIII.
       P. P. Thunderbolt on throne. *R.I.C. 23a.* ................................................... 50    140

483 485

|  | F £ | VF £ |
|---|---|---|
| 483 **Domitian,** 81-96 (Caesar 69-81), recalled Agricola in 83/4 and abandoned the conquest of northern Scotland (ca. 87). Æ *denarius.* IMP. XIX. COS. XIIII. CENS. P. P. P. Minerva stg. l., resting on spear. *R.I.C. 140.* | 25 | 75 |
| 484 Æ *dupondius.* VIRTVTI AVGVSTI S. C. Virtus stg. r. *R.I.C. 393.* | 35 | 85 |
| 484A Æ *as.* MONETA AVGVSTI S. C. Moneta stg. l. *R.I.C. 354b.* | 35 | 85 |
| 485 **Nerva,** 96-98. Æ *denarius.* AEQVITAS AVGVST. Aequitas stg. l. *R.I.C. 13.* | 50 | 120 |
| 485A Æ *as.* LIBERTAS PVBLICA S. C. Libertas stg. l. *R.I.C. 86.* | 55 | 140 |
| 486 **Trajan,** 98-117, established the northern frontier in Britain along the Tyne-Solway line (ca. 100). Æ *aureus.* P. M. TR. P. COS. VI. P. P. S. P. Q. R. Genius stg. l., holding patera and corn-ears. *R.I.C. 347.* | 450 | 1000 |

487 490

| 487 Æ *denarius.* COS. V. P. P. S. P. Q. R. OPTIMO PRINC. Military trophy. *R.I.C. 147.* | 25 | 75 |
|---|---|---|
| 488 Æ *sestertius.* S. P. Q. R. OPTIMO PRINCIPI S. C. Spes walking l., holding flower. *R.I.C. 519.* | 50 | 175 |
| 488A Æ *dupondius.* SENATVS POPVLVSQVE ROMANVS S. C. Emperor advancing between two trophies. *R.I.C. 676.* | 50 | 100 |
| 489 **Hadrian,** 117-138, visited Britain in 122 and initiated the construction of a fortified frontier line (Hadrian's Wall). Æ *aureus.* HISPANIA. Hispania reclining l. *R.I.C. 305.* | 500 | 1200 |
| 490 Æ *denarius.* P. M. TR. P. COS. III. Roma stg. l., holding Victory and spear. *R.I.C. 76.* | 30 | 85 |
| 491 Æ *sestertius.* COS. III. S. C. Neptune stg. r., holding dolphin and trident, foot on prow. *R.I.C. 632.* | 50 | 175 |
| 491A Æ *as.* FELICITATI AVG COS. III. P. P. S. C. Galley travelling l. over waves. *R.I.C. 719.* | 40 | 120 |
| *See also under Category 2.* | | |
| 492 **Sabina,** wife of Hadrian. Æ *denarius.* IVNONI REGINAE. Juno stg. l. *R.I.C. 395a.* | 40 | 120 |
| 493 **Aelius Caesar,** heir of Hadrian, 136-138. Æ *denarius.* CONCORD. TR. POT. COS. II. Concordia seated l. *R.I.C. 436.* | 75 | 200 |
| 493A Æ *as.* TR. POT. COS. II. S. C. Spes walking l., holding flower. *R.I.C. 1067.* | 50 | 130 |

|                                                                                      | F | VF |
|                                                                                      | £ | £ |

494    **Antoninus Pius,** 138-161, ordered the expansion of the Roman province
       to include southern Scotland and constructed the Antonine Wall on the
       Forth-Clyde line (beginning ca. 143). An uprising in northern Britain in the
       150s results in a permanent withdrawal to the Hadrianic frontier early in
       the next reign. *N̸ aureus.* COS. IIII. Togate emperor stg. l., holding globe.
       *R.I.C. 233b.* ..............................................................        400    850
495    *Æ denarius.* PIETATI AVG. COS. IIII. Pietas stg. l. between two children,
       holding two more in her arms. *R.I.C. 313c.* ...............................        25     70

496

496    *Æ sestertius.* SALVS AVG. S. C. Salus stg. l. at altar, feeding snake.
       *R.I.C. 635.* .............................................................          40     160
496A   *Æ dupondius.* TR. POT. XX. COS. IIII. S. C. Providentia stg. l., pointing
       at globe at her feet and holding sceptre. *R.I.C. 2025.* .....................       25     60
       *See also under Categories 2 and 3.*
497    **Antoninus Pius and Marcus Aurelius Caesar**. *Æ denarius.* Obv. Laur.
       hd. of Antoninus Pius r. Rev. AVRELIVS CAESAR AVG PII F. COS. Bare
       hd. of young Marcus Aurelius r. *R.I.C. 417a.* ...............................       50     130

498                                   501

498    **Divus Antoninus Pius,** deified 161. *Æ denarius.* CONSECRATIO.
       Four-storeyed crematorium of Antoninus Pius. *R.I.C. 436.* .................        25     75
499    **Diva Faustina Senior,** wife of Antoninus Pius, deified 141. *Æ denarius.*
       AETERNITAS. Aeternitas stg. l., holding globe and billowing veil. *R.I.C. 351.*     25     75
499A   *Æ sestertius.* AVGVSTA S. C. Ceres stg. l., holding two torches. *R.I.C. 1120.*    30     110
500    **Marcus Aurelius,** 161-180 (Caesar 139-161), re-established Hadrian's Wall
       as the permanent northern frontier of the province, ca. 163. *N̸ aureus.*
       PROV. DEOR. TR. P. XV. COS. III. Providentia stg. l., holding globe and
       cornucopiae. *R.I.C. 19.* ..................................................        450    950
501    *Æ denarius.* PIETAS AVG. Priestly emblems. *R.I.C. 424a.* ..................       25     75
501A   — SALVTI AVG. COS. III. Salus stg. l. at altar, feeding snake. *R.I.C. 222.*        20     70
502    *Æ sestertius.* CONCORD. AVGVSTOR. TR. P. XVI. COS. III. S. C. Marcus
       Aurelius and Lucius Verus stg. face to face, clasping hands. *R.I.C. 826.*          40     160
502A   *Æ as.* HONOS TR. POT. II. COS. II. S. C. Honos stg. r. *R.I.C. 1271a.* ..          30     75

|  | F | VF |
|---|---|---|
|  | £ | £ |

503 **Divus Marcus Aurelius,** deified 180. Æ *denarius.* CONSECRATIO.
Eagle stg. r. on altar. *R.I.C. 272.* ............... 25 70

504                                          506A

504 **Faustina Junior,** daughter of Antoninus Pius, wife of Marcus Aurelius.
Æ *denarius.* FECVNDITAS. Fecunditas stg. r., holding sceptre and child.
*R.I.C. 677.* ............... 25 60
504A Æ *sestertius.* HILARITAS S. C. Hilaritas stg. l. *R.I.C. 1642.* ............... 35 120
505 **Diva Faustina Junior,** deified 175. Æ *as.* S. C. Crescent and seven stars.
*R.I.C. 1714.* ............... 35 80
506 **Lucius Verus,** 161-169. Æ denarius. PAX TR. P. VI. IMP. IIII. COS. II.
Pax stg. l. *R.I.C. 561.* ............... 30 80
506A Æ *dupondius.* TR. P. IIII. IMP. II. COS. II. S. C. Mars stg. r., resting on
spear and shield. *R.I.C. 1387.* ............... 35 95
507 **Lucilla,** daughter of Marcus Aurelius, wife of Lucius Verus. Æ *denarius.*
IVNONI LVCINAE. Juno stg. l., holding child in swaddling clothes.
*R.I.C. 771.* ............... 30 75
507A Æ *sestertius.* PIETAS S. C. Pietas stg. l., altar at feet. *R.I.C. 1756.* ......... 35 120
508 **Commodus,** 177-192 (Caesar 175-177), major warfare on the British
frontier early in the reign; situation restored by Ulpius Marcellus in 184/5,
followed by unrest in the British legions. Æ *denarius.* LIB. AVG. IIII. TR.
P. VI. IMP. IIII. COS. III. P. P. Liberalitas stg. l. *R.I.C. 22.* ............... 30 80

509                                          511

509 Æ *sestertius.* IOVI VICTORI IMP. III. COS. II. P. P. S. C. Jupiter seated l.
*R.I.C. 1612.* ............... 40 140
509A Æ *as.* ANN. AVG. TR. P. VII. IMP. IIII. COS. III. P. P. S. C. Annona stg. l.,
modius at feet. *R.I.C. 339.* ............... 25 70
*See also under Category 2.*
510 **Crispina,** wife of Commodus. Æ *denarius.* CONCORDIA. Clasped hands.
*R.I.C. 279.* ............... 30 75
511 **Pertinax,** January-March 193, formerly governor of Britain, ca. 185-7. Æ
*denarius.* PROVID. DEOR. COS. II. Providentia stg l., reaching up to star.
*R.I.C. 11a.* ............... 250 600

512                                         513A

|       |                                                                                   | F £ | VF £ |
|-------|-----------------------------------------------------------------------------------|-----|------|

512   **Didius Julianus,** March-June 193. Æ *denarius.* CONCORD MILIT.
      Concordia Militum stg. l., holding standards. *R.I.C. 1.* ...........................   375   850
513   **Clodius Albinus,** 195-197 (Caesar 193-195), governor of Britain (from
      191/2) at the time of his imperial proclamation by his troops. Æ *denarius.*
      MINER. PACIF. COS. II. Minerva stg. l. *R.I.C. 7.* ...................................   60    140
513A  — FIDES LEGION. COS. II. Clasped hands holding legionary eagle.
      *R.I.C. 20b.* ................................................................................................   75    175

514                                         516

514   **Septimius Severus,** 193-211, restored the frontier forts in northern Britain
      following the downfall of Clodius Albinus; later repaired Hadrian's Wall,
      and spent the years 208-11 in Britain campaigning in Scotland; divided
      Britannia into two provinces, Superior and Inferior; died at York, February
      211. Æ *denarius.* VIRT AVGG. Roma stg. l., holding Victory, spear and
      shield. *R.I.C. 171a.* ...................................................................................   20    50
514A  — P.M. TR. P. XVIII. COS. III. P. P. Jupiter stg. l. between two children.
      *R.I.C. 240.* .................................................................................................   20    50
      *See also under Category 2.*
515   **Julia Domna,** wife of Septimius Severus, mother of Caracalla and Geta,
      accompanied her husband and sons on the British expedition, 208-211, and
      probably resided in London during the northern campaigns. Æ *denarius.*
      VENERI VICTR. Venus stg. r., resting on column. *R.I.C. 536.* ..............   15    45
515A  — VESTA. Vesta stg. l., holding palladium and sceptre. *R.I.C. 390.* ......   15    45
516   **Caracalla,** 198-217 (Caesar 196-198), accompanied his father and brother
      on the British expedition, 208-211, and led the final campaign in Scotland
      in 210 during Severus' illness; made frontier dispositions before returning
      to Rome and finalized his father's arrangements for the division of Britain
      into two provinces. Æ *antoninianus (double denarius,* introduced in 215).
      VENVS VICTRIX. Venus stg. l., holding Victory and resting on shield.
      *R.I.C. 311c.* ..............................................................................................   30    75
517   Æ *denarius.* PART. MAX. PONT. TR. P. IIII. Trophy with two captives at
      base. *R.I.C. 54b.* ........................................................................................   15    50
517A  — P. M. TR. P. XV. COS. III. P. P. Hercules stg. l., holding olive-branch
      and club. *R.I.C. 192.* ................................................................................   15    50
      *See also under Category 2.*

|  | F | VF |
|---|---|---|
|  | £ | £ |

518 **Plautilla,** wife of Caracalla. Æ *denarius.* PROPAGO IMPERI. Caracalla
and Plautilla clasping hands. *R.I.C. 362.* ............................................. 25 75

519           522A

519 **Geta,** 209-212 (Caesar 198-209), accompanied his father and brother on
the British expedition, 208-211, and took charge of the civil administration
in London during the northern campaigns. Æ *denarius.* PRINC. IVVENTVTIS.
Prince stg. l. beside trophy, holding branch and spear. *R.I.C. 18.* ............ 20 50
519A — FORT RED TR. P. III. COS. II. Fortuna seated l. *R.I.C. 75.* ............... 25 65
*See also under Category 2.*
520 **Macrinus,** 217-218. Æ *denarius.* PROVIDENTIA DEORVM. Providentia
stg. l., globe at feet. *R.I.C. 80.* ...................................................... 35 110
521 **Diadumenian,** 218 (Caesar 217-218). Æ *denarius.* PRINC. IVVENTVTIS.
Prince stg. l., two standards behind. *R.I.C. 109.* ............................... 70 175
522 **Elagabalus,** 218-222. Æ *antoninianus.* MARS VICTOR. Mars advancing r.
*R.I.C. 122.* ...................................................................................... 22 55
522A Æ *denarius.* P. M. TR. P. III. COS. III. P. P. Jupiter seated l., eagle at feet
*R.I.C. 27.* ...................................................................................... 20 40
523 **Julia Paula,** first wife of Elagabalus. Æ *denarius.* CONCORDIA.
Concordia seated l. *R.I.C. 211.* ...................................................... 40 100
524 **Aquilia Severa,** second wife of Elagabalus. Æ *denarius.* CONCORDIA.
Concordia stg. l., altar at feet. *R.I.C. 226.* .................................... 60 150
525 **Julia Soaemias,** mother of Elagabalus. Æ *denarius.* VENVS CAELESTIS.
Venus seated l., child at feet. *R.I.C. 243.* ...................................... 30 75
526 **Julia Maesa,** grandmother of Elagabalus and Severus Alexander. Æ
*denarius.* SAECVLI FELICITAS. Felicitas stg. l., altar at feet. *R.I.C. 271.* 25 60
527 **Severus Alexander,** 222-235 (Caesar 221-222). Æ *denarius.*
PAX AETERNA AVG. Pax stg. l. *R.I.C. 165.* ........................................ 15 40
527A — P. M. TR. P. XIII. COS. III. P. P. Sol advancing l., holding whip. *R.I.C. 123.* 15 40

528

528 Æ *sestertius.* MARS VLTOR S. C. Mars advancing r., with spear and shield.
*R.I.C. 635.* .......................................................................................... 30 85

|       |       |                                                                                                                                 | *F*<br>£ | *VF*<br>£ |
|-------|-------|---------------------------------------------------------------------------------------------------------------------------------|----|-----|

529    **Orbiana,** wife of Severus Alexander. Æ *denarius.* CONCORDIA AVGG.
     Concordia seated l. *R.I.C. 319.* ......................................................................    70    175

530    **Julia Mamaea,** mother of Severus Alexander. Æ *denarius.* VESTA.
     Vesta stg. l. *R.I.C. 362.* ......................................................................    20    50

530A   Æ *sestertius.* FELICITAS PVBLICA S. C. Felicitas stg. facing, hd. l.,
     resting on column. *R.I.C. 676.* ..............................................................    30    85

531

531    **Maximinus I,** 235-238. Æ *denarius.* PAX AVGVSTI. Pax stg. l. *R.I.C. 12.*    20    50

531A   Æ *sestertius.* SALVS AVGVSTI S. C. Salus seated l., feeding snake arising
     from altar. *R.I.C. 85.* ............................................................................    30    85

532    **Maximus Caesar,** son of Maximinus I. Æ *denarius.* PRINC IVVENTVTIS.
     Prince stg. l., two standards behind. *R.I.C. 3.* ......................................    50    175

533    **Gordian I Africanus,** March-April 238, governor of Britannia Inferior
     late in the reign of Caracalla. Æ *denarius.* P. M. TR. P. COS. P. P. Togate
     emperor stg. l. *R.I.C. 1.* ........................................................................    250    600

534    **Gordian II Africanus,** March-April 238. Æ *denarius.* VIRTVS AVGG.
     Virtus stg. l., with shield and spear. *R.I.C. 3.*......................................    250    600

535    **Balbinus,** April-July 238. Æ *antoninianus.* FIDES MVTVA AVGG.
     Clasped hands. *R.I.C. 11.* ......................................................................    75    175

535A   Æ *denarius.* PROVIDENTIA DEORVM. Providentia stg. l., globe at feet.
     *R.I.C. 7.* ..................................................................................................    50    140

536    **Pupienus,** April-July 238. Æ *antoninianus.* AMOR MVTVVS AVGG.
     Clasped hands. *R.I.C. 9a.*......................................................................    75    175

536A   Æ *denarius.* PAX PVBLICA. Pax seated l. *R.I.C. 4.* ..............................    50    140

537    **Gordian III,** 238-244 (Caesar 238). Æ *antoninianus.* LAETITIA AVG. N.
     Laetitia stg. l. *R.I.C. 86.* ......................................................................    15    30

538    Æ *denarius.* DIANA LVCIFERA. Diana stg. r., holding torch. *R.I.C. 127.*    15    30

538A

538A   Æ *sestertius.* AETERNITATI AVG. S.C. Sol stg. l., holding globe. *R.I.C. 297a.*    22    65

539

| | F | VF |
| | £ | £ |
|---|---|---|

539 **Philip I,** 244-249. Æ *antoninianus*. ROMAE AETERNAE. Roma seated l.
R.I.C. 65. ..................................................................... 12 30
539A Æ *sestertius*. SECVRIT. ORBIS S. C. Securitas seated l. *R.I.C. 190.* ..... 22 70
540 **Otacilia Severa,** wife of Philip I. Æ *antoninianus*. PIETAS AVGVSTAE.
Pietas stg. l. *R.I.C. 125c.* ...................................... 15 40
540A Æ *sestertius*. CONCORDIA AVGG. S. C. Concordia seated l. *R.I.C. 203a.* 25 75
541 **Philip II,** 247-249 (Caesar 244-247). Æ *antoninianus*. PRINCIPI IVVENT.
Prince stg. l., holding globe and spear. *R.I.C. 218d.* ................ 20 50
541A Æ *sestertius*. PAX AETERNA S. C. Pax stg. l. *R.I.C. 268c.* ................. 25 80

542                          543

542 **Trajan Decius,** 249-251. Æ *antoninianus*. DACIA. Dacia stg. l., holding
staff with ass's hd. *R.I.C. 12b.* ................................ 15 35
542A Æ *sestertius*. PANNONIAE S. C. The two Pannoniae stg., each holding
standard. *R.I.C. 124a.*............................................. 25 75
543 **Herennia Etruscilla,** wife of Trajan Decius. Æ *antoninianus*. PVDICITIA
AVG. Pudicitia stg. l. *R.I.C. 58b.*............................... 15 35
544 **Herennius Etruscus,** 251 (Caesar 250-251). Æ *antoninianus*. PIETAS
AVGG. Mercury stg. l., holding purse and caduceus. *R.I.C. 142b.*.......... 25 65
545 **Hostilian,** 251 (Caesar 251). Æ *antoninianus*. PRINCIPI IVVENTVTIS.
Apollo seated l., holding branch. *R.I.C. 180.* ......................... 35 85
546 **Trebonianus Gallus,** 251-253. Æ *antoninianus*. FELICITAS PVBLICA.
Felicitas stg. l., resting on column. *R.I.C. 34A.*....................... 12 30
546A Æ *sestertius*. SALVS AVGG S. C. Salus stg. r., feeding snake held in her
arms. *R.I.C. 121a.* .......................................... 25 75
547 **Volusian,** 251-253 (Caesar 251). Æ *antoninianus*. VIRTVS AVGG.
Virtus stg. l. *R.I.C. 186.* ...................................... 12 30
548 **Aemilian,** 253. Æ *antoninianus*. PACI AVG. Pax stg. l., resting on column.
*R.I.C. 8.* ................................................... 50 120
549 **Valerian,** 253-260. Billon antoninianus. FIDES MILITVM. Fides stg. r.,
holding two standards. *R.I.C. 241.*............................. 8 20
550 **Diva Mariniana,** wife of Valerian, deified 253. Billon *antoninianus*.
CONSECRATIO. Empress seated on peacock flying r. *R.I.C. 6.* ............ 45 110

|   | *F* | *VF* |
|---|---|---|
|   | £ | £ |

551 **Gallienus,** 253-268, during whose reign Rome temporarily lost control over Britain when Postumus rebelled and established the independent Gallic Empire in 260. Billon *antoninianus.* VIRT GALLIENI AVG. Emperor advancing r., captive at feet. *R.I.C. 54.* ..................................... 10 25

552

| 552 | — DIANAE CONS. AVG. Doe l. *R.I.C. 176.* ......................................... | 8 | 20 |
|---|---|---|---|
| 552A | — SOLI INVICTO. Sol stg. l., holding globe. *R.I.C. 658.* ....................... | 8 | 18 |
| 553 | **Salonina,** wife of Gallienus. Billon *antoninianus.* VENVS FELIX. Venus seated l., child at feet. *R.I.C. 7.* .................................................... | 8 | 20 |
| 553A | — IVNONI CONS. AVG. Doe l. *R.I.C. 16.* ........................................... | 8 | 20 |
| 554 | **Valerian Junior,** son of Gallienus, Caesar 256-258. Billon *antoninianus.* IOVI CRESCENTI. Infant Jupiter seated on goat r. *R.I.C. 13.* ................ | 15 | 35 |
| 555 | **Divus Valerian Junior,** deified 258. Billon *antoninianus.* CONSECRATIO. Large altar. *R.I.C. 24.*.................................................................. | 12 | 30 |
| 556 | **Saloninus,** 260 (Caesar 258-260). Billon *antoninianus.* PIETAS AVG. Priestly emblems. *R.I.C. 9.*.................................................................. | 12 | 30 |
| 557 | **Macrianus,** usurper in the East, 260-261. Billon *antoninianus.* SOL. INVICTO. Sol stg. l., holding globe. *R.I.C. 12.*....................................... | 35 | 85 |
| 558 | **Quietus,** usurper in the East, 260-261. Billon *antoninianus.* INDVLGENTIAE AVG. Indulgentia seated l. *R.I.C. 5.* .......................... | 35 | 85 |
| 559 | **Postumus,** usurper in the West, 260-268, founder of the 'Gallic Empire' which temporarily detached Britain from the rule of the central government, a state of affairs which continued until Aurelian's defeat of Tetricus in 273. Billon *antoninianus.* HERC. DEVSONIENSI. Hercules stg. r. *R.I.C. 64.* | 12 | 30 |

560

| 560 | — MONETA AVG. Moneta stg. l. *R.I.C. 75.* ..................................... | 10 | 25 |
|---|---|---|---|
| 560A | Æ *sestertius.* FIDES MILITVM. Fides stg. l., holding two standards. *R.I.C. 128.* .................................................................................. | 50 | 140 |
| 561 | **Laelianus,** usurper in the West, 268. Billon *antoninianus.* VICTORIA AVG. Victory advancing r. *R.I.C. 9.* ................................................. | 110 | 275 |
| 562 | **Marius,** usurper in the West, 268. Billon *antoninianus.* CONCORDIA MILITVM. Clasped hands. *R.I.C. 7.* .................................................... | 35 | 85 |
| 563 | **Victorinus,** usurper in the West, 268-270. Billon *antoninianus.* INVICTVS. Sol advancing l. *R.I.C. 114.* ................................................................ | 8 | 20 |

|  | | F | VF |
|---|---|---|---|
|  | | £ | £ |

564 **Tetricus,** usurper in the West, 270-273, defeated by Aurelian, thus ending
the 'Gallic Empire' and the isolation of Britain from the authority of Rome.
Billon *antoninianus.* LAETITIA AVGG. Laetitia stg. l. *R.I.C. 87.*.......... 8 25
*See also under Category 4.*

565 **Tetricus Junior,** son of Tetricus, Caesar 270-273. Billon *antoninianus.*
SPES PVBLICA. Spes walking l., holding flower *R.I.C. 272.*................. 8 20
*See also under Category 4.*

566 **Claudius II Gothicus,** 268-270. Billon *antoninianus.* IOVI STATORI.
Jupiter stg. r. *R.I.C. 52.* ............................................................................ 8 20

567 **Divus Claudius II,** deified 270. Billon *antoninianus.* CONSECRATIO.
Large altar. *R.I.C. 261.* ............................................................................ 8 20
*See also under Category 4.*

568 **Quintillus,** 270. Billon *antoninianus.* DIANA LVCIF. Diana stg. r.,
holding torch. *R.I.C. 49.* ........................................................................ 18 45

569 **Aurelian,** 270-275, restored Britain to the rule of the central government
through his defeat of Tetricus in 273; possibly began construction of the
chain of 'Saxon Shore' forts on the eastern and southern coastlines. Billon
*antoninianus.* ORIENS AVG. Sol stg. l. between two captives. *R.I.C. 63.* 10 25

569A — RESTITVT. ORBIS. Female stg. r., presenting wreath to emperor stg. l.
*R.I.C. 399.* ............................................................................................... 10 25

570 **Aurelian and Vabalathus,** ruler of Palmyra 267-272 and usurper in the
East from 271. Billon *antoninianus.* Obv. Laur. bust of Vabalathus r. Rev.
Rad. bust of Aurelian r. *R.I.C. 381.* ...................................................... 25 70

571                                              574A

571 **Severina,** wife of Aurelian. Billon *antoninianus.* PROVIDEN. DEOR.
Concordia (or Fides) Militum stg. r., facing Sol stg. l. *R.I.C. 9.* ............. 18 45

572 **Tacitus,** 275-276. Billon *antoninianus.* SECVRIT. PERP. Securitas stg. l.,
leaning on column. *R.I.C. 163.* ................................................................ 15 35

573 **Florian,** 276. Billon *antoninianus.* LAETITIA FVND. Laetitia stg. l.
*R.I.C. 34.* ................................................................................................. 30 75

574 **Probus,** 276-282, suppressed governor's revolt in Britain and lifted
restrictions on viticulture in Britain and Gaul. Billon *antoninianus.*
ADVENTVS PROBI AVG. Emperor on horseback l., captive seated
before. *R.I.C. 160.* .................................................................................... 10 25

574A — VICTORIA GERM. Trophy between two captives. *R.I.C. 222.* ......... 15 40

575 **Carus,** 282-283. Billon *antoninianus.* PAX EXERCITI. Pax stg. l., holding
olive-branch and standard. *R.I.C. 75.*...................................................... 15 40

576 **Divus Carus,** deified 283. Billon *antoninianus.* CONSECRATIO. Eagle
facing, hd. l. *R.I.C. 28.* ............................................................................ 18 45

577 **Carinus,** 283-285 (Caesar 282-283). Billon *antoninianus.* SAECVLI
FELICITAS. Emperor stg. r. *R.I.C. 214.* ................................................. 12 35

| | F | VF |
|---|---|---|
| | £ | £ |

578 **Magnia Urbica,** wife of Carinus. Billon *antoninianus.* VENVS VICTRIX.
Venus stg. l., holding helmet, shield at feet. *R.I.C. 343.* ........................... 60 150

579 **Numerian,** 283-284 (Caesar 282-283). Billon *antoninianus.* CLEMENTIA
TEMP. Emperor stg. r., receiving globe from Jupiter stg. l. *R.I.C. 463.* .. 15 40

580 **Diocletian,** 284-305. Æ *argenteus.* VIRTVS MILITVM. The four tetrarchs
sacrificing before gateway of military camp. *R.I.C. 27a (Rome).* ............ 100 250

581 Billon *antoninianus.* IOVI CONSERVAT AVGG. Jupiter stg. l. *R.I.C. 162.* 10 25

582 Æ *follis.* GENIO POPVLI ROMANI. Genius stg. l. R.I.C. 14a *(Alexandria).* 10 30

582A — (post-abdication coinage, after 305). PROVIDENTIA DEORVM QVIES
AVGG. Quies and Providentia stg. facing each other. *R.I.C. 676a (Treveri).* 22 65
*See also under Category 3.*

583 **Maximian,** 286-305 and 306-308, failed in his attempts to suppress the
usurpation of Carausius in Britain. Æ *argenteus.* VICTORIA SARMAT. The
four tetrarchs sacrificing before gateway of military camp. *R.I.C. 37b (Rome).* 100 250

584

584 Billon *antoninianus.* SALVS AVGG. Salus stg. r., feeding snake held in
her arms. *R.I.C. 417.* ................................................................................ 8 20

585 Æ *follis.* SAC. MON. VRB. AVGG. ET CAESS. NN. Moneta stg. l.
*R.I.C. 105b (Rome).* ................................................................................ 12 35

585A — (second reign). CONSERVATORES VRB SVAE. Roma seated in
hexastyle temple. *R.I.C. 84b (Ticinum).* .................................................... 12 35
*See also under Category 3.*

*[For coins of the usurpers **Carausius** and **Allectus** see under Category 3]*

586 **Constantius I,** 305-306 (Caesar 293-305), invaded Britain 296 and defeated
the usurper Allectus, thus restoring the island to the rule of the central
government; Britain now divided into four provinces and the northern
frontier defences reconstructed; died at York, July 306. Æ *argenteus.*
PROVIDENTIA AVGG. The four tetrarchs sacrificing before gateway
of military camp. *R.I.C. 11a (Rome).* ...................................................... 110 275

587

587 Æ *follis.* GENIO POPVLI ROMANI. Genius stg. l. *R.I.C. 26a (Aquileia).* 12 35

587A — SALVIS AVGG. ET CAESS. FEL. KART. Carthage stg. l., holding
fruits. *R.I.C. 30a (Carthage).* .................................................................... 15 40
*See also under Category 3.*

588

|  | F £ | VF £ |
|---|---|---|
| 588 **Galerius,** 305-311 (Caesar 293-305). Æ argenteus. VIRTVS MILITVM. The four tetrarchs sacrificing before gateway of military camp. *R.I.C. 15b (Ticinum).* ............. | 100 | 250 |
| 588A — XC / VI in wreath. *R.I.C. 16b (Carthage).*.......................... | 150 | 400 |
| 589 Æ *follis.* GENIO AVGG ET CAESARVM NN. Genius stg. l. *R.I.C. 11b (Cyzicus).*............... | 12 | 35 |
| 589A — GENIO IMPERATORIS. Genius stg. l. *R.I.C. 101a (Alexandria).*...... | 8 | 25 |
| *See also under Category 3.* | | |
| 590 **Galeria Valeria,** wife of Galerius. Æ *follis.* VENERI VICTRICI. Venus stg. l. *R.I.C. 110 (Alexandria).* .................... | 35 | 85 |
| 591 **Severius II,** 306-307 (Caesar 305-306). Æ *follis.* FIDES MILITVM. Fides seated l. *R.I.C. 73 (Ticinum).* .................... | 35 | 85 |
| *See also under Category 3.* | | |
| 592 **Maximinus II,** 310-313 (Caesar 305-310). Æ *follis.* GENIO CAESARIS. Genius stg. l. *R.I.C. 64 (Alexandria).*.................... | 8 | 25 |
| 592A — GENIO POP. ROM. Genius stg. l. *R.I.C. 845a (Treveri).* .................. | 8 | 20 |
| *See also under Category 3.* | | |

593

| 593 **Maxentius,** 306-312 (Caesar 306). Æ *follis.* CONSERV. VRB. SVAE. Roma seated in hexastyle temple. *R.I.C. 210 (Rome).* ............................. | 10 | 30 |
|---|---|---|
| 594 **Romulus,** son of Maxentius, deified 309. Æ *quarter follis.* AETERNAE MEMORIAE. Temple with domed roof. *R.I.C. 58 (Ostia).* .................... | 35 | 85 |
| 595 **Licinius,** 308-324. Æ *follis.* GENIO AVGVSTI. Genius stg. l. *R.I.C. 198b (Siscia).* ............. | 8 | 20 |
| 595A Æ 3. IOVI CONSERVATORI AVGG. Jupiter stg. l. *R.I.C. 24 (Nicomedia).* | 8 | 20 |
| *See also under Category 3.* | | |
| 596 **Licinius Junior,** son of Licinius, Caesar 317-324. Æ 3. CAESARVM NOSTRORVM around wreath containing VOT. / V. *R.I.C. 92 (Thessalonica).* | 8 | 22 |
| 597 **Constantine I, the Great,** 307-337 (Caesar 306-307), campaigned with his father Constantius I against the Picts in northern Britain, summer 306, and proclaimed emperor by the legions at York on Constantius' death in July; closed the London mint early in 325 ending almost four decades of operation. Æ *follis.* GENIO POP ROM. Genius stg. l. *R.I.C. 719b (Treveri).* | 12 | 35 |
| 598 — SOLI INVICTO COMITI. Sol stg. l. *R.I.C. 307 (Lugdunum).* ............ | 6 | 18 |
| 598A Æ 3. PROVIDENTIAE AVGG. Gateway of military camp. *R.I.C. 153 (Thessalonica).* ............. | 5 | 15 |

599 600

| | F | VF |
|---|---|---|
| | £ | £ |

599 — VIRTVS EXERCIT. Trophy between two captives. *R.I.C. 280 (Treveri).* 12 30

599A Æ 3/4. GLORIA EXERCITVS. Two soldiers stg. either side of two standards.
*R.I.C. 518 (Treveri).* ..................................................................... 4 12
*See also under Category 3.*

600 **'Urbs Roma',** after 330. Æ 3/4. Obv. Helmeted bust of Roma l. Rev.
She-wolf l., suckling twins. *R.I.C. 195 (Nicomedia).* ............................. 5 15

601 604

601 **'Constantinopolis',** after 330. Æ 3/4. Obv. Helmeted bust of
Constantinopolis l. Rev. Victory stg. l., foot on prow. *R.I.C. 339 (Rome).* 5 15

602 **Fausta,** wife of Constantine I. Æ 3. SALVS REIPVBLICAE. Empress
stg. l., holding two children. *R.I.C. 459 (Treveri).*..................................... 18 45
*See also under Category 3.*

603 **Helena,** mother of Constantine I. Æ 3. SECVRITAS REIPVBLICE.
Empress stg. l., holding branch. *R.I.C. 38 (Alexandria).* .......................... 18 40

603A Æ 4 (posthumous issue, 337-340). PAX PVBLICA. Pax stg. l. *R.I.C. 78
(Treveri).* ................................................................................................. 10 25
*See also under Category 3.*

604 **Theodora,** second wife of Constantius I. Æ 4 (posthumous issue, 337-340).
PIETAS ROMANA. Pietas stg. r., holding child. R.I.C. 43 *(Treveri).* .... 12 30

605 **Crispus,** eldest son of Constantine I, Caesar 317-326. Æ 3. CAESARVM
NOSTRORVM around wreath containing VOT. / V. *R.I.C. 68 (Aquileia).* 8 20
*See also under Category 3.*

606 **Delmatius,** nephew of Constantine I, Caesar 335-337. Æ 3/4. GLORIA
EXERCITVS. Two soldiers stg. either side of two standards. *R.I.C. 90
(Antioch)*................................................................................................. 18 45

607 **Hanniballianus,** nephew of Constantine I, Rex 335-337. Æ 4. SECVRITAS
PVBLICA. River-god Euphrates reclining r. *R.I.C. 147 (Constantinople).* 100 225

608 **Constantine II,** 337-340 (Caesar 317-337). Æ 3. BEATA
TRANQVILLITAS. Altar inscribed VOT / IS / XX. *R.I.C. 312 (Treveri).* 8 20

608A Æ 3/4. GLORIA EXERCITVS. Two soldiers stg. either side of standard.
*R.I.C. 392 (Rome).* ................................................................................. 4 10
*See also under Category 3.*

609 **Constans,** 337-350 (Caesar 333-337), visited Britain in 343, the last
reigning emperor to do so. Æ 2. FEL. TEMP. REPARATIO. Soldier r.,
dragging barbarian from hut beneath tree. *R.I.C. 103 (Aquileia).* ............ 10 30

609A                              611B

|  | F | VF |
|---|---|---|
|  | £ | £ |
| 609A — FEL. TEMP. REPARATIO. Emperor stg. l. on galley steered by Victory. *R.I.C. 219 (Treveri).* | 10 | 30 |
| 609B Æ 4. VICTORIAE DD. AVGG. Q. NN. Two Victories stg. face to face. *R.I.C. 195 (Treveri).* | 4 | 10 |
| 610 **Constantius II,** 337-361 (Caesar 324-337). Æ 3/4. GLORIA EXERCITVS. Two soldiers stg. either side of two standards. *R.I.C. 85 (Cyzicus).* | 4 | 12 |
| 611 *Æ siliqua.* VOTIS / XXX. / MVLTIS / XXXX. in wreath. *R.I.C. 207 (Arelate).* | 25 | 70 |
| 611A Æ 2. FEL. TEMP. REPARATIO. Emperor stg. l. on galley. *R.I.C. 218 (Treveri).* | 10 | 30 |
| 611B Æ 3. FEL. TEMP. REPARATIO. Soldier advancing l., spearing fallen horseman. *R.I.C. 189 (Lugdunum).* | 5 | 15 |

*See also under Categories 3 and 4.*

612                              616

| 612 **Magnentius,** usurper in the West, 350-353, temporarily detached Britain from the rule of the legitimate Constantinian dynasty. Æ 1. SALVS DD. NN. AVG. ET CAES. *Chi-Rho* Christian monogram between Alpha and Omega. *R.I.C. 34 (Ambianum).* | 75 | 175 |
|---|---|---|
| 612A Æ 2. FELICITAS REIPVBLICE. Emperor stg. l., holding Victory and labarum. *R.I.C. 264 (Treveri).* | 15 | 40 |
| *See also under Category 4.* | | |
| 613 **Decentius,** brother of Magnentius, Caesar 351-353. Æ 2. VICTORIAE DD. NN. AVG. ET CAE. Two Victories supporting between them shield inscribed VOT. / V. / MVLT. / X. *R.I.C. 146 (Lugdunum).* | 20 | 50 |
| *See also under Category 4.* | | |
| 614 **Vetranio,** 'usurper' in the Balkans, 350. Æ 2. CONCORDIA MILITVM. Emperor stg. l., holding two labara. *R.I.C. 281 (Siscia).* | 50 | 125 |
| 615 **Constantius Gallus,** Caesar under Constantius II, 351-354. Æ 2. FEL. TEMP. REPARATIO. Soldier advancing l., spearing fallen horseman. *R.I.C. 94 (Cyzicus).* | 15 | 40 |
| 616 **Julian II,** 360-363 (Caesar 355-360). *Æ siliqua.* VOT. / X. / MVLT. / XX. in wreath. *R.I.C. 309 (Arelate).* | 25 | 70 |

| | F | VF |
|---|---|---|
| | £ | £ |
| 617 Æ 1. SECVRITAS REIPVB. Bull stg. r. *R.I.C. 411 (Siscia)*.................... | 45 | 140 |
| 617A Æ 3. VOT. / X. / MVLT. / XX. in wreath. *R.I.C. 108 (Sirmium)*. ............ | 8 | 25 |
| 618 **Jovian,** 363-364. Æ 3. VOT. / V. / MVLT. / X. in wreath. *R.I.C. 426 (Siscia)*. | 12 | 35 |
| 619 **Valentinian I,** 364-375 (in the West), during whose reign the Roman province of Britannia was devastated by the simultaneous attack of hordes of invaders on several fronts (the 'Barbarian Conspiracy'); order eventually restored by Count Theodosius, father of the future emperor . *N solidus.* RESTITVTOR REIPVBLICAE. Emperor stg. r., holding standard and Victory. *R.I.C. 2b (Antioch)*. ........................................................ | 120 | 275 |
| 619A Æ 3. GLORIA ROMANORVM. Emperor advancing r., dragging barbarian and holding labarum. *R.I.C. 14a (Siscia)*. ............................... | 5 | 15 |

619B

| 619B — SECVRITAS REIPVBLICAE. Victory advancing l. *R.I.C. 32a (Treveri)*. | 5 | 15 |
|---|---|---|
| 620 **Valens,** 364-378 (in the East). Æ *siliqua.* VRBS ROMA. Roma seated l. *R.I.C. 27e (Treveri)*. ................................................................................. | 25 | 70 |
| 620A Æ 3. SECVRITAS REIPVBLICAE. Victory advancing l. *R.I.C. 42b (Constantinople)*............................................................................................ | 5 | 15 |
| 621 **Procopius,** usurper in the East, 365-366. Æ 3. REPARATIO FEL. TEMP. Emperor stg. r., holding standard and shield. *R.I.C. 17a (Constantinople)*. | 50 | 125 |
| 622 **Gratian,** 367-383 (in the West), overthrown by Magnus Maximus who had been proclaimed emperor by the army in Britain. Æ *siliqua.* VRBS ROMA. Roma seated l. *R.I.C. 27f (Treveri)*. ............................................ | 30 | 75 |
| 623 **Valentinian II,** 375-392 (in the West). Æ 2. REPARATIO REIPVB. Emperor stg. l., raising kneeling female figure. *R.I.C. 20c (Arelate)*. ...... | 10 | 30 |
| 623A Æ 4. SALVS REIPVBLICAE. Victory advancing l., dragging barbarian. *R.I.C. 20a (Alexandria)*. ................................................................................ | 4 | 12 |
| 624 **Theodosius I,** the Great, 379-395 (in the East), son of the Count Theodosius who had cleared Britain of barbarian invaders in the reign of Valentinian I; the Emperor Theodosiua twice restored Britain to the rule of the central government, by his defeat of the usurpers Magnus Maximus (in 388) and Eugenius (in 394). Æ *siliqua.* CONCORDIA AVGGG. Constantinopolis enthroned facing, foot on prow. *R.I.C. 55a (Treveri)*. .............................. | 30 | 75 |

624A

| 624A — VIRTVS ROMANORVM. Roma enthroned facing. *R.I.C. (Aquileia) 28d.* | 30 | 75 |
|---|---|---|
| 624B Æ 2. VIRTVS EXERCIT. Emperor stg. r., foot on captive, holding labarum and globe. *R.I.C. 24b (Heraclea)*. ............................................... | 12 | 35 |

|  | F | VF |
|---|---|---|
|  | £ | £ |

625 **Aelia Flaccilla,** wife of Theodosius I. Æ 2. SALVS REIPVBLICAE.
Victory seated r., inscribing Christian monogram on shield set on cippus.
*R.I.C. 81 (Constantinople).* ........................................................ 25 65

626 627

626 **Magnus Maximus,** usurper in the West, 383-388, proclaimed emperor
by the army in Britain, invaded Gaul, and overthrew the legitimate western
emperor Gratian; possibly reopened the London mint for a brief issue of
precious metal coinage (Rudyard Kipling presented a rather fanciful
version of his career in "Puck of Pook's Hill"). *Æ siliqua.* VIRTVS
ROMANORVM. Roma enthroned facing. *R.I.C. 84b (Treveri).* ............. 35 95
*See also under Category 3.*

627 **Flavius Victor,** son of Magnus Maximus, co-emperor 387-388. Æ 4.
SPES ROMANORVM. Gateway of military camp. *RIC 55b (Aquileia).* 40 100

628 **Eugenius,** usurper in the West, 392-394, recognized in Britain until his
defeat by Theodosius the Great. *Æ siliqua.* VIRTVS ROMANORVM.
Roma seated l. on cuirass. *R.I.C. 106d (Treveri).* ..................................... 120 275

629 **Arcadius,** 395-408 (in the East, co-emperor with his father Theodosius I
from 383). *N solidus.* VICTORIA AVGGG. Emperor stg. r., foot on
captive, holding standard and Victory. *R.I.C. 1205 (Milan).* ................... 100 250

629A 631

629A Æ 2. GLORIA ROMANORVM. Emperor stg. l., holding standard and
shield, captive at feet. *R.I.C. 41 (Antioch).* ............................................. 15 40

630 **Honorius,** 395-423 (in the West, co-emperor with his father Theodosius I
and brother Arcadius from 393), this reign saw the end of Roman rule in
Britain following a succession of usurpations in the province, culminating
in that of Constantine III against whom the Britons rebelled in 409;
Honorius' celebrated 'Rescript' of the following year instructed the
provincials to look to their own defence as he was no longer able to assist
them. *N solidus.* VICTORIA AVGGG. Emperor stg. r., foot on captive,
holding standard and Victory. *R.I.C. 1287 (Ravenna).* ............................. 100 250

630A *Æ siliqua.* VIRTVS ROMANORVM. Roma seated l. on cuirass.
*R.I.C. 1228 (Milan).* ................................................................................. 35 85

631 **Constantine III,** usurper in the West, 407-411, proclaimed emperor by the
army in Britain, but his authority rejected by the Romano-Britons two years
later, thus effectively ending 366 years of Roman rule in Britain. *Æ siliqua.*
VICTORIA AVGGG. Roma enthroned l. *R.I.C. 1532 (Treveri).* ............. 150 325

|     |     | F   | VF  |
|     |     | £   | £   |

632    **Valentinian III,** 425-455 (in the West), during whose reign the Saxon
        conquest of the former Roman province commenced, following the final
        unsuccessful appeal of the Romano-Britons for help addressed to the general
        Aetius in 446. *N solidus.* VICTORIA AVGGG. Emperor stg. facing, foot
        on human-headed serpent. *R.I.C. 2010 (Ravenna).* ...................................    125    300
632A   Æ 4. VOT. PVB. Gateway of military camp. *R.I.C. 2123 (Rome).* ..........    25    75

## 2. ISSUES WITH TYPES REFERRING SPECIFICALLY
## TO THE PROVINCE OF BRITANNIA

Struck in Rome, unless otherwise indicated. These usually commemorate military operations in the
northern frontier region of the province or beyond.

                    633                                        635

|     |     | F   | VF  |
|     |     | £   | £   |

633    **Claudius,** A.D. 41-54. AV aureus, celebrating the early stages of the
        Roman conquest of Britain which commenced in A.D. 43. DE BRITANN
        on architrave of triumphal arch. *R.I.C. 33.* .............................................    1000    2500
634    Æ *denarius.* Similar. *R.I.C. 34.* ...............................................    300    725
634A   Æ *didrachm* of Caesarea in Cappadocia. DE BRITANNIS. Emperor in
        triumphal quadriga r. *R.I.C. 122.* ...............................................    300    750
635    **Hadrian,** 117-138. Æ as, commemorating the restoration of order in the
        province following a serious uprising (or invasion) in the north, probably
        early in the governorship of Q. Pompeius Falco (118-122). BRITANNIA
        PONT. MAX. TR. POT. COS. III. S. C. Britannia seated facing on rock.
        *R.I.C. 577a.* ...............................................    175    425
636    Æ *sestertius,* commemorating Hadrian's visit to the province in 122, when
        he planned and initiated the construction of the northern frontier system
        which bears his name. ADVENTVI AVG. BRITANNIAE S.C. Emperor
        and Britannia stg. either side of altar. *R.I.C. 882.* ....................................    *Extremely rare*

                    637

637    — BRITANNIA S. C. Britannia seated facing, foot resting on rock.
        *R.I.C. 845.* ...............................................    *Extremely rare*

|  | F | VF |
|---|---|---|
|  | £ | £ |

637A   Æ *dupondius* or as. *Similar. R.I.C. 846.*..........................................     *Extremely rare*

638   Æ *sestertius*, commemorating Hadrian's attention to the legionary garrison strength of the province, principally his transfer of *VI Victrix* from Germany in 122. EXERC. BRITANNICVS S. C. Emperor on horseback r., addressing gathering of troops. *R.I.C. 912.* .......................................     *Extremely rare*

638A  — EXERC. BRITANNICVS S.C. Emperor stg. r. on tribunal, addressing gathering of troops. *R.I.C. 913.*.................................................................     *Extremely rare*

639   **Antoninus Pius,** 138-161. *N aureus,* commemorating the conquests in Scotland by the governor Q. Lollius Urbicus (138/9-142/3) at which time construction of the Antonine Wall was begun. BRITAN. IMPERATOR II. Victory stg. l. on globe. *R.I.C. 113.* ........................................................   750   1900

640

640   Æ *sestertius.* BRITANNIA S. C. Britannia seated l. on rock, holding standard. *R.I.C. 742.*...................................................................................   550   1400

641  — BRITAN. IMPERATOR II. S. C. Helmeted Britannia seated l., foot on rock. *R.I.C. 743.* ........................................................................................   550   1450

642  — BRITAN. IMPERATOR II. S. C. Britannia seated l. on globe above waves, holding standard. *R.I.C. 744.* .......................................................   650   1700

643  — BRITAN. IMPERATOR II. S. C. Victory stg. l. on globe. *R.I.C. 719.*   200    500

643A  — BRITANNIA IMPERATOR II. S. C. Britannia seated l. on rock, holding standard. *R.I.C. 745.* ........................................................................   550   1400

644   Æ *as.* IMPERATOR II. S. C. Victory hovering l., holding shield inscribed BRI / TAN. *R.I.C. 732.* ............................................................................    90    225

645   Æ *dupondius,* commemorating the quelling of a serious uprising in the north, ca. 154/5, necessitating the evacuation of the recently constructed Antonine Wall in Scotland. BRITANNIA COS. IIII. S. C. Britannia seated l. on rock, shield and vexillum in background. *R.I.C. 930.* ......................    80    200

|     |     |
| --- | --- |
| *F* | *VF* |
| £ | £ |

646    Æ *as.* Similar. *R.I.C. 934.* ............................................................    75    185
   *Many specimens of this type are carelessly struck on inadequate flans.*
   *Moreover, they have been found in significant quantities on Romano-British*
   *sites, notably in Coventina's Well at Carrawburgh fort on Hadrian's Wall,*
   *raising the interesting possibility that they may have been issued from a*
   *temporary mint in Britain. The style of the engraving is quite regular,*
   *indicating that even if locally produced these coins would have been struck*
   *from normal Roman dies brought to Britain especially for this purpose.*
   *See under Category 3.*

647    **Commodus,** 177-192. Æ *sestertius,* commemorating the victories in
   Scotland of the governor Ulpius Marcellus in 184/5. These were in
   retribution for a major barbarian invasion several years earlier resulting
   in serious damage to Hadrian's Wall, which had been temporarily overrun,
   and the defeat and death of an unknown governor. BRITT. P. M. TR. P.
   VIIII. IMP. VII. COS. IIII. P. P. S. C. Britannia stg. l., holding curved
   sword and helmet. *R.I.C. 437.* ....................................................................    *Extremely rare*

648

648    — VICT. BRIT. P. M. TR. P. VIIII. (or X.) IMP. VII. COS. IIII. P. P. S. C.
   Victory seated r., about to inscribe shield. *R.I.C. 440, 452* ......................    100    260

649

649    **Septimius Severus,** 193-211. *N aureus,* commemorating the success of
   the punitive Roman campaigns in Scotland during 209 and 210 culminating
   in the illness and death of Severus at York in Feb. 211. VICTORIAE BRIT.
   Victory advancing l. *R.I.C. 334.* ...............................................................    1200    3000
650    — VICTORIAE BRIT. Victory advancing r., leading child by hand.
   *R.I.C. 302.* ...................................................................................................    1500    3500
651    Æ *denarius.* VICTORIAE BRIT. Victory advancing r. *R.I.C. 332.* ..........    40    85
651A   — VICTORIAE BRIT. Victory stg. facing beside palm-tree with shield
   attached. *R.I.C. 336.* ..................................................................................    40    85
651B   — VICTORIAE BRIT. Victory stg. l. *R.I.C. 333.* ....................................    40    85
651C   — VICTORIAE BRIT. Victory seated l., holding shield. *R.I.C. 335.* .....    40    80

652

| | F<br>£ | VF<br>£ |
|---|---|---|
| 652  Æ *sestertius.* VICTORIAE BRITTANNICAE S. C. Two Victories placing shield on palm-tree with captives at base. *R.I.C. 818.* ............................. | 300 | 850 |
| 653  — P. M. TR. P. XVIII. COS. III. P. P. S. C. Similar. *R.I.C. 796.* ........... | 175 | 400 |
| 654  Æ *dupondius.* VICT. BRIT. P. M. TR. P. XIX. COS. III. P. P. S. C. Victory stg. r. between two captives, holding vexillum. *R.I.C. 809.* ..................... | 100 | 275 |
| 655  Æ *as.* VICTORIAE BRITTANNICAE S. C. Similar. *R.I.C. 837a.* ......... | 100 | 275 |
| 656  Billon *tetradrachm* of Alexandria in Egypt. NEIKH KATA BRET. Nike flying l. *Milne 2726.* .............................................................................. | *Extremely rare* | |
| 657  **Caracalla, 198-217.** *N aureus,* commemorating the victories achieved by the Romans in Scotland during the campaigns led jointly by Severus and Caracalla in 209, and by Caracalla alone the following year during his father's illness. VICTORIAE BRIT. Victory seated l., holding shield. *R.I.C. 174.* ....................................................................................... | 1200 | 3000 |

658          659A

| | | |
|---|---|---|
| 658  Æ *denarius.* VICTORIAE BRIT. Victory advancing l. *R.I.C. 231.* ......... | 40 | 80 |
| 658A  — VICTORIAE BRIT. Victory advancing r., holding trophy. *R.I.C. 231A.* | 40 | 80 |
| 659  Æ *sestertius.* VICTORIAE BRITTANNICAE S. C. Victory stg. r., erecting trophy to r. of which Britannia stands facing, captive at feet. *R.I.C. 464.* | 250 | 650 |
| 659A  — VICT. BRIT. TR. P. XIIII. COS. III. S.C. Similar. *Cf. R.I.C. 483c.* ... | 225 | 550 |
| 660  Æ *dupondius.* VICTORIAE BRITTANNICAE S. C. Victory stg. r., inscribing shield set on palm-tree. *R.I.C. 467.* ......................................... | 100 | 275 |
| 661  Æ *as.* VICT. BRIT. TR. P. XIIII. COS. III. S. C. Similar. *R.I.C. 490.* ...... | 100 | 250 |
| 662  **Geta, 209-212.** Æ *denarius,* commemorating the victories achieved by his father and brother in Scotland in 209-10 while he and his mother were resident in London. VICTORIAE BRIT. Victory stg. l. *R.I.C. 92.* ......... | 40 | 85 |
| 662A  — VICTORIAE BRIT. Victory advancing r. *R.I.C. 91.* ............................. | 40 | 85 |

663

|  | F | VF |
|  | £ | £ |

663    Æ *sestertius.* VICTORIAE BRITTANNICAE S. C. Victory seated r.,
       inscribing shield set on knee. *R.I.C. 166.* ....................................    275    700

663A   — VICT. BRIT. TR. P. III. COS. II. S. C. Similar. *R.I.C. 172b.* .............    250    575

664    Æ *as.* VICTORIAE BRITTANNICAE S. C. Victory seated l., balancing
       shield on knee. *R.I.C. 191a.* ........................................................    100    275

665    Billon *tetradrachm* of Alexandria in Egypt. NEIKH KATA BRETAN.
       Nike advancing l. *B.M.C. (Alexandria) 1481.* ........................................    *Extremely rare*

## 3. OFFICIAL ROMAN COINAGE STRUCK IN BRITAIN

The London mint, and the associated 'C' mint (possibly Colchester), were created by the usurper
Carausius soon after his seizure of Britain in 287. Prior to this, in the mid-2nd century, there may
have been minting of 'Britannia' asses of Antoninus Pius in the province using dies brought from
Rome, though this has not been firmly established. After the downfall of the rebel British regime in
296 the minting establishment in London (though not the subsidiary mint) was retained by the
tetrarchal government and the succeeding Constantinian administration. Early in 325, however,
Constantine the Great closed the London mint after almost four decades of operation. A possible
brief revival under the usurper Magnus Maximus has been postulated for gold and silver coins
marked 'AVG', 'AVGOB' and 'AVGPS', though the attribution has not received universal
acceptance.

|  | F | VF |
|  | £ | £ |

666    **Antoninus Pius,** 138-161. Æ *as,* struck in northern Britain (?) in 155.
       BRITANNIA COS. IIII. S. C. Britannia seated l. on rock, shield and
       vexillum in background. *R.I.C. 930.* ........................................................    60    150
       *Many poorly struck examples of this type have been found on Romano-
       British sites, notably at Brocolitia (Carrawburgh) fort on Hadrian's Wall
       in Northumberland, where no fewer than 327 specimens were discovered
       in the great votive deposit in the well which formed part of the shrine of the
       water-nymph Coventina. There appears to be a very real possibility that
       many of these 'Britannia' asses had been issued from a temporary mint in
       Britain, most likely situated in the north. The dies, however, are quite regular,
       and would thus have been brought from Rome to the island province for the
       express purpose of supplementing the money supply at a time of crisis.*

667    **Carausius,** usurper in Britain and northwestern Gaul, A.D. 287-293. *N
       aureus,* London. CONSERVAT. AVG. Jupiter stg. l., eagle at feet, ML in
       ex. *R.I.C. 1.* ........................................................    5000    12500

668    Æ *denarius,* London. EXPECTATE VENI. Britannia stg. r. and emperor l.,
       clasping hands, RSR in ex. *R.I.C. 555.* ........................................................    400    1000

669 672A

|   |   | F | VF |
|---|---|---|---|
|   |   | £ | £ |
| 669 | — RENOVAT. ROMANO. She-wolf r., suckling twins, RSR in ex. R.I.C. 571. | 300 | 850 |
| 670 | Billon *antoninianus*, London. COMES AVG. Victory stg. l., S—P in field, ML in ex. R.I.C. 14. | 45 | 110 |
| 670A | — HILARITAS AVG. Hilaritas stg. l., B—E in field, MLXXI in ex. R.I.C. 41. | 30 | 70 |
| 671 | — LAETITIA AVG. Laetitia stg. l., F—O in field, ML in ex. R.I.C. 50. | 30 | 70 |
| 671A | — LEG. II. AVG. Capricorn l., ML in ex. R.I.C. 58. | 80 | 195 |
|   | *Legio II Augusta was stationed at Isca (Caerleon in South Wales).* |   |   |
| 672 | — LEG. XX. V. V. Boar stg. r. R.I.C. 82. | 80 | 195 |
|   | *Legio XX Valeria Victrix was stationed at Deva (Chester in the northwest Midlands).* |   |   |
| 672A | — PAX AVG. Pax stg. l., F—O in field, ML in ex. R.I.C. 101. | 25 | 70 |
| 673 | — Similar, but without mint mark. R.I.C. 880. | 25 | 65 |
| 673A | — PROVIDENT. AVG. Providentia stg. l., B—E in field, MLXXI in ex. R.I.C. 149. | 30 | 70 |
| 674 | — SALVS AVGGG. Salus stg. r., feeding snake held in her arms, S—P in field, ML in ex. R.I.C. 164. | 30 | 70 |
|   | *The reverse legends with triple-ending (AVGGG.) presumably are subsequent to Carausius' recognition by Diocletian and Maximian in 289 following the failure of the latter's attempt to dislodge the usurper from his island stronghold.* |   |   |
| 674A | — TEMPORVM FELICITAS. Felicitas stg. l., B—E in field, ML in ex. R.I.C. 172. | 25 | 70 |
| 675 | — VIRTVS AVGGG. Mars (or Virtus) stg. r., holding spear and shield, S—P in field, MLXXI in ex. R.I.C. 183. | 30 | 70 |
| 676 | Billon *antoninianus*, Colchester (?). CONCORDIA MILIT. Emperor stg. r. and Concordia l., clasping hands, C in ex. R.I.C. 205. | 55 | 130 |
| 676A | — EXPECTATE VENI. Britannia stg. r. and emperor l., clasping hands, MSC in ex. R.I.C. 216. | 100 | 250 |
| 677 | — FELICITAS AVG. Galley with mast and rowers, CXXI in ex. R.I.C. 221. | 80 | 200 |
| 677A | — FORTVNA RAEDVX. Fortuna seated l., SPC in ex. R.I.C. 237. | 40 | 100 |
| 678 | — LAETITIA AVG. Laetitia stg. l., globe at feet, S—P in field, C in ex. R.I.C. 255. | 30 | 70 |
| 678A | — MONETA AVG. Moneta stg. l., CXXI in ex. R.I.C. 287. | 30 | 70 |
| 679 | — ORIENS AVG. Sol stg. l., C in ex. R.I.C. 293. | 35 | 85 |
| 679A | — PAX AVGGG. Pax stg. l., S—P in field, MC in ex. R.I.C. 335. | 30 | 70 |

680

| | F | VF |
| --- | --- | --- |
| | £ | £ |
| 680 — PROVID. AVG. Providentia stg. l., S—P in field, C in ex. *R.I.C. 353.* | 30 | 70 |
| 680A — SALVS AVG. Salus stg. l. at altar, feeding snake, S—C in field, C in ex. *R.I.C. 396.* | 30 | 70 |
| 681 — SPES PVBLICA. Spes walking l., holding flower, S—P in field, C in ex. *R.I.C. 413.* | 30 | 70 |
| 681A — VICTORIA AVG. Victory advancing l., captive at feet, MC in ex. *R.I.C. 429.* | 35 | 85 |
| 682 **Carausius, Diocletian and Maximian,** after 289. Billon *antoninianus,* Colchester (?). Obv. CARAVSIVS ET FRATRES SVI. Conjoined busts of the three emperors l. Rev. PAX AVGGG. Pax stg. l., S—P in field, C in ex. *R.I.C. 1.* | 800 | 2000 |

682A 684A

| 682A — MONETA AVGGG. Moneta stg. l., S—P in field, C in ex. *R.I.C. —.* | 1000 | 2500 |
| --- | --- | --- |
| *See also nos. 693-4 and 698-700 as well as regular Carausian types with the triple-ending 'AVGGG.' on reverse.* | | |
| 683 **Allectus,** usurper in Britain, 293-296. *N aureus,* London. ORIENS AVG. Sol stg. l. between two captives, ML in ex. *R.I.C. 4.* | 7000 | 17500 |
| 684 *Æ antoninianus,* London. LAETITIA AVG. Laetitia stg. l., S—A in field, MSL in ex. *R.I.C. 22.* | 30 | 75 |
| 684A — PAX AVG. Pax stg. l., S—A in field, ML in ex. *R.I.C. 28.* | 35 | 80 |
| 685 — PROVID. AVG. Providentia stg. l., holding globe and cornucopiae, S—P in field, ML in ex. *R.I.C. 36.* | 35 | 85 |
| 685A — SALVS AVG. Salus stg. r., feeding snake held in her arms, S—A in field, MSL in ex. *R.I.C. 42.* | 30 | 75 |
| 686 — TEMPOR. FELICITAS. Felicitas stg. l., S—A in field, ML in ex. *R.I.C. 47.* | 30 | 70 |
| 686A — VICTORIA AVG. Victory advancing l., S—P in field, ML in ex. *R.I.C. 48.* | 30 | 70 |
| 687 *Æ antoninianus,* Colchester (?). AEQVITAS AVG. Aequitas stg. l., S—P in field, C in ex. *R.I.C. 63.* | 30 | 75 |
| 687A — FIDES MILITVM. Fides stg. l., holding two standards, S—P in field, C in ex. *R.I.C. 69.* | 30 | 75 |

688A

| | | F | VF |
| | | £ | £ |
| 688 | — LAETITIA AVG. Laetitia stg. l., S—P in field, CL in ex. *R.I.C. 79.* . | 40 | 100 |

*This form of mint mark has given rise to the alternative identification of this mint as Clausentum (Bitterne, Hants.)*

| 688A | — MONETA AVG. Moneta stg. l., S—P in field, C in ex. *R.I.C. 82.* ..... | 40 | 95 |
| 689 | — PAX AVG. Pax stg. l., S—P in field, C in ex. *R.I.C. 86.* ................... | 35 | 80 |
| 689A | — PROVIDENTIA AVG. Providentia stg. l., globe at feet, S—P in field, C in ex. *R.I.C. 111.*................................ | 30 | 75 |
| 690 | — TEMPORVM FELIC. Felicitas stg. l., S—P in field, CL in ex. *R.I.C. 117.* | 40 | 100 |
| 690A | — VIRTVS AVG. Mars stg. r., holding spear and shield, S—P in field, C in ex. *R.I.C. 121.*................................ | 30 | 75 |
| 691 | Æ *'quinarius'*, London. VIRTVS AVG. Galley l., QL in ex. *R.I.C. 55.* .. | 30 | 75 |

*An experimental denomination issued only during this reign, the types of the so-called 'quinarius' would seem to indicate that it was in some way associated with the operations of the fleet upon which the survival of the rebel regime in Britain was totally dependent.*

692 693

| 692 | Æ *'quinarius'*, Colchester (?). LAETITIA AVG. Galley r., QC in ex. *R.I.C. 124.* ................................ | 35 | 80 |
| 692A | — VIRTVS AVG. Galley l., QC in ex. *R.I.C. 128.* ................................ | 35 | 85 |
| 693 | **Diocletian,** 284-305. Billon *antoninianus* of London, struck by Carausius between 289 and 293. PAX AVGGG. Pax stg. l., S—P in field, MLXXI in ex. *R.I.C. 9.* ................................ | 35 | 85 |
| 694 | Billon *antoninianus* of Colchester (?), same date. PROVID AVGGG. Providentia stg. l., globe at feet, S—P in field, C in ex. *R.I.C. 22.*........... | 35 | 85 |

695

| | F | VF |
|---|---|---|
| | £ | £ |

695 &AElig; *follis,* London. GENIO POPVLI ROMANI. Genius stg. l., LON in ex.
R.I.C. 1a. .......................................................................................................... 125 275
*By the time the central government had recovered control of Britain in 296
the antoninianus had been replaced by the larger follis under Diocletian's
sweeping currency reform. London was retained as an official imperial
mint, but the secondary British establishment (at Colchester?) was now
abandoned. Except for its initial issue in 297 (marked 'LON') the London
mint under the tetrarchic government produced only unsigned folles
throughout its first decade of operation. Perhaps Constantius did not
wish to draw attention to his employment of a mint which had been the
creation of a rebel regime.*

696

| 696 | — Similar, but without mint mark. R.I.C. 6a. .......................................... | 15 | 35 |
|---|---|---|---|

697 — (post-abdication coinage, after 305). PROVIDENTIA DEORVM
QVIES AVGG. Quies and Providentia stg. facing each other (no mint mark).
R.I.C. 77a. ........................................................................................................ 30 65

697A — QVIES AVGG. Quies stg. l., holding branch and sceptre, PLN in ex.
R.I.C. 98. ........................................................................................................ 20 50

698 **Maximian,** 286-305 and 306-308. &Nu; *aureus* of London, struck by
Carausius between 289 and 293. SALVS AVGGG. Salus stg. r., feeding
snake held in her arms, ML in ex. R.I.C. 32. ............................................ *Extremely rare*

699 Billon *antoninianus* of London, same date. PROVIDENTIA AVGGG.
Providentia stg. l., S—P in field, MLXXI in ex. R.I.C. 37. ...................... 35 85

700 Billon *antoninianus* of Colchester (?), same date. PAX AVGGG. Pax stg.
l., S—P in field, C in ex. R.I.C. 42. ............................................................ 35 85

701 &AElig; *follis,* London. GENIO POPVLI ROMANI. Genius stg. l., LON in ex.
R.I.C. 2. ........................................................................................................ 100 250

702 — Similar, but without mint mark. R.I.C. 23b. ........................................... 15 35

703 — (post-abdication coinage, after 305). PROVIDENTIA DEORVM
QVIES AVGG. Quies and Providentia stg. facing each other (no mint mark).
R.I.C. 77b. ..................................................................................................... 30 65

704

|  | F<br>£ | VF<br>£ |
|---|---|---|

704 — (second reign). GENIO POP. ROM. Genius stg. l., PLN in ex. *R.I.C. 90.* 20 40
704A — HERCVLI CONSERVATORI. Hercules stg. l., resting on club,
PLN in ex. *R.I.C. 91.* .............................................................................. 30 75
705 **Constantius I,** 305-306 (Caesar 293-305). Æ *follis,* London (as Caesar).
GENIO POPVLI ROMANI. Genius stg. l., LON in ex. *R.I.C. 4a.* .......... 110 275

706

706 — Similar, but without mint mark. *R.I.C. 30.* ......................................... 15 35
707 — (as Augustus). Similar. *R.I.C. 52a.* ...................................................... 20 45
708 **Divus Constantius I,** deified 306. Æ *follis,* London. MEMORIA FELIX.
Altar flanked by eagles, PLN in ex. *R.I.C. 110.* ...................................... 20 50
709 **Galerius,** 305-311 (Caesar 293-305). Æ *follis,* London (as Caesar).
GENIO POPVLI ROMANI. Genius stg. l., LON in ex. *R.I.C. 4b.* .......... 110 275
710 — Similar, but without mint mark. *R.I.C. 15.* ......................................... 10 25
711 — (as Augustus). Similar. *R.I.C. 42.* ...................................................... 12 30
711A — GENIO POP. ROM. Genius stg. l., PLN in ex. *R.I.C. 86.* ................... 18 45
712 **Severus II,** 306-307 (Caesar 305-306). Æ *follis,* London (as Caesar).
GENIO POPVLI ROMANI. Genius stg. l. (no mint mark). *R.I.C. 58a* ... 35 85
713 — (as Augustus). Similar. *R.I.C. 52c.* ...................................................... 35 85
714 **Maximinus II,** 310-313 (Caesar 305-310). Æ *follis,* London (as Caesar).
GENIO POPVLI ROMANI. Genius stg. l. (no mint mark). *R.I.C. 57.* .... 15 40
715 — GENIO POP. ROM. Genius stg. l., PLN in ex. *R.I.C. 89a.* .................. 15 40
716 — (as Augustus). Similar, but with star in r. field. *R.I.C. 209b.* .............. 12 30
717 **Licinius,** 308-324. Æ *follis,* London. GENIO POP. ROM. Genius stg. l.,
star in r. field, PLN in ex. *R.I.C. 209c.* .................................................... 12 30
717A — Similar, but with S—F in field. *R.I.C. 3.* ............................................ 8 20
718 — SOLI INVICTO COMITI. Sol stg. l., holding globe, S—P in field,
MSL in ex. *R.I.C. 79.* .............................................................................. 10 25
719 **Constantine I, the Great,** 307-337 (Caesar 306-307). Æ *follis,* London
(as Caesar). GENIO POPVLI ROMANI. Genius stg. l. (no mint mark).
*R.I.C. 72.* .................................................................................................. 25 65
719A — GENIO POP. ROM. Genius stg. l., PLN in ex. *R.I.C. 88b.* ................. 15 35

|     |     | F<br>£ | VF<br>£ |
| --- | --- | --- | --- |

720   — PRINCIPI IVVENTVTIS. Prince stg. l., holding standards, PLN in ex.
      *R.I.C. 97.* ...................................................................................   25   60
721   — (as Augustus). ADVENTVS AVG. Emperor on horseback l., captive
      on ground before, star in r. field, PLN in ex. *R.I.C. 133.* .......................   22   55

722

722   — COMITI AVGG. NN. Sol stg. l., holding globe and whip, same mint
      mark. *R.I.C. 155.* ........................................................................   18   45
723   — CONCORD. MILIT. Concordia stg. l., holding standards, same mint
      mark. *R.I.C. 195.* ........................................................................   15   40
724   — MARTI CONSERVATORI. Mars. stg. r., holding spear and shield,
      star in l. field, PLN in ex. *R.I.C. 254.* ...........................................   15   35
724A  — SOLI INVICTO COMITI. Sol stg. l., holding globe, S—F in field,
      MLL in ex. *R.I.C. 27.* ....................................................................   10   25
725   Æ 3, London. VICTORIAE LAETAE PRINC. PERP. Two Victories
      supporting shield, inscribed VOT. / P. R., over altar, PLN in ex. *R.I.C. 159.*   10   25
726   — VIRTVS EXERCIT. Vexillum, inscribed VOT. / XX., between two
      captives, PLN in ex. R.I.C. 191. .....................................................   10   25
727   — BEAT. TRANQLITAS. Altar, inscribed VOT / IS / XX., surmounted
      by globe and three stars, PLON in ex. *R.I.C. 267.* .........................   10   25
727A  — SARMATIA DEVICTA. Victory advancing r., trampling captive,
      PLON and crescent in ex. *R.I.C. 289.* ..........................................   20   45
728   — PROVIDENTIAE AVGG. Gateway of military camp, PLON in ex.
      *R.I.C. 293.* ...................................................................................   10   25
729   **Fausta,** wife of Constantine I. Æ 3, London. SALVS REIPVBLICAE.
      Empress stg. l., holding two children, PLON in ex. *R.I.C. 300.* ...............   60   150
730   **Helena,** mother of Constantine I. Æ 3, London. SECVRITAS REIPVBLICE.
      Empress stg. l., holding branch, PLON in ex. *R.I.C. 299.* .........................   60   150
731   **Crispus,** eldest son of Constantine I, Caesar 317-326. Æ 3, London.
      SOLI INVICTO COMITI. Sol stg. l., holding globe, crescent in l. field,
      PLN in ex. *R.I.C. 144.* ...................................................................   12   30
731A  — VIRTVS EXERCIT. Vexillum, inscribed VOT. / XX., between two
      captives, PLN in ex. *R.I.C. 194.* .....................................................   12   30
732   — BEATA TRANQVILLITAS. Altar, inscribed VOT / IS / XX.,
      surmounted by globe and three stars, P—A in field, PLON in ex. *R.I.C. 211.*   12   30
733   — CAESARVM NOSTRORVM around wreath containing VOT. / X.,
      PLON and crescent in ex. *R.I.C. 291.* ..........................................   12   30

734                                    737A

|      |                                                                                                                                                                        | F £ | VF £ |
|------|------------------------------------------------------------------------------------------------------------------------------------------------------------------------|-----|------|
| 734  | — PROVIDENTIAE CAESS. Gateway of military camp, PLON in ex. *R.I.C. 295.* ............................................................................ | 10  | 25   |
| 735  | **Constantine II,** 337-340 (Caesar 317-337). Æ 3, London (as Caesar). CLARITAS REIPVBLICAE. Sol stg. l., holding globe, crescent in l. field, PLN in ex. *R.I.C. 131.* .............................................................................. | 12  | 30   |
| 736  | — VICTORIAE LAETAE PRINC. PERP. Two Victories supporting shield, inscribed VOT. / P. R., over altar ornamented with wreath, PLN in ex. *R.I.C. 182.* ...................................................................................... | 12  | 30   |
| 737  | — VIRTVS EXERCIT. Vexillum, inscribed VOT. / XX., between two captives, PLON in ex. *R.I.C. 190.* ............................................... | 12  | 30   |
| 737A | — BEATA TRANQVILLITAS. Altar, inscribed VOT / IS / XX., surmounted by globe and three stars, PLON in ex. *R.I.C. 236.* ................. | 10  | 25   |
| 738  | — CAESARVM NOSTRORVM around wreath containing VOT. / X., PLON and crescent in ex. *R.I.C. 292.* ....................................... | 10  | 25   |
| 738A | — PROVIDENTIAE CAESS. Gateway of military camp, PLON in ex. *R.I.C. 296.* ............................................................................ | 10  | 25   |
| 739  | **Constantius II,** 337-361 (Caesar 324-337). Æ 3, London (as Caesar). PROVIDENTIAE CAESS. Gateway of military camp, PLON in ex. *R.I.C. 298.* ............................................................................ | 25  | 60   |
| 740  | **Magnus Maximus,** usurper in the West, 383-388. *N solidus,* London (?). RESTITVTOR REIPVBLICAE. Emperor stg. r., holding labarum and Victory, AVG in ex. *R.I.C. 1.* ...................................................... | \| Unique \| ||

The attribution to London of this rare series has not been firmly established,
though Maximus was certainly proclaimed emperor in Britain and it is
well attested that the principal city of the British provinces bore the name
'Augusta' in the late Roman period (Ammianus Marcellinus XXVII, 8, 7;
XXVIII, 3, 7).*

741

| 741 | — VICTORIA AVGG. Two emperors enthroned facing, Victory hovering in background between them, AVGOB in ex. *R.I.C. 2b.* ......................... | 5000 | 10000 |

*Maximus appears to have struck a similar type in the name of the eastern
emperor Theodosius I (cf. R.I.C. 2a), though it is presently known only
from a silver-gilt specimen preserved in the British Museum.*

|     |     |
| --- | --- |
| *F* | *VF* |
| £ | £ |

742    Æ *siliqua*, London (?). VOT. / V. / MVLT. / X. within wreath, AVG below.
       *R.I.C. 4.* ................................................................................................    850    2000
742A   — VICTORIA AVGG. Victory advancing l., AVGPS in ex. *R.I.C. 3.*....    750    1750

## 4. IMITATIONS OF ROMAN COINS PRODUCED IN BRITAIN

At certain periods during the three and a half centuries of its occupation Roman Britain seems to have been the source of much local imitation of the official imported coinage. This began soon after the Claudian invasion in A.D. 43 when significant quantities of sestertii, dupondii and asses (especially the last) were produced in the newly conquered territory, as evidenced by the frequency of their occurrence in archaeological finds. The technical excellence of many of these 'copies', together with the surprising extent of their minting, would seem to indicate that some, at least, of these coins were produced with official sanction in order to make good an unexpected deficiency in the currency supply. Others are much poorer and well below weight, representing the 'unofficial' branch of this operation, some of it probably emanating from territory as yet unconquered. As conditions in the new province settled down rapid Romanization and urbanization of British society brought a general increase in wealth, and with it a much greater volume of currency flowing into the country. Local imitation now virtually ceased, except for the occasional activities of criminal counterfeiters, and this state of affairs lasted down to the great political crisis and financial collapse of the second half of the 3rd century. At this point large scale minting of imitations of the debased antoniniani of the late 260s and early 270s began in Britain and in the other northwestern provinces, all of which had been seriuolsy affected by the political dislocation of this turbulent era. This class of imitations is usually referred to as 'barbarous radiates', the emperor's spiky crown being a constant and conspicuous feature of the obverses. Most frequently copied were the antoniniani of the Gallic rulers Tetricus Senior and Tetricus Junior (ca. 270-273) and the posthumous issues of Claudius Gothicus (died 270). The quality of the 'barbarous radiates' is variable in the extreme, some exhibiting what appears to be a revival of Celtic art forms, others so tiny that it is virtually impossible to see anything of the design. Their production appears to have ended abruptly with Aurelian's reconquest of the western provinces in 273. A similar phenomenon, though on a lesser scale, occurred in the middle decades of the following century when normal life in Britain was again disrupted, not only by usurpation but additionally by foreign invasion. With supplies of currency from the Continent temporarily disrupted local imitation, particularly of the 'Æ 2' and 'Æ 3' issues of Constantius II and the usurper Magnentius, began in earnest. How long this continued is difficult to determine as life in the island province was now subject to increasingly frequent episodes of dislocation. By now urban life in Britain was in serious decline and when Roman rule ended early in the 5th century, bringing a total cessation of currency supplies, the catastrophic decline in monetary commerce in the former provinces rendered it no longer necessary for the deficiency to be made good.

|     |     |
| --- | --- |
| *F* | *VF* |
| £ | £ |

743    **Agrippa,** died 12 B.C. Æ as, of irregular British mintage, imitating the
       Roman issue made under Agrippa's grandson Caligula, A.D. 37-41.
       S. C. Neptune stg. l., holding dolphin and trident.....................................    40    100
       *The large official issue of Agrippa asses was made shortly before the*
       *Claudian invasion of Britain in A.D. 43 and would thus have comprised*
       *a significant proportion of the 'aes' in circulation at this time. In*
       *consequence, it would soon have become familiar to the new provincials*
       *providing an ideal prototype for imitation.*
744    **Claudius,** 41-54. Æ *sestertius,* of irregular British mintage. SPES
       AVGVSTA S. C. Spes walking l., holding flower.  ...............................    75    250
745    Æ *dupondius,* of irregular British mintage. CERES AVGVSTA S. C.
       Ceres enthroned l., holding corn- ears and torch. ....................................    35    100

746

|  | F<br>£ | VF<br>£ |
|---|---|---|

746 Æ *as*, of irregular British mintage. S. C. Minerva advancing r., brandishing
spear and holding shield............................................................. 30 85
*This is by far the commonest of the Claudian imitations and the prototypes*
*must have represented the bulk of the aes coinage carried by the legions at*
*the time of the invasion. The martial type may well have been specially*
*selected as a suitable theme for the initial import of coinage into the newly*
*conquered territory.*

747 **Nero Claudius Drusus,** father of Claudius, died 9 B.C. Æ *sestertius,* of
irregular British mintage. TI. CLAVDIVS CAESAR AVG. P. M. TR .P.
IMP. S. C. Claudius seated l. on curule chair amidst arms...................... 85 300
*This type was issued by Claudius half a century after his father's death and*
*would thus have been prominently represented in the initial wave of coinage*
*imported into the new province.*

748 **Antonia,** mother of Claudius, died A.D. 37. Æ *dupondius,* of irregular British
mintage. TI. CLAVDIVS CAESAR AVG P.M. TR. P. IMP. P. P. S. C. Claudius
stg. l., holding simpulum.......................................................... 60 175
*Another Claudian issue for a deceased parent, this represents one of only*
*two dupondius types struck during this reign and would have entered*
*Britain in significant quantities at the time of the invasion in A.D. 43.*

749A                                        749B

749C

749 **'Barbarous radiates',** ca. 270-273. British and Continental imitations of
billon *antoniniani,* principally of Divus Claudius II (A), Tetricus Senior
(B) and Tetricus Junior (C). The inscriptions are usually blundered and
the types sometimes unrecognizable. British mintage can only be
established by provenance. ....................................................... 5 10

|  | *F* | *VF* |
|--|-----|------|
|  | £ | £ |

750   **Barbarous 4th century,** mostly of the second half of the century, and
        principally imitated from 'Æ 2' and 'Æ 3' issues of the later Constantinian
        period, notably those of Constantius II ('soldier spearing fallen horseman'
        type), and the usurpers Magnentius and Decentius ('two Victories' type).
        The copies, especially those of Magnentius and Decentius, are often of
        excellent style and execution, though the legends frequently contain small
        errors. Those of Constantius II are sometimes very barbarous and poorly
        struck, occasionally over regular issues of the earlier Constantinian period.
        Again, the likelihood of British mintage can only be established by
        provenance. .............................................................................................   5-8   10-15

## Grading of Hammered Coins

As the name suggests, hammered coins were struck by hand with a hammer. This can lead to the coin being struck off centre, double struck, weak in the design, suffer cracks or flan defects. It is important to take these factors into account when assessing the grade of this series. Value is considerably reduced if the coin is holed, pierced, plugged or mounted.

**Extremely Fine**
Design and legends
sharp and clear.

**Very Fine**
Design and legends
still clear but with
slight evidence of wear
and/or minor damage.

**Fine**
Showing quite a lot of
wear but still with
design and legends
distinguishable.

Anglo-Saxon 'Porcupine' Sceat

Gold Noble

Silver Crown

# EARLY & MIDDLE ANGLO-SAXON KINGDOMS & MINTS (C.650-973)

# EARLY ANGLO-SAXON PERIOD, *c*. 600-*c*. 775

The withdrawal of Roman forces from Britain early in the 5th century A.D. and the gradual decline of central administration resulted in a rapid deterioration of the money supply. The arrival of Teutonic raiders and settlers hastened the decay of urban commercial life and it was probably not until late in the 6th century that renewed political, cultural and commercial links with the kingdom of the Merovingian Franks led to the appearance of small quantities of Merovingian gold *tremisses* (one-third solidus) in England. A purse containing such pieces was found in the Sutton Hoo ship-burial. Native Anglo-Saxon gold *thrymsas* were minted from about the 630s, initially in the style of their continental prototypes or copied from obsolete Roman coinage and later being made in pure Anglo-Saxon style. By the middle of the 7th century the gold coinage was being increasingly debased with silver, and gold had been superseded entirely by about 675.

These silver coins, contemporary with the *deniers or denarii* of the Merovingian Franks, are the first English pennies, though they are commonly known today as *sceattas* (a term more correctly translated as 'treasure' or 'wealth'). They provide important material for the student of Anglo-Saxon art.

Though the earliest sceattas are a transition from the gold thrymsa coinage, coins of new style were soon developed which were also copied by the Frisians of the Low Countries. Early coins appear to have a standard weight of 20 grains (1.29 gms) and are of good silver content, though the quality deteriorates early in the 8th century. These coins exist in a large number of varied types, and as well as the official issues there are mules and other varieties which are probably contemporary imitations. Many of the sceattas were issued during the reign of Aethelbald of Mercia, but as few bear inscriptions it is only in recent years that research has permitted their correct dating and the attribution of certain types to specific areas. Some silver sceattas of groups II and III and most types of groups IV to X were issued during the period (A.D. 716-757) when Aethelbald, King of Mercia, was overlord of the southern English. Though a definitive classification has not yet been developed, the arrangement given below follows the latest work on the series: this list is not exhaustive.

This section has been catalogued in line with research published by Dr D. M. Metcalf. Wherever possible the catalogue number previously in use has been retained. Where it has been necessary to allocate a new and different number, the 'old' S. number is listed, in brackets, at the end of the entry. New entries are given a new number. The primary sceattas are followed by the secondary sceattas and, finally, the continental sceattas. This is not chronologically correct but has been adopted for ease of reference and identification. The reference 'B.M.C.' is to the type given in *British Museum Catalogue: Anglo-Saxon Coins.* Other works of reference include:

North, J. J. *English Hammered Coinage*, Vol. 1, *c.* 650-1272 (1994).
Metcalf, D.M. *Thrymsas and Sceattas in the Ashmolean Museum,* Vols I-III.
Rigold, S. E. 'The two primary series of sceattas', *B.N.J., xxx* (1960).
Sutherland, C. H. V. *Anglo-Saxon Gold Coinage in the light of the Crondall Hoard* (1948).

ᚠᚪᚦᛖᚱᚲ·ᚷᚹᚻᚾᛁᛁᚩᛋᛇᚷᚣᚾᛏᛒᛗᚻᛚᛝᛞᛟᚪᚫᛠᚣᚪ

f   u   th o   r   k . z   w   h   n   i   j  ih  p   x   s   t   b   e   m   l  ng  d  oe  a  Æ  ea  y

Early Anglo-Saxon Runes

## GOLD

|   |   | F | VF |
|---|---|---|---|
|   |   | £ | £ |
| **A.** | **Early pieces, of uncertain monetary status** | | |
| 751 | Thrymsa. Name and portrait of Bishop Leudard (chaplain to Queen Bertha of Kent). ℞. Cross. ................................................................ | *Extremely rare* | |
| 752 | Solidus. Imitating solidi of Roman rulers. Blundered legends, some with runes. ................................................................................ | *Extremely rare* | |

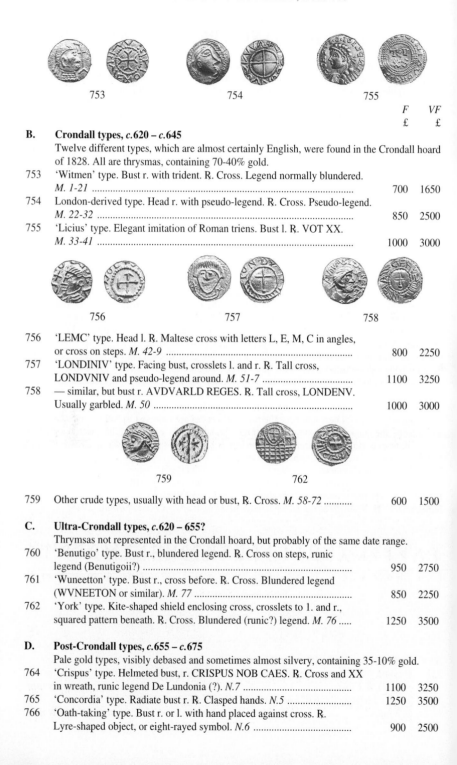

753                        754                        755

|     | F £ | VF £ |
|-----|-----|------|

**B.     Crondall types, c.620 – c.645**

Twelve different types, which are almost certainly English, were found in the Crondall hoard of 1828. All are thrysmas, containing 70-40% gold.

753  'Witmen' type. Bust r. with trident. R. Cross. Legend normally blundered.
     *M. 1-21* ........................................................................................... 700  1650
754  London-derived type. Head r. with pseudo-legend. R. Cross. Pseudo-legend.
     *M. 22-32* ......................................................................................... 850  2500
755  'Licius' type. Elegant imitation of Roman triens. Bust l. R. VOT XX.
     *M. 33-41* ......................................................................................... 1000  3000

756                        757                        758

756  'LEMC' type. Head l. R. Maltese cross with letters L, E, M, C in angles,
     or cross on steps. *M. 42-9* ............................................................ 800  2250
757  'LONDINIV' type. Facing bust, crosslets l. and r. R. Tall cross,
     LONDVNIV and pseudo-legend around. *M. 51-7* .............................. 1100  3250
758  — similar, but bust r. AVDVARLD REGES. R. Tall cross, LONDENV.
     Usually garbled. *M. 50* ................................................................ 1000  3000

759                        762

759  Other crude types, usually with head or bust, R. Cross. *M. 58-72* ........... 600  1500

**C.     Ultra-Crondall types, c.620 – 655?**

Thrymsas not represented in the Crondall hoard, but probably of the same date range.

760  'Benutigo' type. Bust r., blundered legend. R. Cross on steps, runic
     legend (Benutigoii?) ...................................................................... 950  2750
761  'Wuneetton' type. Bust r., cross before. R. Cross. Blundered legend
     (WVNEETON or similar). *M. 77* ...................................................... 850  2250
762  'York' type. Kite-shaped shield enclosing cross, crosslets to l. and r.,
     squared pattern beneath. R. Cross. Blundered (runic?) legend. *M. 76* ..... 1250  3500

**D.     Post-Crondall types, c.655 – c.675**

Pale gold types, visibly debased and sometimes almost silvery, containing 35-10% gold.

764  'Crispus' type. Helmeted bust, r. CRISPUS NOB CAES. R. Cross and XX
     in wreath, runic legend De Lundonia (?). *N.7* ................................... 1100  3250
765  'Concordia' type. Radiate bust r. R. Clasped hands. *N.5* ....................... 1250  3500
766  'Oath-taking' type. Bust r. or l. with hand placed against cross. R.
     Lyre-shaped object, or eight-rayed symbol. *N.6* ............................... 900  2500

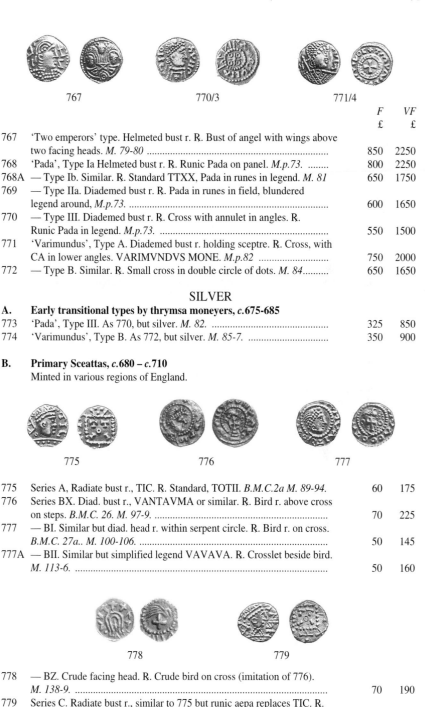

767              770/3              771/4

|  |  | F | VF |
|---|---|---|---|
|  |  | £ | £ |
| 767 | 'Two emperors' type. Helmeted bust r. R. Bust of angel with wings above two facing heads. *M. 79-80* ........ | 850 | 2250 |
| 768 | 'Pada', Type Ia Helmeted bust r. R. Runic Pada on panel. *M.p.73.* ........ | 800 | 2250 |
| 768A | — Type Ib. Similar. R. Standard TTXX, Pada in runes in legend. *M. 81* | 650 | 1750 |
| 769 | — Type IIa. Diademed bust r. R. Pada in runes in field, blundered legend around, *M.p.73.* ........ | 600 | 1650 |
| 770 | — Type III. Diademed bust r. R. Cross with annulet in angles. R. Runic Pada in legend. *M.p.73.* ........ | 550 | 1500 |
| 771 | 'Varimundus', Type A. Diademed bust r. holding sceptre. R. Cross, with CA in lower angles. VARIMVNDVS MONE. *M.p.82* ........ | 750 | 2000 |
| 772 | — Type B. Similar. R. Small cross in double circle of dots. *M. 84* ........ | 650 | 1650 |

## SILVER

**A.    Early transitional types by thrymsa moneyers, *c*.675-685**

| 773 | 'Pada', Type III. As 770, but silver. *M. 82.* ........ | 325 | 850 |
|---|---|---|---|
| 774 | 'Varimundus', Type B. As 772, but silver. *M. 85-7.* ........ | 350 | 900 |

**B.    Primary Sceattas, *c*.680 – *c*.710**
Minted in various regions of England.

775              776              777

| 775 | Series A, Radiate bust r., TIC. R. Standard, TOTII. *B.M.C.2a M. 89-94.* | 60 | 175 |
|---|---|---|---|
| 776 | Series BX. Diad. bust r., VANTAVMA or similar. R. Bird r. above cross on steps. *B.M.C. 26. M. 97-9.* ........ | 70 | 225 |
| 777 | — BI. Similar but diad. head r. within serpent circle. R. Bird r. on cross. *B.M.C. 27a.. M. 100-106.* ........ | 50 | 145 |
| 777A | — BII. Similar but simplified legend VAVAVA. R. Crosslet beside bird. *M. 113-6.* ........ | 50 | 160 |

778              779

| 778 | — BZ. Crude facing head. R. Crude bird on cross (imitation of 776). *M. 138-9.* ........ | 70 | 190 |
|---|---|---|---|
| 779 | Series C. Radiate bust r., similar to 775 but runic aepa replaces TIC. R. Standard, TOTII. *B.M.C. 2b. M. 117-125.* ........ | 40 | 110 |

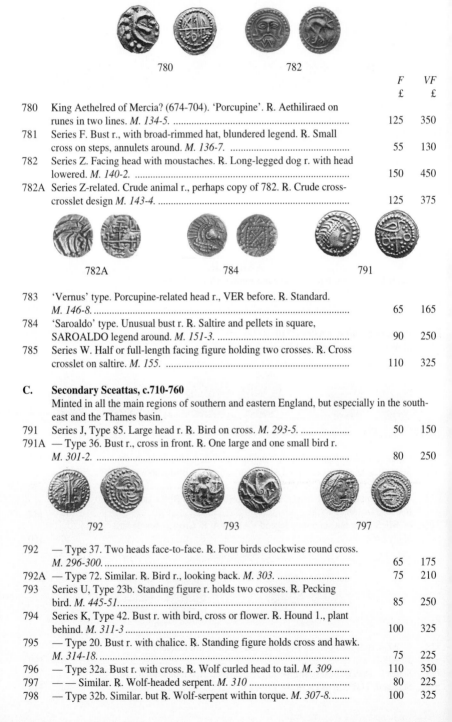

780                    782

|  |  | *F* | *VF* |
|--|--|--|--|
|  |  | £ | £ |

| | | | |
|--|--|--|--|
| 780 | King Aethelred of Mercia? (674-704). 'Porcupine'. ℞. Aethiliraed on runes in two lines. *M. 134-5.* | 125 | 350 |
| 781 | Series F. Bust r., with broad-rimmed hat, blundered legend. ℞. Small cross on steps, annulets around. *M. 136-7.* | 55 | 130 |
| 782 | Series Z. Facing head with moustaches. ℞. Long-legged dog r. with head lowered. *M. 140-2.* | 150 | 450 |
| 782A | Series Z-related. Crude animal r., perhaps copy of 782. ℞. Crude cross-crosslet design *M. 143-4.* | 125 | 375 |

782A                    784                    791

| | | | |
|--|--|--|--|
| 783 | 'Vernus' type. Porcupine-related head r., VER before. ℞. Standard. *M. 146-8.* | 65 | 165 |
| 784 | 'Saroaldo' type. Unusual bust r. ℞. Saltire and pellets in square, SAROALDO legend around. *M. 151-3.* | 90 | 250 |
| 785 | Series W. Half or full-length facing figure holding two crosses. ℞. Cross crosslet on saltire. *M. 155.* | 110 | 325 |

**C.    Secondary Sceattas, c.710-760**

Minted in all the main regions of southern and eastern England, but especially in the south-east and the Thames basin.

| | | | |
|--|--|--|--|
| 791 | Series J, Type 85. Large head r. ℞. Bird on cross. *M. 293-5.* | 50 | 150 |
| 791A | — Type 36. Bust r., cross in front. ℞. One large and one small bird r. *M. 301-2.* | 80 | 250 |

792                    793                    797

| | | | |
|--|--|--|--|
| 792 | — Type 37. Two heads face-to-face. ℞. Four birds clockwise round cross. *M. 296-300.* | 65 | 175 |
| 792A | — Type 72. Similar. ℞. Bird r., looking back. *M. 303.* | 75 | 210 |
| 793 | Series U, Type 23b. Standing figure r. holds two crosses. ℞. Pecking bird. *M. 445-51.* | 85 | 250 |
| 794 | Series K, Type 42. Bust r. with bird, cross or flower. ℞. Hound 1., plant behind. *M. 311-3* | 100 | 325 |
| 795 | — Type 20. Bust r. with chalice. ℞. Standing figure holds cross and hawk. *M. 314-18.* | 75 | 225 |
| 796 | — Type 32a. Bust r. with cross. ℞. Wolf curled head to tail. *M. 309* | 110 | 350 |
| 797 | — — Similar. ℞. Wolf-headed serpent. *M. 310* | 80 | 225 |
| 798 | — Type 32b. Similar. but ℞. Wolf-serpent within torque. *M. 307-8.* | 100 | 325 |

|     |     | F<br>£ | VF<br>£ |
|-----|-----|--------|---------|
| 799 | — Type 33. Bust r., cross in front. R. Wolf's head with long tongue, l. or r. *M. 306.* ................................................................................................ | 110 | 375 |

800          801                    802                    803

| 800 | 'Archer' type. Kneeling archer r. R. Bird on branch r., head turned back. *M. 349.* ................................................................................................ | 325 | 950 |
| 801 | 'Carip' group. Bust r., CARIP. R. Pecking bird, wolf-serpent, or standing figure. *M. 336-40.* ................................................................................. | 150 | 450 |
| 802 | Series O, Type 38. Bust r. in cable border. R. Bird r. in torque. *M. 373-5.* | 85 | 250 |
| 803 | — Type 21. Similar, but bust l. R. Standing figure with two crosses. *M. 376* | 150 | 475 |

804                    805                    806

| 804 | 'Triquetras' eclectic group. Facing bust, man and crosses, winged figure, or bird and branch. R. Interlace pattern. *M.p.425.* ...................................... | 125 | 400 |
| 805 | Series H, Type 39. Pecking bird. R. Round shield with bosses. *M. 283-4.* | 80 | 210 |
| 806 | — Type 49. 'Wodan' head, annulets around. R. Pecking bird. *M. 285-8.* | 90 | 250 |
| 807 | — Type 48. Whorl of 3 wolf heads. R. Round shield with bosses. *M. 289-92.* ............................................................................................. | 80 | 220 |

808                    809A                    810

| 808 | Series G. Bust r., cross before. R. Standard with 3 or 4 X's. *(Minted in Northern France?) M. 267-70.* ................................................. | 60 | 160 |
| 809 | — crude copies, some with bird or bird on cross. *M. 271-4.* ..................... | 40 | 90 |
| 809A | Series M. Prancing dog l. or r. R. Spiral branch. *M. 363-6.* ..................... | 90 | 275 |
| 810 | Series N. Two standing figures. R. Monster looking back r. or l. *M. 368-72.* | 75 | 225 |

811                    813                    815

| 811 | Series O, Type 40. Standing figure holds two crosses. R. As last. *M. 379-81.* | 80 | 235 |
| 812 | — Type 43. Interlace shield. R. As last. *M.p.482.* ................................... | 125 | 375 |
| 813 | — Type 57. Bust r. in cable border. R. Monster looking back l. *M. 377.* . | 125 | 375 |
| 814 | 'Animal mask' group. Facing animal (lion?) mask. R. Bird, figure, monster or cross. *M. 354-6.* . ................................................................................. | 250 | 750 |
| 815 | Series V. Wolf and twins. R. Bird in vine. *M. 453.* ................................. | 150 | 450 |

816                         818                     822

|       |                                                                                      | F     | VF    |
|       |                                                                                      | £     | £     |
| 816   | Series T. Diad. bust r., +LEL. R. 'Porcupine' l. *M. 442-4.* | 110   | 320   |
| 818   | Series L, Type 12. Bust r., LVNDONIA. R. Standing figure holds two crosses. *M. 319-22.* | 125   | 375   |
| 820   | — Type 13. Similar. R. Seated figure holds hawk and cross. *M.p.409.* | 225   | 675   |
| 821   | — Type 14. Similar, but bust l. R. Celtic cross. *M.p.427.* | 135   | 400   |
| 822   | — Type 15. Bust r. with cross, no legend. R. Standing figure holds two crosses. *M. 323-6.* | 80    | 250   |
| 825   | — Type 16. Bust r. with floral scroll. R. Standing figure holds branch and cross, or two branches. *M. 329-30.* | 90    | 275   |
| 827   | — Type 18. Bust r. with cross. R. Standing figure holds cross and bird. *M. 331-3.* | 75    | 225   |
| 828   | — Type 19. Similar, but bust l. *M. 335.* | 90    | 275   |
| 828A  | — Type 34. Bust r. with cross or sceptre. R. Celtic cross. *M. 345-6.* | 110   | 350   |
| 828B  | Series L-related. Bust r. rosettes in field. R. Standing figure holds two crosses. *M. 347.* | 150   | 475   |

829                       831                      832

| 829   | Type 22. Victory standing with wreath. R. Winged figure, or standing figure holding two crosses. *M. 350-1.* | 165   | 500   |
| 830   | Type 23e. Standing figure holds two crosses. R. Whorl of 3 wolf heads. *M. 359-62.* | 85    | 250   |
| 831   | Series S. Female centaur. R. Whorl of 4 wolf heads. *M. 438-41.* | 85    | 250   |
| 832   | Series R. Bust r. or l. Epa, Wigraed, Spi, etc in runes. R. Standard. *M. 391-428.* | 40    | 105   |

833                       834A                     836

| 832B  | Series Q(R), Type 73. Crude radiate bust r. or l. R. Quadruped r. *M. 388.* | 85    | 240   |
| 833   | 'Saltire Standard' types. Bust l. or r. with cross, two standing figures, or double croix ancree. R. Saltire and pellets in square. *M. 432-5.* | 70    | 210   |
| 834   | 'Monita Scorum' type. Small bird looking back, MONITA SCORUM. R. Standard with saltire of annulets. *M.p.436.* | 275   | 800   |
| 834A  | — Bust r., MONITA SCORUM. R. 'porcupine' l., figure with two crosses, or triquetra. *M. 348.* | 300   | 825   |
| 835   | Type 70. Saltire-standard. R. Standard. *M. 436-7.* | 40    | 100   |
| 836   | Series Q, Types QII-IVd Bird l. or r. R. Quadruped l. or r. *M. 386-7.* | 100   | 300   |
| 836A  | — Type QIVe Quadruped both sides. *M.p.501* | 110   | 325   |
| 836B  | — Type QIe Bust r. with cross. R. Walking bird l. *M. 383.* | 125   | 375   |

|      |      |                                                                                                   | F<br>£ | VF<br>£ |
|------|------|---------------------------------------------------------------------------------------------------|--------|---------|
| 836C | — Type QIf Standing figure with two crosses. R. Walking bird l. *M. 384.* | 150 | 475 |
| 836D | — Type QIg Facing head. R. Long-legged quadruped looking back.<br>*M.p.492.* | 200 | 600 |

844                              844A

| 844  | Type 30. Facing 'Wodan' head. R. Two standing figures, or standard.<br>*M. 429-31.* | 150 | 475 |
| 844A | — Type 53. 'Porcupine', similar to 787. R. Stepped cross, annulet at centre.<br>*Mint? M. 258-62.* | 75 | 185 |

## C.  Continental Sceattas, *c.*695-*c.*740
Most are from the Rhine area, or Frisia

786

| 786 | Series E. Porcupine-like figure, body with annulet at one end, triangle at other. R. 'Standard' with four pellets around central annulet. *Dorestad. M. 209-11.* | 30 | 80 |

787                      789                      790

| 787 | — Similar, with triangular fore-leg. R. 'Standard' with four lines and central annulet. *M. 200-5.* | 30 | 70 |
| 788 | — Similar, with parallel lines in curve of body. R. 'Standard' with VICO. *M. 194-8.* | 30 | 75 |
| 789 | — Figure developed into plumed bird. R. Standard. *M. 190-3.* | 35 | 100 |
| 790 | Later issues. R. 'Standard' 'Porcupine'. Innumerable varieties. *M. 214-53.* | 30 | 65 |
| 832A | Type 10. Bust r., AEPA or APA. R. Porcupine modified into profile face. *Mint? M.p.248.* | 175 | 350 |
| 838 | 'Porcupine' R. Small cross, S E D E in angles. *Mint? M. 263.* | 250 | 725 |

839                      840                      843

| 839 | Series D, Type 2c. Bust r., pseudo-runes. R. Plain cross with pellets in angles. *Domburg? M. 158-80.* | 40 | 90 |
| 840 | — Type 8. Standard. R. As 839. *M. 183-6.* | 30 | 65 |
| 841 | 'Maastricht' Type. Crude head l. R. Quatrefoil interlace. *M. 265-6.* | 175 | 550 |
| 843 | Series X. Facing 'Wodan' head. R. Monster l. *Ribe, Jutland, M. 275-81.* | 100 | 250 |
| 843A | — cruder copies. *English, M. 282.* | 125 | 400 |

# KINGS OF NORTHUMBRIA AND BISHOPS OF YORK

The issues associated with pre-Viking Northumbria encompass a late seventh-century emission of gold, the following series of silver sceattas and the subsequent styca coinage. On the fringe of the later are two special issues, Eanred's penny and Wigmund's *solidus,* for neither of which is there yet evidence of use within the kingdom.

The Stycas developed in two phases, becoming a robust currency of small-denomination coins which seem to have been of great practical use. Production must have ceased early in Osberht's reign, although the old money may have continued in circulation until the Viking capture of York in 867. The official styca coinage, however, does appear to have been overwhelmed by irregular issues, which may reflect a period of civil war during the years *c.* 843 to *c.* 855.

The separation of kings and archbishops is no longer regarded as appropriate and the classification is chronological. In the spelling of names *U* for *W* would be appropriate in the Northumbrian context. *W* is based on West Saxon practice, but is used here on grounds of familiarity.

|  |  | F | VF |
|---|---|---|---|
|  |  | £ | £ |
| 762 | **AV thrymsa,** *temp.* Ecgfrith (?) (670-85). Building with tower and window. R̅. Indeterminate legend around cross (*see also under Early Anglo-Saxon Period, Ultra-Crondall types*) | 1250 | 3500 |

**Æ sceattas (a). Regal issues**

| 846 | **Aldfrith** (685-705). Pellet in annulet. R̅. Canine, lying 1., stylized tree | 250 | 600 |
|---|---|---|---|
| 847 | **Eadberht** (737-758). Small cross (mainly). R̅. Stylized stag, to 1. or r. | 80 | 225 |
| 848 | **Aethelwald Moll** (759-765). (A possible, though disputed, issue is known) | | |

849            852

| 849 | **Alchred** (765-774). Small cross. R̅. Stylized stag to 1. or r. | 175 | 450 |
|---|---|---|---|
| 850 | **Aethelred I** (first reign, 774-779/80). R̅. Stylized stag to 1. or r. | 225 | 750 |
| 851 | **Aelfwald I** (779/80-788). R̅. Stylized stag to 1. or r. | 200 | 550 |

**Æ sceattas (b). Joint issues, by kings and archbishops**

| 852 | **Eadberht** with **Abp. Ecgberht** (737-758). Small cross. R̅. Mitred figure holding two crosses | 175 | 450 |
|---|---|---|---|
| 853 | **Aethelwald Moll** with **Abp. Ecgberht** (759-765). Cross each side | 450 | 1250 |
| 854 | **Alchred** with **Abp. Ecgberht** (765-766). Cross each side | 275 | 800 |
| 855 | **Aethelred I,** with **Abp. Eanbald I** (*c.* 779-780). Various motifs. | 175 | 525 |

**Stycas Phase Ia**. Issues in base silver, for kings and archbishop separately, c. 790-830, with moneyers named

| 856 | **Aethelred I** (second reign, 789-796). R̅. CUDHEARD, or others | 100 | 250 |
|---|---|---|---|
| 857 | – R̅. 'Shrine', CUDCILS | 250 | 650 |

858

| | | F £ | VF £ |
|---|---|---|---|
| 858 | **Eardwulf** (first reign, 796-806). ℞. Small cross, CUDHEARD ............. | 600 | 1500 |
| 859 | **Aelfwald II** (806-808). ℞. Small cross, CUDHEARD ............................ | 200 | 550 |
| 860 | **Eanred** (810-841 (total reign)). ℞. CUDHEARD, or others .................. | 45 | 125 |

860                                865

| | | | |
|---|---|---|---|
| 861 | **Abp. Eanbald II** (796-835 (total tenure)). ℞. EADWULF or EDILWEARD ....................................................................................... | 70 | 200 |
| 861A | **Eanred,** *c.* 830. Æ *penny*. Bust right. ℞. Cross, part moline part crosslet.... | 2250 | 7500 |

861                            863A                        870

**Stycas Phase Ib.** Early issues in copper alloy, *c.* 830-835, with moneyers named

| | | | |
|---|---|---|---|
| 862 | **Eanred.** ℞ DAEGBERCT, EADUINI, HEARDWULF or HERRED .... | 25 | 60 |
| 863 | **Abp. Eanbald II** ℞ EADWULF, or EDILWEARD .............................. | 65 | 175 |
| 863A | **Abp. Wigmund** (837-849/50). *N̸ solidus.* Facing bust. ℞. Cross in wreath ............................................................................................... | *Extremely Rare* | |

**Stycas Phase II.** Later issues in copper alloy, *c.* 837-*c.*855, with moneyers named

| | | | |
|---|---|---|---|
| 864 | **Eanred.** ℞ MONNE or others ....................................................... | 15 | 40 |
| 865 | **Aethelred II** (first reign, 841-843/4). ℞. MONNE or others ................. | 15 | 40 |
| 866 | – ℞. Hound 1., LEOFDEGN ............................................................. | 150 | 450 |
| 867 | **Redwulf** (843/4). ℞. MONNE or others .................................................. | 30 | 75 |
| 868 | **Aethelred II** (second reign, 843/4-849/50). ℞. EARDWULF or others ........ | 15 | 45 |
| 869 | **Osberht** (849/50-867). ℞. WINIBERHT or others ............................... | 30 | 80 |
| 870 | **Abp. Wigmund** (837-849/50). ℞. EDILVEARD or others .................. | 20 | 50 |
| 871 | **Abp. Wulfhere** (849/50-900). ℞. WULFRED ....................................... | 65 | 160 |
| 872 | **Irregular Issues** (*c.*843/4-*c.*855). Various types; legends often mere nonsense.................................................................................................. | 15 | 45 |

*Pirie E.J.E. Coins of the Kingdom of Northumbria c.700-867. 1996*

In the kingdom of the Franks a reformed coinage of good quality *deniers* struck on broad flans had been introduced by Pepin in 755 and continued by his son Charlemagne and his descendants. A new coinage of *pennies* of similar size and weighing about 20 grains (1.3 gms) was introduced into England, probably by Offa, the powerful king of Mercia, about 755/780, though early pennies also exist of two little known kings of Kent, Heaberht and Ecgberht, of about the same period.

The silver penny (*Lat.* 'denarius', hence the *d.* of our £ *s. d.*) remained virtually the sole denomination of English coinage for almost five centuries, with the rare exception of occasional gold coins and somewhat less rare silver halfpence. The penny reached a weight of 24 grains, i.e., a 'pennyweight' during the reign of Alfred the Great. Silver pennies of this period normally bear the ruler's name, though not always his portrait, and the name of the moneyer responsible for their manufacture.

Pennies were issued by various rulers of the Heptarchy for the kingdoms of Kent, Mercia, East Anglia and Wessex by the Danish settlers in the Danelaw and the Hiberno-Norse kings of York, and also by the Archbishops of Canterbury and a Bishop of London. Under Eadgar, who became the sole ruler of England, a uniform coinage was instituted throughout the country, and it was he who set the pattern for the 'reformed' coinage of the later Anglo-Saxon and Norman period.

Halfpence were issued by most rulers from Alfred to Eadgar between 871-973 for S. England, and although all are rare today, it is probable that reasonable quantities were made.

Nos. 873-1387 are all silver pennies except where stated.

NB. Many pennies of the early part of this period have chipped flans and prices should be reduced accordingly.

## KINGS OF KENT

|  |  | F | VF |
|---|---|---|---|
|  |  | £ | £ |
| 873 | **Heaberht** (*c.* 765). Monogram for REX. ℞. Five annulets, each containing a pellet, joined to form a cross | 3000 | 8000 |
| 874 | **Ecgberht** (*c.* 780). Similar. ℞. Varied | 850 | 2500 |

875                                   877

| 875 | **Eadberht Praen.** Type 1. (796-798). As illustration. ℞. Varied | 950 | 3000 |
|---|---|---|---|
| 875A | — Type 2. (*c.* 798). His name around Ⓜ, in centre, ℞. Moneyer's name in angles of a tribrach | 925 | 3000 |
| 876 | **Cuthred** (798-807). *Canterbury.* Various types without portrait | 600 | 1600 |
| 877 | — — Portrait. ℞. Cross and wedges or A | 525 | 1450 |

878                                   881

| 878 | **Anonymous** (*c.* 822-823). *Canterbury.* As illustration or 'Baldred' style head | 650 | 2200 |
| 879 | **Baldred** (*c.* 823-825). *Canterbury.* diademed head r. ℞. DRUR CITS within inner circle | 900 | 2850 |

|     |                                                              | F   | VF   |
|-----|--------------------------------------------------------------|-----|------|
|     |                                                              | £   | £    |
| 880 | — Cross each side.................................................................. | 650 | 1750 |
| 881 | *Rochester.* Bust r. R. Cross moline or wheel design............................... | 800 | 2650 |

## ARCHBISHOPS OF CANTERBURY

882

| 881A | **Jaenberht** (765-792). New type (early). Under Ecgberht II of Kent (?). (before *c.* 780 ?) His name around small cross of pellets in centre. R. PONTIFEX in three lines.......................... | 975 | 3250 |
|------|--------|-----|------|
| 882 | Under Offa of Mercia (*c.* 780-792) His name around central ornament or cross and wedges. R. OFFA REX in two lines ..................................... | 750 | 2350 |
| 883 | — His name in three lines. R. OFFA or OFFA REX between the limbs of Celtic cross............................................................................ | 900 | 2750 |
| 884 | **Aethelheard** (el. 792, cons. 793, d. 805). With Offa as overlord. First issue (792-?), with title *Pontifex*........................................ | 800 | 2500 |

885                                   887

| 885  | — Second issue (?-796), with title *Archiepiscopus* .................................. | 725 | 2250 |
|------|--------|-----|------|
| 885A | — Third issue (*c.* 796-798), with title *Archiepiscopus*. His name and AR around EP in centre. R. Moneyer's name, EADGAR or CIOLHARD..... | 850 | 2750 |
| 886  | — With Coenwulf as overlord. (798-800 ?) Fourth Issue. As last. R. King's name in the angles of a tribrach ..................................... | 800 | 2500 |
| 886A | — Fifth issue (*c.* 798-805?). As last R. Coenwulf's name around Ⓜ in centre | 675 | 1850 |
| 887  | **Wulfred** (805-832). group I (805-*c.* 810). As illustration. R. Crosslet, alpha-omega.......................................................................... | 700 | 2250 |
| 888  | — Group II (*c.* 810). As last. R. DOROVERNIA C monogram .............. | 625 | 1850 |
| 889  | — Group III (pre- 823). Bust extends to edge of coin. R. As last ............ | 600 | 1750 |
| 890  | — Groups IV and V (*c.* 822-823). Anonymous under Ecgberht. Moneyer's name in place of the Archbishop's. R. DOROBERNIA CIVITAS in three or five lines.................................................................................... | 700 | 2000 |
| 891  | — Group VI (*c.* 823-825). Baldred type. Crude portrait. R. DRVR CITS in two lines.............................................................................. | 900 | 3000 |
| 892  | — Group VII (*c.* 832). Second monogram (Ecgberht) type. Crude portrait r., PLFRED. R. DORIB C. Monogram as 1035.............. | 825 | 2750 |

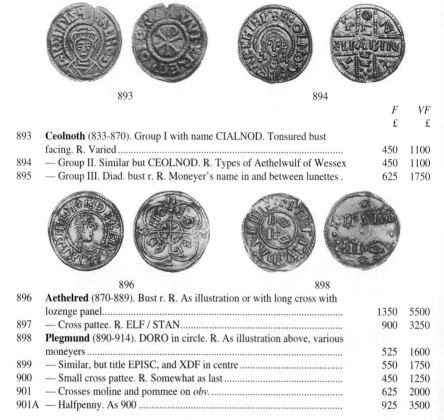

893                                              894

|  |  | F | VF |
|---|---|---|---|
|  |  | £ | £ |
| 893 | **Ceolnoth** (833-870). Group I with name CIALNOD. Tonsured bust facing. R. Varied | 450 | 1100 |
| 894 | — Group II. Similar but CEOLNOD. R. Types of Aethelwulf of Wessex | 450 | 1100 |
| 895 | — Group III. Diad. bust r. R. Moneyer's name in and between lunettes . | 625 | 1750 |

896                                              898

| 896 | **Aethelred** (870-889). Bust r. R. As illustration or with long cross with lozenge panel | 1350 | 5500 |
|---|---|---|---|
| 897 | — Cross pattee. R. ELF / STAN | 900 | 3250 |
| 898 | **Plegmund** (890-914). DORO in circle. R. As illustration above, various moneyers | 525 | 1600 |
| 899 | — Similar, but title EPISC, and XDF in centre | 550 | 1750 |
| 900 | — Small cross pattee. R. Somewhat as last | 450 | 1250 |
| 901 | — Crosses moline and pommee on *obv.* | 625 | 2000 |
| 901A | — Halfpenny. As 900 | 925 | 3500 |

# KINGS OF MERCIA

Until 825 Canterbury was the principal mint of the Kings of Mercia and some moneyers also struck coins for the Kings of Kent and Archbishops of Canterbury.

## GOLD

902                                              903

| 902 | **Offa** (757-796). Gold *dinar*. Copy of Arabic dinar of Caliph Al Mansur, dated 157 A.H. (A.D. 774), with OFFA REX added on *rev.* | *Extremely rare* |
|---|---|---|
| 903 | Gold *penny*. Bust r., moneyer's name. R. Standing figure, moneyer's name | *Extremely rare* |

*A copy of a solidus with a diademed bust appears to read CIOLHEARD and is probably Mercian of this or the following reign.*

# SILVER

904                        905                        906

|  | F £ | VF £ |
|---|---|---|
| 904 Light Coinage. (*c.* 780?-792) *London and Canterbury.* Various types without portraits. Small flans | 425 | 950 |
| 905 — (*c.* 780?-792) *London and Canterbury.* Various types with portraits. Small flans. | 800 | 2250 |
| 906 — East Anglia. Various types with portraits. R. Some with runic letters, small flans | 900 | 3000 |

908                        909

| 907 — — Various types without portraits. R. often with runic letters, small flans | 600 | 1500 |
|---|---|---|
| 908 Heavy Coinage. (*c.* 792-796) *London, Canterbury and East Anglia.* Various types without portraits, large flans. | 500 | 1250 |
| 909 **Cynethryth** (wife of Offa). Coins as light coinage of Offa. As illustration | 1650 | 5250 |
| 910 — *O. As rev.* of last. R. EOBA on leaves of quatrefoil | 850 | 2750 |
| 911 **Eadberht** (Bishop of London, died 787/789). EADBERHT EP in three lines or aDBERHT in two lines within a beaded rectangle, EP below. R. Name of Offa | 900 | 3000 |

912

| 912 **Coenwulf, King of Mercia** (796-821). Gold *penny* or *Mancus* of 30 pence. London, diademed bust of Coenwulf right, finely drawn with four horizontal lines on the shoulders | | *Unique* |
|---|---|---|
| 912A **Penny.** Group I (796-805). *London.* Without portrait. His name in three lines. R. Varied | 525 | 1500 |
| 913 — *Canterbury.* Name around ᛗ as illus. below. R. Moneyer's name in two lines | 625 | 1750 |

914                                      915

|     |                                                                                 | F    | VF   |
|     |                                                                                 | £    | £    |
| 914 | — *Both mints.* Tribrach type                                                  | 325  | 800  |
| 915 | — Group II (*c.* 805-810). *Canterbury.* With portrait. Small flans. Ŗ. Varied but usually cross and wedges | 525  | 1450 |
| 916 | — Groups III and IV (*c.* 810-820). *Canterbury.* Similar but larger flans. Ŗ. Varied | 475  | 1250 |
| 917 | — *Rochester.* Large diad. bust of coarse style. Ŗ. Varied. (Moneyers: Dun, Ealhstan) | 650  | 1750 |
| 918 | — *London.* With portrait generally of Roman style. Ŗ. Crosslet                 | 575  | 1650 |
| 919 | — *E. Anglia.* Crude diad. bust r. Ŗ. Moneyer's name LVL on leaves in arms of cross | 400  | 975  |
| 920 | — — *O.* as last. Ŗ. Various types                                              | 425  | 1000 |

921                                      929

| 921 | **Ceolwulf I** (821-823). *Canterbury.* Group I. Bust r. Ŗ. Varied. (Moneyers: Oba, Sigestef) | 875  | 2750 |
| 922 | — — Group II. Crosslet. Ŗ. Varied                                               | 700  | 2000 |
| 923 | — — Group III. Tall cross with MERCIORŪ. Ŗ. Crosslet. SIGESTEF DOROBERNIA       | 825  | 2650 |
| 924 | — *Rochester.* Group I. Bust r. Ŗ. Varied                                        | 800  | 2500 |
| 925 | — — Group IIA. As last but head r.                                              | 875  | 2750 |
| 926 | — — Group IIB. Ecclesiastical issue by Bp. of Rochester. With mint name, DOROBREBIA, but no moneyer | 950  | 3000 |
| 927 | — *East Anglia.* Crude style and lettering with barbarous portrait. Ŗ. Varied 1250 | 550  | 1500 |
| 928 | **Beornwulf** (823-825). Bust r. Ŗ. Moneyer's name in three lines               | 750  | 2350 |
| 929 | — Ŗ. Cross crosslet in centre                                                    | 725  | 2200 |
| 930 | Crude copy of 928 but moneyer's name in two lines with crosses between          | 900  | 2500 |
| 931 | **Ludica** (825-827). Bust r. Ŗ. Moneyer's name in three lines as 928           | 2500 | 7500 |

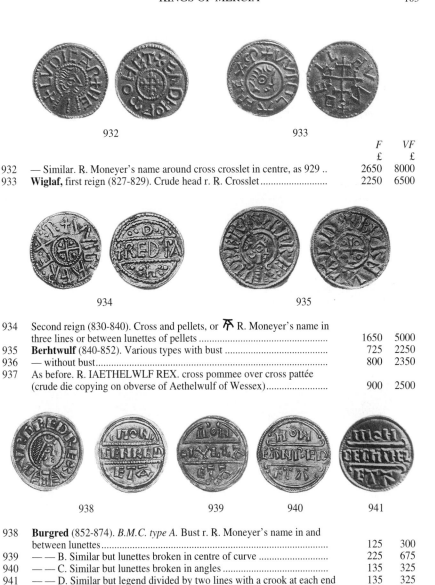

932

933

| | | F | VF |
|---|---|---|---|
| | | £ | £ |
| 932 | — Similar. R. Moneyer's name around cross crosslet in centre, as 929 .. | 2650 | 8000 |
| 933 | **Wiglaf,** first reign (827-829). Crude head r. R. Crosslet .......................... | 2250 | 6500 |

934

935

| 934 | Second reign (830-840). Cross and pellets, or 🐾 R. Moneyer's name in three lines or between lunettes of pellets ..................................... | 1650 | 5000 |
|---|---|---|---|
| 935 | **Berhtwulf** (840-852). Various types with bust ...................................... | 725 | 2250 |
| 936 | — without bust.................................................................................. | 800 | 2350 |
| 937 | As before. R. IAETHELWLF REX. cross pommee over cross pattée (crude die copying on obverse of Aethelwulf of Wessex)....................... | 900 | 2500 |

938                         939              940              941

| 938 | **Burgred** (852-874). *B.M.C. type A.* Bust r. R. Moneyer's name in and between lunettes............................................................................. | 125 | 300 |
|---|---|---|---|
| 939 | — — B. Similar but lunettes broken in centre of curve .......................... | 225 | 675 |
| 940 | — — C. Similar but lunettes broken in angles ......................................... | 135 | 325 |
| 941 | — — D. Similar but legend divided by two lines with a crook at each end | 135 | 325 |
| 942 | — — E. As last, but m above and below............................................... | 450 | 1350 |
| 943 | **Ceolwulf II** (874-*c.* 880). Bust r. R. Two emperors seated. Victory above | 3000 | 9500 |

944                         945

| 944 | — R. Moneyer's name in angles of long cross with lozenge centre......... | 1350 | 4500 |

# KINGS OF EAST ANGLIA

|   |   | F<br>£ | VF<br>£ |
|---|---|---|---|
| 945 | **Beonna,** King of East Anglia, *c.* 758. Æ sceat. Pellet in centre, Runic inscription. R. EFE in Roman characters around saltire cross | 375 | 975 |
| 945A | — Similar. R. WILRED in runic around pellet or cross | 425 | 1200 |
| 945B | — Similar. R. Interlace pattern (large flans) | 800 | 2500 |
| 945C | **Alberht** (749-?). Pellet in centre, AETHELBERT (runic) around R. Rosette in circle, TIAELRED (runic) around. | 1250 | 4000 |

946

| 946 | **Aethelberht** (d. 794). As illustration | 3500 | 13500 |
|---|---|---|---|
| 947 | **Eadwald** (*c.* 798). King's name in three lines. R. Moneyer's name in quatrefoil or around cross | 750 | 2250 |
| 947A | — King's name around cross or ᛗ in centre. R. Moneyer's name in quatrefoil | 800 | 2500 |

948                                 951

| 948 | **Aethelstan I** (*c.* 825-840). Bust r. or l. R. Crosslet or star | 750 | 2500 |
|---|---|---|---|
| 949 | Bust r. R. Moneyer's name in three or four lines | 800 | 2650 |
| 950 | Alpha or A. R. Varied | 275 | 800 |
| 951 | *O.* and *rev.* Cross with or without wedges or pellets in angles | 300 | 850 |
| 952 | — Similar, with king's name both sides | 425 | 1000 |
| 952A | Name around ship in centre. R. Moneyer Eadgar, around cross of pellets or in two lines (Possibly the earliest of his coins.) | 1750 | 6000 |

953                                 954

| 953 | **Aethelweard** (*c.* 840-*c.* 855), A. Omega or cross and crescents. R. Cross with pellets or wedges | 425 | 1000 |
|---|---|---|---|
| 954 | **Edmund** (855-870). Alpha or A. R. Cross with pellets or wedges | 210 | 575 |
| 955 | — *O.* Varied. R. Similar | 210 | 575 |

*For the St. Edmund coins and the Danish issues struck in East Anglia bearing the name of Aethelred I, see Danish East Anglia.*

**Danish East Anglia,** *c*. **885-915**

957

|     |                                                                                                                          | *F* | *VF* |
| --- | ------------------------------------------------------------------------------------------------------------------------ | --- | ---- |
|     |                                                                                                                          | £   | £    |
| 956 | **Aethelstan II** (878-890), originally named Guthrum? Cross pattee. ℞. Moneyer's name in two lines                        | 900 | 2750 |
| 957 | **Oswald** (unknown except from his coins). Alpha or A. ℞. Cross pattee..                                                 | 1350 | 4500 |
| 958 | — Copy of Carolinigian 'temple' type. ℞ Cross and pellets                                                                | 1350 | 4500 |
| 959 | **Aethelred I.** (*c*.870) As last, with name of Aethelred I. ℞. As last, or cross-crosslet                                | 1250 | 3500 |
| 959A | — As 954                                                                                                                 | 900 | 2750 |
| 960 | **St. Edmund,** memorial coinage, Æ *penny,* type as illus. below, various legends of good style                          | 90  | 225  |

    961        962

| 961 | — Similar, but barbarous or semi-barbarous legends | 85  | 200 |
| --- | --------------------------------------------------- | --- | --- |
| 962 | *Halfpenny.* Similar                                | 350 | 975 |

    963        966

| 963 | **St. Martin of Lincoln.** As illustration                                                | 1500 | 5250 |
| --- | ------------------------------------------------------------------------------------------ | ---- | ---- |
| 964 | **Alfred.** (Viking imitations, usually of very barbarous workmanship.) Bust r. ℞. *Londonia* monogram | 650  | 1750 |
| 965 | — Similar, but *Lincolla* monogram                                                         | 825  | 2500 |
| 966 | — Small cross, as Alfred group II *(Br. 6),* various legends, some read REX DORO           | 225  | 525  |
| 967 | — Similar. ℞. 'St. Edmund type' A in centre                                               | 425  | 975  |
| 968 | — Two emperors seated. ℞. As 964. (Previously attributed to Halfdene.)                    | 1650 | 5250 |
| 969 | *Halfpenny.* As 964 and 965                                                                | 350  | 850  |

970

|  | | F £ | VF £ |
|---|---|---|---|
| 970 | — As 966 ................................................................................... | 275 | 625 |

## DANELAW, *c.* 898-915

971                      975

| 971 | **Alfred** (Imitations). ELFRED between ORSNA and FORDA. ℞. Moneyer's name in two lines (occasionally divided by horizontal long cross) ................................................................................... | 400 | 850 |
|---|---|---|---|
| 972 | — *Halfpenny.* Similar, of very crude appearance.................................... | 425 | 1100 |
| 973 | **Alfred/Plegmund.** *Obv.* ELFRED REX PLEGN ............................. | 550 | 1500 |
| 974 | **Plegmund.** Danish copy of 900.................................................... | 425 | 1000 |
| 975 | **Earl Sihtric.** Type as 971. SCELDFOR between GVNDI BERTVS. ℞ SITRIC COMES in two lines.................................................... | 1650 | 5500 |

### Viking Coinage of York?
*References are to 'The Classification of Northumbrian Viking Coins in the Cuerdale hoard', by C. S. S. Lyon and B. H. I. H. Stewart, in Numismatic Chronicle, 1964, p. 281 ff.*

| 975A | **Guthfrith.** GU DE F. RE Small cross. ℞. Moneyer's name in two lines. | 1500 | 5000 |
|---|---|---|---|
| 976 | **Siefred.** C. SIEFRE DIIS REX in two lines. ℞. EBRAICE CIVITAS (or contractions), small cross. *L. & S. Ia, Ie, Ii*............................. | 250 | 675 |
| 977 | — Cross on steps between. ℞. As last. *L. & S. If, Ij* ................................ | 325 | 850 |
| 978 | — Long cross. ℞. As last. *L. & S. Ik*...................................... | 300 | 800 |
| 979 | SIEFREDVS REX, cross crosslet within legend. ℞. As last. *L. & S. Ih*... | 165 | 400 |

980                      984

| 980 | SIEVERT REX, cross crosslet to edge of coin. ℞. As last. *L. & S. Ic, Ig, Im* | 175 | 475 |
|---|---|---|---|
| 981 | — Cross on steps between. ℞. As last. *L. & S. Il*...................................... | 300 | 800 |
| 982 | — Patriarchal cross. ℞. DNS DS REX, small cross. *L. & S. Va*.............. | 250 | 700 |
| 983 | — — ℞. MIRABILIA FECIT, small cross. *L. & S. VIb*......................... | 300 | 800 |
| 984 | REX, at ends of cross crosslet. ℞. SIEFREDVS, small cross. *L. & S. IIIa, b* | 175 | 475 |

| | | *F* | *VF* |
| --- | --- | --- | --- |
| | | £ | £ |
| 985 | — Long cross. R. As last. *L. & S. IIIc* | 165 | 450 |
| 986 | *Halfpenny.* Types as 977, *L. & S. Ib; 980, Ic; and 983, VIb* | 475 | 1200 |
| 987 | **Cnut.** CNVT REX, cross crosslet to edge of coin. R. EBRAICE CIVITAS, small cross. *L. & S. Io, Iq* | 175 | 475 |
| 988 | — — R. CVNNETTI, small cross. *L. & S. IIc* | 165 | 450 |
| 989 | — Long cross. R. EBRAICE CIVITAS, small cross. *L. & S. Id, In, Ir* | 125 | 285 |
| 990 | — — R. CVNNETTI, small cross. *L. & S. IIa, IId* | 110 | 235 |
| 991 | — Patriarchal cross. R. EBRAICE CIVITAS, small cross. *L. & S. Ip, Is* | 95 | 225 |
| 992 | — — R.— *Karolus* monogram in centre. *L. & S . It* | 625 | 1750 |

993            995

| 993 | — — R. CVNNETTI, small cross. *L. & S. IIb, IIe* | 90 | 200 |
| --- | --- | --- | --- |
| 994 | *Halfpenny.* Types as 987, *L. & S. Iq; 989, Id; 991, Is; 992, Iu; 993, IIb and e* | 350 | 825 |
| 995 | As 992, but CVNNETTI around *Karolus* monogram. *L. & S. IIf* | 325 | 800 |
| 996 | **Cnut and/or Siefred.** CNVT REX, patriarchal cross. R. SIEFREDVS, small cross. *L. & S. IIId* | 140 | 375 |
| 997 | — — R. DNS DS REX, small cross. *L. & S. Vc.* | 325 | 800 |

998

| 998 | — — R. MIRABILIA FECIT. *L. & S. VId* | 140 | 325 |
| --- | --- | --- | --- |
| 999 | EBRAICE C, patriarchal cross. R. DNS DS REX, small cross. *L. & S. Vb* | 250 | 650 |

1000            1002

| 1000 | — — R. MIRABILIA FECIT. *L. & S. VIc* | 140 | 325 |
| --- | --- | --- | --- |
| 1001 | DNS DS REX in two lines. R. ALVALDVS, small cross. *L. & S. IVa* | 675 | 2000 |
| 1002 | DNS DS O REX, similar. R. MIRABILIA FECIT. *L. & S. VIa* | 300 | 750 |
| 1003 | *Halfpenny.* As last. *L. & S. VIa* | 475 | 1350 |
| 1004 | **'Cnut'.** Name blundered around cross pattée with extended limbs. R. QVENTOVICI around small cross. *L. & S. VII* | 325 | 925 |

|  | F £ | VF £ |
|---|---|---|
| 1005  *Halfpenny. Similar. L. & S. VII* | 475 | 1300 |

*Possibly not Northumbrian; the reverse copied from the Carolingian coins of Quentovic, N. France.*

**York, early tenth century issues**

1006                                          1009

| 1006  **St. Peter coinage.** Early issues. SCI PETRI MO in two lines. ℞. Cross pattee | 200 | 525 |
|---|---|---|
| 1007  — similar. ℞. 'Karolus' monogram | 825 | 2500 |
| 1008  *Halfpenny. Similar. ℞. Cross pattee* | 625 | 1500 |
| 1009  **Regnald** (blundered types). RAIENALT, head to l. or r. ℞. EARICE CT, 'Karolus' monogram | 1450 | 5250 |

1010

| 1010  — Open hand. ℞. Similar | 1350 | 4000 |
|---|---|---|
| 1011  — Hammer. ℞. Bow and arrow | 1500 | 5500 |
| 1012  Anonymous ℞. Sword | 1350 | 4500 |

## ENGLISH COINS OF THE HIBERNO-NORSE VIKINGS

**Early period, *c.* 919-925**

| 1013  **Sihtric** (921-927). SITRIC REX, sword. ℞. Cross, hammer or T | 1450 | 4750 |
|---|---|---|
| 1014  **St. Peter coinage.** Late issues SCI PETRI MO, sword and hammer. ℞. EBORACEI, cross and pellets | 625 | 1600 |

1015                                          1016

| 1015  — Similar. ℞. Voided hammer | 525 | 1250 |
|---|---|---|
| 1016  — Similar. ℞. Solid hammer | 650 | 1650 |

*St. Peter coins with blundered legends are rather cheaper.*

|  | F | VF |
|  | £ | £ |

**Later period, 939-954** (after the battle of Brunanburh). Mostly struck at York.

1017   **Anlaf Guthfrithsson,** 939-941. Flower type. Small cross, ANLAF REX
       TO D. R. Flower above moneyer's name ............................................. 1750 6500

1018   — Circumscription type, with small cross each side, ANLAF CVNVNC,
       M in field on reverse *(Derby)* .................................................. 1650 4750

1018A— Two line type. ONLAF REX. Large letter both sides *(Lincoln?)*........ 1650 4750

1019                                            1020

1019   — Raven type. As illustration, ANLAF CVNVNC................................. 1500 4500

1020   **Olaf Sihtricsson,** first reign, 941-944. Triquetra type. As illus., CVNVNC.
       R. Danish standard ........................................................................ 1650 5250

1021   — Circumscription type (a). Small cross each side, CVNVNC .............. 1350 4500

1022   — Cross moline type, CVNVN C. R. Small cross ................................ 1450 4750

1023   — Two line type. Small cross. R. ONLAF REX. R. Name in two lines .. 1350 4500

1024   **Regnald Guthfrithsson,** 943-944. Triquetra type. As 1020. REGNALD
       CVNVNC................................................................................................ 1650 5250

1025                                            1030

1025   — Cross moline type. As 1022, but REGNALD CVNVNC................... 1650 5250

1026   **Sihtric Sihtricsson,** *c.* 942. Triquetra type. As 1020, SITRIC CVNVNC 1650 5250

1027   — Circumscription type. Small cross each side ...................................... 1500 4750

1027A **Anonymous?** Two line type. Small cross ELTANGERHT. R.
       RERNART in two lines ......................................................................... 1200 3250

1028   **Eric Blood-axe,** first reign, 948. Two line type. Small cross, ERICVC REX
       A; ERIC REX AL; or ERIC REX EFOR. R. Name in two lines............. 2250 6500

1029   **Olaf Sihtricsson,** second reign, 948-952. Circumscription type (b). Small
       cross each side. ONLAF REX ................................................................ 1500 4500

1029A— Flower type. small cross ANLAF REX R. Flower above moneyer's
       name............................................................................................................ 1650 5500

1029B— Two line type. Small cross, ONLAF REX. R. Moneyer's name in
       two lines .................................................................................................... 1400 4500

1030   **Eric Blood-axe,** second reign, 952-954. Sword type. ERIC REX in two
       lines, sword between. R. Small cross....................................................... 2500 7500

**Later, KINGS OF ALL ENGLAND FROM 959**
All are silver pennies unless otherwise stated

## BEORHTRIC, 786-802

Beorhtric was dependent on Offa of Mercia and married a daughter of Offa.

1031

|  | | F | VF |
|---|---|---|---|
|  | | £ | £ |
| 1031 | As illustration | 3000 | 8500 |
| 1032 | Alpha and omega in centre. R. Omega in centre | 2750 | 8000 |

## ECGBERHT, 802-839

King of Wessex only, 802-825; then also of Kent, Sussex, Surrey, Essex and East Anglia, 825-839, and of Mercia also, 829-830.

| 1033 | *Canterbury.* Group I. Diad. hd. r. within inner circle. R. Various | 800 | 2350 |
|---|---|---|---|
| 1034 | — II. Non-portrait types. R. Various | 625 | 1800 |

1035

| 1035 | — III. Bust r. breaking inner circle. R. DORIB C | 800 | 2500 |
|---|---|---|---|
| 1036 | *London.* Cross potent. R. LVN / DONIA / CIVIT | 1000 | 3500 |
| 1037 | — — R. REDMVND MONE around TA | 800 | 2500 |
| 1038 | *Rochester,* royal mint. Non-portrait types with king's name ECGBEO RHT | 675 | 1850 |
| 1039 | — — Portrait types, ECGBEORHT | 825 | 2650 |
| 1040 | *Rochester,* bishop's mint. Bust r. R. SCS ANDREAS (APOSTOLVS)... | 900 | 3250 |
| 1041 | *Winchester.* SAXON monogram or SAXONIORVM in three lines. R. Cross | 700 | 1850 |

Son of Ecgberht; sub-King of Essex, Kent, Surrey and Sussex, 825-839; King of all southern England, 839-855; King of Essex, Kent and Sussex only, 855-858. No coins are known of his son Aethelbald who ruled over Wessex proper, 855-860.

1043                                    1045

|  |  | F | VF |
|---|---|---|---|
|  |  | £ | £ |
| 1042 | *Canterbury*. Phase I (839-c. 843). Head within inner circle. R. Various. *Br. 3* | 350 | 950 |
| 1043 | — — Larger bust breaking inner circle. R. A. *Br. 1 and 2*...................... | 375 | 1000 |
| 1044 | — — Cross and wedges. R. SAXONIORVM in three lines in centre. *Br. 10* | 275 | 800 |
| 1045 | — — Similar, but OCCINDENTALIVM in place of moneyer. *Br. 11*.... | 300 | 850 |
| 1046 | — Phase II (*c.* 843-848?). Cross and wedges. R. Various, but chiefly a form of cross or a large A. *Br. 4* ........................................................................ | 275 | 800 |
| 1047 | — — New portrait, somewhat as 1043. R. As last. *Br. 7* ......................... | 375 | 1000 |
| 1048 | — — Smaller portrait. R. As last, with *Chi/Rho* monogram. *Br. 7* .......... | 400 | 1200 |

1049                                    1051

| 1049 | — Phase III (*c.* 848/851-*c.* 855). DORIB in centre. R. CANT mon. *Br. 5* | 275 | 800 |
|---|---|---|---|
| 1050 | — — CANT mon. R. CAN M in angles of cross. *Br. 6* .......................... | 400 | 1200 |
| 1051 | — Phase IV (*c.* 855-859). Type as Aethelberht. New neat style bust R. Large voided long cross. *Br. 8* ................................................................. | 350 | 900 |
| 1052 | *Winchester*. SAXON mon. R. Cross and wedges. *Br. 9* .......................... | 400 | 1200 |

Son of Aethelwulf; sub-King of Kent, Essex and Sussex, 858-860; King of all southern England, 860-865/6.

1053

|  | | F | VF |
|---|---|---|---|
|  | | £ | £ |
| 1053 | As illustration above ............................................................. | 325 | 850 |
| 1054 | *O.* Similar, R. Cross fleury over quatrefoil ............................................. | 575 | 1750 |

## AETHELRED I, 865/866-871

Son of Aethelwulf; succeeded his brother Aethelberht.

1055

| 1055 | As illustration ........................................................................... | 350 | 900 |
|---|---|---|---|
| 1056 | Similar, but moneyer's name in four lines ................................................ | 625 | 2000 |

*For another coin with the name Aethelred see 959 under Viking coinages.*

Brother and successor to Aethelred, Alfred had to contend with invading Danish armies for much of his reign. In 878 he and Guthrum the Dane divided the country, with Alfred holding all England south and west of Watling Street. Alfred occupied London in 886.

## Types with portraits

|  | 1057 |  | 1058 |  |  |
| --- | --- | --- | --- | --- | --- |

|  |  | F | VF |
| --- | --- | --- | --- |
|  |  | £ | £ |
| 1057 | Bust r. R. As Aethelred I. *Br. 1* (*name often* AELBRED) | 400 | 1000 |
| 1058 | — R. Long cross with lozenge centre, as 944, *Br. 5* | 1250 | 4000 |
| 1059 | — R. Two seated figures, as 943. *Br. 2* | 4750 | 15000 |
| 1060 | — R. As Archbp. Aethered; cross within large quatrefoil. *Br. 3* | 1500 | 5000 |

|  | 1061 |  | 1062 |  |  |
| --- | --- | --- | --- | --- | --- |

| 1061 | *London.* Bust. r. R. LONDONIA monogram | 850 | 2500 |
| --- | --- | --- | --- |
|  | *Copies made of tin at the Wembley Exhibition are common* |  |  |
| 1062 | — R. Similar, but with moneyer's name added | 950 | 2750 |
| 1063 | — *Halfpenny.* Bust r. or rarely l. R. LONDONIA monogram as 1061 | 350 | 875 |
| 1064 | *Gloucester.* R. Æ GLEAPA in angles of three limbed cross | 2500 | 7500 |

## Types without portraits

| 1065 | King's name on limbs of cross, trefoils in angles. R. Moneyer's name in quatrefoil. *Br. 4.* | 2000 | 6250 |
| --- | --- | --- | --- |

|  | 1066 |  | 1069 |  |  |
| --- | --- | --- | --- | --- | --- |

| 1066 | Cross pattée. R. Moneyer's name in two lines. *Br. 6* | 325 | 675 |
| --- | --- | --- | --- |
| 1067 | — As last, but neater style, as Edw, the Elder | 325 | 700 |
| 1068 | — *Halfpenny.* As 1066 | 300 | 675 |
| 1069 | *Canterbury.* As last but DORO added on *obv. Br. 6a* | 375 | 800 |
| 1070 | *Exeter?* King name in four lines. R. EXA vertical | 2250 | 7000 |
| 1071 | *Winchester?* Similar to last, but PIN | 2250 | 7000 |
| 1071A | *Oxford.* Elfred between OHSNA and FORDA. R. Moneyer's name in two lines (much commoner as a Viking Imitation see 971) | 675 | 2000 |
| 1072 | 'Offering penny'. Very large and heavy. AELFRED REX SAXORVM in four lines. R. ELIMO in two lines i.e. (*Elimosina,* alms) | *Extremely rare* |  |

*For other pieces bearing the name of Alfred see under the Viking coinages.*

Edward, the son of Alfred, aided by his sister Aethelflaed 'Lady of the Mericians', annexed all England south of the Humber and built many new fortified boroughs to protect the kingdom.

1074                                            1078

|  | | *F*<br>£ | *VF*<br>£ |
|---|---|---|---|

**Rare types**

| 1073 | *Br. 1. Bath?* R. BA | 1250 | 4000 |
|---|---|---|---|
| 1074 | — 2. *Canterbury.* Cross moline in pommee. R. Moneyer's name | 900 | 3000 |
| 1075 | — 3. *Chester?* Small cross. R. Minster | 1200 | 3750 |
| 1076 | — 4. — Small cross. R. Moneyer's name in single line | 725 | 2000 |
| 1077 | — 5. — R. Two stars | 850 | 2750 |

1081                                            1082

| 1078 | — 6. — R. Flower above central line, name below | 1000 | 3500 |
|---|---|---|---|
| 1079 | — 7. — R. Floral design with name across field | 1200 | 3750 |
| 1080 | — 8. — R. Bird holding twig | 1750 | 6500 |
| 1081 | — 9. — R. Hand of Providence, several varieties | 1500 | 4500 |
| 1082 | — 10. — R. City gate of Roman style | 1250 | 4000 |
| 1083 | — 11. — R. Anglo-Saxon burg | 1000 | 3500 |

**Ordinary types**

1084                                            1087

| 1084 | *Br. 12.* Bust l. R. Moneyer's name in two lines | 600 | 1750 |
|---|---|---|---|
| 1086 | — *12a.* Similar, but bust r. of crude style | 725 | 2000 |
| 1087 | — 13. Small cross. R. Similar (to 1084) | 175 | 475 |
| 1087A | — — As last, but in *gold* | *Extremely rare* | |
| 1088 | *Halfpenny.* Similar to last | 675 | 1750 |
| 1088A | — — R. Hand of Providence | 950 | 3250 |

Aethelstan, the eldest son of Eadward, decreed that money should be coined only in a borough, that every borough should have one moneyer and that some of the more important boroughs should have more than one moneyer.

1089

|  | | F | VF |
|---|---|---|---|
|  | | £ | £ |
| 1089 | **Main issues.** Small cross. R. Moneyer's name in two lines | 200 | 550 |
| 1090 | Diad. bust r. R. As last | 725 | 2250 |
| 1091 | — R. Small cross | 650 | 1750 |
| 1092 | Small cross both sides | 275 | 675 |

1093          1094

| 1093 | — Similar, but mint name added | 250 | 625 |
|---|---|---|---|
| 1094 | Crowned bust r. As illustration. R. Small cross | 500 | 1350 |
| 1095 | — Similar, but mint name added | 525 | 1450 |
| 1096 | **Local Issues.** *N. Mercian mints.* Star between two pellets. R. As 1089 | 850 | 2250 |
| 1097 | — Small cross. R. Floral ornaments above and below moneyer's name | 925 | 2750 |
| 1098 | — Rosette of pellets each side | 325 | 850 |
| 1099 | — Small cross one side, rosette on the other side | 350 | 875 |

1100          1104

| 1100 | *N.E. mints.* Small cross. R. Tower over moneyer's name | 1000 | 3500 |
|---|---|---|---|
| 1101 | Similar, but mint name added | 1100 | 3750 |
| 1102 | — Bust in high relief r. or l. R. Small cross | 725 | 2000 |
| 1103 | — Bust r. in high relief. R. Cross-crosslet | 725 | 2000 |
| 1104 | 'Helmeted' bust or head r. R. As last or small cross | 750 | 2250 |
| 1104A | Halfpenny, small cross. R. Moneyer's name in two lines | 675 | 1700 |

Eadmund, the brother of Aethelstan, extended his realm over the Norse kingdom of York.

1105                                    1107

|  |  | F | VF |
|---|---|---|---|
|  |  | £ | £ |
| 1105 | Small cross, rosette or annulet. R. Moneyer's name in two lines with crosses or rosettes between | 200 | 550 |
| 1106 | Crowned bust r. R. Small cross | 475 | 1350 |
| 1107 | Similar, but with mint name | 525 | 1450 |
| 1108 | Small cross either side, or rosette on one side | 300 | 850 |
| 1109 | Cross of five pellets. R. Moneyer's name in two lines | 275 | 725 |
| 1110 | Small cross. R. Flower above name | 1200 | 3500 |
| 1111 | 'Helmeted' bust r. R. Cross-crosslet | 750 | 2250 |

1111                                    1112

| 1112 | *Halfpenny.* small cross, R. Moneyer's name in two lines or one line between rosettes | 625 | 1650 |
|---|---|---|---|
| 1112A | — Flower. R. As 1105 | 825 | 2250 |

## EADRED, 946-955

Eadred was another of the sons of Eadward. He lost the kingdom of York to Eric Bloodaxe.

1113                                    1115

| 1113 | As illustration. R. Moneyer's name in two lines | 180 | 425 |
|---|---|---|---|
| 1114 | — Similar, but mint name after REX | 525 | 1350 |
| 1115 | Crowned bust r. As illustration | 475 | 1250 |
| 1116 | — R. Similar, with mint name added | 525 | 1350 |

| | F | VF |
|---|---|---|
| | £ | £ |
| 1117 Rosette. R. As 1113.................................................................. | 300 | 750 |
| 1118 Small cross. R. Rosette ........................................................ | 300 | 750 |
| 1119 — R. Flower enclosing moneyer's name. *B.M.C. II*.............. | 1100 | 3250 |
| 1120 *Halfpenny*. Similar to 1113 ................................................... | 575 | 1350 |

## HOWEL DDA, d. 949/950

Grandson of Rhodri Mawr, Howel succeeded to the kingdom of Dyfed *c.* 904, to Seisyllog *c.* 920 and became King of Gwynedd and all Wales, 942.

1121

| 1121 HOPÆL REX, small cross or rosette. R. Moneyer's name in two lines  . | 7500 | 25000 |
|---|---|---|

## EADWIG, 955-959

Elder son of Eadmund, Eadwig lost Mercia and Northumbria to his brother Eadgar in 957.

| 1122 | | 1123 |
|---|---|---|

| 1122 *Br. 1*. Type as illustration......................................................... | 325 | 750 |
|---|---|---|
| 1123 — — Similar, but mint name in place of crosses .................................... | 575 | 1450 |
| 1124 — *2*. As 1122, but moneyer's name in one line...................................... | 850 | 2500 |
| 1125 — *3*. Similar. R. Floral design ................................................... | 1250 | 3750 |
| 1126 — *4*. Similar. R. Rosette or small cross...................................... | 475 | 1250 |
| 1127 — *5*. Bust r. R. Small cross ................................................... | 2250 | 7500 |

1128

| 1128 *Halfpenny*. Small cross. R. Flower above moneyer's name .................... | 900 | 2500 |
|---|---|---|
| 1128A— Similar. R. PIN (Winchester) across field............................................. | 1000 | 3250 |
| 1128B— Star. R. Moneyer's name in two lines................................................. | 800 | 2000 |

King in Mercia and Northumbria from 957; King of all England 959-975.

It is now possible on the basis of the lettering to divide up the majority of Eadgar's coins into issues from the following regions: N.E. England, N.W. England, York, East Anglia, Midlands, S.E. England, Southern England, and S.W. England. (See 'Anglo-Saxon Coins', ed. R. H. M. Dolley.)

1129                                        1135

|  |  | F | VF |
|---|---|---|---|
|  |  | £ | £ |
| 1129 | *Br I*. Small cross. R. Moneyer's name in two lines, crosses between, trefoils top and bottom | 145 | 325 |
| 1130 | — — R. Similar, but rosettes top and bottom (a N.W. variety) | 165 | 375 |
| 1131 | — — R. Similar, but annulets between | 175 | 400 |
| 1132 | — — R. Similar, but mint name between (a late N.W. type) | 240 | 650 |
| 1133 | — *2*. — R. Floral design | 1000 | 3000 |
| 1134 | — *4*. Small cross either side | 150 | 325 |
| 1135 | — — Similar, with mint name | 225 | 600 |
| 1136 | — — Rosette either side | 200 | 550 |
| 1137 | — — Similar, with mint name | 300 | 800 |
| 1138 | — *5*. Large bust to r. R. Small cross | 625 | 1650 |
| 1139 | — — Similar, with mint name | 650 | 1750 |
| 1140 | *Halfpenny*. (8.5 grains.) *Br. 3*. Small cross. R. Flower above name | 850 | 2500 |
| 1140A | — — R. Mint name around cross (Chichester) | 1000 | 3000 |
| 1140B | — Bust r. R. 'Londonia' monogram | 650 | 1750 |

For Eadgar 'reform' issues see overleaf

In 973 Eadgar introduced a new coinage. A royal portrait now became a regular feature and the reverses normally have a cruciform pattern with the name of the mint in addition to that of the moneyer. Most fortified towns of burghal status were allowed a mint, the number of moneyers varying according to their size and importance: some royal manors also had a mint and some moneyers were allowed to certain ecclesiastical authorities. In all some seventy mints were active about the middle of the 11th century (see list of mints pp. 128-9).

The control of the currency was retained firmly in the hands of the central government, unlike the situation in France and the Empire where feudal barons and bishops controlled their own coinage. Coinage types were changed at intervals to enable the Exchequer to raise revenue from new dies and periodic demonetization of old coin types helped to maintain the currency in a good state. No halfpence were minted during this period. During the latter part of this era, full pennies were sheared into 'halfpennies' and 'farthings'. They are far rarer than later 'cut' coins.

**Eadgar, 959-975** *continued*

1141

|  | F | VF |
|---|---|---|
|  | £ | £ |
| 1141 **Penny.** Type 6. Small bust l. R. Small cross, name of moneyer and mint. | 675 | 1800 |

## EDWARD THE MARTYR, 975-978

Son of Eadgar and Aethelflaed, Eadward was murdered at Corfe Castle, reputedly on the orders of his stepmother Aelfthryth.

1142

| 1142  Type as illustration above ........................................................................ | 750 | 2000 |
|---|---|---|

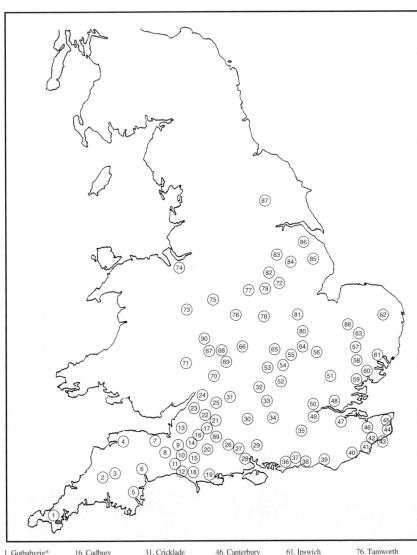

| | | | | | |
|---|---|---|---|---|---|
| 1. Gothabyrig* | 16. Cadbury | 31. Cricklade | 46. Canterbury | 61. Ipswich | 76. Tamworth |
| 2. Launceston | 17. Bruton | 32. Oxford | 47. Rochester | 62. Norwich | 77. Derby |
| 3. Lydford | 18. Dorchester | 33. Wallingford | 48. Horndon | 63. Thetford | 78. Leicester |
| 4. Barnstaple | 19. Wareham | 34. Reading | 49. Southwark | 64. Huntingdon | 79. Nottingham |
| 5. Totnes | 20. Shaftesbury | 35. Guildford | 50. London | 65. Northampton | 80. Melton Mowbray |
| 6. Exeter | 21. Warminster | 36. Chichester | 51. Hertford | 66. Warwick | 81. Stamford |
| 7. Watchet | 22. Bath | 37. Cissbury | 52. Aylesbury | 67. Worcester | 82. Newark |
| 8. Taunton | 23. Bristol | 38. Steyning | 53. Buckingham | 68. Pershore | 83. Torksey |
| 9. Langport | 24. Berkeley | 39. Lewes | 54. Newport Pagnell | 69. Winchcombe | 84. Lincoln |
| 10. Petherton | 25. Malmesbury | 40. Hastings | 55. Bedford | 70. Gloucester | 85. Horncastle |
| 11. Crewkerne | 26. Wilton | 41. Romney | 56. Cambridge | 71. Hereford | 86. Caistor |
| 12. Bridport | 27. Salisbury | 42. Lympne | 57. Bury St Edmunds | 72. Grantham* | 87. York |
| 13. Axbridge | 28. Southampton | 43. Hythe | 58. Sudbury | 73. Shrewsbury | 88. Wilton. Norfolk* |
| 14. Ilchester | 29. Winchester | 44. Dover | 59. Maldon | 74. Chester | 89. Frome |
| 15. Miborne Port | 30. Bedwyn | 45. Sandwich | 60. Colchester | 75. Stafford | 90. Droitwich |

*Possible location of uncertain mint*

He was the son of Eadgar and Aelfthryth. His reign was greatly disturbed by incursions of Danish fleets and armies which massive payments of money failed to curb. He was known as 'The Unready', from UNREDE, meaning 'without counsel', ie. he was without good advice.

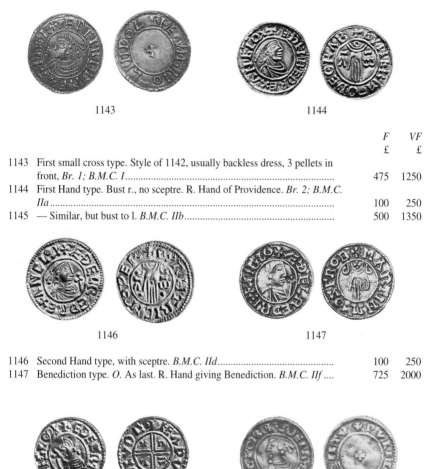

1143      1144

|  | F<br>£ | VF<br>£ |
|---|---|---|
| 1143   First small cross type. Style of 1142, usually backless dress, 3 pellets in front, *Br. 1; B.M.C. I* | 475 | 1250 |
| 1144   First Hand type. Bust r., no sceptre. R. Hand of Providence. *Br. 2; B.M.C. IIa* | 100 | 250 |
| 1145   — Similar, but bust to l. *B.M.C. IIb* | 500 | 1350 |

1146      1147

| 1146   Second Hand type, with sceptre. *B.M.C. IId* | 100 | 250 |
|---|---|---|
| 1147   Benediction type. *O.* As last. R. Hand giving Benediction. *B.M.C. IIf* | 725 | 2000 |

1148      1150

| 1148   CRVX type. *Br. 3; B.M.C. IIIa* | 80 | 180 |
|---|---|---|
| 1149   — Lightweight issue. Small flan, sceptre slants into drapery | 80 | 185 |
| 1150   Intermediate small cross type. Somewhat as 1143, no pellets, similar bust to CRVX type (1148) but no sceptre | 675 | 2000 |

1151                                        1152

|      |                                                      | F | VF |
|------|------------------------------------------------------|---|----|
|      |                                                      | £ | £  |
| 1151 | Long cross type. *Br. 5; B.M.C. IVa* | 85 | 200 |
| 1152 | Helmet type. *Br. 4; B.M.C. VIII* | 90 | 225 |
| 1153 | — — Similar, but struck in **gold** | *Extremely rare* | |

1154                                        1156

|        |                                                             | F | VF |
|--------|-------------------------------------------------------------|---|-----|
| 1154   | Last small cross type. As 1143, but different style | 75 | 160 |
| 1154A  | Similar, but bust r. | 235 | 675 |
| 1155   | — Similar, but bust to edge of coin. *B.M.C. Id* | 350 | 1000 |
| 1156   | Agnus Dei type. *c.* 1009. *Br. 6; B.M.C. X* | 3250 | 10500 |

Son of Swegn Forkbeard, King of Denmark, Cnut was acclaimed King by the Danish fleet in England in 1014 but was forced to leave. He returned in 1015 and in 1016 agreed on a division of the country with Eadmund Ironsides, the son of Aethelred. No coins of Eadmund are known and on his death in November 1016 Cnut secured all England, marrying Emma of Normandy, widow of Aethelred.

## Main types

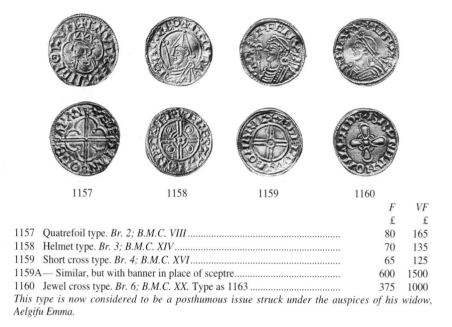

| | | | 1157 | 1158 | 1159 | 1160 |

| | F | VF |
| | £ | £ |
| --- | --- | --- |
| 1157  Quatrefoil type. *Br. 2; B.M.C. VIII* | 80 | 165 |
| 1158  Helmet type. *Br. 3; B.M.C. XIV* | 70 | 135 |
| 1159  Short cross type. *Br. 4; B.M.C. XVI* | 65 | 125 |
| 1159A— Similar, but with banner in place of sceptre | 600 | 1500 |
| 1160  Jewel cross type. *Br. 6; B.M.C. XX.* Type as 1163 | 375 | 1000 |

*This type is now considered to be a posthumous issue struck under the auspices of his widow, Aelgifu Emma.*

## HAROLD I, 1035-1040

Harold, the son of Cnut and Aelgifu of Northampton, initially acted as regent for his half-brother Harthacnut on Cnut's death, was then recognised as King in Mercia and the north, and King throughout England in 1037.

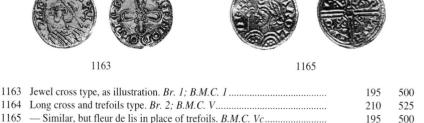

| | | 1163 | 1165 | | |

| | | | |
| --- | --- | --- | --- |
| 1163  Jewel cross type, as illustration. *Br. 1; B.M.C. 1* | | 195 | 500 |
| 1164  Long cross and trefoils type. *Br. 2; B.M.C. V* | | 210 | 525 |
| 1165  — Similar, but fleur de lis in place of trefoils. *B.M.C. Vc* | | 195 | 500 |

He was the son of Cnut but lost the throne to his half-brother Harold owing to his absence in Denmark. On Harold's death he recovered his English realm.

|  | | F | VF |
|---|---|---|---|
|  | | £ | £ |
| 1166 | **Early period, 1036.** Jewel cross type, as 1163; bust l. *Br. 1; B.M.C. I* ... | 850 | 2400 |

1167  1168

| 1167 | — Similar, but bust r. *B.M.C. Ia* ............................................................. | 750 | 2000 |
|---|---|---|---|
| 1168 | **Restoration, 1040-1042.** Arm and sceptre type, with name Harthacnut. | | |
|  | *Br. 2; B.M.C. II* ...................................................................................... | 650 | 1600 |

1169  1170

| 1169 | — Similar, but with name 'Cnut' ............................................................. | 325 | 800 |
|---|---|---|---|
| 1170 | **Danish types,** of various designs, some of English type mostly struck at | | |
|  | Lund, Denmark (now Sweden) ................................................................. | 200 | 525 |

## EDWARD THE CONFESSOR, 1042-1066

Edward was the son of Aethelred II and Emma of Normandy. A number of new mints were opened during his reign.

1171  1173

| 1170A | Arm and Sceptre type. *B.M.C. IIIc* ..................................................... | 800 | 2250 |
|---|---|---|---|
| 1171 | PACX type, cross extends to edge of coin. *Br. 4; B.M.C. IV* .................. | 150 | 400 |
| 1172 | — Similar, but cross ends at legend. *B.M.C. IVa* ................................... | 150 | 400 |
| 1173 | Radiate type. *Br. 2; B.M.C. I* ................................................................. | 85 | 175 |

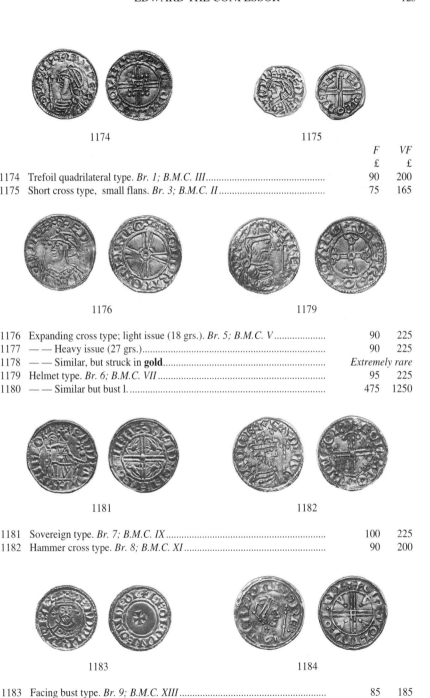

1174                         1175

|      |                                                                    | F | VF |
|------|--------------------------------------------------------------------|---|----|
|      |                                                                    | £ | £  |
| 1174 | Trefoil quadrilateral type. *Br. 1; B.M.C. III* | 90 | 200 |
| 1175 | Short cross type, small flans. *Br. 3; B.M.C. II* | 75 | 165 |

1176                         1179

| 1176 | Expanding cross type; light issue (18 grs.). *Br. 5; B.M.C. V* | 90 | 225 |
| 1177 | —— Heavy issue (27 grs.) | 90 | 225 |
| 1178 | —— Similar, but struck in **gold** | *Extremely rare* | |
| 1179 | Helmet type. *Br. 6; B.M.C. VII* | 95 | 225 |
| 1180 | —— Similar but bust l. | 475 | 1250 |

1181                         1182

| 1181 | Sovereign type. *Br. 7; B.M.C. IX* | 100 | 225 |
| 1182 | Hammer cross type. *Br. 8; B.M.C. XI* | 90 | 200 |

1183                         1184

| 1183 | Facing bust type. *Br. 9; B.M.C. XIII* | 85 | 185 |
| 1184 | Pyramids type. *Br. 10; B.M.C. XV* | 90 | 200 |

1185

| | F £ | VF £ |
|---|---|---|
| 1185 Transitional Pyramids type. *B.M.C. XIV*............................................... | 950 | 2750 |

*Most York coins of this reign have an annulet in one quarter of the reverse.*

## HAROLD II, 1066

Harold was the son of Godwin Earl of Wessex. He was the brother-in-law of Edward the Confessor and was recognised as King on Edward's death. He defeated and killed Harald of Norway who invaded the north, but was himself defeated and killed at the Battle of Hastings by William of Normandy.

1186                                                          1187

| | F | VF |
|---|---|---|
| 1186 Bust l. with sceptre. ℞. PAX across centre of *rev. B.M.C. I*..................... | 475 | 975 |
| 1187 Similar, but without sceptre. *B.M.C. Ia* .................................................... | 550 | 1350 |
| 1188 Bust r. with sceptre *B.M.C. 1b* ................................................................ | 1000 | 3500 |

In late Anglo-Saxon and Norman times coins were struck in the King's name at a large number of mints distributed in centres of population, and in times of emergency in places of refuge, across England and Wales. During the 10th century the use of a mint signature was sporadic but from the Reform type of Edgar the mint name is almost invariably given, usually in conjunction with that of the moneyer responsible, e.g. EDGAR ON BERCLE. At the peak, 71 mints struck the quatrefoil type of Cnut and 65 the PAXS type of William I and they provide a valuable insight into the economic and social structures of the period.

The output of the mints varied enormously and a dozen are exceptionally rare. Approximately 100,000 pennies survive, half of which emanate from the great centres of London, Canterbury, Lincoln, Winchester and York. At the other end of the scale a mint such as Rochester is known from about 500 coins, Derby from around 250, Guildford 100, Bedwyn 25, Horncastle 4 and Pershore 1. Many of these coins, particularly those from the great Scandinavian hoards, are in museum collections and are published in the Sylloge of Coins of the British Isles (SCBI) series.

There are too many type for mint combinations, over 1500 Saxon and 1000 Norman, to price each individually and our aim is to give an indication of value for the commonest Saxon and Norman type, in VF condition, for each of the 102 attested mints (excluding Baronial of Stephen's reign), and for a further 10 mints whose location or attribution is uncertain. The threshold VF price for a Norman coin (W1 PAXS type £375) exceeds that for a Saxon coin (Cnut short cross £125) accounting for the difference in starting level. Prices for coins in lower grade would be less and there is a premium for the rarer types for each mint, but for many types, e.g. in the reigns of Harthacnut or Henry I, the value of the type itself far exceeds that of many of the constituent mints and a scarce mint is only worth a modest premium over a common one.

We also give the most characteristic mint signatures (often found abbreviated) and the reigns for which the mint is known. There are many pitfalls in identifying mints, not least that Saxon and Norman spelling is no more reliable than that of other ages and that late Saxon coins were widely imitated in Scandinavia. There is extensive literature and the specialist in this fascinating series can, for further details, consult J J North, English Hammered Coinage Vol.1.

| Alf | — | Alfred the Great | Hd1 | — | Harold I |
| EdE | — | Edward the Elder | HCn | — | Harthacnut |
| A'stn | — | Aethelstan | EdC | — | Edward the Confessor |
| Edm | — | Edmund | Hd2 | — | Harold II |
| Edw | — | Edwig | W1 | — | William I |
| Edg | — | Edgar | W2 | — | William II |
| EdM | — | Edward the Martyr | H1 | — | Henry I |
| Ae2 | — | Aethelred | St | — | Stephen |
| Cn | — | Cnut | | | |

Berkeley                    Hastings

| | SAXON | NORMAN |
|---|---|---|
| | *VF* | *VF* |
| | £ | £ |
| Axbridge (AXAN, ACXEPO) Edg, Ae2, Cn, HCn | 2000 | — |
| Aylesbury (AEGEL, AEEL), Ae2, Cn, EdC | 1500 | — |
| Barnstable (BARD, BEARDA) Edw, Edg, Ae2-Hd1, EdC, W1, H1 | 650 | 950 |
| Bath (BADAN) EdE-A'stn, Edw-EdC, W1-St | 275 | 460 |
| Bedford (BEDAN, BEDEFOR) Edw-St | 250 | 460 |
| Bedwyn (BEDEPIN) EdC, W1 | 1000 | 2500 |
| Berkeley (BEORC, BERCLE) EdC | 5000 | — |
| Bramber (BRAN) St | — | 2500 |
| Bridport (BRYDI, BRIPVT) A'stn, Ae2, Cn, HCn, EdC-W1 | 650 | 650 |
| Bristol (BRICSTO, BRVCSTO) Ae2-St | 275 | 400 |
| Bruton (BRIVT) Ae2, Cn, HCn, EdC | 1500 | — |
| Buckingham (BVCIN) Edg, EdM-Hd1, HCn, EdC | 1500 | — |
| Bury St.Edmunds (EDMVN, S.EDM) EdC, W1, H1, St | 600 | 500 |
| Cadbury (CADANBY) Ae2, Cn | 3500 | — |
| Caistor (CASTR, CESTR) EdM, Ae2, Cn | 3500 | — |
| Cambridge (GRANTE) Edg-St | 200 | 500 |
| Canterbury (DORO, CAENTPA, CNTL) Alf, A'stn, Edr, Edg-St | 125 | 375 |
| Cardiff (CIVRDI, CAIERDI) W1, H1, St, Mat | — | 800 |
| Carlisle (CARD, EDEN) H1, St | — | 1500 |
| Castle Rising (RISINGE) St (type II-VII) | — | 900 |
| Chester (LEIGE, LEGECE, CESTRE) A'stn, Edm, Edg-St | 250 | 450 |
| Chichester (CISSAN, CICEST) A'stn, Edg, Ae2-St | 200 | 375 |
| Christchurch (orig. Twynham) (TVEHAM, TPIN) W1, H1 | — | 1500 |
| Cissbury (SIDESTEB, SIDMES) Ae2, Cn | 1250 | — |
| Colchester (COLN, COLECES) Ae2-St | 175 | 400 |
| Crewkerne (CRVCERN) Ae2, Cn, Hd1 | 2500 | — |
| Cricklade (CROCGL, CRECCELAD, CRIC) Ae2-W2 | 650 | 650 |
| Derby (DEORBY, DERBI) A'stn, Edm, Edg-St | 500 | 600 |
| Dorchester (DORCE, DORECES) Ae2-H1 | 500 | 600 |
| Dover (DOFERA, DOFRN) A'stn, Edg, Ae2-St | 175 | 400 |
| Droitwich (PICC, PICNEH) EdC, Hd2 | 3000 | — |
| Dunwich (DVNE) St | — | 950 |
| Durham (DVNE, DVRHAM, DVNHO) W1-St | — | 1750 |
| Exeter (EAXA, EAXCESTRE, IEXECE) Alf, A'stn, Edw-St | 175 | 400 |
| Frome (FRO) Cn, HCn, EdC | 3000 | — |
| Gloucester (GLEAP, GLEPECE, GLOPEC) Alf, A'stn, Edg-St | 275 | 400 |
| Grantham (GRANTHA, GRE) Ae2 | 3500 | — |
| Guildford (GYLD, GILDEFRI) EdM-W2 | 750 | 1750 |
| Hastings (HAESTINGPOR, AESTI) Ae2-St | 225 | 450 |
| Hedon (HEDVN) St | — | 5000 |
| Hereford (HEREFOR, HRFRD) A'stn, Edg, Ae2-St | 300 | 450 |
| Hertford (HEORTF, HRTFI, RET) A'stn, Edw-EdC, W1-H1 | 250 | 1000 |
| Horncastle (HORN) EdM, Ae2 | 4000 | — |
| Horndon (HORNIDVNE) EdC | 4000 | — |
| Huntingdon (HVNTEN, HVTD) Edg, Ae2-St | 200 | 750 |
| Hythe (HIÐEN, HIDI) EdC, W1, W2 | 2500 | 800 |
| Ilchester (GIFELCST, GIVELC, IVELCS) Edg, Ae2-St | 450 | 850 |
| Ipswich (GIPESWIC, GYPES) Edg-St | 200 | 400 |
| Langport (LANCPORT, LAGEPOR) A'stn, Cn-EdC | 1500 | — |
| Launceston (LANSTF, LANSA, SANCTI STEFANI) Ae2, W1-H1 | 3000 | 1250 |
| Leicester (LIHER, LEHRE, LEREC) A'stn, Edg, Ae2-St | 300 | 450 |
| Lewes (LAEPES, LEPEEI, LAPA) A'stn, Edg-St | 200 | 450 |
| Lincoln (LINCOLN, NICOLE) Edr, Edg-St | 125 | 375 |
| London (LVNDO, LVNDENE) Alf, A'stn, Edw-St | 125 | 375 |
| Lydford (LYDANFOR) Edg-EdC | 250 | — |
| Lympne (LIMENE, LIMNA) A'stn, Edg-Cn | 650 | — |
| Maldon (MAELDVN, MIEL) A'stn, Edg, Ae2-Hd1, EdC-W2 | 250 | 750 |
| Malmesbury (MALD, MEALDMES, MELME) Edg, Ae2-W2 | 700 | 1000 |
| Marlborough (MAERLEBI) W1, W2 | — | 2500 |
| Melton Mowbray (MEDELTV) Ae2, Cn | 4000 | — |
| Milborne Port (MYLE) Ae2, Cn | 4000 | — |
| Newark (NEWIR, NIWOR) Edg-Cn | 3000 | — |
| Newcastle (CAST) St | — | 1250 |

| | SAXON | NORMAN |
|---|---|---|
| | *VF* | *VF* |
| | £ | £ |
| Newport (NIPANPO, NIPEPORT) Edw, Edg, EdC | 3000 | — |
| Northampton (HAMTVN, HMTI, NORHAM) Edw, Edg-St | 250 | 400 |
| Norwich (NORDPIC) A'stn-Edr, Edg-St | 150 | 375 |
| Nottingham (SNOTING) A'stn, Ae2-St | 500 | 850 |
| Oxford (OXNA, OCXEN, OXENFO) Alf, A'stn, Edr-St | 250 | 400 |
| Pembroke (PEI, PAN, PAIN) H1, St | — | 1500 |
| Pershore (PERESC) EdC | 6000 | — |
| Petherton (PEDR, PEDI) Cn, EdC | 5000 | — |
| Pevensey (PEFNESE, PEVEN) W1-St | — | 1500 |
| Reading (READIN, REDN) EdC | 4000 | — |
| Rhuddlan (RVDILI) W1 | — | 3000 |
| Rochester (ROFEC, ROFSC) A'stn, Edg-H1 | 250 | 1000 |
| Romney (RVMED, RVMNE) Ae2-H1 | 300 | 450 |
| Rye (RIE) St | — | 2000 |
| Salisbury (SEREB, SEARB, SALEB) Ae2-EdC, W1-St | 225 | 375 |
| Sandwich (SANDPI) EdC, W1-St | 250 | 400 |
| Shaftesbury (SCEFTESB, CEFT, SAFTE) A'stn, Edg-St | 300 | 450 |
| Shrewsbury (SCROB, SCRVBS, SALOP) A'stn, Edg, Ae2-St | 250 | 400 |
| Southampton (HAMPIC, HAMTVN) A'stn, Edw-Cn | 400 | — |
| Southwark (SVDBY, SVDGE, SVDPERC) Ae2-St | 125 | 375 |
| Stafford (STAFFO, STAEF) A'stn, Edg, Ae2-Hd1, EdC, W1-St | 350 | 500 |
| Stamford (STANFORD) Edg-St | 125 | 400 |
| Steyning (STAENIG, STENIC) Cn-W2, St | 200 | 400 |
| Sudbury (SVDBI, SVBR) Ae2, Cn, EdC, W1-St | 350 | 450 |
| Swansea (SVENSEI) St | — | 2000 |
| Tamworth (TOMPEARÐ, TAMPRÐ) A'stn, Edg-Hd1, EdC, W1-St | 900 | 650 |
| Taunton (TANTVNE) Ae2-St | 450 | 500 |
| Thetford (ÐEOTFOR, DTF, TETFOR) Edg-St | 125 | 375 |
| Torksey (TVRC, TORC) EdM-Cn | 2000 | — |
| Totnes (DARENT, TOTANES, TOTNES) A'stn, Edw-HCn, W2, H1 | 250 | 1100 |
| Wallingford (PELINGA, PALLIG) A'stn, Edm, Edg, Ae2-H1 | 250 | 450 |
| Wareham (PERHAM, PERI) A'stn, Edg-St | 300 | 450 |
| Warminster (PORIME) Ae2-Hd1, EdC | 2000 | — |
| Warwick (PAERINC, PERPIC, PAR) A'stn (?), Edg-St | 400 | 600 |
| Watchet (PECED, PICEDI, WACET) Ae2-EdC, W1-St | 800 | 1000 |
| Wilton (PILTVNE) Edg-St | 175 | 400 |
| Winchcombe (WENCLES, PINCEL, PINCL) Edg, Ae2, Cn, HCn-W1 | 900 | 900 |
| Winchester (PINTONIA, PINCEST) Alf, A'stn, Edw-St | 125 | 375 |
| Worcester (PIGER, PIHREC, PIREC) EdM, Ae2-St | 350 | 450 |
| York (EBORACI, EFORPIC, EVERWIC) A'stn, Edm, Edg-St | 125 | 400 |

*Mints of uncertain identification or location*

| | | |
|---|---|---|
| "Brygin" (BRYGIN) Ae2 | 2500 | — |
| "Dyr/Dernt" (DYR, DERNE, DERNT) EdC | 1000 | — |
| "Weardburh" (PEARDBV) A'stn, Edg | 2500 | — |
| Abergavenny (?) (FVNI) W1 | — | 1500 |
| Gothabyrig (GEODA, GODABYRI, IODA) Ae2-HCn | 2000 | — |
| Eye (?) (EI, EIE) St | — | 1250 |
| Peterborough (?) (BVRI) W1, St | — | 3000 |
| Richmond, Yorks (?) (R1) St (type 1) | — | 2000 |
| St Davids (?) (DEVITVN) W1 | — | 1500 |
| Wilton, Norfolk (?) (PILTV) Ae2 (LSC) | 2000 | — |
| Bamborough (BCI, CIB, OBCI) Henry of Northumberland | — | 3500 |
| Corbridge (COREB) Henry of Northumberland | — | 4500 |

Aylesbury

Barnstaple

Cricklade

Dunwich

Exeter

Frome

Guildford

Horncastle

Ilchester

London

Milborne Port

Newark

Oxford

Pevensey

Rochester

Stafford

Torksey

Winchcombe

York

# NORMAN MINTS (WILLIAM I TO HENRY I)

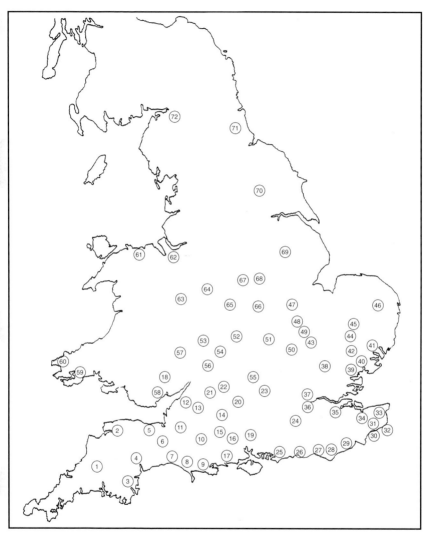

| | | | | | |
|---|---|---|---|---|---|
| 1. Launceston | 13. Bath | 25. Chichester | 37. London | 49. Huntingdon | 61. Rhuddlan |
| 2. Barnstaple | 14. Marlborough | 26. Steyning | 38. Hertford | 50. Bedford | 62. Chester |
| 3. Totnes | 15. Wilton | 27. Lewes | 39. Maldon | 51. Northampton | 63. Shrewsbury |
| 4. Exeter | 16. Salisbury | 28. Pevensey | 40. Colchester | 52. Warwick | 64. Stafford |
| 5. Watchet | 17. Christchurch | 29. Hastings | 41. Ipswich | 53. Worcester | 65. Tamworth |
| 6. Taunton | 18. Abergavenny* | 30. Romney | 42. Sudbury | 54. Winchcombe | 66. Leicester |
| 7. Bridport | 19. Winchester | 31. Hythe | 43. Cambridge | 55. Oxford | 67. Derby |
| 8. Dorchester | 20. Bedwyn | 32. Dover | 44. Bury | 56. Gloucester | 68. Nottingham |
| 9. Wareham | 21. Malmesbury | 33. Sandwich | 45. Thetford | 57. Hereford | 69. Lincoln |
| 10. Shaftesbury | 22. Cricklade | 34. Canterbury | 46. Norwich | 58. Cardiff | 70. York |
| 11. Ilchester | 23. Wallingford | 35. Rochester | 47. Stamford | 59. Pembroke | 71. Durham |
| 12. Bristol | 24. Guildford | 36. Southwark | 48. Peterborough | 60. St Davids* | 72. Carlisle |

* Possible location of uncertain mint

There were no major changes in the coinages following the Norman conquest. The controls and periodic changes of the type made in the previous reigns were continued. Nearly seventy mints were operating during the reign of William I; these had been reduced to about fifty-five by the middle of the 12th century and, under Henry II, first to thirty and later to eleven. By the second half of the 13th century the issue of coinage had been centralized at London and Canterbury, with the exception of two ecclesiastical mints. Of the thirteen types with the name PILLEMVS, PILLELM, etc. (William), the first eight have been attributed to the Conqueror and the remaining five to his son William Rufus. Cut 'halfpennies' and 'farthings' were still made in this period and are scarce until the later issues of Henry I and Stephen.

From William I to Edward II inclusive all are silver pennies unless otherwise stated.

## WILLIAM I, 1066-1087

William Duke of Normandy was the cousin of Edward the Confessor. After securing the throne of England he had to suppress several rebellions.

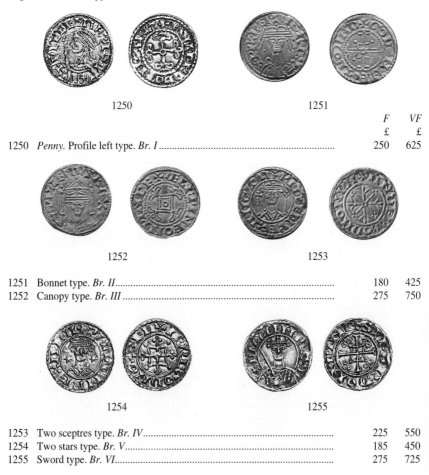

1250                                    1251

|  | F £ | VF £ |
|---|---|---|
| 1250  *Penny.* Profile left type. *Br. I* | 250 | 625 |

1252                                    1253

| 1251  Bonnet type. *Br. II* | 180 | 425 |
| 1252  Canopy type. *Br. III* | 275 | 750 |

1254                                    1255

| 1253  Two sceptres type. *Br. IV* | 225 | 550 |
| 1254  Two stars type. *Br. V* | 185 | 450 |
| 1255  Sword type. *Br. VI* | 275 | 725 |

|           | 1256 |                    | 1257 |       |       |
|-----------|------|--------------------|------|-------|-------|

| | | F | VF |
|---|---|---|---|
| | | £ | £ |
| 1256 | Profile right type. *Br VII* ...................................................................... | 325 | 800 |
| 1257 | PAXS type. *Br. VIII* ......................................................................... | 175 | 375 |

## WILLIAM II, 1087-1100

William Rufus was the second son of William I, his elder brother Robert succeeded to the Dukedom of Normandy. He was killed while hunting in the New Forest.

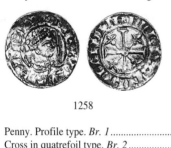

| | 1258 | | 1259 | | |
|---|---|---|---|---|---|

| 1258 | Penny. Profile type. *Br. 1* ................................................................ | 525 | 1200 |
|---|---|---|---|
| 1259 | Cross in quatrefoil type. *Br. 2* ......................................................... | 450 | 1050 |

| | 1260 | | 1261 | | |
|---|---|---|---|---|---|

| 1260 | Cross voided type. *Br. 3* .................................................................. | 450 | 1050 |
|---|---|---|---|
| 1261 | Cross pattée and fleury type. *Br. 4* .................................................. | 475 | 1100 |

1262

| 1262 | Cross fleury and piles type. *Br. 5* ..................................................... | 575 | 1250 |
|---|---|---|---|

Fifteen types were minted during this reign. In 1106-7 provision was made for minting round halfpence again, none having been struck since the time of Eadgar, but relatively few can have been made. The standard of coinage manufacture was now beginning to deteriorate badly. Many genuine coins were being cut to see if they were plated counterfeits and there was a reluctance by the public to accept such damaged pieces. About 1107-8 an extraordinary decision was taken to order the official mutilation of all new coins by snicking the edges, thus ensuring that cut coins had to be accepted. Pennies of types VII to XII (Nos. 1268-1273) usually have a cut in the flan that sometimes penetrated over a third of the way across the coin.

At Christmas 1124 the famous 'Assize of the Moneyers' was held at Winchester when all the moneyers in England were called to account for their activities and a number are said to have been mutilated for issuing coins of inferior quality.

The dates and the order of Henry's issues have been modified several times since Brooke. The main changes are as follows: BMC 11 preceded 10 and BMC 9 follows 6. The order of BMC 7 and 8 remains uncertain. The issues were not made for equal periods of time, as BMC 15 began in early 1125. The contemporary chronicles mention the round halfpenny (and farthings) and the order to snick whole coins under 1107 or 1108. The halfpennies are now dated to agree with these references when BMC 6 and 9 pennies were current. A few pennies of BMC 6 are snicked as are most of the halfpennies. Snicks continue to be used on coins of BMC 13 and 14, though the cut is smaller and only a quarter to a half of the coins are snicked. [Brooke 1916; Archibald and Conté SNC 1990; Blackburn RNS 1990.]

1263             1263A

|  | F £ | VF £ |
|---|---|---|
| 1263 **Penny.** *Br.* I. Annulets type | 400 | 100 |
| 1263A— II. Profile l. R. Cross fleury | 300 | 750 |

1264             1265

| 1264 — III. PAX type | 250 | 625 |
|---|---|---|
| 1265 — IV. Facing bust. R. Five annulets and four piles | 350 | 850 |

1266             1267

| 1266 — V. — R. Voided cross with fleur in each angle | 625 | 1500 |
|---|---|---|
| 1267 — VI. Pointing bust and stars type | 875 | 2500 |

1268

1269

1270

1271

1272

1273

1274

1275                                           1276

| | F | VF |
|---|---|---|
| | £ | £ |
| 1275  Br. XIV. Pellets in quatrefoil type ............................................................ | 175 | 525 |
| 1276  — XV. Quadrilateral on cross fleury type ................................................ | 135 | 325 |

1277

| | F | VF |
|---|---|---|
| 1277  *Halfpenny.* Facing head. R. Cross potent with pellets in angles ............... | 1250 | 3250 |
| 1277A— As above R. Struck from a penny die of type IX ................................ | 1750 | 5500 |

## STEPHEN, 1135-1154
### and the Civil War and Anarchy, 1138-1153

Stephen of Blois, Count of Boulogne and a nephew of Henry I, hastily crossed the Channel on his uncle's death and secured the throne for himself, despite Henry's wishes that his daughter Matilda should succeed him. She was the widow of the German emperor Henry V, and was then married to Geoffrey, Count of Anjou. Two years later Matilda arrived in England to claim the throne, supported by her half-brother Robert of Gloucester.

During the protracted civil war that ensued Matilda and later her son, Henry of Anjou, set up an alternative court at Bristol and held much of the west of England, striking coins at mints under their control. Many irregular coins were struck during this troubled period, some by barons in their own name. Particularly curious are the coins from the Midlands and E. Anglia which have Stephen's head defaced, now believed to have been issued during the Interdict of 1148. In 1153, following the death of Stephen's son, Eustace, a treaty between the two factions allowed for the succession of Matilda's son Henry and a uniform coinage was once more established throughout the kingdom.

*B.M.C. Norman Kings*, 2 vols. (1916). *M.*— Mack, R. P., 'Stephen and the Anarchy 1135-54', *BNJ, XXXV* (1966), pp. 38-112.

**Regular regal issuess**

1278                    1280

|  |  | F | VF |
|---|---|---|---|
|  |  | £ | £ |
| 1278 | **Penny.** Cross moline (Watford) type. Bust r., with sceptre. R. Cross moline with lis in angles. *B.M.C. I; M. 3-42* | 200 | 500 |
| 1279 | — Similar, but obv. reads PERERIC or PERERICM. *M. 43-50* | 475 | 1250 |
| 1280 | Voided cross type. Facing bust with sceptre. R. Voided cross pattée with mullets in angles. *East and South-east mints only. B.M.C. II; M. 53-66* | 225 | 550 |

1281                    1282

| 1281 | Cross fleury type. Bust l. with sceptre. R. Cross fleury with trefoils in angles. *East and South-east mints only. B.M.C. VI; M. 77-99* | 350 | 850 |
| 1282 | Cross pommee (Awbridge) type. Bust half-left with sceptre. R. Voided cross pommee with lis in angles. *B.M.C. VII; M. 99z-135b* | 235 | 600 |

*For B.M.C. types III, IV & V, see 1300-1302.*

# LOCAL AND IRREGULAR ISSUES OF THE CIVIL WAR

## A. Coins struck from erased or defaced dies (interdict of 1148)

1283

|  | | F<br>£ | VF<br>£ |
|---|---|---|---|
| 1283 | As 1278, with king's bust defaced with long cross. *East Anglian Mints.*<br>*M. 137-147* | 600 | 1500 |
| 1284 | — Similar, but king's bust defaced with small cross. *Nottingham. M. 149* | 550 | 1350 |
| 1285 | — Similar, but sceptre defaced with bar or cross. *Nottingham, Lincoln*<br>*and Stamford. M. 148 and 150-154* | 475 | 1200 |
| 1286 | — Similar, but king's name erased. *Nottingham. M. 157* | 425 | 975 |
| 1286A | — Other defacements | 450 | 1000 |

## B. South-Eastern variant

| 1287 | As 1278, but king holds mace instead of sceptre. *Canterbury. M. 158* .... | 850 | 2500 |
|---|---|---|---|

## C. Eastern variants

1288

| 1288 | As 1278, but roundels in centre or on limbs of cross or in angles. *Suffolk*<br>*mints. M. 159-168* | 575 | 1350 |
|---|---|---|---|
| 1288A | As 1278, but star before sceptre and annulets at tips of *fleurs on reverse.*<br>*Suffolk mints. M. 188* | 675 | 1650 |
| 1289 | As 1278, but thick plain cross with pellet at end of limbs, lis in angles.<br>*Lincoln. M. 169-173* | 700 | 1750 |
| 1290 | — Similar, but thick plain cross superimposed on cross moline. *M. 174.* | 650 | 1500 |
| 1290A | As 1278. ℞. Quadrilateral over voided cross. *M. 176* | 875 | 2500 |
| 1290B | As 1278. ℞. Long cross to edge of coin, fleurs outwards in angles. *Lincoln.*<br>*M. 186-187* | 875 | 2500 |

|  | F £ | VF £ |
|---|---|---|

### D. Southern variants

1291 As 1278, but with large rosette of pellets at end of obverse legend.
*M. 184-185* ............................................................................................. 600 1350

1292 — Similar, but star at end of obverse legend. *M. 187y* ............................ 475 1000

1293 Crowned bust r. or l. with rosette of pellets before face in place of sceptre.
R. As 1280, but plain instead of voided cross. *M. 181-183* ...................... 700 1750

1291        1295

1295 As 1278, but usually collar of annulets. R. Voided cross moline with
annulet at centre. *Southampton. M. 207-212* ............................................ 250 575

### E. Midland variants

1296

1296 As 1278, but cross moline on reverse has fleured extensions into legend.
*Leicester. M. 177-178* ............................................................................. 700 1750

1297 As 1278 but crude work. R. Voided cross with lis outwards in angles.
*Tutbury. M. 179* ...................................................................................... 750 2000

1298        1300

1298 Somewhat similar. R. Voided cross with martlets in angles. *Derby. M. 175* 1350 4250

1299 As 1278. R. Plain cross with T-cross in each angle. *M. 180* ..................... 850 2350

1300 Facing bust with three annulets on crown. R. Cross pattée, fleurs inwards
in angles. *Northampton or Huntingdon (?). B.M.C. III; M. 67-71* ........... 1100 3000

1301                                    1302

|  | F | VF |
|---|---|---|
|  | £ | £ |

1301  Facing bust with three fleurs on crown. R. Lozenge fleury, annulets in
       angles. *Lincoln or Nottingham. B.M.C. IV; M. 72-75*............................ 750 | 2000
1302  Bust half-right with sceptre. R. Lozenge with pellet centre, fleurs inwards
       in angles. *Leicester. B.M.C. V; M. 76* ...................................................... 1250 | 3500
1303  **Robert,** Earl of Leicester(?). As 1280, but reading ROBERTVS. *M. 269* 1850 | 6500

### F. North-east and Scottish border variants

1304  As 1278, but star before sceptre and annulets at tips of fleurs on reverse.
       *M. 188* ............................................................................................... 675 | 1650
1305  As 1278, but a voided cross extending to outer circle of reverse.
       *M. 189-192* ......................................................................................... 675 | 1650
1306  As 1278, but crude style, with Stephen's name. *M. 276-279 and 281-282* 575 | 1350
1307  — Similar. R. Cross crosslet with cross-pattée and crescent in angles.
       *M. 288* ............................................................................................... 1350 | 3500
1308  **David I** (K. of Scotland). As 1305, but with name DAVID REX. *M. 280* 1750 | 4500
1309  **Henry** (Earl of Northumberland, son of K. David). hENRIC ERL.
       As 1278. *M. 283-285*............................................................................ 1850 | 4750
1310  — Similar. R. Cross fleury. *M. 286-287* ................................................ 1850 | 4750
1311  — As 1307, but with name NENCI : COM on obverse. *M. 289* .............. 2000 | 5000

### G. 'Ornamented' series. *So-called 'York Group' but probably minted in Northern France*

1312  As 1278, with obverse inscription NSEPEFETI, STEFINEI or RODBDS.
       R. WISÐ. GNETA, etc., with ornament(s) in legend (sometimes retro-
       grade). *M. 215-216 and 227*.................................................................. 1350 | 4000

1313                                    1315

1313  Flag type. As 1278, but king holds lance with pennant, star to r. R. As
       1278, mostly with four ornaments in legend. *M. 217*............................ 900 | 2250
1313A— Similar, but with eight ornaments in reverse inscription. *M. 217*........ 950 | 2500
1314  As 1278, but STIEN and ornaments, sceptre is topped by pellet in lozenge.
       R. Cross fleury over plain cross, ornaments in place of inscription. *M. 218* 1200 | 3250
1314A King stg. facing, holding sceptre and long standard with triple-tailed
       pennon. R. Cross pattee, crescents and quatrefoils in angles, pellets around,
       ornaments in legend ............................................................................. 1750 | 5250
1315  **Stephen and Queen Matilda.** Two standing figures holding sceptre, as
       illustration. R. Ornaments in place of inscription. *M. 220*....................... 1750 | 5500

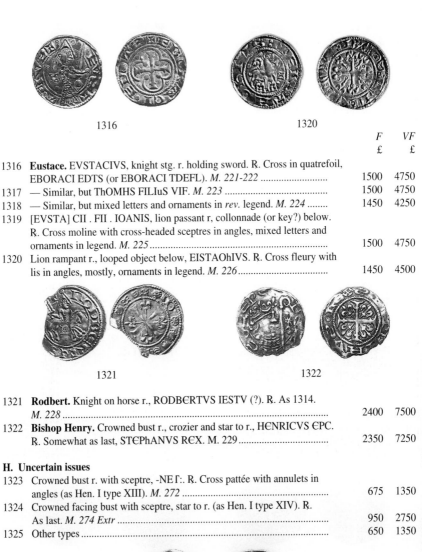

1316                                      1320

|                                                                                                                | F | VF |
|                                                                                                                | £ | £ |

1316  **Eustace.** EVSTACIVS, knight stg. r. holding sword. R. Cross in quatrefoil,
      EBORACI EDTS (or EBORACI TDEFL). *M. 221-222* .......................... 1500 4750

1317  — Similar, but ThOMHS FILIuS VIF. *M. 223* ...................................... 1500 4750

1318  — Similar, but mixed letters and ornaments in *rev.* legend. *M. 224* ........ 1450 4250

1319  [EVSTA] CII . FII . IOANIS, lion passant r, collonnade (or key?) below.
      R. Cross moline with cross-headed sceptres in angles, mixed letters and
      ornaments in legend. *M. 225* ...................................................................... 1500 4750

1320  Lion rampant r., looped object below, EISTAOhIVS. R. Cross fleury with
      lis in angles, mostly, ornaments in legend. *M. 226* ................................... 1450 4500

1321                                      1322

1321  **Rodbert.** Knight on horse r., RODBERTVS IESTV (?). R. As 1314.
      *M. 228* ............................................................................................................ 2400 7500

1322  **Bishop Henry.** Crowned bust r., crozier and star to r., HENRICVS EPC.
      R. Somewhat as last, STEPhANVS REX. M. 229 ................................... 2350 7250

### H. Uncertain issues

1323  Crowned bust r. with sceptre, -NEΓ:. R. Cross pattée with annulets in
      angles (as Hen. I type XIII). *M. 272* ...................................................... 675 1350

1324  Crowned facing bust with sceptre, star to r. (as Hen. I type XIV). R.
      As last. *M. 274 Extr* ................................................................................... 950 2750

1325  Other types ..................................................................................................... 650 1350

1326

1326  **Matilda,** Dowager Empress, Countess of Anjou (in England 1139-1148).
      As 1278, but cruder style, MATILDI IMP. etc. *M. 230-240* .................... 950 2750

1326A Obv. similar. R. Cross pattée over cross fleury (Cardiff hoard) .............. 950 2750

1326B Similar, but triple pellets or plumes at end of cross (Cardiff hoard) ........ 1000 3000

| | F<br>£ | VF<br>£ |
|---|---|---|
| 1326C **Henry of Neubourg,** Bust r., R. As 1276A or 1278 .............................. | 1650 | 4500 |
| 1327 **Duke Henry,** son of Matilda and Geoffrey of Anjou, Duke of Normandy<br>from 1150 (in England 1147-1149-1150 and 1153-1154). As 1278 but<br>hENRICVS, etc. *M. 241-245* ................................................................. | 1350 | 4250 |
| 1327A As 1295 but hENRIC. *M. 246*................................................................. | 1350 | 4250 |
| 1327B As 1326B, but hENNENNVS R, etc....................................................... | 1500 | 4500 |
| 1328 Obverse as 1278. R. Cross crosslet in quatrefoil. *M. 254*...................... | 1500 | 4500 |
| 1329 Crowned bust r. with sceptre. R. Cross fleury over quadrilateral fleury.<br>*M. 248-253*................................................................................................ | 1500 | 4500 |

1330                          1331

| | | |
|---|---|---|
| 1330 Crowned facing bust, star each side. R. Cross botonnée over a quadri-<br>lateral pommée. *M. 255-258* .................................................................... | 1750 | 5500 |
| 1331 Obverse as 1330. R. Voided cross botonnée over a quadrilateral pommée.<br>*M. 259-261* ............................................................................................. | 1750 | 5500 |
| 1331A **Robert,** Earl of Gloucester, 1143-7, Lion. r. R. Cross fleury.................. | 1350 | 3750 |
| 1332 **William,** Earl of Gloucester (succeeded his father, Earl Robert, in 1147).<br>Type as Henry of Anjou, no. 1329. *M. 262* ......................................... | 1600 | 4750 |
| 1333 Type as Henry of Anjou, no. 1330. *M. 263* ......................................... | 1750 | 5500 |
| 1334 Type as Henry of Anjou, no. 1331. *M. 264-268* ................................... | 1750 | 5500 |
| 1334A — Lion. R. Cross fleury................................................................. | 1250 | 3500 |
| 1335 **Brian Fitzcount,** Lord of Wallingford (?). Type as Henry of Anjou,<br>no. 1330. *M. 270* ..................................................................................... | 2750 | 8000 |
| 1336 **Patrick,** Earl of Salisbury (?). Helmeted bust r. holding sword, star behind.<br>R. As Henry of Anjou, no. 1329. *M. 271* .............................................. | 2750 | 8250 |

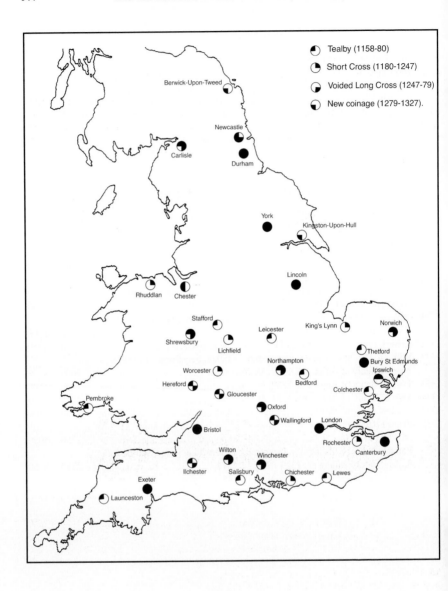

## HENRY II, 1154-1189

### Cross-and-crosslets ('Tealby') Coinage, 1158-1180

Coins of Stephen's last type continued to be minted until 1158. Then a new coinage bearing Henry's name replaced the currency of the previous reign which contained a high proportion of irregular and sub-standard pennies. The new Cross and Crosslets issue is more commonly referred to as the 'Tealby' coinage, as over 5000 of these pennies were discovered at Tealby, Lincolnshire, in 1807. Thirty mints were employed in this re-coinage, but once the re-minting had been completed not more than a dozen mints were kept open. The issue remained virtually unchanged for twenty-two years apart from minor variations in the king's portrait. The coins tend to be poorly struck on irregular plans.

Cut coins occur with varying degrees of frequency during this issue, according to the type and local area.

The price quoted for coins in this section allows for the usual poor quality strike.

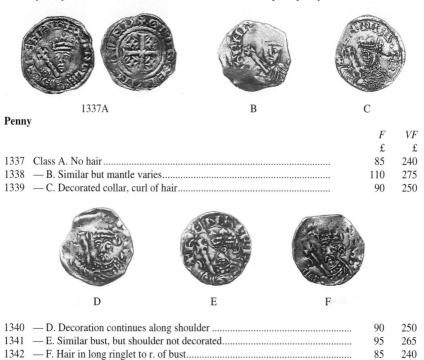

| 1337A | B | C |

**Penny**

|  |  | F | VF |
|---|---|---|---|
|  |  | £ | £ |
| 1337 | Class A. No hair | 85 | 240 |
| 1338 | — B. Similar but mantle varies | 110 | 275 |
| 1339 | — C. Decorated collar, curl of hair | 90 | 250 |

| D | E | F |

| 1340 | — D. Decoration continues along shoulder | 90 | 250 |
| 1341 | — E. Similar bust, but shoulder not decorated | 95 | 265 |
| 1342 | — F. Hair in long ringlet to r. of bust | 85 | 240 |

### Mints and classes of the Cross-and-Crosslets coinage

Approximate dates for the various classes are as follows:
A 1158-1161, B and C 1161-1165, D 1165-1168, E 1168-1170 and F 1170-1180.

| Bedford | A - - - - - | Ilchester | A B C D - F | Pembroke | A - - - - - |
|---|---|---|---|---|---|
| Bristol | A B C D E F | Ipswich | - B C D E F | Salisbury | A - - - - - |
| Bury St. Edmunds | A B C D E F | Launceston | A - - - - - | Shrewsbury | A - - - - - |
| Canterbury | A B C D E F | Leicester | A - - - - - | Stafford | A - C - - - |
| Carlisle | A - C D E F | Lewes | - - - - ? F | Thetford | A - C D - F |
| Chester | A - - D - - | Lincoln | A B C D E F | Wallingford | A - - - - - |
| Colchester | A - C - E - | London | A B C D E F | Wilton | A - - - - - |
| Durham | A B C - - - | Newcastle | A - C D E F | Winchester | A - C D ? - |
| Exeter | A B C D - - | Northampton | A - C ? - - | York | A - C D - - |
| Gloucester | A - - - - - | Norwich | A B C D - F |  |  |
| Hereford | A - C - - - | Oxford | A - - D E - |  |  |

*The publishers would like to thank the late Prof. Jeffrey Mass for re-organising and updating the short cross series. All illustrations were kindly supplied by Prof. Mass.*

### 'Short Cross' coinage of Henry II (1180-1189)

In 1180 a coinage of new type, known as the Short Cross coinage, replaced the Tealby issue. The new coinage is remarkable in that it covers not only the latter part of the reign of Henry II, but also the reigns of his sons Richard and John and on into the reign of his grandson Henry III, and the entire issue bears the name 'hENRICVS'. There are no English coins with the names of Richard or John. The Short Cross coins can be divided chronologically into various classes: ten mints were operating under Henry II and tables of mints, moneyers and classes are given for each reign.

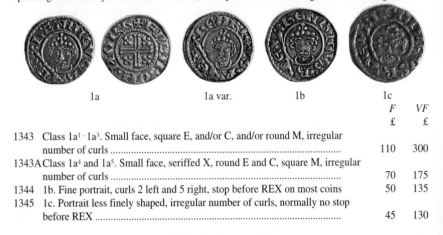

| | 1a | 1a var. | 1b | 1c | |
|---|---|---|---|---|---|
| | | | | | F | VF |
| | | | | | £ | £ |

| 1343 | Class 1a¹ - 1a³. Small face, square E, and/or C, and/or round M, irregular number of curls ............................................................................ | 110 | 300 |
|---|---|---|---|
| 1343A | Class 1a⁴ and 1a⁵. Small face, seriffed X, round E and C, square M, irregular number of curls ............................................................................ | 70 | 175 |
| 1344 | 1b. Fine portrait, curls 2 left and 5 right, stop before REX on most coins | 50 | 135 |
| 1345 | 1c. Portrait less finely shaped, irregular number of curls, normally no stop before REX ............................................................................ | 45 | 130 |

# RICHARD I, 1189-1199

Pennies of Short Cross type continued to be issued throughout the reign, all bearing the name hENRICVS. The coins of class 4, which have very crude portraits, continued to be issued in the early years of the next reign. The only coins bearing Richard's name are from his territories of Aquitaine and Poitou in western France.

| 2 | 3 | 4a | 4b |
|---|---|---|---|

| 1346 | 2. Chin whiskers made of small curls, no side whiskers, almost always 5 pearls to crown, frequently no collar, sometimes RE/X ...................... | 85 | 250 |
|---|---|---|---|
| 1347 | 3. Large or small face, normally 7 pearls to crown, chin and side whiskers made up of small curls ............................................................ | 65 | 185 |
| 1348A | 4a. Normally 7 pearls to crown, chin and side whiskers made up of small pellets, hair consisting of 2 or more non-parallel crescents left and right | 60 | 165 |
| 1348B | 4a* Same as last, but with reverse colon stops (instead of single pellets) | 75 | 200 |
| 1348C | 4b Normally 7 pearls to crown, chin and side whiskers made up of small pellets, single (or parallel) crescents as hair left and right, frequent malformed letters ............................................................................ | 50 | 135 |

**'Short Cross' coinage** *continued.* All with name hЄNRICVS

The Short Cross coins of class 4 continued during the early years of John's reign, but in 1205 a re-coinage was initiated and new Short Cross coins of better style replaced the older issues. Coins of classes 5a and 5b were issued in the re-coinage in which sixteen mints were employed. Only ten of these mints were still working by the end of class 5. The only coins to bear John's name are the pennies, halfpence and farthings issues for Ireland.

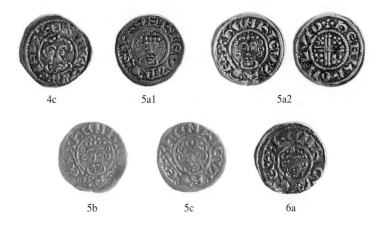

| 4c | 5a1 | 5a2 |
|----|-----|-----|
| 5b | 5c | 6a |

|  |  | F | VF |
|---|---|---|---|
|  |  | £ | £ |
| 1349 | 4c. Reversed S, square face at bottom, 5 pearls to crown, normally single crescents as hair left and right.................................................................. | 75 | 225 |
| 1350A | 5a1 Reversed or regular S, irregular curved lines as hair (or circular curls containing no pellets), cross pattee as initial mark on reverse, *London and Canterbury* only ...................................................................................... | 175 | 450 |
| 1350B | 5a2 Reversed S, circular curls left and right (2 or 3 each side) containing single pellets, cross pomme as initial mark on reverse............................ | 70 | 175 |
| 1350C | 5a/5b or 5b/5a........................................................................................ | 60 | 150 |
| 1351 | 5b. Regular S, circular pelleted curls, cross pattee as initial mark on reverse | 45 | 130 |
| 1352 | 5c. Slightly rounder portrait, letter X in the form of a St. Andrew's cross | 40 | 115 |
| 1353 | 6a. Smaller portrait, with smaller letter X composed of thin strokes or, later, short wedges................................................................................. | 45 | 135 |

*For further reading and an extensive listing of the English Short Cross Coinage see:*
**Sylloge of Coins of the British Isles.** *The J. P. Mass Collection of English Short Cross Coins 1180-1247*

**'Short Cross' coinage** *continued* (1216-47)

The Short Cross coinage continued for a further thirty years during which time the style of portraiture and workmanship deteriorated. By the 1220s minting had been concentrated at London and Canterbury, one exception being the mint of the Abbot of Bury St. Edmunds.

Halfpenny and farthing dies are recorded early in this issue; a few halfpennies and now farthings have been discovered. See nos 1357 D-E.

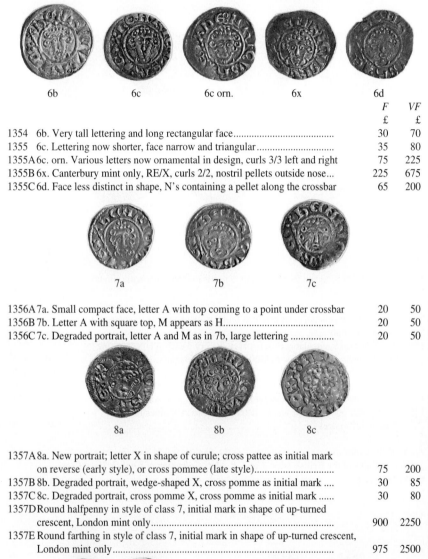

| 6b | 6c | 6c orn. | 6x | 6d |
|----|----|----|----|----|

|  |  | F | VF |
|---|---|---|---|
|  |  | £ | £ |
| 1354 | 6b. Very tall lettering and long rectangular face............................... | 30 | 70 |
| 1355 | 6c. Lettering now shorter, face narrow and triangular............................ | 35 | 80 |
| 1355A | 6c. orn. Various letters now ornamental in design, curls 3/3 left and right | 75 | 225 |
| 1355B | 6x. Canterbury mint only, RE/X, curls 2/2, nostril pellets outside nose... | 225 | 675 |
| 1355C | 6d. Face less distinct in shape, N's containing a pellet along the crossbar | 65 | 200 |

|  | 7a |  | 7b |  | 7c |
|---|---|---|---|---|---|

| 1356A | 7a. Small compact face, letter A with top coming to a point under crossbar | 20 | 50 |
| 1356B | 7b. Letter A with square top, M appears as H.......................................... | 20 | 50 |
| 1356C | 7c. Degraded portrait, letter A and M as in 7b, large lettering ................. | 20 | 50 |

|  | 8a |  | 8b |  | 8c |
|---|---|---|---|---|---|

| 1357A | 8a. New portrait; letter X in shape of curule; cross pattee as initial mark on reverse (early style), or cross pommee (late style)............................... | 75 | 200 |
| 1357B | 8b. Degraded portrait, wedge-shaped X, cross pomme as initial mark .... | 30 | 85 |
| 1357C | 8c. Degraded portrait, cross pomme X, cross pomme as initial mark ...... | 30 | 80 |
| 1357D | Round halfpenny in style of class 7, initial mark in shape of up-turned crescent, London mint only........................................................................ | 900 | 2250 |
| 1357E | Round farthing in style of class 7, initial mark in shape of up-turned crescent, London mint only.................................................................................. | 975 | 2500 |

|  | 1357D |  | 1357E |
|---|---|---|---|

**Moneyer tables for the short cross coinage**

*Fine*

**Henry II:**

*London:* Aimer (1a-b), Alain (1a-b), Alain V (1a-b), Alward (1b), Davi (1b-c),
Fil Aimer (1a-b), Gefrei (1c), Gilebert (1c), Godard (1b), Henri (1a-b),
Henri Pi (1a), Iefrei (1a-b), Iohan (1a-b), Osber (1b), Pieres (1a-c),
Pieres M (1a-b), Randvl (1a-b), Ravl (1b-c), Reinald (1a-b), Willelm (1a-b)　　45
*Carlisle:* Alain (1b-c)　　85
*Exeter:* Asketil (1a-b), Iordan (1a-b), Osber (1a-b), Ravl (1b), Ricard (1b-c),
Roger (1a-c)　　75
*Lincoln:* Edmvnd (1b-c), Girard (1b), Hvgo (1b), Lefwine (1b-c), Rodbert (1b),
Walter (1b), Will. D.F. (1b), Willelm (1b-c)　　65
*Northampton:* Filip (1a-b), Hvgo (1a-b), Ravl (1a-c), Reinald (1a-c), Simvn (1b),
Walter (1a-c), Willelm (1a-b)　　50
*Oxford:* Asketil (1b), Iefrei (1b), Owein (1b-c), Ricard (1b-c), Rodbert (1b),
Rodbt. F. B. (1b), Sagar (1b)　　70
*Wilton:* Osber (1a-b), Rodbert (1a-b)　　75
*Winchester:* Adam (1a-c), Clement (1a-b), Gocelm (1a-c), Henri (1a),
Osber (1a-b), Reinier (1b), Rodbert (1a-b)　　45
*Worcester:* Edrich (1b), Godwine (1b-c), Osber (1b-c), Oslac (1b)　　75
*York:* Alain (1a-b), Efrard (1a-c), Gerard (1a-b), Hvgo (1a-c), Hunfrei (1a-b),
Isac (1a-b), Tvrkil (1a-c), Willelm (1a-b)　　45

**Richard I**

*London:* Aimer (2-4a), Fvlke (4a-b), Henri (4a-b), Ravl (2), Ricard (2-4b),
Stivene (2-4b), Willelm (2-4b)　　50
*Canterbury:* Goldwine (3-4b), Hernavd (4b), Hve (4b), Ioan (4b), Meinir (2-4b),
Reinald/Reinavd (2-4b), Roberd (2-4b), Samvel (4b), Simon (4b), Vlard (2-4b)　　50
*Carlisle:* Alein (3-4b)　　125
*Durham:* Adam (4a), Alein (4a-b), Pires (4b)　　150
*Exeter:* Ricard (3)　　135
*Lichfield:* Ioan (2)　　2500
*Lincoln:* Edmvnd (2), Lefwine (2), Willelm (2)　　100
*Northampton:* Giferei (4a), Roberd (3), Waltir (3)　　110
*Northampton or Norwich:* Randvl (4a-b), Willelm (4a-b)　　100
*Shrewsbury:* Ive (4a-b), Reinald/Reinavd (4a-b), Willem (4a)　　175
*Winchester:* Adam (3), Gocelm (3), Osbern (3-4a), Pires (4a), Willelm (3-4a)　　65
*Worcester:* Osbern (2)　　250
*York:* Davi (4a-b), Efrard/Everard (2-4b), Hvgo/Hve (2-4a), Nicole (4a-b),
Tvrkil (2-4a)　　60

**John**

*London:* Abel (5c-6a), Adam (5b-c), Beneit (5b-c), Fvlke (4c-5b), Henri (4c-5b/5a),
Ilger (5b-6a), Ravf (5c-6a), Rener (5a/b-5c), Ricard (4c-5b), Ricard B (5b-c),
Ricard T (5a/b-5b), Walter (5c-6a), Willelm (4c-5b), Willelm B (5a/b-5c),
Willelm L (5b-c), Willelm T (5b-c)　　40
*Canterbury:* Goldwine (4c-5c), Hernavd/Arnavd (4c-5c), Hve (4c-5c), Iohan (4c-5c),
Iohan B (5b-c), Iohan M (5b-c), Roberd (4c-5c), Samvel (4c-5c), Simon (4c-5c)　　40
*Bury St Edmunds:* Fvlke (5b-c)　　90
*Carlisle:* Tomas (5b)　　110
*Chichester:* Pieres (5b/a-5b), Ravf (5b/a-5b), Simon (5b/a-5b), Willelm (5b)　　80
*Durham:* Pieres (5a-6a)　　90
*Exeter:* Gileberd (5a-b), Iohan (5a-b), Ricard (5a-b)　　75

*Ipswich:* Alisandre (5b-c), Iohan (5b-c) — 60
*Kings Lynn:* Iohan (5b), Nicole (5b), Willelm (5b) — 125
*Lincoln:* Alain (5a), Andrev (5a-5c), Hve (5a/b-5c), Iohan (5a), Ravf (5a/b-5b),
Ricard (5a-5b/a), Tomas (5a/b-5b) — 40
*Northampton:* Adam (5b-c), Roberd (5b), Roberd T (5b) — 60
*Northampton or Norwich:* Randvl (4c) — 80
*Norwich:* Gifrei (5a/b-5c), Iohan (5a-c), Renald/Renavd (5a-c) — 60
*Oxford:* Ailwine (5b), Henri (5b), Miles (5b) — 70
*Rochester:* Alisandre (5b), Hvnfrei (5b) — 90
*Winchester:* Adam (5a-c), Andrev (5b-c), Bartelme (5b-c), Henri (5a), Iohan (5a-c),
Lvkas (5b-c), Miles (5a-c), Ravf (5b-c), Ricard (5a-b) — 40
*York:* Davi (4c-5b), Nicole (4c-5c), Renavd (5b), Tomas (5a/b-5b) — 45

## Henry III

*London:* Abel (6b-7a), Adam (7b-c), Elis (7a-b), Giffrei (7b-c), Ilger (6b-7b),
Ledvlf (7b-c), Nichole (7c-8c), Ravf (6b-7b), Ricard (7b), Terri (7a-b),
Walter (6b-c) — 20
*Canterbury:* Arnold (6c/6x, 6x), Henri (6b-6c/d, 7a-c), Hivn/Ivn (6b-7b),
Iohan (6b-7c, 8b-c), Ioan Chic (7b-c), Ioan F. R. (7b-c), Nichole (7c, 8b-c),
Osmvnd (7b-c), Robert (6b, 7b-c), Robert Vi (7c), Roger (6b-7b),
Roger of R (7a-b), Salemvn (6x, 7a-b), Samvel (6b-d, 7a), Simon (6b-d, 7a-b),
Tomas (6d, 7a-b), Walter (6b-7a), Willem (7b-c, 8b-c), Willem Ta (7b-c) — 20
*Bury St Edmunds:* Iohan (7c-8c), Norman (7a-b), Ravf (6c-d, 7a), Simvnd (7b-c),
Willelm (7a) — 35
*Durham:* Pieres (7a) — 80
*Winchester:* Henri (6c) — 125
*York:* Iohan (6c), Peres (6c), Tomas (6c), Wilam (6c) — 125

Irregular Local Issue
Rhuddlan (in chronological order) — 95
Group I (c. 1180 – pre 1205) Halli, Tomas, Simond
Group II (c.1205 – 1215) Simond, Henricus

Rhuddlan

## 'Long Cross' coinage (1247-72)

By the middle of Henry's reign the coinage in circulation was in a poor state, being worn and clipped. In 1247 a fresh coinage was ordered, the new pennies having the reverse cross extended to the edge of the coin to help safeguard the coins against clipping. The earliest of these coins have no mint or moneyers' names. A number of provincial mints were opened for producing sufficient of the Long Cross coins, but these were closed again in 1250, only the royal mints of London and Canterbury and the ecclesiastical mints of Durham and Bury St. Edmunds remained open.

In 1257, following the introduction of new gold coinages by the Italian cities of Brindisi (1232), Florence (1252) and Genoa (1253), Henry III issued a gold coinage in England. This was a gold 'Penny' valued at 20 silver pence and twice the weight of the silver penny. The coinage was not a success, being undervalued, and it ceased to be minted after a few years; few coins have survived.

Cut halfpennies and farthings are common for this period, with a greater concentration in the early part. They are up to 100 times commoner than in late Anglo-Saxon times.

## Without sceptre

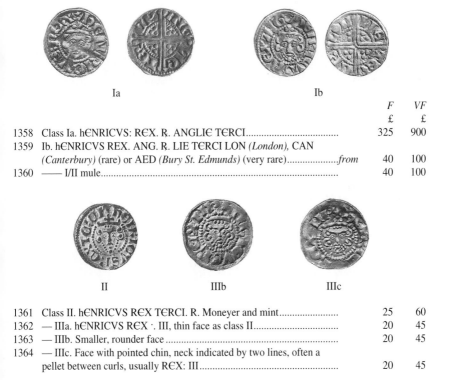

Ia           Ib

| | | F | VF |
|---|---|---|---|
| | | £ | £ |
| 1358 | Class Ia. hENRICVS: REX. R. ANGLIE TERCI.................................... | 325 | 900 |
| 1359 | Ib. hENRICVS REX. ANG. R. LIE TERCI LON *(London)*, CAN *(Canterbury)* (rare) or AED *(Bury St. Edmunds)* (very rare)...................*from* | 40 | 100 |
| 1360 | —— I/II mule......................................................................................... | 40 | 100 |

II          IIIb          IIIc

| | | | |
|---|---|---|---|
| 1361 | Class II. hENRICVS REX TERCI. R. Moneyer and mint...................... | 25 | 60 |
| 1362 | — IIIa. hENRICVS REX ·. III, thin face as class II................................ | 20 | 45 |
| 1363 | — IIIb. Smaller, rounder face ................................................................. | 20 | 45 |
| 1364 | — IIIc. Face with pointed chin, neck indicated by two lines, often a pellet between curls, usually REX: III...................................................... | 20 | 45 |

## With sceptre

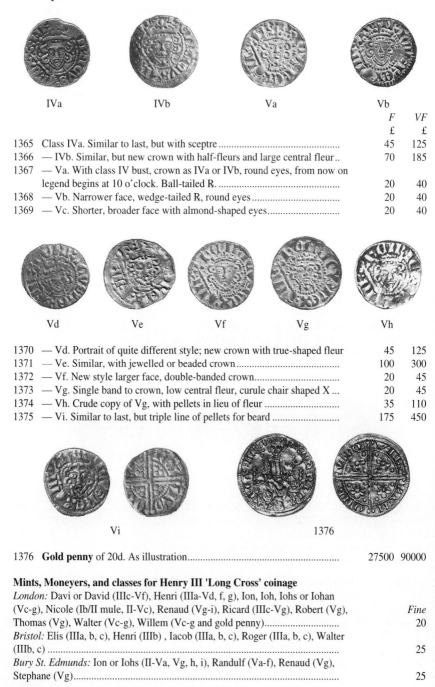

IVa IVb Va Vb

|  | F | VF |
|---|---|---|
|  | £ | £ |
| 1365 Class IVa. Similar to last, but with sceptre ............................................. | 45 | 125 |
| 1366 — IVb. Similar, but new crown with half-fleurs and large central fleur.. | 70 | 185 |
| 1367 — Va. With class IV bust, crown as IVa or IVb, round eyes, from now on legend begins at 10 o'clock. Ball-tailed Ŗ. ............................................. | 20 | 40 |
| 1368 — Vb. Narrower face, wedge-tailed Ŗ, round eyes ................................... | 20 | 40 |
| 1369 — Vc. Shorter, broader face with almond-shaped eyes .......................... | 20 | 40 |

Vd Ve Vf Vg Vh

| 1370 — Vd. Portrait of quite different style; new crown with true-shaped fleur | 45 | 125 |
|---|---|---|
| 1371 — Ve. Similar, with jewelled or beaded crown ....................................... | 100 | 300 |
| 1372 — Vf. New style larger face, double-banded crown................................. | 20 | 45 |
| 1373 — Vg. Single band to crown, low central fleur, curule chair shaped X ... | 20 | 45 |
| 1374 — Vh. Crude copy of Vg, with pellets in lieu of fleur ............................ | 35 | 110 |
| 1375 — Vi. Similar to last, but triple line of pellets for beard ......................... | 175 | 450 |

Vi 1376

| 1376 **Gold penny** of 20d. As illustration............................................................. | 27500 | 90000 |
|---|---|---|

## Mints, Moneyers, and classes for Henry III 'Long Cross' coinage

*London:* Davi or David (IIIc-Vf), Henri (IIIa-Vd, f, g), Ion, Ioh, Iohs or Iohan (Vc-g), Nicole (Ib/II mule, II-Vc), Renaud (Vg-i), Ricard (IIIc-Vg), Robert (Vg), Thomas (Vg), Walter (Vc-g), Willem (Vc-g and gold penny)..............................

*Fine*

20

*Bristol:* Elis (IIIa, b, c), Henri (IIIb) , Iacob (IIIa, b, c), Roger (IIIa, b, c), Walter (IIIb, c) ............................................................................................................... 25

*Bury St. Edmunds:* Ion or Iohs (II-Va, Vg, h, i), Randulf (Va-f), Renaud (Vg), Stephane (Vg)................................................................................................. 25

*Fine*

*Canterbury:* Alein (Vg, h), Ambroci (Vg), Gilbert (II-Vd/c mule, Vf, g), Ion, Ioh, Iohs, or Iohanes (IIIe-Vd, f, g), Nicole or Nichole (Ib/II mule, II-Vh), Ricard (Vg, h), Robert (Vc-h), Roger (Vh), Walter (Vc-h), Willem or Willeme (Ib/II mule, II-Vd, f, g) ....................................................................................... 20

*Carlisle:* Adam (IIIa, b), Ion (IIIa, b), Robert (IIIa, b), Willem (IIIa, b) ............. 50

*Durham:* Philip (IIIb), Ricard (V, b, c), Roger (Vg), Willem (Vg) ...................... 70

*Exeter:* Ion (II-IIIc), Philip (II-IIIc), Robert (II-IIIc), Walter (II-IIIb) ................. 30

*Gloucester:* Ion (II-IIIc), Lucas (II-IIIc), Ricard (II-IIIc), Roger (II-IIIc) ........... 35

*Hereford:* Henri (IIIa, b), Ricard (IIIa, b, c), Roger (IIIa, b, c), Walter (IIIa, b, c) 40

*Ilchester:* Huge (IIIa, b, c), Ierveis (IIIa, b, c), Randulf (IIIa, b, c), Stephe (IIIa, b, c)............................................................................................................ 70

*Lincoln:* Ion (II-IIIc), Ricard (II-IIIc), Walter (II-IIIc), Willem (II-IIIc)............. 25

*Newcastle:* Adam (IIIa, b), Henri (IIIa, b, c), Ion (IIIa, b, c), Roger (IIIa, b, c).. 25

*Northampton:* Lucas (II-IIIb), Philip (II-IIIc), Tomas (II-IIIc), Willem (II-IIIc) 25

*Norwich:* Huge (II-IIIc), Iacob (II-IIIc), Ion (II-IIIc), Willem (II-IIIc) ............... 30

*Oxford:* Adam (II-IIIc), Gefrei (II-IIIc), Henri (II-IIIc), Willem (II-IIIc) ........... 35

*Shrewsbury:* Lorens (IIIa, b, c), Nicole (IIIa, b, c), Peris (IIIa, b, c), Ricard (IIIa, b, c) ...................................................................................................................... 45

*Wallingford:* Alisandre (IIIa, b), Clement (IIIa, b), Ricard (IIIa, b), Robert (IIIa, b) ............................................................................................................................ 60

*Wilton:* Huge (IIIb, c), Ion (IIIa, b, c), Willem (IIIa, b, c) .................................. 35

*Winchester:* Huge (II-IIIc), Iordan (II-IIIc), Nicole (II-IIIc), Willem (II-IIIc) .... 25

*York:* Alain (II-IIIb), Ieremie (II-IIIb), Ion (II-IIIc), Rener (II-IIIc), Tomas (IIIb, c) 25

## EDWARD I, 1272-1307

**'Long Cross' coinage** (1272-79). With name hENRICVS

The earliest group of Edward's Long Cross coins are of very crude style and known only of Durham and Bury St. Edmunds. Then, for the last class of the type, pennies of much improved style were issued at London, Durham and Bury, but in 1279 the Long Cross coinage was abandoned and a completely new coinage substituted.

Cut halfpennies and farthings also occur for this issue, and within this context are not especially rare.

VI                                                          VII

|  |  | F | VF |
|---|---|---|---|
|  |  | £ | £ |
| 1377 | Class VI. Crude face with new realistic curls, Є and N ligate ................. | 25 | 60 |
| 1378 | — VII. Similar, but of improved style, usually with Lombardic U ......... | 40 | 125 |

### Mints, moneyers, and classes for Edward I 'Long Cross' coinage
*London:* Phelip (VII), Renaud (VII) ...................................................*from*   40
*Bury St. Edmunds:* Ioce (VII), Ion or Ioh (VI, VII) ...........................*from*   25
*Durham:* Roberd (VI), Robert (VII) .................................................*from*  250

**New Coinage** (from 1279).

A major re-coinage was embarked upon in 1279 which introduced new denominations. In addition to the penny, halfpence and farthings were also minted and, for the first time, a fourpenny piece called a 'Groat', wt. 89 grs., (from the French *Gros*).

The groats, though ultimately unsuccessful, were struck from more than thirty obverse dies and form an extensive series with affinities to the pence of classes 1c to 3g. The precise chronology is still uncertain and they are arranged in accordance with the classification set out in SCBI 39.

As mint administration was now very much centralized, the practice of including the moneyer's name in the coinage was abandoned (except for a few years at Bury St. Edmunds). Several provincial mints assisted with the re-coinage during 1279-81, then minting was again restricted to London, Canterbury, Durham and Bury.

The provincial mints were again employed for a subsidiary re-coinage in 1299-1302 in order to remint lightweight coins and the many illegal *esterlings* (foreign copies of the English pennies, mainly from the Low Countries), which were usually of poorer quality than the English coins.

|  | F | VF |
|---|---|---|
|  | £ | £ |

1379A **Groat.** *London.* Variety a. (Fox 5). Small crowned bust within a quatrefoil of
three lines, flowers in spandrels. Flat crown with pellet ornaments, drapery of
two wedges with rosette below ................................................................ 1450   5000

1379B — b. (Fox 6). Larger face with flat hair. Unusual crescent crown carrying
pearl ornaments, drapery with rosette in centre ....................................... 1450   5000

1379C — c. (Fox 3). Similar face with bushy hair. Crown with plain band and
pearl ornaments, drapery is foreshortened circle with rosette in centre.... 1500   5500

1379D — d. (Fox 7). New portrait with smaller pointed face, trefoils in spandrels.
Crown with spearhead ornaments, drapery is segment of a circle with
rosette in centre ....................................................................................... 1500   5500

1379E

1379E — e. (Fox 4). Larger oval face with bushy hair, flowers in spandrels. Crown
with spearhead ornaments, thick curved drapery without rosette............. 1450   5000

1379F — f. (Fox 1). Broader face and shorter hair. Crown with spread side fleurs,
drapery of two wedges, trefoil of pellets below....................................... 1650   6500

1379G —— (Fox 2). Quatrefoil of two lines. Drapery of two wedges, trefoil of
pellets below ............................................................................................ 1500   5500

1379H

1379H— g. (Fox -). Quatrefoil of two lines. Crown with bifoliate side fleurs, drapery
of two wedges with annulet (?) on breast, two annulets after ANG ........ 1750   6500

*Edward I groats were often mounted as brooches and gilt. Such specimens are worth
considerably less*

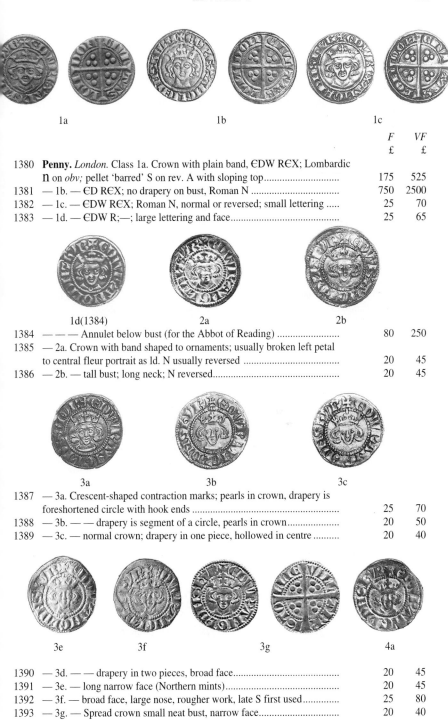

1a 1b 1c

|  | F | VF |
|---|---|---|
|  | £ | £ |

1380 **Penny.** *London.* Class 1a. Crown with plain band, ЄDW RЄX; Lombardic

 Ռ on *obv;* pellet 'barred' S on rev. A with sloping top ........................... 175 525

1381 — 1b. — ЄD RЄX; no drapery on bust, Roman N ................................. 750 2500

1382 — 1c. — ЄDW RЄX; Roman N, normal or reversed; small lettering ..... 25 70

1383 — 1d. — ЄDW R;—; large lettering and face ......................................... 25 65

1d(1384) 2a 2b

1384 ——— Annulet below bust (for the Abbot of Reading) ........................ 80 250

1385 — 2a. Crown with band shaped to ornaments; usually broken left petal

 to central fleur portrait as ld. N usually reversed ..................................... 20 45

1386 — 2b. — tall bust; long neck; N reversed................................................. 20 45

3a 3b 3c

1387 — 3a. Crescent-shaped contraction marks; pearls in crown, drapery is

 foreshortened circle with hook ends ......................................................... 25 70

1388 — 3b. —— drapery is segment of a circle, pearls in crown................... 20 50

1389 — 3c. — normal crown; drapery in one piece, hollowed in centre ......... 20 40

3e 3f 3g 4a

1390 — 3d. —— drapery in two pieces, broad face........................................ 20 45

1391 — 3e. — long narrow face (Northern mints)............................................. 20 45

1392 — 3f. — broad face, large nose, rougher work, late S first used.............. 25 80

1393 — 3g. — Spread crown small neat bust, narrow face................................ 20 40

4b        4c        4d        4e

|  |  | F £ | VF £ |
|---|---|---|---|
| 1394 | — 4a. Comma-shaped contraction mark, late S always used, C and Є open | 20 | 45 |
| 1395 | — 4b. Similar, but face and hair shorter............................................... | 20 | 40 |
| 1396 | — 4c. Larger face with more copious hair; nick to band of crown .......... | 25 | 60 |
| 1397 | — 4d. Pellet at beginning of *obv.* and *rev.* legend .................................... | 20 | 40 |
| 1398 | — 4e. Three pellets on breast, ropy hair, pellet in *rev.* legend (no pellets on Bury or Durham) ................................................................. | 20 | 45 |

5a              5b

| 1399 | — 5a. Well spread coins, pellet on breast, face as 1398, A normally unbarred | 35 | 85 |
|---|---|---|---|
| 1400 | — 5b. Coins more spread, tall lettering, long narrow face, pellet on breast | 35 | 85 |

6a        6b        7a        7b

| 1401 | — 6a. Smaller coins, smaller lettering with closed E (from now on) initial cross almost plain, crown with wide fleurs, crude appearance....... | 75 | 225 |
|---|---|---|---|
| 1402 | — 6b. Initial cross pattée ........................................................................ | 40 | 120 |
| 1403 | — 7a. Rose on breast (except Bury), short hair; almond-shaped eyes, double barred N...................................................................................... | 30 | 90 |

8b             8c

| 1404 | — 7b. Rose on breast (London only) longer hair, new crown.................. | 45 | 125 |
|---|---|---|---|
| 1405 | — 8a. Crown resembling 7b with central fleur usually broken................ | 25 | 50 |
| 1406 | — 8b. Similar to 1405 with wider drapery, top-tilted S ........................... | 25 | 55 |
| 1406A | — 8c — — Crown with very arched band................................................. | 35 | 90 |

9a          9b

|  | F £ | VF £ |
|---|---|---|
| 1407 — 9a. Drapery of two wedges, pellet eyes, crown of 8a-b or new flatter one; often star on breast .......................................................... | 20 | 40 |
| 1408 — 9b. Small coins; Roman N, normal, un-barred, or usually of pot-hook form; often star or (very rarely) pellet on breast. Some Durham coins are from locally made dies................................................................ | 20 | 40 |
| 1408A– 9c. Larger crude lettering with barred A and abbreviation marks. (only found in combination with dies of 9b or 10ab, except Bury)........... | 30 | 100 |

10ab

| 1409 — 10ab. ЄDWARD. Bifoliate crown (converted 9b or new taller one). Narrow incurved lettering. ...................................................... | 20 | 40 |
|---|---|---|
| 1409A— 10ab. Similar with annulet on breast or a pellet each side of head and on breast ......................................................................... | 75 | 200 |
| 1409B— 10ab. ЄDWAR (rarely ЄDWR). Similar to 1409. A few early coins have the trifoliate crown of 9b. ................................................ | 20 | 40 |

10cf1              10cf2

Crown 1     Crown 2     Crown 3     Crown 4     Crown 5

| 1410 — 10cf1. Crown 1 (Axe-shaped central fleur, wedge-shaped petals). ЄDWA from now on. Stub-tailed. R........................................... | 20 | 40 |
|---|---|---|
| 1411 — 10cf2. Crown 2 (Well-shaped central lis, no spearheads). Spreading hair. | 20 | 40 |

| | 10cf3 | | 10cf4 | | 10cf5 | F | VF |
|---|---|---|---|---|---|---|---|
| | | | | | | £ | £ |

| | | F | VF |
|---|---|---|---|
| | | £ | £ |
| 1412 | — 10cf3. Crown 3 (Left-hand arrowhead inclines to right). Early coins have the broken lettering of 10cf2; later have new lettering with .......... round-backed Є. .................................................................... | 20 | 40 |
| 1413 | — 10cf4. Crown 4 (Neat with hooked petal to right-hand side fleur)...... | 25 | 75 |
| 1414 | — 10cf5. Crown 5 (taller and more spread, right-hand ornament inclines to left). Later coins are on smaller flans................................................. | 20 | 50 |

*For a more detailed classification of Class 10, see 'Sylloge of British Coins, 39, The J. J. North Collection, Edwardian English Silver Coins 1279-1351', The Classification of Class 10, c. 1301-10, by C. Wood.*

*Prices are for full flan, well struck coins.*
*The prices for the above types are for London. For coins of the other mints see following pages; types are in brackets, prices are for the commonest type of each mint.*

| Berwick Type 1 | Type II | Type III | Type IV |
|---|---|---|---|

| | | F | VF |
|---|---|---|---|
| 1415 | *Berwick-on-Tweed.* (Blunt types I-IV) Local dies ..................................... | 20 | 50 |
| 1416 | *Bristol.* (2; 3b; c, d; 3f, g; 9b)............................................................ | 20 | 45 |
| 1417 | *Bury St. Edmunds.* Robert de Hadelie (3c, d, g; 4a, b, c)........................ | 40 | 110 |
| 1418 | — Villa Sci Edmundi (4e; 5b; 6b; 7a; 8ab, 9a – 10 cf 5)......................... | 20 | 45 |
| 1419 | *Canterbury.* (2; 3b-g; 4; 5; 7a; 7b; 9;10)........................................... | 20 | 40 |
| 1420 | *Chester.* (3g; 9b) ................................................................................. | 35 | 90 |
| 1421 | *Durham.* Plain cross mm (9b; 10ab; 10cf 2-3; 10cf 5) ......................... | 20 | 45 |
| 1422 | — Bishop de Insula (2; 3b, c, e, g; 4a)................................................. | 20 | 45 |
| 1423 | — Bishop Bec (4b-e; 5b; 6b; 7b; 9a, 9b, 10) with *mm.* cross moline ....... | 20 | 45 |
| 1424 | — — (4b) cross moline in one angle of *rev.*......................................... | 135 | 425 |
| 1425 | *Exeter.* (9b)...................................................................................... | 35 | 80 |
| 1426 | *Kingston-upon-Hull.* (9b)................................................................... | 40 | 100 |
| 1427 | *Lincoln.* (3c, d, f, g)........................................................................... | 20 | 40 |
| 1428 | *Newcastle-upon-Tyne.* (3e; 9b; 10ab)................................................. | 20 | 40 |
| 1429 | *York.* Royal mint (2; 3b, c, d, e, f; 9b) ............................................... | 20 | 40 |
| 1430 | — Archbishop's mint (3e, f; 9b). R. Quatrefoil in centre ...................... | 20 | 40 |
| 1431 | **Halfpenny,** *London.* Class 3b. ЄDWR ANGL DNS hYB, drapery composed of curved line with wedges above........................................... | 35 | 110 |
| 1432 | — 3c Drapery composed of two wedges ................................................ | 20 | 50 |

| | 1434A | | 1433 | | |
|---|---|---|---|---|---|

| | | F | VF |
|---|---|---|---|
| 1433 | — 3g. New wide crown, thick-waisted S, drapery as 3b........................ | 25 | 60 |
| 1433A | — — 4c. Narrower crown, drapery of two unequal wedges ................... | 30 | 85 |
| 1433B | — — Similar, pellet before LON.......................................................... | 35 | 100 |

| | F | VF |
|---|---|---|
| | £ | £ |
| 1434 — 4e. Single-piece collar with (usually) three pellets on breast .............. | 40 | 120 |
| 1434A— 6. Small face with short hair, large coarse crown, closed Є ............... | 40 | 125 |
| 1435 — 7. Larger face with square jaw, open Є, usually double-barred N....... | 35 | 110 |
| 1436 — 8. Similar, new crown with straight sides ......................................... | 35 | 110 |
| 1437 — 10. ЄDWAR R ANGL DNS hYB, bifoliate or trifoliate crown, new waisted letters.................................................................................... | 30 | 85 |

*The above prices are for London; halfpence of the mints given below were also struck.*

| | | |
|---|---|---|
| 1438 *Berwick-on-Tweed.* (Blunt types I, II and III)...................................... | 50 | 150 |
| 1439 *Bristol.* Class 3c, 3g, 4c................................................................ | 30 | 90 |
| 1440 *Lincoln.* Class 3c ............................................................................ | 35 | 110 |
| 1441 *Newcastle.* Class 3e, single pellet in each angle of *rev.* ........................... | 45 | 140 |
| 1442 *York.* Class 3c-e................................................................................ | 35 | 100 |

1443A 1445

| | | |
|---|---|---|
| 1443 **Farthing,** *London.* Class 1a. Base silver issue (6.65 grains), ЄDWARDVS RЄX. bifoliate crown with no intermediate jewels, inner circle. R. LONDONIЄNSIS, (rarely LONDRIЄNSIS), ..................................... | 40 | 135 |
| 1443A— 1c. Similar trifoliate crown ...................................................... | 30 | 110 |
| 1444 — 2. Smaller face, trifoliate crown with intermediate jewels ................ | 25 | 70 |
| 1445 — 3c. New tapering face, wide at top, crown with curved band. ............ | 25 | 70 |
| 1445A— 3de. Sterling silver issue (5.51 grains.) Є R ANGLIЄ bust (usually) to bottom of coin, no inner circle. R. LONDONIЄNSIS.......................... | 30 | 90 |
| 1446 — 3g. Similar, new wide crown with curving side fleurs........................ | 20 | 65 |
| 1446A— 4de. Similar to 3de. R. CIVITAS LONDON ...................................... | 35 | 125 |
| 1446B — 5. Similar, crude wide crown. ....................................................... | 35 | 125 |
| 1447 — 6-7. New large face with wide cheeks, pellet or almond eyes............. | 35 | 130 |
| 1448 — 8. Similar, small rounded face, tall crude crown .............................. | 30 | 100 |
| 1449 — 9a. Є R ANGL DN, small tapering face, (a variety has the face of class 6-7) ............................................................................................. | 30 | 100 |
| 1449A— 9b. Small ugly face, usually wide crown with outwards-sloping sides. . | 45 | 150 |
| 1450 — 10 ЄDWARDVS REX (-, A, AN or ANG,) large bust within inner circle *Type 1450 often appears on oval flans.* | 20 | 50 |

*It is now thought that the order of London Farthings is class 4de, 6-7, 5, 9a, 8, 9b*

1446 1452

| | | |
|---|---|---|
| 1451 *Berwick-on-Tweed.* (Blunt type I, IIIb)...................................... | 110 | 350 |
| 1452 *Bristol.* Class 2, 3c, 3de................................................................ | 30 | 90 |
| 1453 *Lincoln.* Class 3de.......................................................................... | 35 | 100 |
| 1453A*Newcastle.* Class 3de, R NOVI CASTRI.............................................. | 175 | 625 |
| 1454 *York.* Class 2, 3c, 3de.................................................................... | 40 | 125 |

*For further information see Farthings and Halfpennies, Edward I and II, Paul and Bente R Withers, 2001*

The coinage of this reign differs only in minor details from that of Edward I. No groats were issued in the years *c.* 1282-1351.

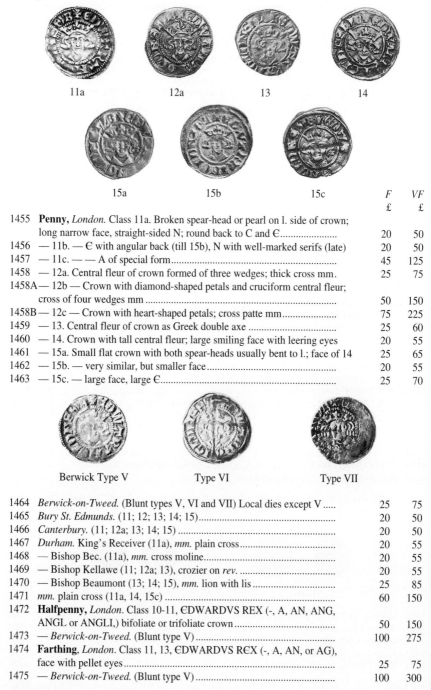

|  |  |  |  |
|---|---|---|---|
| 11a | 12a | 13 | 14 |

|  |  |  | F | VF |
|---|---|---|---|---|
| 15a | 15b | 15c | £ | £ |

| | | F | VF |
|---|---|---|---|
| 1455 | **Penny,** *London.* Class 11a. Broken spear-head or pearl on l. side of crown; long narrow face, straight-sided N; round back to C and Є...................... | 20 | 50 |
| 1456 | — 11b. — Є with angular back (till 15b), N with well-marked serifs (late) | 20 | 50 |
| 1457 | — 11c. — — A of special form.................................................................. | 45 | 125 |
| 1458 | — 12a. Central fleur of crown formed of three wedges; thick cross mm. | 25 | 75 |
| 1458A | — 12b — Crown with diamond-shaped petals and cruciform central fleur; cross of four wedges mm .................................................................... | 50 | 150 |
| 1458B | — 12c — Crown with heart-shaped petals; cross patte mm..................... | 75 | 225 |
| 1459 | — 13. Central fleur of crown as Greek double axe ................................... | 25 | 60 |
| 1460 | — 14. Crown with tall central fleur; large smiling face with leering eyes | 20 | 55 |
| 1461 | — 15a. Small flat crown with both spear-heads usually bent to l.; face of 14 | 25 | 65 |
| 1462 | — 15b. — very similar, but smaller face.................................................. | 20 | 55 |
| 1463 | — 15c. — large face, large Є................................................................. | 25 | 70 |

|  |  |  |
|---|---|---|
| Berwick Type V | Type VI | Type VII |

| | | F | VF |
|---|---|---|---|
| 1464 | *Berwick-on-Tweed.* (Blunt types V, VI and VII) Local dies except V ..... | 25 | 75 |
| 1465 | *Bury St. Edmunds.* (11; 12; 13; 14; 15)................................................. | 20 | 50 |
| 1466 | *Canterbury.* (11; 12a; 13; 14; 15) ........................................................ | 20 | 50 |
| 1467 | *Durham.* King's Receiver (11a), *mm.* plain cross................................... | 20 | 55 |
| 1468 | — Bishop Bec. (11a), *mm.* cross moline................................................ | 20 | 55 |
| 1469 | — Bishop Kellawe (11; 12a; 13), crozier on *rev.* .................................. | 20 | 55 |
| 1470 | — Bishop Beaumont (13; 14; 15), *mm.* lion with lis ............................... | 25 | 85 |
| 1471 | *mm.* plain cross (11a, 14, 15c).............................................................. | 60 | 150 |
| 1472 | **Halfpenny,** *London.* Class 10-11, ЄDWARDVS REX (-, A, AN, ANG, ANGL or ANGLI,) bifoliate or trifoliate crown ............................................ | 50 | 150 |
| 1473 | — *Berwick-on-Tweed.* (Blunt type V).................................................... | 100 | 275 |
| 1474 | **Farthing,** *London.* Class 11, 13, ЄDWARDVS RЄX (-, A, AN, or AG), face with pellet eyes.............................................................................. | 25 | 75 |
| 1475 | — *Berwick-on-Tweed.* (Blunt type V).................................................... | 100 | 300 |

During Edward's early years small quantities of silver coin were minted following the standard of the previous two reigns, but in 1335 halfpence and farthings were produced which were well below the .925 Sterling silver standard. In 1344 an impressive gold coinage was introduced comprising the Florin or Double Leopard valued at six shillings, and its half and quarter, the Leopard and the Helm. The design of the Florin was based on the contemporary gold of Philip de Valois of France.

The first gold coinage was not successful and it was replaced later the same year by a heavier coinage, the Noble, valued at 6s. 8d, i.e., 80 pence, half a mark or one third of a pound, together with its fractions. The Noble was lowered in weight in two stages over the next few years, being stabilized at 120 grains in 1351. With the signing of the Treaty of Bretigni in 1360 Edward's title to the Kingdom of France was omitted from the coinage, but it was resumed again in 1369.

In 1344 the silver coinage had been re-established at the old sterling standard, but the penny was reduced in weight to just over 20 grains and in 1351 to 18 grains. Groats were minted again in 1351 and were issued regularly henceforth until the reign of Elizabeth.

Subsequent to the treaty with France which gave England a cross-channel trading base at Calais, a mint was opened there in 1363 for minting gold and silver coins of English type. In addition to coins of the regular English mints, the Abbot of Reading also minted silver pence, halfpence and farthings with a scallop shell in one quarter of the reverse while coins from Berwick display one or two boar's or bear's heads.

There is evidence of re-use of dies at later periods, e.g. 3rd coinage halfpennies.

For further study of the English Hammered Gold Coinage see: Sylloge of Coins of the British Isles, 47, the Herbert Schneider Collection Volume One, by Peter Woodhead. 1996.

*Mintmarks*

| 6 | 1 | 2 | 3 | 74 | 4 | 5 | 7a |

| | | | |
|---|---|---|---|
| 1334-51 | Cross pattée (6) | 1356 | Crown (74) |
| 1351-2 | Cross 1 (1) | 1356-61 | Cross 3 (4) |
| 1351-7 | Crozier on cross end (76a, *Durham*) | 1361-9 | Cross potent (5) |
| 1352-3 | Cross 1 broken (2) | 1369-77 | Cross pattée (6) |
| 1354-5 | Cross 2 (3) | | Plain cross (7a) |

*The figures in brackets refer to the plate of mintmarks in Appendix III.*

# GOLD

**Third coinage, 1344-51**
**First period, 1344**

| 1476 | 1477 | 1478 |

|  | F<br>£ | VF<br>£ |
|---|---|---|
| 1476 **Double-florin.** (=6s.; wt. 108 grs.). King enthroned beneath canopy; crowned leopard's head each side. R. Cross in quatrefoil ......... | 25000 | 125000 |
| 1477 **Florin.** Leopard sejant with banner l. R. Somewhat as last..................... | 12500 | 35000 |
| 1478 **Half-florin .** Helmet on fleured field. R. Floriate cross ......................... | 6000 | 17500 |

**Second period, 1344-46**

1479

| 1479 **Noble** (=6s. 8d., wt. 138.46 grs.). King stg. facing in ship with sword and shield. R. L in centre of royal cross in tressure........................................ | 4250 | 15000 |
|---|---|---|
| 1479A**Half-noble.** Similar.................................................................................. | 2250 | 7500 |
| 1480 **Quarter-noble.** Shield in tressure. R. As last........................................ | 950 | 2750 |

**Third period, 1346-51**

| 1481 **Noble** (wt. 128.59 grs.). As 1479, but Є in centre; large letters ............... | 1000 | 2750 |
|---|---|---|
| 1482 **Half-noble.** Similar................................................................................ | 975 | 3000 |
| 1483 **Quarter-noble.** As 1480, but Є in centre................................................ | 300 | 800 |

**Fourth coinage, 1351-77**
*Reference:* L. A. Lawrence, *The Coinage of Edward III from 1351.*
**Pre-treaty period, 1351-61.** With French title.

| 1484 **Noble** (wt. 120 grs.), series B (1351). Open Є and C, Roman M; *mm.* cross 1 (1)............................................................................................ | 675 | 1650 |
|---|---|---|
| 1485 — — *rev.* of series A (1351). Round lettering, Lombardic M and N; closed inverted Є in centre .............................................................................. | 725 | 1850 |

|      |      |      | F | VF |
|------|------|------|------|------|
|      |      |      | £ | £ |
| 1486 | C (1351-1352). Closed Є and C, Lombardic M; *mm.* cross 1 (1) | | 550 | 1200 |
| 1487 | D (1352-1353). *O.* of series C. R. *Mm.* cross 1 broken (2) | | 1250 | 3750 |

1488                                    1498

| 1488 | E (1354-1355). Broken letters, V often has a nick in r. limb; *mm.* | | | |
|------|------|------|------|------|
|      | cross 2 (3) | | 550 | 1250 |
| 1489 | F (1356). *Mm.* crown (74) | | 725 | 2000 |
| 1490 | G (1356-1361). *Mm.* cross 3 (4). Many varieties | | 525 | 1100 |
| 1491 | **Half-noble,** B. As noble with *rev.* of series A, but closed Є in centre not | | | |
|      | inverted | | 450 | 1100 |
| 1492 | C. *O.* as noble. *Rev.* as last | | 475 | 1250 |
| 1493 | E. As noble | | 675 | 1850 |
| 1494 | G. As noble. Many varieties | | 350 | 900 |
| 1495 | **Quarter-noble,** B. Pellet below shield. R̟. Closed Є in centre | | 250 | 625 |
| 1496 | C. *O.* of series B. *Rev.* details as noble | | 300 | 850 |
| 1497 | E. *O.* as last. *Rev.* details as noble, pellet in centre | | 275 | 750 |
| 1498 | G. *Mm.* cross 3 (4). Many varieties | | 200 | 475 |

**Transitional treaty period, 1361.** French title omitted, replaced by that of Aquitaine on the noble and (rarely) on the half-noble, but not on the quarter-noble; irregular sized letters; *mm.* cross potent (5).

1499

| 1499 | **Noble.** R̟. Pellets or annulets at corners of central panel | | 575 | 1450 |
|------|------|------|------|------|

1500                    1503

|      |                                                                                      | *F* £ | *VF* £ |
|------|--------------------------------------------------------------------------------------|-------|--------|
| 1500 | **Half-noble.** Similar................................................................ | 275   | 700    |
| 1501 | **Quarter-noble.** Similar. Many varieties. Pellet and rarely Є in centre.... | 185   | 375    |

**Treaty period, 1361-69.** Omits FRANC, new letters, usually curule-shaped X; *mm.* cross potent(5).

| 1502 | **Noble.** *London.* Saltire or nothing before ЄDWARD .............................. | 550 | 1150 |
|------|----------------------------------------------------------------------------------------|-----|------|
| 1503 | — Annulet before ЄDWARD (with, rarely, crescent on forecastle)........ | 525 | 1100 |
| 1504 | *Calais.* C in centre of *rev.,* flag at stern of ship ...................................... | 600 | 1250 |
| 1505 | — — without flag ................................................................................. | 600 | 1250 |

1506                              1508

| 1506 | **Half-noble.** *London.* Saltire before ЄDWARD...................................... | 325 | 850 |
|------|----------------------------------------------------------------------------------------|-----|------|
| 1507 | — Annulet before ЄDWARD................................................................. | 350 | 875 |
| 1508 | *Calais.* C in centre of *rev.,* flag at stern of ship ...................................... | 625 | 1450 |
| 1509 | — — without flag ................................................................................. | 725 | 1850 |
| 1510 | **Quarter-noble.** *London.* As 1498. R. Lis in centre.............................. | 185 | 375 |
| 1511 | — — annulet before ЄDWARD............................................................. | 185 | 375 |
| 1512 | *Calais.* R. Annulet in centre................................................................ | 200 | 475 |
| 1513 | — — cross in circle over shield........................................................... | 235 | 575 |
| 1514 | — R. Quatrefoil in centre; cross over shield........................................ | 275 | 675 |
| 1515 | — — crescent over shield..................................................................... | 325 | 750 |

**Post-treaty period, 1369-1377.** French title resumed.

| 1516 | **Noble.** *London.* Annulet before ЄD. R. Treaty period die.................. | 725 | 2000 |
|------|----------------------------------------------------------------------------------------|-----|------|
| 1517 | — — — crescent on forecastle............................................................. | 575 | 1350 |
| 1518 | — — — post-treaty letters. R. Є and pellet in centre............................ | 550 | 1250 |
| 1519 | — — — R. Є and saltire in centre......................................................... | 625 | 1500 |
| 1520 | *Calais.* Flag at stern. R. Є in centre ................................................... | 600 | 1450 |

1521

|  | | F | VF |
|---|---|---|---|
|  | | £ | £ |
| 1521 | — — *Rev.* as 1518, with Є and pellet in centre | 575 | 1350 |
| 1522 | — As 1520, but without flag. R. Є in centre | 600 | 1450 |
| 1523 | **Half-noble.** *London. O.* Treaty die. *Rev.* as 1518 | 950 | 2750 |
| 1524 | *Calais.* Without AQT, flag at stern. R. Є in centre | 850 | 2250 |
| 1525 | — — R. Treaty die with C in centre | 875 | 2350 |

## SILVER

**First coinage, 1327-35** (0.925 fineness)

1526             1530

| 1526 | **Penny.** *London.* As Edw. II; class XVd with Lombardic n's | 300 | 850 |
|---|---|---|---|
| 1527 | *Bury St. Edmunds.* Similar | 400 | 1000 |
| 1528 | *Canterbury; mm.* cross pattée with pellet centre | 200 | 550 |
| 1529 | — — three extra pellets in one quarter | 185 | 500 |
| 1530 | *Durham.* R. Small crown in centre | 575 | 1650 |
| 1530A | *Reading.* R. Escallop in 2nd quarter | 650 | 1750 |
| 1531 | *York.* As 1526, but quatrefoil in centre of *rev;* three extra pellets in TAS quarter | 175 | 475 |
| 1532 | — — — pellet in each quarter of *mm.* | 175 | 475 |
| 1534 | — — — Roman N's on *obv.* | 175 | 475 |
| 1535 | *Berwick* (1333-1342, Blunt type VIII). Bear's head in one quarter of *rev.* | 475 | 1250 |
| 1536 | **Halfpenny.** *London.* Indistinguishable from EDWARD II (cf. 1472) | 50 | 150 |
| 1537 | *Berwick* (Bl. VIII). Bear's head in one or two quarters | 65 | 200 |
| 1538 | **Farthing.** *London.* Indistinguishable from those of EDWARD II (cf. 1474) | 25 | 75 |
| 1539 | *Berwick* (Bl. VIII). As 1537 | 50 | 150 |

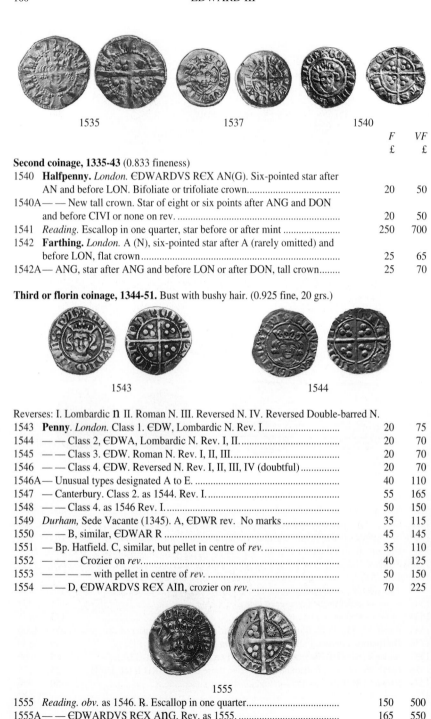

1535        1537        1540

| | F £ | VF £ |
|---|---|---|

**Second coinage, 1335-43** (0.833 fineness)

1540  **Halfpenny.** *London.* ЄDWARDVS RЄX AN(G). Six-pointed star after AN and before LON. Bifoliate or trifoliate crown ..................................... 20  50

1540A— — New tall crown. Star of eight or six points after ANG and DON and before CIVI or none on rev. .................................................. 20  50

1541  *Reading.* Escallop in one quarter, star before or after mint ..................... 250  700

1542  **Farthing.** *London.* A (N), six-pointed star after A (rarely omitted) and before LON, flat crown .......................................................................... 25  65

1542A— ANG, star after ANG and before LON or after DON, tall crown ........ 25  70

**Third or florin coinage, 1344-51.** Bust with bushy hair. (0.925 fine, 20 grs.)

1543        1544

Reverses: I. Lombardic ᴎ II. Roman N. III. Reversed N. IV. Reversed Double-barred N.

1543  **Penny.** *London.* Class 1. ЄDW, Lombardic N. Rev. I. ............................ 20  75

1544  — — Class 2, ЄDWA, Lombardic N. Rev. I, II. .................................... 20  70

1545  — — Class 3. ЄDW. Roman N. Rev. I, II, III. ..................................... 20  70

1546  — — Class 4. ЄDW. Reversed N. Rev. I, II, III, IV (doubtful) .............. 20  70

1546A— Unusual types designated A to E. ......................................................... 40  110

1547  — Canterbury. Class 2. as 1544. Rev. I. ................................................... 55  165

1548  — — Class 4. as 1546 Rev. I. ................................................................... 50  150

1549  *Durham,* Sede Vacante (1345). A, ЄDWR rev.  No marks ..................... 35  115

1550  — — B, similar, ЄDWAR R ....................................................................... 45  145

1551  — Bp. Hatfield. C, similar, but pellet in centre of *rev.* ........................... 35  110

1552  — — — Crozier on *rev.* .......................................................................... 40  125

1553  — — — — with pellet in centre of *rev.* .................................................. 50  150

1554  — — D, ЄDWARDVS RЄX Aᴎ, crozier on *rev.* ................................... 70  225

1555

1555  *Reading. obv.* as 1546. Ŗ. Escallop in one quarter ............................... 150  500

1555A— — ЄDWARDVS RЄX AᴎG. Rev. as 1555. ....................................... 165  550

1556  *York. obv.* as 1546. Ŗ. Quatrefoil in centre ........................................... 20  60

| | F | VF |
|---|---|---|
| | £ | £ |
| 1557 **Halfpenny.** *London.* ЄDWARDVS RЄX ................................................ | 15 | 35 |
| 1558 — — ЄDWARDVS RЄX An............................................................... | 15 | 40 |
| 1559 — — as 1558 with pellet or small saltire each side of crown and/or in | | |
| one reverse quarter............................................................................... | 25 | 75 |
| 1560 — *Reading.* as 1557. Rev. Escallop in one quarter................................ | 200 | 550 |
| 1561 — — as 1558. Rev. as 1560................................................................ | 225 | 575 |
| 1562 **Farthing.** *London.* ЄDWARDVS RЄX ................................................. | 25 | 75 |
| 1562A *Reading.* As S.1562. Rev. as 1560. ................................................. | 250 | 800 |
| 1562B — — ЄDWARDVS RЄX An. Rev. as 1560 ........................................ | 275 | 825 |

**Fourth coinage, 1351-77**
*Reference:* L. A. Lawrence, *The Coinage of Edward III from 1351.*
*A large variety of mules exist between styles and issue.*
**Pre-treaty period, 1351-61.** With French title.

1563                          1567

| 1563 **Groat** (=4d., 72 grs.). *London,* series B (1351). Roman M, open C and Є; | | |
|---|---|---|
| *mm.* cross 1............................................................................................ | 175 | 550 |
| 1564 — — — crown in each quarter...................................................... | 1500 | 6000 |
| 1565 — C (1351-2). Lombardic m, closed C and Є, R with wedge-shaped tail; | | |
| *mm.* cross 1............................................................................................ | 45 | 165 |
| 1566 — D (1352-3). R with normal tail; *mm.* cross 1 or cross 1 broken (2) ..... | 60 | 225 |
| 1567 — E (1354-5). Broken letters, V often with nick in r. limb; *mm.* cross 2 (3) | 45 | 165 |
| 1568 — — — lis on breast ..................................................................... | 60 | 200 |
| 1569 — F (1356). *Mm.* crown (74)......................................................... | 65 | 200 |

1570                          1572

| 1570 — G (1356-61). Usually with annulet in one quarter and sometimes under | | |
|---|---|---|
| bust, *mm.* cross 3 (4). Many varieties ...................................................... | 40 | 150 |
| 1571 *York,* series D. As London ......................................................... | 150 | 475 |
| 1572 — E. As London .......................................................................... | 65 | 185 |

1573                                    1574

|      |                                                                                      | F | VF |
|------|--------------------------------------------------------------------------------------|---|----|
|      |                                                                                      | £ | £  |
| 1573 | **Halfgroat.** *London,* series B. As groat                                           | 80 | 275 |
| 1574 | — C. As groat                                                                        | 30 | 100 |
| 1575 | — D. As groat                                                                        | 30 | 110 |
| 1576 | — E. As groat                                                                        | 30 | 110 |
| 1577 | — F. As groat                                                                        | 35 | 120 |
| 1578 | — G. As groat                                                                        | 30 | 100 |
| 1579 | — — — annulet below bust                                                             | 35 | 110 |
| 1580 | *York,* series D. As groat                                                           | 70 | 225 |
| 1581 | — E. As groat                                                                        | 45 | 150 |
| 1582 | — — — lis on breast                                                                  | 60 | 200 |
| 1583 | **Penny.** *London.* Series A (1351). Round letters, Lombardic M and ñ, annulet in each quarter; *mm.* cross pattee | 60 | 250 |

1584                1587                      1591

|      |                                                                                      | F | VF |
|------|--------------------------------------------------------------------------------------|---|----|
| 1584 | — C. Details as groat, but annulet in each quarter                                    | 20 | 60 |
| 1585 | — D. Details as groat, but annulet in each quarter                                    | 25 | 75 |
| 1586 | — E. Sometimes annulet in each quarter                                                | 20 | 60 |
| 1587 | — F. Details as groat                                                                 | 25 | 75 |
| 1588 | — G. Details as groat                                                                 | 20 | 60 |
| 1589 | — — — annulet below bust                                                              | 20 | 60 |
| 1590 | — — — saltire in one quarter                                                          | 35 | 125 |
| 1591 | *Durham,* Bp. Hatfield. Series A. As 1583, but extra pellet in each quarter, VIL LA crozier DVRREM | 75 | 250 |
| 1592 | — C. Details as groat. R. Crozier, CIVITAS DVNELMIE                                   | 20 | 70 |
| 1593 | — D — — —                                                                            | 25 | 80 |
| 1594 | — E — — —                                                                            | 30 | 90 |
| 1595 | — F — R. Crozier, CIVITAS DVREME                                                      | 25 | 80 |
| 1596 | — G — — —                                                                            | 25 | 75 |
| 1597 | — — — — — annulet below bust                                                         | 25 | 85 |
| 1598 | — — — — — saltire in one quarter                                                     | 35 | 115 |
| 1599 | — — — — — annulet on each shoulder                                                   | 30 | 100 |
| 1600 | — — — — — trefoil of pellets on breast                                               | 30 | 100 |
| 1601 | — — — R. Crozier, CIVITAS DVRELMIE                                                    | 40 | 150 |

|  |  | F | VF |
|---|---|---|---|
|  |  | £ | £ |
| 1602 | *York,* Royal Mint. Series D ........................................ | 25 | 80 |
| 1603 | — — E ........................................................... | 20 | 70 |
| 1604 | — Archb. Thoresby. Series D. R. Quatrefoil in centre ........... | 25 | 90 |
| 1605 | — — G — ...................................................... | 20 | 65 |
| 1606 | — — — annulet or saltire on breast ........................ | 25 | 85 |
| 1607 | **Halfpenny.** *London.* Series E. ЄDWARDVS RЄX AႶ .......... | 70 | 250 |
| 1608 | — G, but with *obv.* of F (*mm.* crown). Annulet in one quarter ........ | 100 | 375 |
| 1609 | **Farthing.** *London.* Series E. ЄDWARDVS RЄX ................. | 75 | 250 |
| 1609A | — — Series G. Annulet in one quarter ........................ | 80 | 275 |

**Transitional treaty period, 1361.** French title omitted, irregular sized letters; *mm.* cross potent (5).

| 1610 | **Groat.** *London.* Annulet each side of crown ..................... | 275 | 900 |

|  | 1611 |  | 1612 |  |  |
|---|---|---|---|---|---|
| 1611 | **Halfgroat.** Similar, but only seven arches to tressure ............ |  | | 100 | 300 |
| 1612 | **Penny,** *London.* Omits RЄX, annulet in two upper qtrs. of *mm* ........ |  | | 75 | 250 |
| 1613 | *York,* Archb. Thoresby. Similar, but quatrefoil enclosing pellet in centre of *rev.* ................................................... |  | | 50 | 160 |
| 1614 | *Durham.* Bp. Hatfield. Similar. R. Crozier, CIVITAS DORЄLMЄ ........ |  | | 65 | 200 |
| 1615 | **Halfpenny.** Two pellets over *mm.,* ЄDWARDVS RЄX AႶ ........ |  | | 75 | 250 |

**Treaty period, 1361-69.** French title omitted, new letters, usually 'Treaty' X, rarely curule chair X *mm.* cross potent (5).

| 1616 | **Groat,** *London.* Many varieties .............................. | 70 | 200 |
| 1617 | — Annulet before ЄDWARD ................................... | 75 | 225 |
| 1618 | — Annulet on breast ........................................ | 100 | 300 |

1617                             1619

| 1619 | *Calais.* As last .................................................. | 120 | 350 |

1621        1635

| | F £ | VF £ |
|---|---|---|
| 1620 **Halfgroat,** *London.* As groat | 35 | 110 |
| 1621 — — Annulet before ЄDWARDVS | 35 | 120 |
| 1622 — — Annulet on breast | 40 | 150 |
| 1623 *Calais.* As last | 75 | 250 |
| 1624 **Penny,** *London.* ЄDWARD ANGL R, etc. | 30 | 90 |
| 1625 — — — pellet before ЄDWARD | 30 | 100 |
| 1626 *Calais.* R. VILLA CALЄSIE | 100 | 300 |
| 1627 *Durham.* R. CIVITAS DVNЄLMIS | 45 | 150 |
| 1628 — R. Crozier, CIVITAS DVREMЄ | 35 | 125 |
| 1629 *York,* Archb. Thoresby. Quatrefoil in centre of *rev.,* ЄDWARDVS DЄI G REX AN | 35 | 125 |
| 1630 — — — ЄDWARDVS REX ANGLI | 25 | 90 |
| 1631 — — — — quatrefoil before ЄD and on breast | 30 | 95 |
| 1632 — — — — annulet before ЄD | 30 | 100 |
| 1633 — — — ЄDWARD ANGL R DNS HYB | 35 | 125 |
| 1634 **Halfpenny.** ЄDWARDVS REX AN, pellet stops | 20 | 80 |
| 1635 — Pellet before ЄD, annulet stops | 25 | 90 |
| 1636 **Farthing.** ЄDWARDVS REX, pellet stops | 80 | 275 |

**Post-treaty period, 1369-77.** French title resumed, X like St. Andrew's cross; *mm.* 5, 6, 7a.

1637        1639

| | | |
|---|---|---|
| 1637 **Groat.** Various readings, *mm.* cross pattee | 90 | 300 |
| 1638 — — row of pellets across breast (chain mail) | 300 | 1000 |
| 1639 — row of annulets below bust (chain mail); *mm.* cross potent with four pellets | 325 | 1050 |
| 1640 **Halfgroat.** Various readings | 110 | 300 |

1640A

| | F £ | VF £ |
|---|---|---|
| 1640A— Thin portrait of Richard II | 125 | 450 |
| 1641   — row of pellets one side of breast (chain mail) | 150 | 525 |
| 1642   **Penny,** *London.* No marks on breast | 35 | 120 |
| 1643   — Pellet or annulet on breast | 40 | 125 |
| 1644   — Cross or quatrefoil on breast | 30 | 100 |
| 1645   *Durham,* Bp. Hatfield. *Mm.* 7a, CIVITAS DVΠOLM, crozier | 35 | 120 |
| 1646   — — — — annulet on breast | 40 | 125 |
| 1647   — — — — lis on breast | 35 | 120 |
| 1648   *York.* Archb. Thoresby or Neville. R̵. Quatrefoil in centre | 25 | 90 |
| 1649   — — — lis on breast | 30 | 100 |
| 1650   — — — annulet on breast | 30 | 100 |
| 1651   — — — cross on breast | 35 | 110 |

1652

| | | |
|---|---|---|
| 1652   **Farthing.** ЄDWARD RЄX ANGL, large head without neck | 100 | 350 |

*For further reading see:*
**Halfpennies and Farthings of Edward III and Richard II.** *Paul and Bente R. Withers, 2002.*

There was no change in the weight standard of the coinage during this reign and the coins evolve from early issues resembling those of Edward III to late issues similar to those of Henry IV.

There is no overall, systematic classification of the coins of Richard II but a coherent scheme for the gold coinage has been worked out and is published in the Schneider Sylloge (SCBI 47). This classification has been adopted here.

Reference: *Silver coinages of Richard II, Henry IV and V.* (B.N.J. 1959-60 and 1963).

*Mintmark:* cross pattée (6)

|  | F £ | VF £ |
|---|---|---|

## GOLD

| | | F | VF |
|---|---|---|---|
| 1653 | **Noble,** *London.* Style of Edw. III. IA. Lis over sail ............................... | 750 | 1850 |

1654                                    1658

| 1654 | — IB. Annulet over sail .............................................................. | 675 | 1450 |
|---|---|---|---|
| 1655 | French title omitted. IIA. Crude style, saltire over sail. IIB. Fine style, trefoil over sail. IIC. Porcine style, no mark over sail ............................ | 725 | 1650 |
| 1656 | French title resumed. IIIA. Fine style, no marks ................................. | 700 | 1600 |
| 1657 | — IIIB. Lis on rudder. IIIC. Trefoil by shield ................................... | 750 | 1850 |
| 1658 | Henry IV style. IVA. Escallop on rudder. IVB. Crescent on rudder ........ | 850 | 2500 |
| 1659 | *Calais.* Style of Edw. III, IA, Edw. III lettering ............................... | 950 | 3000 |
| 1660 | Style of Edw. III. IB. New lettering. Voided quatrefoil over sail ........... | 700 | 1600 |

1661                                    1662

| 1661 | French title omitted. IIA. Crude style, no marks. IIB. Fine style, trefoil over sail. IIC. Porcine style, no marks ........................................... | 675 | 1500 |
|---|---|---|---|
| 1662 | French title resumed. IIIA. Fine style, no marks ................................. | 725 | 1650 |
| 1663 | — IIIB. Lion on rudder. IIIC. Two pellets by shield ............................ | 850 | 2250 |
| 1664 | **Half-noble,** *London.* With altered *obv.* of Edw. III. Usually muled with *rev.* or altered *rev.* of Edw. III .................................................. | 825 | 2250 |

1665                 1673

|  |  | F | VF |
|---|---|---|---|
|  |  | £ | £ |
| 1665 | Style of Edw. III. IB. No marks or saltire over sail | 725 | 2000 |
| 1666 | French title omitted. IIA. New style, no marks | 725 | 2000 |
| 1667 | French title resumed. IIIA. No marks. IIIB. Lion on rudder | 750 | 2100 |
| 1668 | Henry IV style. IVB. Crescent on rudder | 850 | 2500 |
| 1669 | *Calais.* Mule with *obv.* or *rev.* of Edw. III | 1250 | 3500 |
| 1670 | Style of Edw. III. IB. Quatrefoil over sail | 1100 | 3250 |
| 1671 | Late style. French title. IIIA. No marks. IIIB. Saltire by rudder | 975 | 3000 |
| 1672 | **Quarter-noble,** *London.* IA. R in centre of *rev.* | 350 | 875 |
| 1673 | IB Lis in centre of *rev.* | 325 | 800 |
| 1674 | — lis or cross over shield | 350 | 875 |

1675                 1677

| 1675 | IIIA. Pellet in centre of *rev.* | 325 | 800 |
|---|---|---|---|
| 1676 | IIIB. Trefoil of annulets over shield or trefoils in spandrels | 400 | 975 |
| 1677 | IVA. Escallop over shield | 375 | 900 |

## SILVER

1679                 1682

| 1678 | **Groat.** I. Style of Edw. III, F *(i.e. et)* before FRANC, etc. | 300 | 1000 |
|---|---|---|---|
| 1679 | II. New lettering, retrograde Z before FRANC, etc. | 275 | 900 |
| 1680 | III. Bust with bushy hair, 'fishtail' serifs to letters | 300 | 1000 |
| 1681 | IV. New style bust and crown, crescent on breast | 950 | 3500 |
| 1682 | **Halfgroat.** II. New lettering; with or without French title | 175 | 600 |
| 1683 | III. As 1680 | 225 | 750 |
| 1684 | — — with *obv.* die of Edw. III (1640A) | 300 | 950 |

|                                                                                               | F    | VF   |
|                                                                                               | £    | £    |
| 1685  IV. As 1681, but no crescent........................................................     | 525  | 2000 |
| 1686  **Penny,** *London.* I Lettering as 1678, RICARDVS REX ANGLIE..........                 | 165  | 500  |
| 1688  — II. As 1679, Z FRANC lis on breast ......................................             | 175  | 525  |

1689                                   1692

| 1689  — III. As 1680, RICARD REX AnGLIE, fish-tail letters ......................             | 185  | 600  |
| 1690  *York.* I. Early style, usually with cross or lis on breast, quatrefoil in centre       |      |      |
|        of *rev* ...................................................................................  | 45   | 185  |
| 1691  — II. New bust and letters, no marks on breast.........................................  | 45   | 185  |
| 1692  — Local dies. Pellet above each shoulder, cross on breast, REX ANGLIE                    |      |      |
|        or ANGILIE...............................................................................    | 45   | 200  |
| 1693  — — — REX DNS EB .............................................................................| 90   | 350  |
| 1694  — — — REX ANG FRANC...............................................................            | 80   | 300  |
| 1695  — III. As 1680, REX ANGL Z FRANC (scallop after TAS) ..................                  | 65   | 250  |
| 1696  — IV. Very bushy hair, new letters, R. R in centre of quatrefoil .............           | 150  | 500  |
| 1697  *Durham.* Cross or lis on breast, DVNOLM .............................................   | 100  | 375  |

1698                 1699                 1701                 1704

| 1698  **Halfpenny.** Early style. LONDON, saltire or annulet (rare) on breast ....           | 50   | 160  |
| 1699  Intermediate style. LONDON, no marks on breast...................................       | 30   | 95   |
| 1700  Type III. Late style. Similar, but fishtail letters .......................................| 30   | 100  |
| 1700A Type IV. Short, stubby lettering..................................................          | 35   | 120  |
| 1701  **Farthing.** Small bust and letters ................................................       | 90   | 300  |
| 1703  Similar but no neck ...................................................................      | 85   | 275  |
| 1704  Rose in each angle of *rev.* instead of pellets ............................................| 125  | 400  |
| 1704A Large head with broad face as Henry IV .................................................   | 135  | 425  |

*For further reading see:*
**Halfpennies and Farthings of Edward III and Richard II.** *Paul and Bente R. Withers, 2002..*

## HENRY IV, 1399-1413

In 1412 the standard weights of the coinage were reduced, the noble by 12 grains and the penny by 3 grains, partly because there was a scarcity of bullion and partly to provide revenue for the king, as Parliament had not renewed the royal subsidies. As in France, the royal arms were altered, three fleur-de-lis taking the place of the four or more lis previously displayed.

*Mintmark:* cross pattée (6)

### GOLD

**Heavy coinage, 1399-1412**

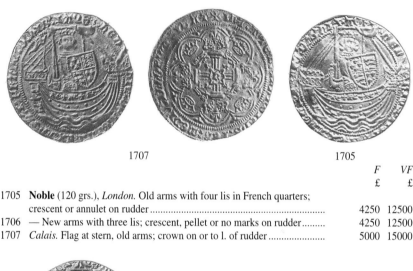

|  | | 1707 | 1705 | | |
| --- | --- | --- | --- | --- | --- |

|  |  | F £ | VF £ |
| --- | --- | --- | --- |
| 1705 | **Noble** (120 grs.), *London.* Old arms with four lis in French quarters; crescent or annulet on rudder | 4250 | 12500 |
| 1706 | — New arms with three lis; crescent, pellet or no marks on rudder | 4250 | 12500 |
| 1707 | *Calais.* Flag at stern, old arms; crown on or to l. of rudder | 5000 | 15000 |

|  | | 1708 | 1710 | | |
| --- | --- | --- | --- | --- | --- |

| 1708 | — — new arms; crown or saltire on rudder | 4750 | 14000 |
| --- | --- | --- | --- |
| 1709 | **Half-noble,** *London.* Old arms | 3250 | 9500 |
| 1710 | — new arms | 3000 | 9000 |
| 1711 | *Calais.* New arms | 4250 | 12500 |
| 1712 | **Quarter-noble,** *London.* Crescent over old arms | 950 | 3000 |
| 1713 | — — — new arms | 900 | 2750 |
| 1714 | *Calais.* New arms. R. *Mm.* crown | 1250 | 3500 |

1715

|      |      | F     | VF    |
|------|------|-------|-------|
|      |      | £     | £     |

**Light coinage, 1412-13**

1715 **Noble** (108 grs.). Trefoil, or trefoil and annulet, on side of ship. R. Trefoil
in one quarter ........................................................................................... 1250   3250

1716 **Half-noble.** Similar, but always with annulet........................................... 2000   5250

1717

1717 **Quarter-noble.** Trefoils, or trefoils and annulets beside shield, lis above. R.
Lis in centre............................................................................................ 475   1100

# SILVER

**Heavy coinage, 1399-1412**

1718                              1722                              1723

| | | | |
|---|---|---|---|
| 1718 **Halfgroat** (36 grs.). Star on breast ............................................................ | 1000 | 3250 | |
| 1718A— Muled with Edw. III (1640A) *obv.* ...................................................... | 700 | 2000 | |
| 1719 **Penny,** *London.* Similar, early bust with long neck.............................. | 500 | 1500 | |
| 1720 — later bust with shorter neck, no star ....................................................... | 500 | 1500 | |
| 1722 *York* Bust with broad face, round chin................................................. | 275 | 850 | |
| 1723 **Halfpenny.** Early small bust................................................................ | 125 | 450 | |
| 1724 — later large bust, with rounded shoulders, ........................................... | 125 | 450 | |
| 1725 **Farthing.** Face without neck ................................................................... | 525 | 1500 | |

**Light coinage, 1412-13**

|      |                                                                                                 | F    | VF   |
| ---- | ----------------------------------------------------------------------------------------------- | ---- | ---- |
|      |                                                                                                 | £    | £    |
| 1726 | **Groat** (60 grs.). I. Pellet to l., annulet to r. of crown; altered die of Richard II ........ | 1500 | 5000 |
| 1727 | New dies; II. Annulet to l., pellet to r. of crown, 8 or 10 arches to tressure                   | 1350 | 4750 |
| 1728 | — III. Similar but 9 arches to tressure ........                                                 | 1250 | 4500 |
| 1729 | **Halfgroat.** Pellet to l., annulet to r. of crown ........                                     | 550  | 1500 |
| 1730 | Annulet to l., pellet to r. of crown ........                                                    | 350  | 900  |
| 1731 | **Penny,** *London.* Annulet and pellet by crown; trefoil on breast and before CIVI ........     | 350  | 950  |
| 1732 | — — annulet or slipped trefoil before LON ........                                               | 350  | 950  |
| 1733 | — Pellet and annulet by crown ........                                                           | 375  | 1000 |
| 1734 | *York.* Annulet on breast. R. Quatrefoil in centre ........                                      | 150  | 550  |
| 1735 | *Durham.* Trefoil on breast, DVnOLM ........                                                     | 150  | 550  |
| 1737 | **Halfpenny.** New dies; annulets by crown or neck, or no marks ........                         | 125  | 500  |
| 1738 | **Farthing.** Face, no bust; trefoil after RЄX ........                                          | 525  | 1500 |

*For further information see:*
**Halfpennies and Farthings of Henry IV, V and VI.** *Paul and Bente R. Withers, 2003.*

There was no change of importance in the coinage of this reign. There was, however, a considerable development in the use of privy marks which distinguished various issues, except for the last issue of the reign when most marks were removed. The Calais mint, which had closed in 1411, did not re-open until just before the end of the reign.

*Mintmarks*

Cross pattee (4)      Pierced cross with      Pierced cross (18).
                      pellet centre (20)

## GOLD

|      |                                                                                          | F<br>£ | VF<br>£ |
|------|------------------------------------------------------------------------------------------|--------|---------|
| 1739 | **Noble.** A. Quatrefoil over sail and in second quarter of *rev.* Short broad letters, no other marks | 1250   | 3500    |
| 1740 | — B. Ordinary letters; similar, or with annulet on rudder                                 | 725    | 1750    |
| 1741 | — C. Mullet by sword arm, annulet on rudder                                               | 675    | 1450    |

1742

|      |                                                                                          | F<br>£ | VF<br>£ |
|------|------------------------------------------------------------------------------------------|--------|---------|
| 1742 | — — — broken annulet on side of ship                                                      | 625    | 1300    |
| 1743 | —D. Mullet and annulet by sword arm, trefoil by shield, broken annulet on ship           | 675    | 1500    |

1744

|      |                                                                                          | F<br>£ | VF<br>£ |
|------|------------------------------------------------------------------------------------------|--------|---------|
| 1744 | — E. Mullet, or mullet and annulet by sword arm, trefoil by shield, pellet by sword point and in one quarter, annulet on side of ship | 650    | 1450    |
| 1745 | — — Similar, but trefoil on ship instead of by shield                                     | 700    | 1600    |
| 1746 | — F. Similar, but no pellet at sword point, trefoil in one quarter                         | 750    | 1800    |
| 1747 | — G. No marks; annulet stops, except for mullet after first word                          | 850    | 2000    |
| 1748 | **Half-noble.** B. As noble; Hen. IV *rev.* die                                           | 1350   | 4000    |
| 1749 | — C. Broken annulet on ship, quatrefoil below sail                                        | 650    | 1500    |

| | | F £ | VF £ |
|---|---|---|---|
| 1750 | — — Mullet over shield, broken annulet on *rev.* ..................................... | 575 | 1250 |
| 1751 | — F. Similar, but no annulet on ship, usually trefoil by shield ............... | 750 | 2250 |

1752                                              1756

| | | | |
|---|---|---|---|
| 1752 | — F/E. As last, but pellet in 1st and annulet in 2nd quarter .................... | 750 | 2250 |
| 1753 | — G. As noble, but quatrefoil over sail, mullet sometimes omitted after first word of *rev.*.................................................................................... | 650 | 1750 |
| 1754 | **Quarter-noble.** A. Lis over shield and in centre of *rev.* Short broad letters; quatrefoil and annulet beside shield, stars at corners of centre on *rev.*...... | 575 | 1500 |
| 1755 | — C. Ordinary letters; quatrefoil to l., quat. and mullet to r. of shield..... | 325 | 800 |
| 1756 | — — — annulet to l., mullet to r. of shield ............................................. | 275 | 600 |
| 1757 | — F. Ordinary letters; trefoil to l., mullet to r. of shield........................... | 300 | 675 |
| 1758 | — G. — no marks, except mullet after first word ..................................... | 325 | 700 |

## SILVER

| | | | |
|---|---|---|---|
| 1759 | **Groat.** A. Short broad letters; 'emaciated' bust......................................... | 925 | 3000 |

1759

| | | | |
|---|---|---|---|
| 1760 | — — muled with Hen. IV *obv*.................................................................... | 975 | 3500 |
| 1761 | — — muled with Hen. IV *rev*.................................................................... | 925 | 3000 |

1762                                              1765

| | | | |
|---|---|---|---|
| 1762 | B. Ordinary letters; 'scowling' bust............................................................ | 275 | 950 |
| 1762A | — — mullet in centre of breast................................................................. | 300 | 1000 |
| 1762B | — — mullet to r. of breast ........................................................................ | 325 | 1050 |
| 1763 | — — muled with Hen. IV........................................................................... | 475 | 1500 |
| 1764 | C. Normal bust .......................................................................................... | 200 | 700 |
| 1765 | — — mullet on r. shoulder ........................................................................ | 100 | 375 |

|  | *F* | *VF* |
|---|---|---|
|  | £ | £ |
| 1766 — — R muled with Hen. IV | 475 | 1500 |
| 1767 G. Normal bust; no marks | 225 | 750 |
| 1768 **Halfgroat.** A. As groat, but usually with annulet and pellet by crown .... | 425 | 1200 |
| 1769 B. Ordinary letters; no marks | 300 | 850 |
| 1770 — — muled with Hen. IV *obv.* | 475 | 1500 |
| 1771 C. Tall neck, broken annulet to l. of crown | 95 | 325 |
| 1772 — — — mullet on r. shoulder | 100 | 350 |

1773                                        1774

| 1773 — — — mullet in centre of breast | 95 | 300 |
|---|---|---|
| 1774 F. Annulet and trefoil by crown, mullet on breast | 100 | 325 |
| 1775 G. New neat bust: no marks. | 100 | 350 |
| 1776 **Penny.** *London.* A. Letters, bust and marks as 1768 | 200 | 650 |
| 1777 — Altered Hen. IV *obv.* with mullet added to l. of crown | 350 | 1050 |

1778                                        1791

| 1778 — C. Tall neck, mullet and broken annulet by crown | 25 | 100 |
|---|---|---|
| 1779 — D. Similar, but whole annulet | 30 | 110 |
| 1780 — F. Mullet and trefoil by crown | 35 | 125 |
| 1781 — G. New neat bust, no marks, DI GRA | 35 | 135 |
| 1782 *Durham.* C. As 1778 but quatrefoil at end of legend | 35 | 125 |
| 1783 — D. As 1779 | 35 | 125 |
| 1784 — G. Similar, but new bust. R. Annulet in one qtr. | 40 | 140 |
| 1785 *York.* C. As 1778, but quatrefoil in centre of *rev.* | 20 | 80 |
| 1786 — D. Similar, but whole annulet by crown | 25 | 85 |
| 1787 — E. As last, but pellet above mullet | 40 | 140 |
| 1788 — F. Mullet and trefoil by crown | 20 | 80 |
| 1789 — — Trefoil over mullet to l., annulet to r. of crown | 35 | 110 |
| 1790 — G. Mullet and trefoil by crown (London dies) | 30 | 100 |
| 1791 — — Mullet and lis by crown, annulet in one qtr. (usually local dies).... | 30 | 110 |
| 1792 **Halfpenny.** A. Emaciated bust, annulets by crown | 100 | 350 |
| 1793 — altered dies of Hen. IV | 120 | 450 |
| 1794 C. Ordinary bust, broken annulets by crown | 20 | 80 |
| 1795 D. Annulets, sometimes broken, by hair | 20 | 80 |

1796

1798

|  | | F | VF |
|---|---|---|---|
|  | | £ | £ |
| 1796 | F. Annulet and trefoil by crown | 20 | 80 |
| 1797 | G. New bust; no marks, (usually muled with Henry VI annulet *rev.*) | 35 | 135 |
| 1797A | **Farthing.** *London.* B. Very large head | 250 | 750 |
| 1798 | — G. Small face with neck | 135 | 450 |
| 1798A | *Calais.* G. as 1798, VILLA CALIS | 325 | 1000 |

*For further information see:*
**Halfpennies and Farthings of Henry IV, V and VI.** *Paul and Bente R. Withers, 2003.*

The supply of gold began to dwindle early in the reign, which accounts for the rarity of gold after 1426. The Calais mint had reopened just before the death of Henry V and for some years a large large amount of coin was struck there. It soon stopped minting gold; the mint was finally closed in 1440. A royal mint at York was opened for a short time in 1423/4.

Marks used to denote various issues become more prominent in this reign and can be used to date coins to within a year or so.

Reference: C. A. Whitton Heavy Coinage of Henry VI. (B.N.J. 1938-41).

*Mintmarks*

| 136 | 7a | 105 | 18 | 133 | 8 | 9 | 15 |

| | | | | |
|---|---|---|---|
| 1422-7 | Incurved pierced cross (136) | 1422-34 | Cross pommée (133) |
| 1422-3 | Lis (105, York) | 1427-34 | Cross patonce (8) |
| 1422-60 | Plain cross (7a, intermittently | | Cross fleury (9) |
| | Lis (105, on gold) | 1434-35 | Voided cross (15) |
| 1422-27 | Pierced cross (18) | 1435-60 | Cross fleury (9) |
| 1460 | Lis (105, on rev. of some groats) | | |

*For Restoration mintmarks see page 198.*

## GOLD

1799

|  | | *F* | *VF* |
|---|---|---|---|
| | **Annulet issue, 1422-7** | £ | £ |
| 1799 | **Noble.** *London.* Annulet by sword arm, and in one spandrel on *rev.;* trefoil stops on *obv.* with lis after hЄnRIC, annulets on *rev.,* with mullet after IhC ................................................................................................ | 525 | 1100 |
| 1800 | — Similar, but *obv.* from Henry V die ....................................................... | 950 | 2500 |
| 1801 | — As 1799, but Flemish imitative coinage................................................ | 350 | 900 |
| 1802 | *Calais.* As 1799, but flag at stern and C in centre of *rev* ......................... | 725 | 2000 |

1803

|  | | F | VF |
|---|---|---|---|
|  | | £ | £ |
| 1803 | — — with h in centre of *rev.* | 575 | 1400 |
| 1804 | *York.* As London, but with lis over stern | 700 | 1850 |

1805

| 1805 | **Half-noble.** *London.* As 1799 | 325 | 900 |
|---|---|---|---|
| 1806 | — Similar, but *obv.* from Henry V die | 725 | 2000 |
| 1807 | *Calais.* As noble, with C in centre of *rev.* | 700 | 2000 |
| 1808 | — — with h in centre of *rev.* | 675 | 1750 |
| 1809 | *York.* As noble | 750 | 2250 |
| 1810 | **Quarter-noble.** *London.* Lis over shield; *mm.* large lis | 200 | 450 |
| 1811 | — — — trefoil below shield | 220 | 500 |
| 1812 | — — — pellet below shield | 225 | 525 |
| 1813 | *Calais.* Three lis over shield; *mm.* large lis | 300 | 700 |

1814                                         1819

| 1814 | — Similar but three lis around shield | 250 | 600 |
|---|---|---|---|
| 1815 | — As 1810, but much smaller *mm.* | 225 | 550 |
| 1816 | *York.* Two lis over shield | 250 | 600 |

|                                                                          | *F* | *VF* |
|                                                                          | £   | £    |

**Rosette-mascle issue, 1427-30**

| 1817 | **Noble.** *London.* Lis by sword arm and in *rev.* field; stops, rosettes, or rosettes and mascles .................................................................................. | 825 | 2000 |
| 1818 | *Calais.* Similar, with flag at stern ................................................................. | 1100 | 3000 |
| 1819 | **Half-noble.** *London.* Lis in *rev.* field; stops, rosettes and mascles ........... | 1250 | 3500 |
| 1820 | *Calais.* Similar, flag at stern; stops, rosettes .......................................... | 1350 | 4000 |
| 1821 | **Quarter-noble.** *London.* As 1810; stops, as noble ................................. | 600 | 1350 |
| 1822 | — without lis over shield .......................................................................... | 625 | 1500 |
| 1823 | *Calais.* Lis over shield, rosettes r. and l., and rosette stops ..................... | 650 | 1650 |

**Pinecone-mascle issue, 1430-4**

1824

| 1824 | **Noble.** Stops, pinecones and mascles ..................................................... | 750 | 1850 |
| 1825 | **Half-noble.** *O.* Rosette-mascle die. *R.* As last .......................................... | 1750 | 5500 |
| 1826 | **Quarter-noble.** As 1810, but pinecone and mascle stops ....................... | 750 | 1850 |

**Leaf-mascle issue, 1434-5**

| 1827 | **Noble.** Leaf in waves; stops, saltires with two mascles and one leaf ....... | 1750 | 5500 |
| 1828 | **Half-noble.** (Fishpool hoard and Reigate hoard) .................................... | 1650 | 5250 |
| 1829 | **Quarter-noble.** As 1810; stops, saltire and mascle; leaf on inner circle of *rev.* | 750 | 1850 |

**Leaf-trefoil issue, 1435-8**

| 1830 | **Noble.** Stops, leaves and trefoils ............................................................. | 1750 | 5250 |
| 1830A | **Half-noble.** .............................................................................................. | 1850 | 6000 |
| 1831 | **Quarter-noble.** Similar .......................................................................... | 750 | 2000 |

**Trefoil issue, 1438-43**

| 1832 | **Noble.** Trefoil to left of shield and in *rev.* legend .................................. | 1750 | 5250 |

**Leaf-pellet issue, 1445-54**

| 1833 | **Noble.** Annulet, lis and leaf below shield .............................................. | 2000 | 6500 |

**Cross-pellet issue, 1454-60**

| 1834 | **Noble.** Mascle at end of *obv.* legend ...................................................... | 2250 | 7000 |

*Muling exists in Henry VI coins spanning two or three issues. Full flan coins in the smaller denominations are difficult to find.*

# SILVER

**Annulet issue, 1422-7**

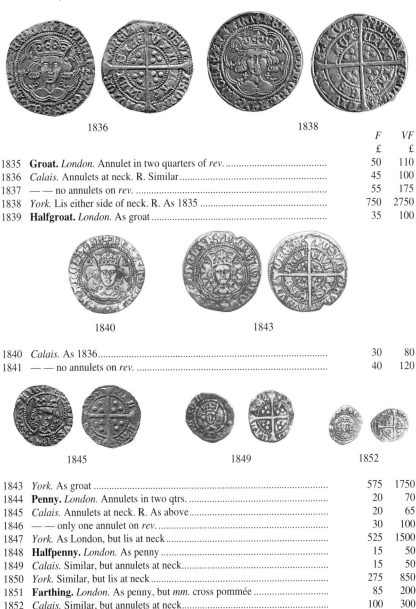

| | 1836 | 1838 | | |
|---|---|---|---|---|
| | | | F | VF |
| | | | £ | £ |
| 1835 | **Groat.** *London.* Annulet in two quarters of *rev.* | | 50 | 110 |
| 1836 | *Calais.* Annulets at neck. R. Similar | | 45 | 100 |
| 1837 | — — no annulets on *rev.* | | 55 | 175 |
| 1838 | *York.* Lis either side of neck. R. As 1835 | | 750 | 2750 |
| 1839 | **Halfgroat.** *London.* As groat | | 35 | 100 |

| | 1840 | 1843 | | |
|---|---|---|---|---|
| 1840 | *Calais.* As 1836 | | 30 | 80 |
| 1841 | — — no annulets on *rev.* | | 40 | 120 |

| | 1845 | 1849 | 1852 | |
|---|---|---|---|---|
| 1843 | *York.* As groat | | 575 | 1750 |
| 1844 | **Penny.** *London.* Annulets in two qtrs. | | 20 | 70 |
| 1845 | *Calais.* Annulets at neck. R. As above | | 20 | 65 |
| 1846 | — — only one annulet on *rev.* | | 30 | 100 |
| 1847 | *York.* As London, but lis at neck | | 525 | 1500 |
| 1848 | **Halfpenny.** *London.* As penny | | 15 | 50 |
| 1849 | *Calais.* Similar, but annulets at neck | | 15 | 50 |
| 1850 | *York.* Similar, but lis at neck | | 275 | 850 |
| 1851 | **Farthing.** *London.* As penny, but *mm.* cross pommée | | 85 | 200 |
| 1852 | *Calais.* Similar, but annulets at neck | | 100 | 300 |
| 1852A | *York.* Similar, but lis at neck | | 425 | 1250 |

|  | F £ | VF £ |
|---|---|---|

**Annulet-trefoil sub-issue**

| 1854 | **Groat.** *Calais,* as 1836 but trefoil to l. of crown. ..................................... | 60 | 175 |
| 1855 | **Halfgroat.** *Calais,* similar, only known with annulet or rosette mascle *rev.* | 60 | 200 |
| 1856 | **Penny.** *Calais.* Similar, only one annulet on *rev* ..................................... | 60 | 200 |

**Rosette-mascle issue, 1427-30.** All with rosettes (early) or rosettes and mascles somewhere in the legends.

| 1858 | **Groat.** *London.* ......................................................................................... | 50 | 150 |

1859             1861

| 1859 | *Calais* ............................................................................................................ | 45 | 110 |
| 1860 | — mascle in two spandrels (as illus. 1863) ............................................. | 50 | 135 |
| 1861 | **Halfgroat.** *London.* ...................................................................................... | 65 | 250 |
| 1862 | *Calais* ............................................................................................................ | 35 | 100 |

1863             1872

| 1863 | — mascle in two spandrels, as illustrated ............................................... | 40 | 110 |
| 1864 | **Penny.** *London.* ........................................................................................... | 75 | 300 |
| 1865 | *Calais* ............................................................................................................ | 30 | 100 |
| 1866 | *York.* Archb. Kemp. Crosses by hair, no rosette ..................................... | 25 | 85 |
| 1867 | — — Saltires by hair, no rosette ................................................................ | 30 | 90 |
| 1868 | — — Mullets by crown ................................................................................ | 25 | 85 |
| 1869 | *Durham,* Bp. Langley. Large star to l. of crown, no rosette, DVnOLMI | 40 | 135 |
| 1870 | **Halfpenny,** *London* ...................................................................................... | 15 | 50 |
| 1871 | *Calais* ............................................................................................................ | 15 | 50 |
| 1872 | **Farthing,** *London* ......................................................................................... | 100 | 350 |
| 1873 | *Calais. Mm.* cross pommée ....................................................................... | 120 | 400 |

**Pinecone-mascle issue, 1430-4.** All with pinecones and mascles in legends.

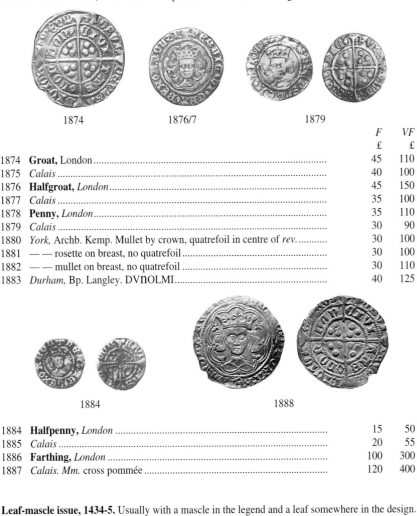

1874        1876/7              1879

|  |  | F | VF |
|---|---|---|---|
|  |  | £ | £ |
| 1874 | **Groat,** London | 45 | 110 |
| 1875 | *Calais* | 40 | 100 |
| 1876 | **Halfgroat,** *London* | 45 | 150 |
| 1877 | *Calais* | 35 | 100 |
| 1878 | **Penny,** *London* | 35 | 110 |
| 1879 | *Calais* | 30 | 90 |
| 1880 | *York,* Archb. Kemp. Mullet by crown, quatrefoil in centre of *rev.* | 30 | 100 |
| 1881 | — — rosette on breast, no quatrefoil | 30 | 100 |
| 1882 | — — mullet on breast, no quatrefoil | 30 | 110 |
| 1883 | *Durham,* Bp. Langley. DVnOLMI | 40 | 125 |

1884                    1888

| 1884 | **Halfpenny,** *London* | 15 | 50 |
|---|---|---|---|
| 1885 | *Calais* | 20 | 55 |
| 1886 | **Farthing,** *London* | 100 | 300 |
| 1887 | *Calais. Mm.* cross pommée | 120 | 400 |

**Leaf-mascle issue, 1434-5.** Usually with a mascle in the legend and a leaf somewhere in the design.

| 1888 | **Groat.** *London.* Leaf below bust, all appear to read DOnDOn | 135 | 500 |
|---|---|---|---|
| 1889 | — — *rev.* of last or next coinage | 110 | 350 |
| 1890 | *Calais.* Leaf below bust, and usually below MCVM | 90 | 250 |
| 1891 | **Halfgroat.** *London.* Leaf under bust, pellet under TAS and DON | 110 | 325 |

1892                    1897

| | F £ | VF £ |
|---|---|---|
| 1892 *Calais.* Leaf below bust, and sometimes on *rev.* | 110 | 300 |
| 1893 **Penny.** *London.* Leaf on breast, no stops on *rev.* | 50 | 125 |
| 1894 *Calais.* Leaf on breast and below SIЄ | 60 | 150 |
| 1895 **Halfpenny.** *London.* Leaf on breast and on *rev.* | 30 | 75 |
| 1896 *Calais.* Leaf on breast and below SIЄ | 65 | 175 |

**Leaf-trefoil issue, 1435-8.** Mostly with leaves and trefoil of pellets in the legends.

| | F £ | VF £ |
|---|---|---|
| 1897 **Groat.** *London.* Leaf on breast | 70 | 180 |
| 1898 — without leaf on breast | 65 | 175 |
| 1899 *Calais.* Leaf on breast | 475 | 1350 |
| 1900 **Halfgroat.** *London.* Leaf on breast; *mm.* plain cross | 55 | 160 |
| 1901 — *O. mm.* cross fleury; leaf on breast | 50 | 150 |
| 1902 — — without leaf on breast | 60 | 160 |
| 1902A *Calais.* leaf on breast, mule with leaf mascle *rev.* | 125 | 400 |
| 1903 **Penny.** *London.* Leaf on breast | 45 | 125 |
| 1903A *Calais.* Similar | 250 | 700 |
| 1904 *Durham,* Bp. Neville. Leaf on breast. R. Rings in centre, no stops, DVnOLM | 100 | 300 |
| 1905 **Halfpenny.** *London.* Leaf on breast | 20 | 50 |
| 1906 — without leaf on breast | 20 | 60 |
| 1906A *Calais.* leaf on breast, mule with leaf mascle rev. | 100 | 275 |
| 1907 **Farthing.** *London.* Leaf on breast; stops, trefoil and saltire on *obv.* | 95 | 275 |

**Trefoil issue, 1438-43.** Trefoil of pellets either side of neck and in legend, leaf on breast.

1909                    1911A

| | F £ | VF £ |
|---|---|---|
| 1908 **Groat.** *London.* Sometimes a leaf before LON. | 70 | 225 |
| 1909 — Fleurs in spandrels, sometimes extra pellet in two qtrs. | 100 | 300 |
| 1910 — Trefoils in place of fleurs at shoulders, none by neck, sometimes extra pellets | 80 | 240 |
| 1911 *Calais* | 185 | 600 |
| 1911A **Halfgroat,** *London* Similar, but trefoil after DEUM and sometimes after POSUI Mule only with leaf trefoil *obv.* | 100 | 300 |
| 1911B — *Calais Obv.* Similar to 1911, mule with leaf mascle *rev.* | 275 | 800 |
| 1912 **Halfpenny,** *London* | 20 | 65 |
| 1912A **Farthing,** *London* | 125 | 350 |

**Trefoil pellet issue, 1443-5**

| 1912 | 1913 | 1915 | 1917 |
|------|------|------|------|

|  | F £ | VF £ |
|---|---|---|
| 1913 **Groat.** Trefoils by neck, pellets by crown, small leaf on breast; sometimes extra pellet in two quarters | 110 | 325 |

**Leaf-pellet issue, 1445-54.** Leaf on breast, pellet each side of crown, except where stated.

| | F | VF |
|---|---|---|
| 1914 **Groat.** AnGL; extra pellet in two quarters | 60 | 175 |
| 1915 *Similar,* but AnGLI | 50 | 160 |
| 1916 — — trefoil in *obv.* legend | 65 | 200 |
| 1917 Leaf on neck, fleur on breast, often extra pellet in two quarters | 50 | 160 |
| 1918 As last, but two extra pellets by hair | 150 | 500 |
| 1919 **Halfgroat.** As 1914 *mm.*Cross patonce | 60 | 160 |
| 1920 Similar, but *mm.* plain cross, some times no leaf on breast, no stops | 55 | 150 |
| 1921 **Penny.** *London.* Usually extra pellets in two quarters | 40 | 100 |
| 1922 — — pellets by crown omitted | 40 | 110 |
| 1923 — — trefoil in legend | 45 | 125 |
| 1924 *York,* Archb. Booth. R. Quatrefoil and pellet in centre | 30 | 90 |
| 1925 — — two extra pellets by hair (local dies) | 30 | 90 |
| 1926 *Durham,* Bp. Neville. Trefoil in *obv.* legend. R. Two rings in centre of cross | 50 | 135 |

| 1927 | 1932 |
|------|------|

| | F | VF |
|---|---|---|
| 1927 — — Similar, but without trefoil | 50 | 140 |
| 1928 **Halfpenny.** Usually extra pellet in two quarters | 15 | 50 |
| 1929 — *mm.* plain cross | 15 | 50 |
| 1930 **Farthing.** As last | 100 | 325 |

**Unmarked issue, 1453-4**

| | F | VF |
|---|---|---|
| 1931 **Groat.** No marks on *obv.;* two extra pellets on *rev.* | 375 | 1200 |
| 1932 — four extra pellets on *rev.* | 450 | 1350 |
| 1933 **Halfgroat.** As 1931 | 225 | 600 |

|                                                                                          | F<br>£ | VF<br>£ |
|------------------------------------------------------------------------------------------|--------|---------|

**Cross-pellet issue, 1454-60**

1934 **Groat.** Saltire either side of neck, pellets by crown, leaf and fleur on breast,
extra pellets on *rev.* ................................................................................. 275 850

1935 Saltire on neck, no leaf, pellets by crown, usually mullets in legend; extra
pellets on *rev.* ............................................................................................ 85 250

1935                              1940

| 1936 | — Similar, but mascles in place of mullets on *obv.* ................................... | 95 | 300 |
|------|-----------------------------------------------------------------------------------|-----|-----|
| 1937 | — — pellets by hair instead of by crown ................................................. | 135 | 450 |
| 1938 | **Halfgroat.** Saltire on neck, pellets by crown and on *rev.*, mullets in legend | 200 | 600 |
| 1939 | **Penny.** *London.* Saltire on neck, pellets by crown and on *rev.*, mascle(s), or mullet and mascle in legend ................................................................ | 135 | 450 |
| 1940 | *York,* Archb. Wm. Booth. Saltires by neck, usually leaf on breast, pellets by crown. ℞. Cross in quatrefoil in centre. .............................................. | 25 | 85 |
| 1941 | *Durham,* Bp. Laurence Booth. Saltire and B or B only at neck, pellets by crown. ℞. Rings in centre......................................................................... | 40 | 125 |
| 1942 | **Halfpenny.** Saltires by neck, usually two extra pellets on *rev.* ............... | 35 | 120 |
| 1943 | Similar, but saltire on neck, sometimes mullet after hЄПRIC .................... | 25 | 70 |
| 1944 | **Farthing**. Saltire on neck, usually pellets by crown and on *rev.*, but known without either. ...................................................................................... | 125 | 375 |

**Lis-pellet issue, 1456-60**

1945

1945 **Groat.** Lis on neck; pellets by crown. ℞. Extra pellets .......................... 175 650

*For further information see:*
**Halfpennies and Farthings of Henry IV, V and VI.** *Paul and Bente R. Withers, 2003.*

## EDWARD IV, First Reign, 1461-70

In order to increase the supply of bullion to the mint the weight of the penny was reduced to 12 grains in 1464, and the current value of the noble was raised to 8s. 4d. Later, in 1465, a new gold coin was issued, the Ryal or 'Rose Noble', weighing 120 grains and having a value of 10s. However, as 6s. 8d. had become the standard professional fee the old noble was missed, and a new coin was issued to take its place, the Angel of 80 grains.

Royal mints were opened at Canterbury and York to help with the re-coinage, and other mints were set up at Bristol, Coventry and Norwich, though they were not open for long.

*Reference:* C. E. Blunt and C. A Whitton, *The Coinage of Edward IV and Henry VI (Restored),* B.N.J. 1945-7.

*Mintmarks*

| 105 | 9 | 7a | 33 | 99 | 28 | 74 | 11 |
|-----|---|-----|-----|-----|-----|-----|-----|

| 1461-4 | Lis (105) | 1467-70 | Lis (105, *York*) | |
| | Cross fleury (9) | 1467-8 | Crown (74) | (often |
| | Plain cross (7a) | | Sun (28) | combined) |
| 1464-5 | Rose (33 and 34) | 1468-9 | Crown (74) | (sometimes |
| 1464-7 | Pall (99, *Canterbury*) | | Rose (33) | combined) |
| 1465-6 | Sun (28) | 1469-70 | Long cross | |
| 1466-7 | Crown (74) | | fitchee (l.c.f) (11) | (often |
| | | | Sun (28) | combined) |

## GOLD

**Heavy coinage, 1461-4**

| | | F | VF |
|---|---|---|---|
| | | £ | £ |

| 1946 | **Noble** (=6s. 8d., wt. 108 grs.). Normal type, but *obv.* legend commences at top left, lis below shield; *mm.*-/lis (Spink's sale May 1993) | 2250 | 6750 |
| 1947 | — Quatrefoil below sword arm; *mm.* rose/lis | 2500 | 8000 |
| 1948 | — R. Roses in two spandrels; *mm.* rose | 2650 | 9500 |
| 1949 | **Quarter-noble** | 1750 | 4500 |

1946                              1950

|                    |  F   |  VF  |
|                    |  £   |  £   |

**Light coinage, 1464-70**

1950 **Ryal** or rose-noble (=10s., wt. 120 grs.), *London*. As illustration. Large
       fleurs in spandrels; *mm.* 33-74 ................................................................ 550 1250
1951 — — Small trefoils in spandrels; *mm.* 74-11 ............................................ 550 1250

1952

1952 — Flemish imitative coinage (mostly 16th cent. on a large flan) ............. 400 850
1953 *Bristol*. B in waves, large fleurs; *mm.* sun, crown .................................... 650 1600
1954 — — small fleurs in spandrels; *mm.* sun, crown .................................... 675 1650
1955 *Coventry*. C in waves; *mm.* sun .......................................................... 1250 3000
1956 *Norwich*. 𝕅 in waves; *mm.* sun, rose .................................................... 1300 3250
1957 *York*. Є in waves, large fleurs in spandrels, *mm.* sun, lis ........................ 625 1500
1958 — — small fleurs, *mm.* sun. lis ............................................................ 650 1600
1959 **Half-ryal.** *London*. As 1950 ................................................................ 475 1100
1960 *Bristol*. B in waves; *mm.* sun, sun/crown ............................................... 675 1650
1961 *Coventry*. C in waves; *mm.* sun ........................................................... 2500 8000
1962 *Norwich*. 𝕅 in waves; *mm.* rose .......................................................... 2250 6500

1963                          1965

1963 *York*. Є in waves; *mm.* 28, 105, 33/105 .................................................. 475 1100
1963A Similar but lis instead of Є in waves (probably York) ............................. 575 1350
1964 **Quarter-ryal.** Shield in tressure of eight arcs, rose above. R. Somewhat
       as half ryal; *mm.* sun/rose ..................................................................... 750 2000
1965 Shield in quatrefoil, R. Є above, rose on l., sun on r.; *mm.* 33/28-74/33 .. 275 600
1966 — — sun on l., rose on r.; *mm.* 74-11 .................................................... 300 650

1967

|  | F £ | VF £ |
|---|---|---|
| 1967 **Angel** (=6s. 8d., wt. 80 grs.). St. Michael spearing dragon. R. Ship, rays of sun at masthead, large rose and sun beside mast; *mm.*-/33 | 3500 | 10500 |
| 1968 — — small rose and sun at mast; *mm.*-/74 | 3750 | 12500 |

## SILVER

**Heavy coinage, 1461-4**

| | | |
|---|---|---|
| 1969 **Groat** (60 grs.). Group I, lis on neck, pellets by crown; *mm.* 9, 7a, 105, 9/105 | 125 | 375 |
| 1970 — Lis on breast, no pellets; *mm.* plain cross, 7a/105 | 135 | 425 |
| 1971 — — with pellets at crown; *mm.* plain cross | 135 | 425 |

1972

| | | |
|---|---|---|
| 1972 II, quatrefoils by neck, crescent on breast; *mm.* rose | 125 | 375 |
| 1973 III, similar but trefoil on breast; *mm.* rose | 110 | 325 |
| 1974 — — — eye in *rev.* inner legend, *mm.* rose | 110 | 300 |
| 1975 — Similar, but no quatrefoils by bust | 175 | 550 |
| 1976 — — Similar, but no trefoil on breast | 150 | 450 |
| 1977 IV, annulets by neck, eye after TAS; *mm.* rose | 200 | 650 |

1974                    1978

| | | |
|---|---|---|
| 1978 **Halfgroat.** I, lis on breast, pellets by crown and extra pellets in two qtrs.; *mm.* 9, 7a | 325 | 1000 |

|      |                                                                      | *F* | *VF* |
|------|----------------------------------------------------------------------|-----|------|
|      |                                                                      | £   | £    |
| 1979 | II, quatrefoils at neck, crescent on breast; *mm.* rose              | 250 | 650  |
| 1980 | III, similar, but trefoil on breast, eye on *rev.*; *mm.* rose       | 185 | 500  |
| 1981 | — Similar, but no mark on breast                                     | 185 | 500  |
| 1982 | IV, annulets by neck, sometimes eye on *rev.*; *mm.* rose            | 200 | 600  |
| 1983 | **Penny** (15 grs.), *London.* I, marks as 1978, but mascle after RЄX; *mm.* plain cross | 225 | 650  |
| 1984 | II, quatrefoils by neck; *mm.* rose                                  | 175 | 475  |

1985

| 1985  | III, similar, but eye after TAS; *mm.* rose                        | 150 | 425 |
|-------|-------------------------------------------------------------------|-----|-----|
| 1986  | IV, annulets by neck; *mm.* rose                                   | 175 | 475 |
| 1987  | *York,* Archb. Booth. Quatrefoils by bust, voided quatrefoil in centre of *rev.; mm.* rose | 100 | 250 |
| 1988  | *Durham. O.* of Hen. VI. R. DVႶOLIႶ                                | 110 | 275 |
|       | *Some of the Durham pennies from local dies may belong to the heavy coinage period, but if so they are indistinguishable from the light coins.* |     |     |
| 1989  | **Halfpenny.** I, as 1983, but no mascle                          | 75  | 200 |
| 1990  | II, quatrefoils by bust; *mm.* rose                               | 40  | 100 |
| 1991  | — saltires by bust; *mm.* rose                                    | 35  | 90  |
| 1992  | III, no marks by bust; *mm.* rose                                 | 35  | 90  |
| 1992A | —saltires by bust, eye after TAS, *mm.* rose                      | 85  | 225 |
| 1993  | IV, annulets by bust; *mm.* rose                                  | 40  | 100 |
| 1994  | **Farthing.** I, pellets by crown, extra pellets on rev., with or without lis on breast | 175 | 500 |
| 1994A | II. saltires by bust; *mm.* rose                                  | 185 | 525 |
| 1994B | III, no marks by bust; *mm.* rose                                 | 150 | 475 |

**Light coinage, 1464-70.** There is a great variety of groats and we give only a selection. Some have pellets in one quarter of the reverse, or trefoils over the crown; early coins have fleurs on the cusps of the tressure, then trefoils or no marks on the cusps, while the late coins have only trefoils.

| 1995 | **Groat** (48 grs.), *London.* Annulets at neck, eye after TAS; *mm.* 33 (struck from heavy dies, IV) | 95  | 300 |
|------|------------------------------------------------------------------------------------------------------|-----|-----|
| 1996 | — — — Similar, but new dies, eye after TAS or DOႶ                                                    | 100 | 350 |
| 1997 | — Quatrefoils at neck, eye; rose (heavy dies, III)                                                    | 75  | 225 |
| 1998 | — — — Similar, but new dies, eye in *rev.* legend                                                    | 75  | 225 |
| 1999 | — No marks at neck, eye; *mm* rose                                                                   | 125 | 400 |

2000                            2002

**Light coinage, silver,** *continued.*

|  |  | F £ | VF £ |
|---|---|---|---|
| 2000 | — Quatrefoils at neck, no eye; *mm.* 33, 74, 28, 74/28, 74/33, 11/28 ....... | 40 | 125 |
| 2001 | — — — rose or quatrefoil on breast; *mm.* 33, 74/28.............................. | 45 | 160 |
| 2002 | — No marks at neck; *mm.* 28, 74, 11/28, 11............................................. | 50 | 180 |
| 2003 | — Trefoils or crosses at neck; *mm.* 11/33, 11/28, 11.............................. | 45 | 160 |
| 2004 | *Bristol.* B on breast, quatrefoils at neck; *mm.* 28/33, 28, 28/74, 74, 74/28 | 50 | 180 |
| 2005 | — — trefoils at neck; *mm.* sun .............................................................. | 75 | 250 |
| 2006 | — — no marks at neck; *mm.* sun............................................................. | 135 | 450 |
| 2007 | — Without B, quatrefoils at neck; *mm.* sun............................................ | 135 | 450 |

*Bristol is variously rendered as BRESTOLL, BRISTOLL, BRESTOW, BRISTOW.*

| 2008 | *Coventry.* C on breast, quatrefoils at neck, COVETRE; *mm.* 28/33, 28... | 95 | 275 |
|---|---|---|---|
| 2009 | — — Local dies, similar; *mm.* rose ........................................................ | 125 | 350 |
| 2010 | — — — as last, but no C or quatrefoils.................................................... | 125 | 350 |
| 2011 | Norwich. Π on breast, quatrefoils at neck, ΠORWIC or ΠORVIC, *mm.* 28/33, 28...................................................................................................... | 85 | 250 |
| 2012 | *York.* Є on breast, quatrefoils at neck, ЄBORACI; *mm.* 28, 105/74, 105, 105/28........................................................................................................... | 50 | 160 |
| 2013 | — Similar, but without Є on breast, *mm.* lis............................................. | 70 | 225 |
| 2014 | — Є on breast, trefoils at neck; *mm.* 105/28, 105.................................... | 65 | 200 |
| 2015 | **Halfgroat.** London. Annulets by neck (heavy dies); *mm.* 33 ................... | 200 | 500 |
| 2016 | — Quatrefoils by neck; *mm.* 33/-, 28/-, 74, 74/28 .................................. | 40 | 135 |
| 2017 | — Saltires by neck; *mm.* 74, 74/28 ........................................................ | 55 | 175 |
| 2018 | — Trefoils by neck; *mm.* 74, 74/28, 11/28 ............................................. | 55 | 175 |
| 2019 | — No marks by neck; *mm.* 11/28 ............................................................. | 90 | 275 |
| 2020 | *Bristol.* Saltires or crosses by neck; *mm.* 33/28, 28, 74, 74/- ................ | 125 | 350 |
| 2021 | — Quatrefoils by neck; *mm.* 28/-, 74, 74/- ............................................ | 110 | 325 |
| 2022 | — Trefoils by neck; *mm.* crown.............................................................. | 135 | 375 |
| 2023 | — No marks by neck; *mm.* 74/28 ............................................................ | 150 | 400 |
| 2024 | *Canterbury,* Archb. Bourchier (1464-7). Knot below bust; quatrefoils by neck; *mm.* 99/-, 99, 99/33, 99/28.................................................... | 30 | 110 |
| 2025 | — — — quatrefoils omitted *mm.* 99........................................................ | 30 | 110 |
| 2026 | — — — saltires by neck; *mm.* 99/-, 99/28 ............................................. | 35 | 120 |
| 2026A | — — — trefoils by neck; *mm.* 99................................................................ | 35 | 120 |

2027                                              2030

|      |                                                                                                          | F £ | VF £ |
|------|----------------------------------------------------------------------------------------------------------|-----|------|
| 2027 | — — — wedges by hair and/or neck; *mm.* 99, 99/–, 99/33, 99/28 .......... | 35  | 120  |
| 2028 | — — As 2024 or 2025, but no knot................................................. | 40  | 125  |
| 2029 | — Royal mint (1467-9). Quatrefoils by neck; *mm.* 74, 74/- .................... | 35  | 110  |
| 2030 | — — Saltires by neck; *mm.* 74/-, 74................................................ | 35  | 110  |
| 2031 | — — Trefoils by neck; *mm.* 74, 74/-, 74/28, 33 ................................. | 30  | 100  |
| 2032 | — No marks by neck; *mm.* sun ...................................................... | 60  | 175  |
| 2033 | *Coventry.* Crosses by neck; *mm.* sun............................................... | 475 | 1350 |
| 2034 | *Norwich.* Quatrefoils or saltires by neck; *mm.* sun ........................ | 450 | 1250 |
| 2035 | *York.* Quatrefoils by neck; *mm.* sun, lis, lis/- ................................ | 60  | 175  |
| 2036 | — Saltires by neck; *mm.* lis ......................................................... | 60  | 170  |
| 2037 | — Trefoils by neck; *mm.* lis, lis/-................................................. | 65  | 185  |
| 2038 | — Є on breast, quatrefoils by neck; *mm.* lis/-................................ | 65  | 185  |
| 2039 | **Penny** (12 grs.), *London.* Annulets by neck (heavy dies); *mm.* rose ........ | 135 | 400  |
| 2040 | — Quatrefoils by neck; *mm.* 74, sun. crown.................................... | 35  | 100  |
| 2041 | — Trefoil and quatrefoil by neck; *mm.* crown................................. | 35  | 115  |
| 2042 | — Saltires by neck; *mm.* crown ................................................... | 35  | 110  |
| 2043 | — Trefoils by neck; *mm.* crown, long cross fitchée ......................... | 35  | 110  |
| 2044 | — No marks by neck; *mm.* long cross fitchée ................................. | 120 | 325  |
| 2045 | *Bristol.* Crosses, quatrefoils or saltires by neck, BRISTOW; *mm.* crown | 125 | 350  |
| 2046 | — Quatrefoils by neck; BRI(trefoil)STOLL ..................................... | 125 | 375  |
| 2047 | — Trefoil to r. of neck BRISTOLL ................................................. | 135 | 400  |
| 2048 | *Canterbury,* Archb. Bourchier. Quatrefoils or saltires by neck, knot on | | |
|      | breast; *mm.* pall ......................................................................... | 60  | 160  |
| 2049 | — — Similar, but no marks by neck ............................................... | 60  | 160  |
| 2050 | — — As 2048, but no knot.............................................................. | 65  | 175  |
| 2051 | — — Crosses by neck, no knot....................................................... | 65  | 175  |
| 2052 | — Royal mint. Quatrefoils by neck; *mm.* crown ............................. | 125 | 400  |
| 2053 | — *Durham,* King's Receiver (1462-4). Local dies, mostly with rose in | | |
|      | centre of *rev.*; *mm.* 7a, 33............................................................. | 25  | 70   |
| 2054 | — Bp. Lawrence Booth (1465-70). B and D by neck, B on *rev.*; *mm.* 33 | 30  | 125  |
| 2055 | — — Quatrefoil and B by neck; *mm.* sun........................................ | 25  | 100  |
| 2056 | — — B and quatrefoil by neck; *mm.* crown .................................... | 30  | 125  |
| 2057 | — — D and quatrefoil by neck; *mm.* crown .................................... | 30  | 110  |
| 2058 | — — Quatrefoils by neck; *mm.* crown ........................................... | 30  | 110  |
| 2059 | — — Trefoils by neck; *mm.* crown................................................. | 30  | 110  |
| 2060 | — Lis by neck; *mm.* crown ........................................................... | 25  | 100  |
| 2061 | *York,* Sede Vacante (1464-5). Quatrefoils at neck, no quatrefoil in centre | | |
|      | of *rev.; mm.* sun, rose................................................................... | 35  | 135  |
| 2062 | — Archb. Neville (1465-70). Local dies, G and key by neck, quatrefoil | | |
|      | on *rev.; mm.* sun, plain cross........................................................ | 25  | 95   |

2063 2068

|  | | F | VF |
|---|---|---|---|
|  | | £ | £ |
| 2063 | — — London-made dies, similar; *mm.* 28, 105, 11 ................................. | 30 | 125 |
| 2064 | — — Similar, but no marks by neck; *mm.* large lis................................. | 35 | 125 |
| 2065 | — — — Quatrefoils by neck; *mm.* large lis ........................................... | 35 | 125 |
| 2066 | — — — Trefoils by neck; *mm.* large lis................................................... | 25 | 100 |
| 2067 | **Halfpenny,** *London.* Saltires by neck; *mm.* 34, 28, 74 ........................... | 20 | 75 |
| 2068 | — Trefoils by neck; *mm.* 28, 74, 11........................................................ | 20 | 75 |
| 2069 | — No marks by neck; *mm.* 11................................................................. | 35 | 125 |
| 2070 | *Bristol.* Crosses by neck; *mm.* crown...................................................... | 75 | 225 |
| 2071 | — Trefoils by neck; *mm.* crown.............................................................. | 70 | 200 |
| 2072 | *Canterbury.* Archb. Bourchier. No marks; *mm.* pall............................... | 60 | 150 |
| 2072A | — — Trefoils by neck, *mm.* pall............................................................. | 60 | 150 |
| 2073 | — Royal mint. Saltires by neck; *mm.* crown .......................................... | 55 | 135 |
| 2074 | — — Trefoils by neck; *mm.* crown.......................................................... | 50 | 130 |
| 2074A | *Norwich.* Quatrefoils by neck., *mm.* Sun ................................................ | 225 | 650 |
| 2075 | *York.* Royal mint. Saltires by neck; *mm.* lis/-, sun/-................................ | 45 | 125 |
| 2076 | — — Trefoils by neck; *mm.* lis/- ............................................................. | 40 | 110 |
| 2077 | **Farthing,** *London.* ЄDWARD DI GRA RЄX, trefoils by neck, *mm.* crown | 250 | 675 |

*Full flan coins are difficult to find in the smaller denominations.*

*For further information see:*
**Halfpennies and Farthings of Edward IV to Henry VII.** *Paul and Bente R. Withers, 2004.*

The coinage of this short restoration follows closely that of the previous reign. Only angel gold was issued, the ryal being discontinued. Many of the coins have the king's name reading hЄnRICV—another distinguishing feature is an R that looks like a B.

*Mintmarks*

Cross pattée (6)                              Rose (33, Bristol)
Restoration cross (13)                        Lis (105)
Trefoil (44 and 45)                           Short cross fitchée (12)

## GOLD

2078

|  |  | *F* | *VF* |
|---|---|---|---|
|  |  | £ | £ |
| 2078 | **Angel,** *London.* As illus. but no B; *mm.* -/6, 13, -/105, none | 1100 | 2750 |
| 2079 | *Bristol.* B in waves; *mm.* -/13, none | 1500 | 4500 |
| 2080 | **Half-angel,** *London.* As 2078; *mm.* -/6, -/13, -/105 | 1600 | 4500 |
| 2081 | *Bristol.* B in waves; *mm.* -/13 | 2500 | 6500 |

## SILVER

2082                                      2084

| 2082 | **Groat,** *London.* Usual type; *mm.* 6, 6/13, 6/105, 13, 13/6, 13/105, 13 /12 | 125 | 375 |
|---|---|---|---|
| 2083 | *Bristol.* B on breast; *mm.* 13, 13/33, 13/44, 44, 44/13, 44/33, 44/12 | 175 | 600 |
| 2084 | *York.* Є on breast; *mm.* lis, lis/sun | 135 | 450 |
| 2085 | **Halfgroat,** *London.* As 2082; *mm.* 13, 13/- | 150 | 500 |
| 2086 | *York.* Є on breast; *mm.* lis | 275 | 750 |
| 2087 | **Penny,** *London.* Usual type; *mm.* 6, 13, 12 | 175 | 550 |

| | F | VF |
| --- | --- | --- |
| | £ | £ |
| 2087A *Bristol*. Similar; *mm.* 12 ............................................................ | 350 | 900 |
| 2088 *York*. G and key by neck; *mm.* lis ............................................ | 175 | 500 |
| 2089 **Halfpenny,** *London.* As 2087; *mm.* 12, 13, ................................. | 70 | 200 |
| 2090 *Bristol*. Similar; *mm.* cross .................................................... | 200 | 550 |

## EDWARD IV, Second Reign, 1471-83

The Angel and its half were the only gold denominations issued during this reign. The main types and weight standards remained the same as those of the light coinage of Edward's first reign. The use of the 'initial mark' as a mintmark to denote the date of issue was now firmly established.

*Mintmarks*

| 33 | 105 | 12 | 55 | 44 | 55 | 28 | 56 | 17 |
| --- | --- | --- | --- | --- | --- | --- | --- | --- |

| 30 | 37 | 6 | 18 | 19 | 20 | 31 | 11 | 38 |
| --- | --- | --- | --- | --- | --- | --- | --- | --- |

| 1471-83 | Rose (33, *York & Durham*) | 1473-7 | Cross pattée (6) |
| | Lis (105, *York*) | | Pierced cross 1 (18) |
| 1471 | Short cross fitchee (12) | 1477-80 | Pierced cross and |
| 1471-2 | Annulet (large, 55) | | pellet (19) |
| | Trefoil (44) | | Pierced cross 2 (18) |
| | Rose (33, *Bristol*) | | Pierced cross, central |
| 1471-3 | Pansy (30, *Durham*) | | pellet (20) |
| 1472-3 | Annulet (small, 55) | | Rose (33, *Canterbury*) |
| | Sun (28, *Bristol*) | 1480-3 | Heraldic cinquefoil (31) |
| 1473-7 | Pellet in annulet (56) | | Long cross fitchee |
| | Cross and four pellets (17) | | (11, *Canterbury*) |
| | Cross in circle (37) | 1483 | Halved sun and rose (38) |
| | | | (Listed under Ed. IV/V.) |

## GOLD

2091         2093

| | F | VF |
| --- | --- | --- |
| | £ | £ |
| 2091 **Angel.** *London*. Type as illus.; *mm.* 12, 55, 56, 17, 18, 19, 31 ................. | 450 | 975 |
| 2092 *Bristol*. B in waves; *mm.* small annulet.......................................... | 1750 | 4500 |
| 2093 **Half-angel.** As illus.; *mm.* 55, cross in circle, 19, 20/19, 31 .................... | 450 | 950 |

|      |      |
|------|------|
| *F*  | *VF* |
| £    | £    |

| | | |
|---|---|---|
| 2094 | King's name and title on rev.; *mm.* 12/- | 475 | 1250 |
| 2095 | King's name and the title both sides; *mm.* 55/- | 500 | 1350 |

## SILVER

2096                                    2101

| | | | |
|---|---|---|---|
| 2096 | **Groat,** *London*. Trefoils on cusps, no marks by bust; *mm.* 12-37 | 50 | 160 |
| 2097 | — — roses by bust; *mm.* pellet in annulet | 80 | 250 |
| 2098 | — Fleurs on cusps; no marks by bust; *mm.* 18-20 | 55 | 175 |
| 2099 | — — pellets by bust; *mm.* pierced cross | 80 | 240 |
| 2100 | — — rose on breast; *mm.* 31 | 50 | 165 |
| 2101 | *Bristol.* B on breast no marks by bust; *mm.* 33, 33/55, 28/55, 55, 55/-, 28 | 135 | 375 |
| 2102 | *York.* Є on breast no marks by bust; *mm.* lis | 125 | 350 |
| 2103 | **Halfgroat,** *London.* As 2096; *mm.* 12-31 | 45 | 135 |
| 2104 | *Bristol.* B on breast; *mm.* 33/12 | 225 | 650 |
| 2105 | *Canterbury* (Royal mint). As 2103; *mm.* 33, 11, 11/31, 31 | 35 | 100 |

2106

| | | | |
|---|---|---|---|
| 2106 | — C on breast; *mm.* rose | 30 | 90 |
| 2107 | — — R. C in centre; *mm.* rose | 30 | 90 |
| 2108 | — — R. Rose in centre; *mm.* rose | 30 | 90 |
| 2109 | *York.* No. Є on breast; *mm.* lis | 100 | 250 |
| 2110 | **Penny,** *London.* No marks by bust; *mm.* 12-31 | 35 | 110 |
| 2111 | *Bristol.* Similar; *mm.* rose | 175 | 525 |
| 2112 | *Canterbury* (Royal). Similar; *mm.* 33, 11 | 45 | 135 |
| 2113 | — C on breast; *mm.* rose | 75 | 200 |
| 2114 | *Durham,* Bp. Booth (1471-6). No marks by neck; *mm.* 12, 44 | 25 | 90 |

2115                                    2116

| | | | |
|---|---|---|---|
| 2115 | — — D in centre of *rev.;* B and trefoil by neck; *mm.* 44, 33, 56 | 25 | 90 |
| 2116 | — — — two lis at neck; *mm.* rose | 30 | 100 |
| 2117 | — — — crosses over crown, and on breast; *mm.* rose | 30 | 100 |

|      |      |      |      | F | VF |
|------|------|------|------|---|----|
|      |      |      |      | £ | £  |

| | | |
|---|---|---|
| 2118 | ——— crosses over crown, V under CIVI; *mm.* rose, pansy ................. | 30 | 95 |
| 2119 | ——— B to l. of crown, V on breast and under CIVI ........................... | 25 | 90 |
| 2120 | —— As last but crosses at shoulders ................................................ | 25 | 90 |
| 2121 | — Sede Vacante (1476). R. D in centre; *mm.* rose ................................... | 30 | 95 |
| 2122 | — Bp. Dudley (1476-83). V to r. of neck; as last ................................... | 25 | 90 |

2123                    2125                              2134

| | | |
|---|---|---|
| 2123 | —— D and V by neck; as last, but *mm.* 31 ............................................. | 25 | 80 |

*Nos. 2117-2123 are from locally-made dies.*

| | | |
|---|---|---|
| 2124 | **York,** Archb. Neville (1471-2). Quatrefoils by neck. R. Quatrefoil; *mm.* 12 (over lis) .............................................................................................. | 45 | 135 |
| 2125 | —— Similar, but G and key by neck; *mm.* 12 (over lis) ........................ | 25 | 75 |
| 2126 | — Neville suspended (1472-5). As last, but no quatrefoil in centre of *rev.* | 35 | 110 |
| 2126A | —— no marks by bust, similar; *mm.* annulet ......................................... | 45 | 125 |
| 2127 | —— No marks by neck, quatrefoil on *rev.; mm.* 55, cross in circle, 33 . | 25 | 75 |
| 2128 | —— Similar but Є and rose by neck; *mm.* rose...................................... | 25 | 75 |
| 2129 | — Archb. Neville restored (1475-6). As last, but G and rose.................. | 25 | 85 |
| 2130 | —— Similar, but G and key by bust........................................................ | 20 | 75 |
| 2131 | — Sede Vacante (1476). As 2127, but rose on breast; *mm.* rose.............. | 25 | 90 |
| 2132 | — Archb. Lawrence Booth (1476-80). B and key by bust, quatrefoil on *rev.; mm.* 33, 31 ....................................................................................... | 20 | 75 |
| 2133 | — Sede Vacante (1480). Similar, but no quatrefoil on rev.; *mm.* rose ..... | 25 | 90 |
| 2134 | — Archb. Rotherham (1480-3). T and slanting key by neck, quatrefoil on *rev.; mm.* 33 ......................................................................................... | 20 | 80 |
| 2135 | ——— Similar, but star on breast ......................................................... | 40 | 100 |
| 2136 | ——— Star on breast and to r. of crown ................................................ | 45 | 125 |
| 2137 | **Halfpenny,** *London.* No marks by neck; *mm.* 12-31 ................................. | 25 | 80 |
| 2138 | — Pellets at neck; *mm.* pierced cross..................................................... | 40 | 110 |
| 2139 | *Canterbury* (Royal). C on breast and in centre of *rev.; mm.* rose.............. | 70 | 170 |
| 2140 | — C on breast only; *mm.* rose................................................................ | 65 | 160 |
| 2141 | — Without C either side; *mm.* 11 ......................................................... | 65 | 160 |
| 2142 | *Durham,* Bp. Booth. No marks by neck. R. DЄR Ā̄M, D in centre; *mm.* rose ...................................................................................................... | 125 | 350 |
| 2142A | —— Lis either side of neck. R. D or no mark in centre ......................... | 135 | 400 |
| 2142B | —— B to l. of crown, crosses at shoulders. R. D. in centre; *mm.* rose.... | 135 | 400 |
| 2143 | ——— Bp. Dudley V to l. of neck; as last ............................................. | 130 | 375 |

*Full flan coins are very difficult to find in the small denominations.*

On 12th February, 1483, the prolific cinquefoil coinage of Edward IV came to an end and an indenture between the king and the new master of the mint, Bartholomew Reed, saw the introduction of the sun and rose mintmark.

Edward IV died on 9th April, 1483, but the sun and rose coinage continued, essentially unaltered, through the short reign of Edward V and into the reign of Richard III, ending with the indenture of 20th July, 1483, with Robert Brackenbury, who had been Richard's ducal treasurer, and the introduction of the boar's head mintmark.

New dies prepared after the accession of Richard III on 26th June, 1483, bear his name but coins of the sun and rose coinage struck under Edward IV and Edward V can only be distinguished by arranging the dies in sequence. This is possible for the angels (Schneider Sylloge, SCBI 47, p.41) but has not yet been achieved for the silver coinage.

*Mintmark:* Halved sun and rose.

|  | F | VF |
|---|---|---|
|  | £ | £ |
| 2144   **Angel.** Type As 2091, reading EDWARD DEI GRA (Edward IV)......... | 1500 | 4500 |
| 2144A— Similar but reading EDWARD DI GRA (Edward V).......................... | 5250 | 15000 |

2145

| 2145   **Half-angel.** As 2093 (probably Edward IV)............................................ | 2250 | 6500 |

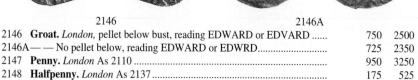

2146                                    2146A

| 2146   **Groat.** *London,* pellet below bust, reading EDWARD or EDVARD ...... | 750 | 2500 |
| 2146A— — No pellet below, reading EDWARD or EDWRD.......................... | 725 | 2350 |
| 2147   **Penny.** *London* As 2110 ........................................................ | 950 | 3250 |
| 2148   **Halfpenny.** *London* As 2137................................................. | 175 | 525 |

Richard's ruthless seizure of the crown left a core of bitter opposition which coalesced around Henry
Tudor, earl of Richmond who had found asylum in Brittany. At Bosworth on 22 August, 1485,
Richard was killed on the battlefield and the War of the Roses ended.

Richard's coinage follows the pattern of previous reigns. The portrait on the silver denominations
remains stylised, though increasingly distinctive. It can be divided into three types according to
mintmark. Type 1, the first sun and rose coinage, lasted 24 days to 20th July 1483. Type 2, the
boar's head coinage, was issued until about June 1484. Type 3, the second sun and rose coinage, was
struck until the end of the reign (Schneider Sylloge, SCBI 47, pp. 41-2).

It is evident that coin dies were stored in a 'loose-box' system which led to extensive muling
between types. As an interim measure, after the indenture of 20th July, 1483, at least eleven existing
sun and rose obverse dies, both gold and silver, were overpunched with the boar's head mark. The
seven overpunched groat dies included four Edward IV/V dies, then still in use, and three dies of
Richard III type 1.

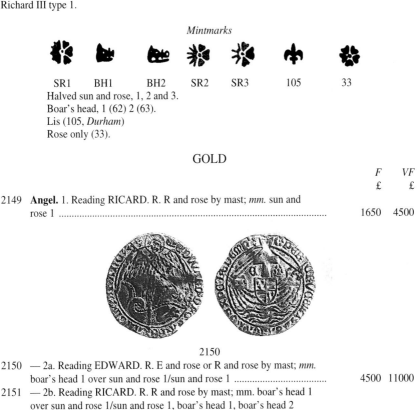

*Mintmarks*

| SR1 | BH1 | BH2 | SR2 | SR3 | 105 | 33 |

Halved sun and rose, 1, 2 and 3.
Boar's head, 1 (62) 2 (63).
Lis (105, *Durham*)
Rose only (33).

## GOLD

| | F £ | VF £ |
|---|---|---|
| 2149 **Angel.** 1. Reading RICARD. R. R and rose by mast; *mm.* sun and rose 1 ........................................................................................... | 1650 | 4500 |

2150

| | | |
|---|---|---|
| 2150 — 2a. Reading EDWARD. R. E and rose or R and rose by mast; *mm.* boar's head 1 over sun and rose 1/sun and rose 1 .................................. | 4500 | 11000 |
| 2151 — 2b. Reading RICARD. R. R and rose by mast; mm. boar's head 1 over sun and rose 1/sun and rose 1, boar's head 1, boar's head 2 (often muled) ........................................................................................ | 1500 | 4000 |

2152                                              2153

|       |                                                                   | F    | VF   |
|-------|-------------------------------------------------------------------|------|------|
|       |                                                                   | £    | £    |
| 2152  | — 3. Reading RICARD or RICAD; *mm.* sun and rose 2 ..............  | 1450 | 3750 |
| 2153  | **Half-angel.** 2b. R. R and rose by mast; *mm.* boar's head 1 ....... | 3250 | 8500 |

## SILVER

SR1

2154                                              2155

| 2154 | **Groat.** *London.* Reading RICARD 1. *mm.* sun and rose 1 ............... | 400  | 1050 |
|------|----------------------------------------------------------------------------|------|------|
| 2155 | — 2a. Reading EDWARD; *mm.* boar's head 1 over sun and rose 1/sun           |      |      |
|      | and rose 1 ................................................................ | 1250 | 3000 |

BH2/1                                            SR2

2156                                             2158

| 2156 | — 2b. Reading RICARD; *mm.* boar's head 1 over sun and rose 1/sun           |      |      |
|------|----------------------------------------------------------------------------|------|------|
|      | and rose 1, boar's head 1, boar's head 2 (often muled) ................     | 450  | 1100 |
| 2157 | — 3. *mm.* sun and rose 2, sun and rose 3 ...............................    | 400  | 975  |
| 2158 | — — Pellet below bust, *mm.* sun and rose 2, sun and rose 3 ..............   | 425  | 1050 |
| 2159 | *York.* 3. *mm.* sun and rose 2/- ........................................   | 850  | 2250 |
| 2160 | **Halfgroat.** *London.* 2a. Reading EDWARD; *mm.* boar's head 1 over sun   |      |      |
|      | and rose 1/- (the *mm.* is indistinct) ....................................  | 1350 | 4000 |

2160                                             2161

| 2161 | — 2b. Reading RICARD; *mm.* boar's head 2/- .......................... | 850 | 2500 |
|------|------------------------------------------------------------------------|-----|------|

|      |                                                                                    | F<br>£ | VF<br>£ |
|------|------------------------------------------------------------------------------------|--------|---------|
| 2162 | — 3. *mm.* sun and rose 2, sun and rose 2/-                                         | 550    | 1350    |
| 2163 | — — Pellet below bust; *mm.* sun and rose 2                                         | 650    | 1500    |

2164

| 2164 | **Penny.** *London.* 2a. Reading EDWARD; *mm.* boar's head 1 over sun |      |      |
|------|-----------------------------------------------------------------------|------|------|
|      | and rose 1/-                                                          | 1200 | 3500 |
| 2165 | — 2b. Reading RICARD; *mm.* boar's head 1/-                            | 1000 | 3000 |

2166

| 2166 | *York.* Archb. Rotherham. T and upright key at neck. R. Quatrefoil in centre; |     |     |
|------|--------------------------------------------------------------------------------|-----|-----|
|      | *mm.* boar's head 1/-                                                           | 175 | 525 |
| 2167 | — — *mm.* rose/-                                                                | 150 | 475 |
| 2168 | — No marks at neck; *mm.* sun and rose 2/-                                      | 200 | 600 |

2169                    2171

| 2169  | *Durham.* Bp. Sherwood. S on breast. R. D in centre; *mm.* lis/-            | 135 | 375  |
|-------|------------------------------------------------------------------------------|-----|------|
| 2170  | **Halfpenny.** *London.* 2b. No marks by neck; *mm.* boar's head 1/-        | 150 | 575  |
| 2171  | — 3. *mm.* sun and rose 2/-                                                  | 125 | 375  |
| 2171A | **Farthing.** *London.* 3. *mm.* sun and rose 2/-                           | 750 | 2000 |

# THE HOUSE OF TUDOR, 1485-1603

## HENRY VII, 1485-1509

For the first four years of his reign Henry's coins differ only in name and mintmark from those of his predecessors, but in 1489 radical changes were made in the coinage. Though the pound sterling had been a denomination of account for centuries, a pound coin had never been minted. Now a magnificent gold pound was issued, and, from the design of the king enthroned in majesty, was called a 'Sovereign'. A small simplified version of the Sovereign portrait was at the same time introduced on the silver pence. The reverse of the gold 'Sovereign' had the royal arms set in the centre of a Tudor rose. A few years later the angel was restyled and St. Michael, who is depicted about to thrust Satan into the Pit with a cross-topped lance, is no longer a feathered figure but is clad in armour of Renaissance style. A gold ryal of ten shillings was also minted again for a brief period.

The other major innovation was the introduction of the shilling in the opening years of the 16th century. It is remarkable for the very fine profile portrait of the king which replaces the representational image of a monarch that had served on the coinage for the past couple of centuries. This new portrait was also used on groats and halfgroats but not on the smaller denominations.

*Mintmarks*

| 39 | 41 | 40 | 42 | 33 | 11 | 7a | 123 |

| 105 | 76b | 31 | 78 | 30 | 91 | 43 | 57 |

| 85 | 94 | 118 | 21 | 33 | 53 |

| 1485-7 | Halved sun and rose (39) | 1495-8 | Pansy (30) |
| | Lis upon sun and rose (41) | | Tun (123, *Canterbury*) |
| | Lis upon half rose (40) | | Lis (105, York) |
| | Lis-rose dimidiated (42) | 1498-9 | Crowned leopard's head (91) |
| | Rose (33, *York*) | | Lis issuant from rose (43) |
| 1487 | Lis (105) | | Tun (123, *Canterbury*) |
| | Cross fitchée (11) | 1499-1502 | Anchor (57) |
| 1487-8 | Rose (33) | 1502-4 | Greyhound's head (85) |
| | Plain cross (7a, *Durham*) | | Lis (105, profile issue only) |
| 1488-9 | No marks | | Martlet (94, *York*) |
| 1489-93 | Cinquefoil (31) | 1504-5 | Cross-crosslet (21) |
| | Crozier (76b, *Durham*) | 1504-9 | Martlet (94, (*York, Canterbury*) |
| 1492 | Cross fitchée (11, gold only) | | Rose (33, *York* and |
| 1493-5 | Escallop (78) | | *Canterbury*) |
| | Dragon (118, gold only) | 1505-9 | Pheon (53) |
| | Lis (105, *Canterbury and York* | | |
| | Tun (123, *Canterbury*) | | |

# GOLD

|   | F | VF |
|---|---|---|
|   | £ | £ |

2172 **Sovereign** (20s; wt. 240 gr.). Group I. Large figure of king sitting on backless throne. R. Large shield crowned on large Tudor rose. *mm.* 31 .. 16500 60000

2173 — Group II. Somewhat similar but throne has narrow back, lis in background. R. Large Tudor rose bearing small shield. *mm.* -/11 ............ 15000 47500

2174

2174 — III. King on high-backed very ornamental throne, with greyhound and dragon on side pillars. R. Shield on Tudor rose; *mm.* dragon ............ 10500 30000

2175 — IV. Similar but throne with high canopy breaking legend and broad seat, *mm.* 105/118, (also with no *obv.* i.c. *mm.* 105/118, very rare).................. 9500 25000

2176 — Narrow throne with a portcullis below the king's feet (like Henry VIII); *mm.* 105/21, 105/53................................................................................. 8500 22500

2177 **Double-sovereign** and **Treble-sovereign** from same dies as 2176. These piedforts were probably intended as presentation pieces *mm.* 105/21, 105/53 *Extremely rare*

2178

2178 **Ryal** (10s.). As illustration: *mm.* -/11 ...................................................... 8000 24500

2179 **Angel** (6s. 8d). I. Angel of old type with one foot on dragon. R. PER CRVCEM. etc., *mm.* 39, 40, (also muled both ways).............................. 850 2250

2179A— With Irish title, and legend over angel head. mm. 33/-........................ 875 2350

2180 — — Name altered from RICARD? and h on *rev.* from R. mm. 41/39, 41/40, 41/-, 39/? ........................................................................................ 925 2500

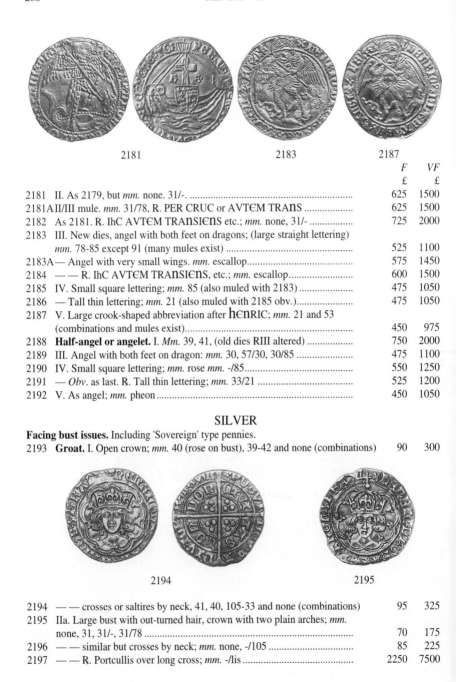

2181      2183      2187

|  | F £ | VF £ |
|---|---|---|
| 2181   II. As 2179, but *mm.* none. 31/-. | 625 | 1500 |
| 2181A II/III mule. *mm.* 31/78, R̸. PER CRUC or AVT€M TRAns | 625 | 1500 |
| 2182   As 2181. R̸. IhC AVT€M TRAnSI€nS etc.; *mm.* none, 31/- | 725 | 2000 |
| 2183   III. New dies, angel with both feet on dragons; (large straight lettering) *mm.* 78-85 except 91 (many mules exist) | 525 | 1100 |
| 2183A — Angel with very small wings. *mm.* escallop | 575 | 1450 |
| 2184   — — R̸. IhC AVT€M TRAnSI€nS, etc.; *mm.* escallop | 600 | 1500 |
| 2185   IV. Small square lettering; *mm.* 85 (also muled with 2183) | 475 | 1050 |
| 2186   — Tall thin lettering; *mm.* 21 (also muled with 2185 obv.). | 475 | 1050 |
| 2187   V. Large crook-shaped abbreviation after h€nRIC; *mm.* 21 and 53 (combinations and mules exist) | 450 | 975 |
| 2188   **Half-angel or angelet.** I. *Mm.* 39, 41, (old dies RIII altered) | 750 | 2000 |
| 2189   III. Angel with both feet on dragon: *mm.* 30, 57/30, 30/85 | 475 | 1100 |
| 2190   IV. Small square lettering; *mm.* rose *mm.* -/85 | 550 | 1250 |
| 2191   — *Obv.* as last. R̸. Tall thin lettering; *mm.* 33/21 | 525 | 1200 |
| 2192   V. As angel; *mm.* pheon | 450 | 1050 |

## SILVER

**Facing bust issues.** Including 'Sovereign' type pennies.

| 2193   **Groat.** I. Open crown; *mm.* 40 (rose on bust), 39-42 and none (combinations) | 90 | 300 |
|---|---|---|

2194      2195

| 2194   — — crosses or saltires by neck, 41, 40, 105-33 and none (combinations) | 95 | 325 |
|---|---|---|
| 2195   IIa. Large bust with out-turned hair, crown with two plain arches; *mm.* none, 31, 31/-, 31/78 | 70 | 175 |
| 2196   — — similar but crosses by neck; *mm.* none, -/105 | 85 | 225 |
| 2197   — — R̸. Portcullis over long cross; *mm.* -/lis | 2250 | 7500 |

| 2198 | 2199 | 2201 |

|  | F | VF |
|---|---|---|
|  | £ | £ |

2198 **Groat.** IIIa. Bust as IIa. Crown with two jewelled arches, *mm.* 31 .......... | 225 | 650
2198A IIIb. Similar, but new bust with realistic hair *mm.* 78, 30......................... | 60 | 160
2199 IIIc. Bust as IIIb, but crown with one plain and one jewelled arch, *mm.*
30-21 and none.................................................................................................. | 50 | 150
2199A IIId. As last, but plainer letters. mm 57, 85, 33 and none ....................... | 60 | 160
2200 IVa. Wide single arch crown; arch is single or double bar with 4 crockets;
*mm.* 85, 85/33, 21 ............................................................................................ | 65 | 185
2201 IVb. — Similar, but arch is double bar with 6 uprights or crockets as jewels;
*mm.* 85, 21/85, 21 ........................................................................................... | 65 | 185
2202 **Halfgroat,** *London.* I. Open crown, tressure unbroken; *mm.* 40/-, 40/39
(R. III mule) .................................................................................................... | 200 | 600
2203 — IIIa. Double arched crown, rosettes on tressure; mm. escallop .......... | 135 | 400
2204 — IIIb. Similar, nothing on tressure. R. Lozenge panel in centre; *mm.* lis | 35 | 100
2205 — — Similar, but also with lis on breast; mm. lis.................................... | 40 | 110
2206 — IIIc. Unarched crown with tressure broken. R. Lozenge panel in centre;
*mm.* lis ............................................................................................................. | 30 | 90
2206A— — — Similar but smaller dies and much smaller lettering................. | 35 | 100

| 2207 | 2211 |

2207 *Canterbury,* Archb. Morton. I. Open crown, crosses by neck. R. M in centre;
*mm.* tun/- .......................................................................................................... | 40 | 110
2208 — — II. Similar, but double-arched crown; no *mm.* .............................. | 35 | 100
2209 III King and Archb. jointly. As last but without M ; (a) early lettering,
trefoil stops; *mm.* lis, tun and lis/lis ............................................................. | 30 | 95
2210 — — (b) ornate lettering, rosette stops; *mm.* tun, lis in combinations ..... | 25 | 80
2211 — — (c) — saltire or no stops; *mm.* 123, 123 & 30/123........................ | 25 | 75
2212 *York,* Royal mint. (a) Double-arched crown, lis on breast (rarely omitted).
R. Lozenge panel in centre; *mm.* lis......................................................... | 45 | 125
2213 — — (b) Similar, but unarched crown, tressure broken, *mm.* lis. ............ | 35 | 100

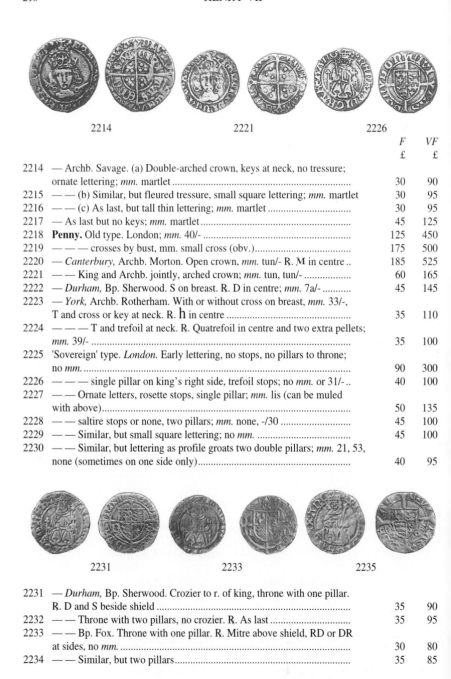

2214          2221          2226

| | F £ | VF £ |
|---|---|---|
| 2214 — Archb. Savage. (a) Double-arched crown, keys at neck, no tressure; ornate lettering; *mm.* martlet | 30 | 90 |
| 2215 — — (b) Similar, but fleured tressure, small square lettering; *mm.* martlet | 30 | 95 |
| 2216 — — (c) As last, but tall thin lettering; *mm.* martlet | 30 | 95 |
| 2217 — As last but no keys; *mm.* martlet | 45 | 125 |
| 2218 **Penny.** Old type. London; *mm.* 40/- | 125 | 450 |
| 2219 — — — crosses by bust, mm. small cross (obv.) | 175 | 500 |
| 2220 — *Canterbury,* Archb. Morton. Open crown, *mm.* tun/- R. M in centre .. | 185 | 525 |
| 2221 — — King and Archb. jointly, arched crown; *mm.* tun, tun/- | 60 | 165 |
| 2222 — *Durham,* Bp. Sherwood. S on breast. R. D in centre; *mm.* 7a/- | 45 | 145 |
| 2223 — *York,* Archb. Rotherham. With or without cross on breast, *mm.* 33/-, T and cross or key at neck. R. h in centre | 35 | 110 |
| 2224 — — — T and trefoil at neck. R. Quatrefoil in centre and two extra pellets; *mm.* 39/- | 35 | 100 |
| 2225 'Sovereign' type. *London.* Early lettering, no stops, no pillars to throne; no *mm.* | 90 | 300 |
| 2226 — — — single pillar on king's right side, trefoil stops; no *mm.* or 31/- .. | 40 | 100 |
| 2227 — — Ornate letters, rosette stops, single pillar; *mm.* lis (can be muled with above) | 50 | 135 |
| 2228 — — saltire stops or none, two pillars; *mm.* none, -/30 | 45 | 100 |
| 2229 — — Similar, but small square lettering; no *mm.* | 45 | 100 |
| 2230 — — Similar, but lettering as profile groats two double pillars; *mm.* 21, 53, none (sometimes on one side only) | 40 | 95 |

2231          2233          2235

| | F £ | VF £ |
|---|---|---|
| 2231 — *Durham,* Bp. Sherwood. Crozier to r. of king, throne with one pillar. R. D and S beside shield | 35 | 90 |
| 2232 — — Throne with two pillars, no crozier. R. As last | 35 | 95 |
| 2233 — — Bp. Fox. Throne with one pillar. R. Mitre above shield, RD or DR at sides, no *mm.* | 30 | 80 |
| 2234 — — Similar, but two pillars | 35 | 85 |

|  |  | *F* | *VF* |
|---|---|---|---|
|  |  | £ | £ |
| 2235 | *York,* Archb. Rotherham. Keys below shield; early lettering, trefoil stops, no pillars to throne, no *mm.* | 30 | 80 |
| 2236 | — — — single pillar | 30 | 75 |
| 2237 | — — — — ornate lettering, rosette or no stops, | 30 | 80 |
| 2238 | — — — two pillars sometimes with crosses between legs of throne | 30 | 75 |
| 2239 | **Halfpenny,** *London.* I. Open crown; *mm.* 40, 42 | 40 | 120 |
| 2240 | — — — trefoils at neck; no *mm.,* rose | 50 | 135 |
| 2241 | — — — crosses at neck; *mm.* rose, cross fitchée | 40 | 120 |
| 2242 | — II. Double arched crown; *mm.* cinquefoil, none | 25 | 75 |
| 2243 | — — — saltires at neck; no *mm.* | 30 | 75 |
| 2244 | — IIIa. Crown with single arch, ornate lettering; no *mm.,* pansy | 20 | 60 |
| 2244A | — IIIb. Similar but with rosette stops; *mm.* none, rose, lis | 30 | 80 |

2245                              2248

| 2245 | — IIIc. Much smaller portrait; *mm.* pheon, lis, none | 20 | 60 |
|---|---|---|---|
| 2246 | *Canterbury,* Archb. Morton. I. Open crown, crosses by neck; R. M in centre | 65 | 200 |
| 2247 | — — II. Similar, but arched crown, saltires by bust; *mm.* profile eye (82) | 65 | 175 |
| 2247A | — — — no marks at neck | 50 | 150 |
| 2248 | — III. King and Archb. Arched crown; *mm.* lis, none | 45 | 110 |

2249                              2250

| 2249 | *York,* Archb. Savage. Arched crown, key below bust to l or r. *mm.* martlet | 50 | 135 |
|---|---|---|---|
| 2250 | **Farthing,** *London.* hЄNRIC DI GRA RЄX (A), arched crown | 150 | 500 |

*No.s 2239-49 have *mm.* on *obv.* only.

**Profile issue**

| 2251 | Testoon (ls.). Type as groat. hЄNRIC (VS); *mm.* lis | 6250 | 15000 |
|---|---|---|---|
| 2252 | — hЄNRIC VII; *mm.* lis | 6750 | 16500 |

2253

| 2253 | — hЄNRIC SЄPTIM; *mm.* lis | 7250 | 17500 |
|---|---|---|---|

2254                                    2258

|      |                                                                                                 | F    | VF   |
|------|-------------------------------------------------------------------------------------------------|------|------|
|      |                                                                                                 | £    | £    |
| 2254 | **Groat,** *Tentative issue* (contemporary with full-face groats). Double band to crown, hENRIC VII; *mm.* none, 105/-, -/105: 105/85, 105, 85, 21 ..... | 140  | 475  |
| 2255 | — — — tressure on *obv.; mm.* cross-crosslet........................................... | 2500 | 6500 |
| 2256 | — — hENRIC (VS); *mm.* 105, -/105, 105/ 85, none............................. | 350  | 1000 |
| 2257 | — — hENRIC SEPTIM; *mm.* -/105 ...................................................... | 2500 | 6500 |
| 2258 | *Regular issue.* Triple band to crown; *mm.* 21, 53 (both *mm.*s may occur on *obv.* or *rev.* or both) ........................................ | 95   | 300  |
| 2259 | **Halfgroat,** *London.* As last; *mm.* 105, 53/105, 105/53, 53...................... | 75   | 250  |
| 2260 | — — no numeral after King's name, no *mm.*, -/lis................................. | 325  | 850  |

2261                                    2262

|       |                                                                                      |     |     |
|-------|--------------------------------------------------------------------------------------|-----|-----|
| 2261  | *Canterbury,* King and Archb. As London, but *mm.* 94, 33, 94/33............ | 65  | 175 |
| 2262  | *York,* Archb. Bainbridge. As London, but two keys below shield; *mm.* 94, 33, 33/94.................................................................................... | 65  | 175 |
| 2262A | — Similar but no keys; *mm.* rose................................................................. | 75  | 225 |

2263

|       |                                                                                      |     |     |
|-------|--------------------------------------------------------------------------------------|-----|-----|
| 2263  | — — XB beside shield; *mm.* rose/martlet ............................................... | 250 | 700 |
| 2263A | — — Similar but two keys below shield *mm.* rose(?)/martlet................. | 300 | 800 |

Henry VIII is held in ill-regard by numismatists as being the author of the debasement of England's gold and silver coinage; but there were also other important numismatic innovations during his reign. For the first sixteen years the coinage closely followed the pattern of the previous issues, even to the extent of retaining the portrait of Henry VII on the larger silver coins.

In 1526, in an effort to prevent the drain of gold to continental Europe, the value of English gold was increased by 10%, the sovereign to 22s. 0d. and the angel to 7s. 4d., and a new coin valued at 4s. 6d.—the Crown of the Rose—was introduced as a competitor to the French *écu au soleil*. The new crown was not a success and within a few months it was replaced by the Crown of the Double Rose valued at 5s but made of gold of only 22 carat fineness, the first time gold had been minted below the standard 23c. At the same time the sovereign was again revalued to 22s. 6d. and the angel to 7s. 6d., with a new coin, the George Noble, valued at 6s. 8d. (one-third pound).

The royal cyphers on some of the gold crowns and half-crowns combine the initial of Henry with those of his queens: Katherine of Aragon, Anne Boleyn and Jane Seymour. The architect of this coinage reform was the chancellor, Cardinal Thomas Wolsey, who besides his other changes had minted at York a groat bearing his initials and cardinal's hat in addition to the other denominations normally authorized for the ecclesiastical mints.

When open debasement of the coinage began in 1544 to help finance Henry's wars, the right to coin of the archbishops of Canterbury and York and of the bishop of Durham was not confirmed. Instead, a second royal mint was opened in the Tower as in subsequent years were six others, at Southwark, York, Canterbury, Bristol, Dublin and Durham House in the Strand. Gold, which fell to 23c. in 1544, 22c. in 1545, and 20c. in 1546 was much less debased than silver which declined to 9oz 2dwt. in 1544, 6oz 2dwt. in 1545 and 4oz 2dwt. in 1546. At this last standard the blanched silver surface of the coins soon wore away to reveal the copper alloy beneath which earned for Henry the nickname 'Old Coppernose'.

*Mintmarks*

| 53 | 69 | 70 | 108 | 33 | 94 | 73 | 11 |
| 105 | 22 | 23 | 30 | 78 | 15 | 24 | 110 |
| 52 | 72a | 44 | 8 | 65a | 114 | 121 | 90 |
| 36 | 106 | 56 | S | E | 116 | 135 |

| | | | |
|---|---|---|---|
| 1509-26 | Pheon (53) | 1509-14 | Martlet (94, *York*) |
| | Castle (69) | 1509-23 | Radiant star (22, *Durham & York*) |
| | Castle with H (70, gold) | 1513-18 | Crowned T (135, Tournai) |
| | Portcullis crowned (108) | 1514-26 | Star (23, *York & Durham*) |
| | Rose (33, *Canterbury*) | | Pansy (30, *York*) |
| | Martlet (94, *Canterbury*) | | Escallop (78, *York*) |
| | Pomegranate (73, but broader, *Cant.*) | | Voided cross (15, *York*) |
| | Cross fitchée (11, *Cant.*) | 1523-26 | Spur rowel (24, *Durham*) |
| | Lis (105, *Canterbury, Durham*) | | |
| 1526-44 | Rose (33) | 1526-32 | Cross patonce (8, *Cant.*) |
| | Lis (105) | | T (114, *Canterbury*) |

|         | Sunburst 110)                      |         |                          |
|---------|------------------------------------|---------|--------------------------|
|         | Arrow (52)                         |         | Uncertain mark (121,     |
|         | Pheon (53)                         |         | *Canterbury*)            |
|         | Lis (106)                          | 1529-44 | Radiant star (22, *Durham*) |
|         | Star (23, *Durham*)                | 1530-44 | Key (90, *York*)         |
| 1526-9  | Crescent (72a, *Durham*)           | 1533-44 | Catherine wheel (36,     |
|         | Trefoil (44 variety,               |         | *Canterbury*)            |
|         | *Durham*)                          | 1544-7  | Lis (105 and 106)        |
|         | Flower of eight petals and         |         | Pellet in annulet (56)   |
|         | circle centre (*Durham*)           |         | S (Southwark)            |
| 1526-30 | Cross (7a, sometimes               |         | Є or E (Southwark)       |
|         | slightly voided, *York*)           | 1546-7  | WS monogram (116, *Bristol*) |
|         | Acorn (65a, *York*)                |         |                          |

# GOLD

**First coinage, 1509-26**

|  |  | F | VF |
|--|--|---|----|
|  |  | £ | £ |

2264  **Sovereign** (20s.). Similar to last sov. of Hen. VII; *mm*. 108 .................... 5500  14500

2264A **Ryal** (10s.) King in ship holding sword and shield. R. Similar to 1950, *mm*.-/108 .......................................................................................... *Extremely rare*

2265  **Angel** (6s. 8d.). As Hen. VIII, but hЄnRIC? VIII DI GRA RЄX, etc.; *mm*. 53, 69, 70, 70/69, 108, R. May omit h and rose, or rose only; *mm*. 69, 108 ... 500  1100

2266  **Half-angel.** Similar (sometimes without VIII), *mm*, 69, 70, 108/33, 108 ... 425  950

2265

**Second coinage, 1526-44**

2267

2267  **Sovereign** (22s. 6d.). As 2264, R. single or double tressure *mm*. 110, 105, 105/52.................................................................................................. 5250  13500

2268  **Angel** (7s. 6d.). As 2265, hЄnRIC VIII D(I) G(RA) R(ЄX) etc,; *mm*. 110, 105.................................................................................................... 675  1750

2269  **Half-angel.** Similar; *mm*. lis ...................................................... 700  1850

2270                                    2272

|  |  | F | VF |
|---|---|---|---|
|  |  | £ | £ |

2270  **George-noble** (6s. 8d.). As illustration; *mm.* rose ............................ 4250 12000
2270A— Similar, but more modern ship with three masts, without initials hR. R.
St. George brandishing sword behind head. ......................................... 5750 17500
2271  **Half-George-noble.** Similar to 2270 *mm* rose, lis .............................. 6500 18000
2272  **Crown of the rose** (4s. 6d., 23 c. 3 ¹/₂ gr.). As illustration; *mm.* rose,
two legend varieties ..................................................................... 4750 13500
2273  **Crown of the double-rose** (5s., 22 c). Double-rose crowned, hK (Henry and
Katherine of Aragon) both crowned in field. R. Shield crowned; *mm.* rose   450   900
2274  — hK both sides; *mm.* rose/lis, lis, arrow ......................................... 450   900
2275* — hK/hA or hA/hK; *mm.* arrow......................................................... 800  2250
2276* — hR/hK or hI/hR; *mm.* arrow......................................................... 700  1750
2277  — hA (Anne Boleyn); *mm.* arrow ..................................................... 800  2250
2278  — hA/hR; *mm.* arrow..................................................................... 775  2250

2279                                    2285

2279  — hI (Jane Seymour); *mm.* arrow...................................................... 525  1250
2280* — hK/hI; *mm.* arrow ...................................................................... 750  2000
2281  — hR/hI; *mm.* arrow ...................................................................... 725  1900
2282  — hR (Rex); *mm.* arrow .................................................................. 475  1050
2283  — — *mm.* pheon............................................................................. 700  1850
2284  **Halfcrown.** Similar but king's name henric 8 on *rev.*, no initials; *mm.* rose  750  2250
2285  — hK uncrowned on *obv.; mm.* rose .................................................. 400   950
2286  — hK uncrowned both sides; *mm.* rose/lis, lis, arrow .......................... 425  1000
2287  — hI uncrowned both sides; *mm.* arrow ............................................. 575  1450
2288  — hR uncrowned both sides; hIB REX; *mm.* pheon.......................... 600  1500

*The hK initials may on later coins refer to Katherine Howard (Henry's fifth wife).

**Third coinage, 1544-7**

2291

|       |                                                                                                          | *F* £ | *VF* £ |
|-------|----------------------------------------------------------------------------------------------------------|-------|--------|
| 2289  | **Sovereign,** I (20s., Wt. 200 gr., 23 c.). As illustration but king with larger face and larger design; *mm.* lis ..................................... | 6750  | 20000  |
| 2290  | II (20s., wt. 200 or 192 grs., 23, 22 or 20 ct.). *Tower.* As illustration; *mm.* lis, pellet in annulet/lis ...................................................................... | 3000  | 8250   |
| 2291  | — *Southwark.* Similar; *mm.* S, Є/S ............................................. | 2750  | 8000   |
| 2292  | — — Similar but Є below shield; *mm.* S/Є ......................................... | 3250  | 8500   |
| 2293  | — *Bristol.* As London but *mm.* WS/- ................................................... | 3500  | 9500   |

2294

| 2294  | **Half-sovereign** (wt. 100 or 96 gr.), *Tower.* As illus.; *mm.* lis, pellet in annulet ..................................................................................... | 525   | 1350   |
|-------|----------------------------------------------------------------------------------------------------------|-------|--------|
| 2295  | — Similar, but with annulet on inner circle (either or both sides) ........ | 550   | 1500   |
| 2296  | *Southwark. Mm.* S ...................................................................... | 550   | 1500   |
| 2297  | — Є below shield; *mm.* S, Є, S/Є, Є/S, (known without sceptre; *mm.* S) ...................................................................................... | 525   | 1400   |
| 2298  | *Bristol.* Lombardic lettering; *mm.* WS, WS/- ....................................... | 900   | 2500   |
| 2299  | **Angel** (8s., 23 c). Annulet by angel's head and on ship, һєɴʀɪᴄ' 8; *mm.* lis ...................................................................................... | 425   | 950    |
| 2300  | — Similar, but annulet one side only or none ..................................... | 450   | 1000   |
| 2301  | **Half-angel.** Annulet on ship; *mm.* lis ............................................... | 450   | 950    |
| 2302  | — No annulet on ship; *mm.* lis ........................................................... | 525   | 1100   |

2303                                      2304

| 2303  | — Three annulets on ship; *mm.* lis ..................................................... | 575   | 1350   |
|-------|----------------------------------------------------------------------------------------------------------|-------|--------|
| 2304  | **Quarter-angel** Angel wears armour; *mm.* lis ..................................... | 425   | 950    |
| 2304A | — Angel wears tunic; *mm.* lis ............................................................. | 450   | 1000   |

|      |                                                                                          | F<br>£ | VF<br>£ |
|------|------------------------------------------------------------------------------------------|--------|---------|
| 2305 | **Crown,** *London.* Similar to 2283, but hɛnRIC' 8 ; Lombardic lettering; mm . 56        | 475    | 1100    |
| 2306 | — without RVTILAnS; *mm.* 56                                                              | 500    | 1150    |
| 2307 | — — — with annulet on inner circle                                                        | 525    | 1200    |
| 2307A| — King's name omitted. DEI GRA both sides, *mm.* 56                                       | 675    | 1650    |
| 2308 | — *Southwark.* As 2306; *mm.* S, Є, E/S, Є/-, E/Є                                         | 550    | 1350    |
| 2309 | *Bristol.* hɛnRIC VIII. ROSA etc. R. D G, etc.; *mm.*-/WS                                 | 425    | 950     |
| 2310 | — Similar but hɛnRIC(VS) 8 R. DЄI) G(RA); *mm.* -/WS, WS                                   | 450    | 975     |
| 2311 | **Halfcrown,** *London.* Similar to 2288; *mm.* 56, 56/-                                   | 350    | 800     |
| 2312 | — — with annulet on inner circle *mm.* 56                                                 | 375    | 825     |
| 2313 | *Southwark.* As 2311; *mm.* S                                                             | 425    | 950     |
| 2314 | — *O.* hɛnRIC 8 ROSA SINЄ SPIn. R. DЄI GRA, etc.; *mm.* Є                                 | 450    | 975     |
| 2315 | *Bristol. O.* RVTILAnS, etc. R. hɛnRIC 8; *mm.* WS/-                                       | 525    | 1250    |

*For other gold coins in Henry's name see page 219-20.*

# SILVER

**First coinage, 1509-26**

2316                                              2327

|      |                                                                                          |     |      |
|------|------------------------------------------------------------------------------------------|-----|------|
| 2316 | **Groat.** Portrait of Hen. VII. *London mm.* 53, 69, 108, 108 over 135                   | 95  | 300  |
| 2317 | — *Tournai; mm.* crowned T. R. CIVITAS TORnACЄn*                                          | 425 | 1250 |
| 2318 | **Halfgroat.** Portrait of Hen. VII. London; *mm.* 108, 108/-                             | 95  | 325  |
| 2319 | — *Canterbury,* Archb. Warham. POSVI *rev.*; *mm.* rose                                   | 110 | 350  |
| 2320 | — — — WA above shield; *mm.* martlet                                                      | 75  | 225  |
| 2321 | — — — WA beside shield; *mm.* cross fitchee                                               | 75  | 225  |
| 2322 | — — CIVITAS CAnTOR *rev.,* similar; *mm.* 73, 105, 11/105                                  | 60  | 175  |
| 2323 | — *York,* POSVI *rev.,* Archb. Bainbridge (1508-14). Keys below shield; *mm.* martlet     | 55  | 150  |
| 2324 | — — — XB beside shield no keys; *mm.* martlet                                             | 60  | 160  |
| 2325 | — — — Archb. Wolsey (1514-30). Keys and cardinal's hat below shield; *mm.* 94, 22         | 135 | 400  |
| 2326 | — — CIVITAS ЄBORACI *rev.* Similar; *mm.* 22, 23, 30, 78, 15, 15/78                        | 50  | 150  |
| 2327 | — — As last with TW beside shield; *mm.* voided cross                                     | 85  | 250  |
| 2327A| — *Tournai.* As 2317                                                                      | 625 | 1750 |

*Other non-portrait groats and half-groats exist of this mint, captured during an invasion of France in 1513. (Restored to France in 1518.)

|      | 2332 | 2335 | 2336 |

|      |                                                                                      | F | VF |
|------|--------------------------------------------------------------------------------------|-----|-----|
|      |                                                                                      | £ | £ |
| 2328 | **Penny,** 'Sovereign' type, *London; mm.* 69, 108 /- ............................... | 50 | 125 |
| 2329 | — *Canterbury.* WA above shield; *mm.* martlet................................... | 95 | 275 |
| 2330 | — — — WA beside shield; *mm.* 73/-.................................................... | 70 | 175 |
| 2331 | — *Durham,* Bp. Ruthall (1509-23). TD above shield; *mm.* lis............ | 35 | 90 |
| 2332 | — — — TD beside shield; *mm.* lis, radiant star.................................... | 35 | 90 |
| 2333 | — — — Bp. Wolsey (1523-9). DW beside shield, cardinal's hat below; *mm.* spur rowel...... | 135 | 400 |
| 2334 | **Halfpenny.** Facing bust, hЄNRIC DI GRA RЄX (AGL). *London; mm.* 69, 108/- .......... | 20 | 65 |
| 2335 | — *Canterbury.* WA beside bust; *mm.* 73/-, 11 ..................................... | 60 | 170 |
| 2335A | — *York.* Key below bust, *mm.* star, escallop ..................................... | 75 | 225 |
| 2336 | **Farthing.** *mm.* 108/-, hЄNRIC DI GRA RЄX, portcullis. ℞. CIVITAS LОNDОN, rose in centre of long cross.......................... | 225 | 575 |

## Second coinage, 1526-44

|      | 2337 | 2337D | 2337E |

|      |                                                                                      | F | VF |
|------|--------------------------------------------------------------------------------------|-----|-----|
| 2337 | **Groat.** His own young portrait. *London;* Laker bust A, large renaissance-style bust, crown arch breaking inner circle. Roman/Roman lettering, roses in cross-ends; *mm.* rose ............. | 375 | 1250 |
| 2337A | — — Roman/Lombardic lettering, saltires in cross-ends; *mm.* rose .... | 200 | 650 |
| 2337B | — — Lombardic/Lombardic lettering, roses in cross-ends; *mm.* rose | 250 | 850 |
| 2337C | — — Lombardic/Lombardic lettering, saltires in cross-ends; *mm.* rose | 150 | 500 |
| 2337D | — Laker bust B, smaller face with pointed nose, crown arch does not break inner circle. Lombardic lettering; *mm.* rose ............... | 85 | 300 |
| 2337E | — Laker bust D, larger squarer face with roman nose, fluffy hair, crown arch does not break inner circle. Lombardic lettering; *mm.* 33, 105, 110, 52, 53 (sometimes muled)..................... | 75 | 250 |
| 2338 | — — with Irish title HIB; reads hЄNRIC 8; *mm.* 53, 105, 53/105, 105/53, | 275 | 750 |
| 2339 | — *York,* Archb. Wolsey. TW beside shield, cardinal's hat below; *mm.* voided cross, acorn, muled (both ways) ............................. | 80 | 275 |
| 2340 | — — — omits TW; *mm.* voided cross ................................................. | 275 | 850 |

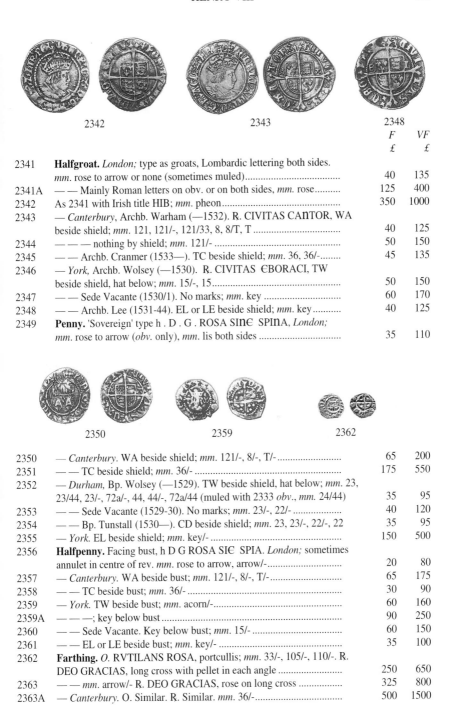

2342      2343      2348

|  |  | F | VF |
|---|---|---|---|
|  |  | £ | £ |
| 2341 | **Halfgroat.** *London;* type as groats, Lombardic lettering both sides. *mm.* rose to arrow or none (sometimes muled) | 40 | 135 |
| 2341A | — — Mainly Roman letters on obv. or on both sides, *mm.* rose | 125 | 400 |
| 2342 | As 2341 with Irish title HIB; *mm.* pheon | 350 | 1000 |
| 2343 | — *Canterbury,* Archb. Warham (—1532). R. CIVITAS CAⱮTOR, WA beside shield; *mm.* 121, 121/-, 121/33, 8, 8/T, T | 40 | 125 |
| 2344 | — — — nothing by shield; *mm.* 121/- | 50 | 150 |
| 2345 | — — Archb. Cranmer (1533—). TC beside shield; *mm.* 36, 36/- | 45 | 135 |
| 2346 | — *York,* Archb. Wolsey (—1530). R. CIVITAS ЄBORACI, TW beside shield, hat below; *mm.* 15/-, 15 | 50 | 150 |
| 2347 | — — Sede Vacante (1530/1). No marks; *mm.* key | 60 | 170 |
| 2348 | — — Archb. Lee (1531-44). EL or LE beside shield; *mm.* key | 40 | 125 |
| 2349 | **Penny.** 'Sovereign' type h . D . G . ROSA SIⱮЄ SPIⱮA, *London; mm.* rose to arrow (*obv.* only), *mm.* lis both sides | 35 | 110 |

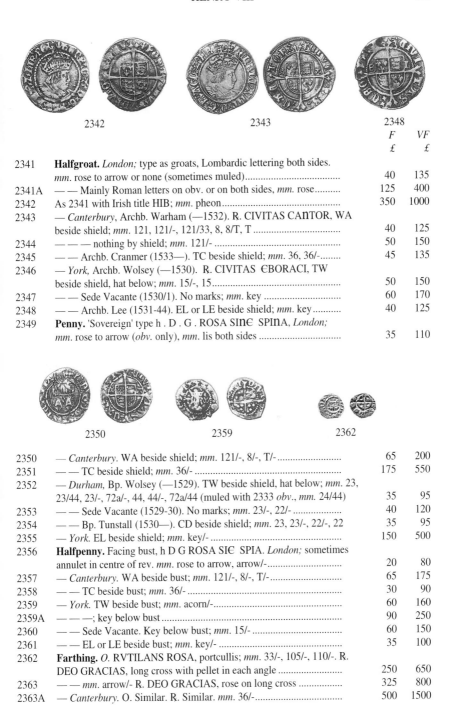

2350      2359      2362

| 2350 | — *Canterbury.* WA beside shield; *mm.* 121/-, 8/-, T/- | 65 | 200 |
|---|---|---|---|
| 2351 | — — TC beside shield; *mm.* 36/- | 175 | 550 |
| 2352 | — *Durham,* Bp. Wolsey (—1529). TW beside shield, hat below; *mm.* 23, 23/44, 23/-, 72a/-, 44, 44/-, 72a/44 (muled with 2333 *obv., mm.* 24/44) | 35 | 95 |
| 2353 | — — Sede Vacante (1529-30). No marks; *mm.* 23/-, 22/- | 40 | 120 |
| 2354 | — — Bp. Tunstall (1530—). CD beside shield; *mm.* 23, 23/-, 22/-, 22 | 35 | 95 |
| 2355 | — *York.* EL beside shield; *mm.* key/- | 150 | 500 |
| 2356 | **Halfpenny.** Facing bust, h D G ROSA SIЄ SPIA. *London;* sometimes annulet in centre of rev. *mm.* rose to arrow, arrow/- | 20 | 80 |
| 2357 | — *Canterbury.* WA beside bust; *mm.* 121/-, 8/-, T/- | 65 | 175 |
| 2358 | — — TC beside bust; *mm.* 36/- | 30 | 90 |
| 2359 | — *York.* TW beside bust; *mm.* acorn/- | 60 | 160 |
| 2359A | — — —; key below bust | 90 | 250 |
| 2360 | — — Sede Vacante. Key below bust; *mm.* 15/- | 60 | 150 |
| 2361 | — — EL or LE beside bust; *mm.* key/- | 35 | 100 |
| 2362 | **Farthing.** *O.* RVTILANS ROSA, portcullis; *mm.* 33/-, 105/-, 110/-. R. DEO GRACIAS, long cross with pellet in each angle | 250 | 650 |
| 2363 | — — *mm.* arrow/- R. DEO GRACIAS, rose on long cross | 325 | 800 |
| 2363A | — *Canterbury.* O. Similar. R. Similar. *mm.* 36/- | 500 | 1500 |

2364                                              2368

|      | F    | VF   |
|------|------|------|
|      | £    | £    |

**Third coinage, 1544-7** (Silver progressively debased. 9oz (2dwt), 6oz (2dwt) 4oz (2dwt)).

| 2364 | **Testoon.** *Tower.* hᴇnRIC'. VIII, etc. R. Crowned rose between crowned h and R.POSVI, etc.; *mm.* lis, lis and 56, lis/two lis | 850 | 4000 |
|------|---|---|---|
| 2365 | — hᴇnRIC 8, *mm.* 105 and 56, 105/56, 105 and 56/56, 56 | 600 | 2250 |
| 2366 | — — annulet on inner circle of rev. or both sides; *mm.* pellet in annulet | 625 | 2350 |
| 2367 | — *Southwark.* As 2365. R. CIVITAS Lonᴅon; *mm.* S, ᴇ, S/ᴇ, ᴇ/S | 650 | 2500 |
| 2368 | — *Bristol.* mm.-/WS monogram. (Tower or local dies.) | 675 | 2750 |

| 2384 | Bust 1 | Bust 2 | Bust 3 | | |
|------|--------|--------|--------|---|---|
| 2369 | **Groat.** *Tower.* As ill. above, busts 1, 2, 3; *mm.* lis/-, lis | | | 75 | 285 |
| 2369A | Bust 1, R. As second coinage; i.e. saltires in forks; *mm.* lis | | | 85 | 350 |
| 2370 | Bust 2 or 3 annulet on inner circle, both sides or rev. only | | | 80 | 325 |
| 2371 | *Southwark.* As 2367, busts 1, 2, 3, 4; no *mm.* or lis/-; S or S and ᴇ or ᴇ in forks | | | 75 | 300 |
| 2372 | *Bristol.* Mm.-/WS monogram, Bristol bust and Tower bust 2 or 3 | | | 80 | 300 |
| 2373 | *Canterbury.* Busts 1, 2, (2 var); no *mm,* or lis/– | | | 80 | 325 |
| 2374 | *York.* Busts 1 var., 2, 3, no *mm.* | | | 75 | 300 |
| 2375 | **Halfgroat.** *Tower.* As 2365, bust 1; *mm.* lis, none | | | 60 | 200 |
| 2376 | *Southwark.* As 2367, bust 1; no *mm.*; S or ᴇ and S in forks | | | 100 | 325 |
| 2377 | *Bristol.* Mm.-/WS monogram | | | 65 | 200 |
| 2378 | *Canterbury.* Bust 1; no *mm.* | | | 40 | 135 |
| 2379 | *York.* Bust 1; no *mm.* | | | 50 | 175 |
| 2380 | **Penny.** *Tower.* Facing bust; no *mm.* or lis/- | | | 30 | 110 |
| 2381 | *Southwark.* Facing bust; *mm.* S/-, ᴇ/-, -/ᴇ | | | 75 | 250 |
| 2382 | *Bristol.* Facing bust; no *mm.* (Tower dies or local but truncated at neck) | | | 45 | 135 |
| 2383 | *Canterbury.* Facing bust; no *mm.* | | | 30 | 110 |
| 2384 | *York.* Facing bust; no *mm.* | | | 30 | 110 |
| 2385 | **Halfpenny.** *Tower.* Facing bust; pellet in annulet in *rev.* centre, no *mm.* or lis/- | | | 65 | 200 |
| 2386 | *Bristol.* Facing bust; no *mm.* | | | 65 | 200 |
| 2387 | *Canterbury.* Facing bust; no *mm.*, (some read H 8) | | | 40 | 125 |
| 2388 | *York.* Facing bust; no *mm.* | | | 35 | 110 |
| 2388A | **Farthing** *obv.* Rose. R. Cross and pellets | | | 500 | 1500 |

These coins were struck during the reign of Edward VI but bear the name and portrait of Henry VIII, except in the case of the half-sovereigns which bear the youthful head of Edward.

*Mintmarks*

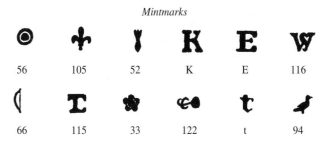

| 56 | 105 | 52 | K | E | 116 |

| 66 | 115 | 33 | 122 | t | 94 |

## GOLD

|  |  | F | VF |
|---|---|---|---|
|  |  | £ | £ |
| 2389 | **Sovereign** (20 c), *London.* As no. 2290, but Roman lettering; *mm.* lis | 3750 | 9500 |
| 2390 | — *Bristol.* Similar but *mm.* WS .......................................................... | 4000 | 10000 |

2391

2391A

| 2391 | **Half-sovereign.** As 2294, but with youthful portrait with sceptre. *Tower*; *mm.* 52, 105, 94 (various combinations)............................................. | 450 | 1350 |
|---|---|---|---|
| 2391A | — Similar but no sceptre; *mm.* 52, 52/56 ............................................ | 475 | 1450 |
| 2392 | — — — K below shield; *mm.*-/K, none,. E/- ...................................... | 475 | 1450 |
| 2393 | — — — grapple below shield; *mm.* 122, none, 122/-, -/122................ | 525 | 1500 |
| 2394 | — *Southwark. Mm.* E, E/-, -/E, Є /E. Usually Є or E (sometimes retrograde) below shield (sceptre omitted; *mm.* -/E).................................. | 450 | 1350 |
| 2394A | — — — R. As 2296; *mm.*-/S................................................................ | 600 | 1600 |

2395

| | | F | VF |
|---|---|---|---|
| | | £ | £ |
| 2395 | **Crown.** Similar to 2305. *London; mm.* 52, 52/-, -/K, 122, 94, ............ | 425 | 1100 |
| 2396 | — Similar but transposed legends without numeral; *mm.* -/arrow ....... | 500 | 1350 |
| 2396A | — As 2395, but omitting RVTILANS; *mm.* arrow ............................. | 450 | 1200 |
| 2396B | Similar, but RVTILANS both sides; *mm.* arrow ................................ | 500 | 1300 |
| 2397 | — *Southwark.* Similar to 2396; *mm.* E .............................................. | 550 | 1500 |
| 2398 | — — King's name on *obv.*; *mm.* E/-, -/E ............................................ | 500 | 1300 |
| 2399 | **Halfcrown.** Similar to 2311. *London; mm.* 52, K/-, 122/-, 94, -/52..... | 450 | 1200 |
| 2399A | As last but E over h on *rev.*, *mm.* 56/52.......................................... | 650 | 1750 |
| 2399B | As 2399 but RVTILANS etc. on both sides, *mm.* arrow ..................... | 550 | 1500 |
| 2400 | — *Southwark. mm.* E, E/-, -/E ................................................................ | 425 | 1100 |

## SILVER

AR (4oz .333)

| 2401 | **Testoon.** *Tower.* As 2365 with lozenge stops one side; -/56, 56.......... | 1350 | 6000 |
|---|---|---|---|

Bust 4               Bust 5               Bust 6

*Some of the Bristol testoons, groats and halfgroats with WS monogram were struck after the death of Henry VIII but cannot easily be distinguished from those struck during his reign.*

| 2403 | **Groat.** *Tower.* Busts 4, 5, 6 (and, rarely, 2). Ɍ. POSVI, etc.; *mm.* 105-94 and none (frequently muled)................................................................. | 70 | 300 |
|---|---|---|---|
| 2404 | — *Southwark.* Busts 4, 5, 6. Ɍ. CIVITAS LONDON; no *mm.* -/E; lis/-, -/lis, K/E; roses or crescents or S and Є in forks, or rarely annulets ... | 70 | 275 |
| 2405 | — *Durham House.* Bust 6. Ɍ. REDDE CVIQUE QVOD SVVM EST; *mm.* bow .................................................................................................. | 150 | 500 |
| 2406 | — *Bristol. mm.* WS on *rev.* Bristol bust B, Tower bust 2 and 3........... | 75 | 300 |
| 2407 | — — *mm.* TC on *rev.* Similar, Bristol bust B ...................................... | 85 | 325 |
| 2408 | — *Canterbury.* Busts 5, 6; no *mm.* or rose/- ........................................ | 70 | 275 |
| 2409 | — *York.* Busts 4, 5, 6; no *mm.* or lis/-, -/lis ......................................... | 70 | 275 |

| | | F £ | VF £ |
|---|---|---|---|
| 2410 | **Halfgroat.** Bust 1. *Tower.* POSVI, etc.; *mm.* 52, 52/-, 52/K , -/K, 52/122, 122, -/122 ....................................................................................... | 65 | 225 |

2411

| | | F £ | VF £ |
|---|---|---|---|
| 2411 | — *Southwark.* CIVITAS LONDON; *mm.* E, -/E, none, 52/E, K/E ...... | 55 | 185 |
| 2412 | — *Durham House.* R. REDD, etc.; *mm.* bow, -/bow ........................... | 350 | 1000 |
| 2413 | — *Bristol. Mm.* WS on *rev.* ................................................................... | 65 | 225 |
| 2414 | — — *mm.* TC on *rev.* ......................................................................... | 70 | 250 |
| 2415 | — *Canterbury.* No *mm.* or t/-, -/t, ...................................................... | 40 | 140 |
| 2416 | — *York.* No *mm.*, bust 1 and three quarter facing .............................. | 50 | 175 |

2418                    2422                    2427

| | | F £ | VF £ |
|---|---|---|---|
| 2417 | **Penny.** *Tower.* CIVITAS LONDON. Facing bust; *mm.* 52/-, -/52, -/K, 122/-, -/122, none................................................................................ | 35 | 110 |
| 2418 | — — three-quarter bust; no *mm.* ......................................................... | 35 | 120 |
| 2419 | — *Southwark.* As 2417; *mm.* E, -/E................................................... | 40 | 130 |
| 2420 | — *Durham House.* As groat but shorter legend; *mm.* -/bow ............... | 425 | 900 |
| 2421 | — *Bristol.* Facing busts, as 2382 but showing more body, no *mm.* ..... | 60 | 185 |
| 2422 | — *Canterbury.* Similar to 2417 ............................................................. | 30 | 100 |
| 2423 | — — three-quarters facing bust; no *mm.*.............................................. | 35 | 110 |
| 2424 | — *York.* Facing bust; no *mm.* .............................................................. | 30 | 110 |
| 2425 | — — three-quarters facing bust; no *mm.*.............................................. | 40 | 125 |
| 2426 | **Halfpenny.** *Tower.* 52?, none............................................................. | 25 | 100 |
| 2427 | — *Canterbury.* No *mm.*, sometimes reads H8 ...................................... | 30 | 110 |
| 2428 | — *York.* No *mm.* .................................................................................. | 25 | 95 |

### Coinage in his own name

The 4 oz. 2.5dwt coins of Henry VIII and those issued under Edward in 1547 and 1548 caused much disquiet, yet at the same time government was prevented by continuing financial necessity from abandoning debasement. A stratagem was devised which entailed increasing the fineness of silver coins, thereby making them appear sound, while at the same time reducing their weight in proportion so that in practice they contained no more silver than hitherto. The first issue, ordered on 24 January 1549, at 8 oz.2 dwt. fine produced a shilling which, at 60 gr., was so light that it was rapidly discredited and had to be replaced in April by another at 6 oz. 2 dwt. Weighing 80 gr., these later shillings proved acceptable.

Between April and August 1551 the issue of silver coins was the worst ever – 3 oz. 2dwt. fine at 72s per lb. before retrenchment came in August, first by a 50% devaluation of base silver coin and then by the issue of a fine standard at 11oz. 1dwt. 'out of the fire'. This was the equivalent of 11oz.3dwt. commixture, and means that since sterling was only 11oz. 2dwt., this issue, which contained four new denominations – the crown, halfcrown, sixpence and threepence – was in effect the finest ever issued under the Tudors.

Some base 'pence' were struck in parallel with the fine silver, but at the devalued rate, they and the corresponding 'halfpence' were used as halfpence and farthings respectively.

The first dates on English coinage appear in this reign, first as Roman numerals and then on the fine issue crowns and halfcrowns of 1551-3, in Arabic numerals.

*Mintmarks*

| 66 | 52 | 35 | 115 | E | 53 | 122 |
| t | T | 111 | Y | 126 | 94 | 91A |
| 92 | 105 | y | 97 | 123 | 78 | 26 |

| | | | |
|---|---|---|---|
| 1547-8 | Arrow (52) | | |
| | E (Southwark) | | |
| 1548-50 | Bow (66, *Durham House*) | 1550 | Martlet (94) |
| 1549 | Arrow (52) | 1550 | Leopard's head (91A) |
| | Grapple (122) | 1550-1 | Lion (92) |
| | Rose (35, *Canterbury*) | | Lis (105, *Southwark*) |
| | TC monogram (115, *Bristol*) | | Rose (33) |
| | Pheon (53) | 1551 | Y or y (117, *Southwark*) |
| | t or T (*Canterbury*) | | Ostrich's head (97, gold only) |
| 1549-50 | Swan (111) | 1551-3 | Tun (123) |
| | Roman Y (*Southwark*) | | Escallop (78) |
| 1549-50 | 6 (126 gold only) | 1552-3 | Pierced mullet (26, *York*) |

# GOLD

**First period, Apr. 1547-Jan. 1549**

2429                               2431

| | F | VF |
|---|---|---|
| | £ | £ |
| 2429 **Half-sovereign** (20 c). As 2391, but reading EDWARD 6. Tower; *mm.* arrow | 1350 | 4000 |
| 2430 — *Southwark* (Sometimes with E or Є below shield); *mm.* E | 1250 | 3000 |
| 2431 **Crown.** RVTILANS, etc., crowned rose between ER both crowned. R. EDWARD 6, etc., crowned shield between ER both crowned; *mm.* arrow, E over arrow/- | 2350 | 7250 |
| 2431A— *Obv.* as last. R. As 2305, *mm.* 52/56 | 2000 | 5500 |
| 2432 **Halfcrown.** Similar to 2431, but initials not crowned; *mm.* arrow | 1750 | 5250 |

**Second period, Jan. 1549-Apr. 1550**

2433

| | | |
|---|---|---|
| 2433 **Sovereign** (22 ct). As illustration; *mm.* arrow, –/arrow, Y, | 3000 | 8500 |
| 2434 **Half-sovereign.** Uncrowned bust. *London.* TIMOR etc., MDXLIX on *obv. mm.* arrow | 2750 | 7500 |

2435

| | | |
|---|---|---|
| 2435 — — SCVTVM, etc., as illustration; *mm.* arrow, **6,** Y | 950 | 2600 |

|     |     |
| --- | --- |
|  *F* | *VF* |
|  £ | £ |

2436 — *Durham House.* Uncrowned, 1/2 length bust with MDXLVIII at end of
*obv.* legend; *mm.* bow; SCVTVM etc. ....................................................... 4500 12500
2437 — Normal, uncrowned bust. LVCERNA, etc., on *obv.; mm.* bow .......... 4000 10500

2438                                2441

2438 — Crowned bust. *London.* EDWARD VI, etc. R. SCVTVM, etc.; *mm.* 52,
122, 111/52, 111, Y, 94.............................................................................. 900 2500
2439 — *Durham House.* Crowned, half-length bust; *mm.* bow ........................ 4500 12500
2440 — — King's name on *obv.* and *rev.; mm.* bow (mule of 2439/37) .......... 4750 13000
2441 **Crown.** Uncrowned bust, as 2435; *mm.* 6, Y, 52/-, Y/-............................. 950 2850
2442 — Crowned bust, as 2438; *mm.* 52, 122, 111, Y (usually *obv.* only)....... 900 2500
2443 **Halfcrown.** Uncrowned bust; R. As 2441, *mm.* arrow, Y, Y/-, 52/- ........ 1000 2850
2444 — Crowned bust, as illus. above; *mm.* 52, 52/111, 111, 122, Y, Y/- ....... 875 2350
2445 — Similar, but king's name on *rev.*, *mm.* 52, 122 ..................................... 900 2500
**Third period, 1550-3**
2446 **'Fine' sovereign** (30s.). King on throne; *mm.* 97, 123 ............................. 12500 32500
2447 **Double sovereign.** From the same dies, *mm.* 97 ...................................... 25000 80000

2444                                2448

2448 **Angel** (10s.). As illustration; *mm.* 97, 123............................................. 4750 13500
2449 **Half-angel.** Similar, *mm.* 97 ................................. 8500 25000
2450 **Sovereign.** (=20s.). Half-length figure of king r., crowned and holding
sword and orb. R. Crowned shield with supporters; *mm.* y, tun ............... 2350 6000

2450

2451

| | F | VF |
|---|---|---|
| | £ | £ |

2451  **Half-sovereign**. As illustration above; *mm.* y, tun ................................... 1000 2750
2452  **Crown**. Similar, but *rev.* SCVTVM etc., *mm.* y, tun............................... 1200 3000
2453  **Halfcrown**. Similar, *mm.* tun, y................................................................. 1250 3500

*\*Small denominations often occur creased or straightened.*

## SILVER

**First period, Apr. 1547-Jan. 1549**

2454

2454  **Groat**. Crowned bust r. *Tower*. R. Shield over cross, POSVI, etc.; *mm.* arrow   675   2000
2455  — As last, but EDOARD 6, *mm.* arrow..................................................... 800   2250
2456  *Southwark. Obv.* as 2454. R. CIVITAS LONDON; *mm.*-/E or none,
        sometimes S in forks................................................................................ 650   2000
2457  **Halfgroat**. *Tower. Obv.* as 2454; *mm.* arrow............................................. 425   1000
2458  *Southwark*. As 2456; *mm.* arrow, E on reverse only................................. 400   950

          2459                              2460

2459  *Canterbury*. Similar. No *mm.*, reads EDOARD or EDWARD (rare)....... 275   750
2460  **Penny**. *Tower*. As halfgroat, but E.D.G. etc. R. CIVITAS LONDON; *mm.*
        arrow ........................................................................................................ 275   950
2461  *Southwark*. As last, but *mm.* -/E................................................................ 325   1000
2462  *Bristol*. Similar, but reads ED6DG or E6DG no *mm.* ............................... 250   850
2463  **Halfpenny**. *Tower*. *O.* As 2460, *mm.* E (?). R. Cross and pellets ........... 275   900
2464  *Bristol*. Similar, no *mm.* but reads E6DG or EDG................................... 300   950

## Second period, Jan. 1549-Apr. 1550

At all mints except Bristol, the earliest shillings of 1549 were issued at only 60 grains but of 8 oz. 2 dwt standard. This weight and size were soon increased to 80 grains, (S.2466 onwards), but the fineness was reduced to 6 oz. 2 dwt so the silver content remained the same. Dies, mm G were prepared for a coinage of 80gr shillings at York, but were not used. Coins from the *mm* are found suitably overmarked, from other mints, S.2466-8. The shilling bust types are set out in *J. Bispham 'The Base Silver Shillings of Edward VI; BNJ 1985.*

Bust 1                        2465A                        Bust 2

|                                                                                      |  F  |  VF  |
|--------------------------------------------------------------------------------------|-----|------|
| **60 gr; 8oz. 2 dwt.**                                                               |  £  |  £   |
| 2465 **Shilling**. *Tower*. Broad bust with large crown. *Obv*. TIMOR etc. MDXLIX. R. Small, oval garnished shield dividing ER. EDWARD VI etc., *mm*. 52, no *mm*, Bust 1; *mm*, –/52, Bust 2 | 225 | 800 |
| 2465A *Southwark*. As last, Bust 1, *mm*. Y, EY/Y                                     | 200 | 750  |
| 2465B *Canterbury*. As last, Bust 1, *mm*. -/rose                                    | 275 | 1000 |
| 2465C *Durham House*. Bust with elaborate tunic and collar TIMOR etc. MDXLIX. R. Oval shield, very heavily garnished in different style. EDWARD VI etc., *mm*. bow (2469) | 250 | 900 |

Bust 3                        Bust 4                        Bust 5

|                                                                                      |  F  |  VF  |
|--------------------------------------------------------------------------------------|-----|------|
| **80 gr; 6oz. 2 dwt.**                                                               |     |      |
| 2466 *Tower*. Tall, narrow bust with small crown. *Obv*. EDWARD VI etc. MDXLIX or MDL. R. As 2465 but TIMOR etc., Busts 3, 4 and 5, *mm*. 52-91a (frequently muled) | 125 | 475 |
| 2466A— *Obv*. as last, MDXLIX. R. Heavily garnished shield, Durham House style, Bust 3 *mm*. grapple | 350 | 1250 |
| 2466B *Southwark*. As 2466, Busts 3, 4 and 5 *mm*. Y, Y/swan                          | 125 | 400  |
| 2466C — — — Bust 3; R. as 2466A. *mm*. Y                                             | 350 | 1250 |
| 2467 *Bristol*. *Obv*. similar to 2466, Bust 3 or local die R. Shield with heavy curved garniture or as 2466, *mm*. TC, or rose over G | 650 | 2500 |

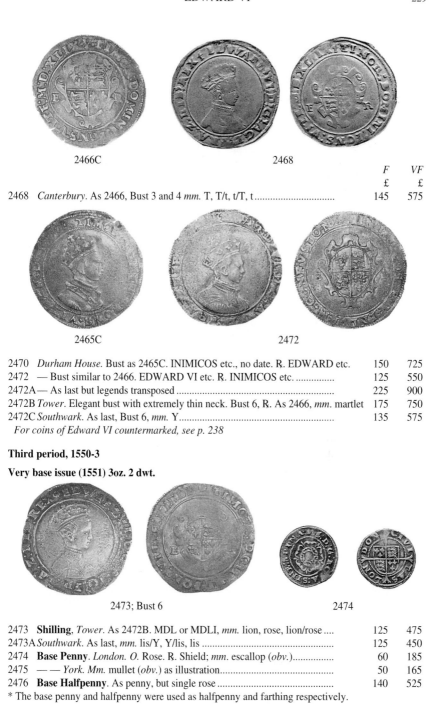

2466C                2468

| | F | VF |
| | £ | £ |

2468  *Canterbury*. As 2466, Bust 3 and 4 *mm*. T, T/t, t/T, t .............................. 145 575

2465C                2472

2470  *Durham House*. Bust as 2465C. INIMICOS etc., no date. R. EDWARD etc.  150 725
2472  — Bust similar to 2466. EDWARD VI etc. R. INIMICOS etc. ............... 125 550
2472A— As last but legends transposed ............................................................ 225 900
2472B *Tower*. Elegant bust with extremely thin neck. Bust 6, R. As 2466, *mm*. martlet 175 750
2472C *Southwark*. As last, Bust 6, *mm*. Y............................................................ 135 575
   *For coins of Edward VI countermarked, see p. 238*

**Third period, 1550-3**

**Very base issue (1551) 3oz. 2 dwt.**

2473; Bust 6                2474

2473  **Shilling**, *Tower*. As 2472B. MDL or MDLI, *mm*. lion, rose, lion/rose .... 125 475
2473A *Southwark*. As last, *mm*. lis/Y, Y/lis, lis ..................................................... 125 450
2474  **Base Penny**. *London*. O. Rose. R. Shield; *mm*. escallop (*obv*.)................ 60 185
2475  — — *York*. *Mm*. mullet (*obv*.) as illustration............................................ 50 165
2476  **Base Halfpenny**. As penny, but single rose .......................................... 140 525
* The base penny and halfpenny were used as halfpenny and farthing respectively.

**Fine silver issue, (1551-3) 11oz. 3 dwt.**

2478

|                                                                                                                           | F    | VF   |
|                                                                                                                           | £    | £    |
| 2478 **Crown**. King on horseback with date below horse. ℞. Shield on cross; *mm.* y. 1551; tun, 1551-3 (1553, wire line inner circle may be missing) . | 675  | 1750 |

2479

| 2479 **Halfcrown**. Walking horse with plume; *mm.* y, 1551 ............................. | 550 | 1250 |
| 2480 Galloping horse without plume; *mm.* tun, 1551-3 ................................... | 575 | 1300 |
| 2481 Large walking horse without plume; *mm.* tun, 1553................................ | 950 | 3000 |

2482                                                                    2483

| 2482 **Shilling**. Facing bust, rose l., value XII r. *mm.* y, tun (several bust varieties) | 85  | 350 |
| 2483 **Sixpence**. *London*. Similar, as illustration; *mm.* y/-, -/y, y, tun (bust varieties)................................................................................................ | 110 | 425 |
| 2484 *York*. As last, but CIVITAS ЄBORACI; *mm.* mullet ............................. | 135 | 525 |

2485                                    2486

|   |   | F | VF |
|---|---|---|---|
|   |   | £ | £ |
| 2485 | **Threepence**. *London*. As sixpence, but III; *mm*. tun | 150 | 625 |
| 2486 | *York*. As 2484, but III by bust | 275 | 975 |

2487                    2487A

| 2487 | **Penny**. 'Sovereign' type; *mm*. tun | 825 | 3000 |
|---|---|---|---|
| 2487A | **Farthing.** *O*. Portcullis, R Cross and Pellets | 750 | 2500 |

Mary brought English coins back to the sterling standard and struck all her gold coins at the traditional fineness of 0.995. The mintmarks usually appear at the end of the first or second word of the legends.

Pomegranate ♟    Halved rose and castle ✤

## GOLD

2488

|      |                                                                 | F | VF |
|------|-----------------------------------------------------------------|------|------|
|      |                                                                 | £ | £ |
| 2488 | **'Fine' Sovereign** (30s.). Queen enthroned. R. Shield on rose, MDLIII, MDLIIII and undated, *mm.* pomegranate, half-rose (or mule) ................. | 2850 | 7250 |
| 2489 | **Ryal** (15s.). As illus, MDLIII. R. As 1950 but A DNO etc. *mm.* pomegranate/- ........................................................................................... | 8250 | 25000 |

2489                                            2490

| 2490 | **Angel** (10s.). Class I, annulet stops; *mm.* pomegranate. ........................... | 1100 | 2750 |
|------|--------------------------------------------------------------------------------|------|------|
| 2490A | — Class II, pellet stops, *mm.* pomegranate (often muled with class I reverse) | 1200 | 3000 |
| 2490B | — Class III, pellet stops, large Roman letters, *mm.* half-rose and castle.. | 1350 | 3500 |
| 2491 | **Half-angel**. Similar; *mm.* pomegranate, pomegranate/- ........................... | 2350 | 6500 |

## SILVER

2492

|  | F | VF |
|  | £ | £ |

2492 **Groat**. Crowned bust l. R. VERITAS, etc.; *mm.* pomegranate, pome-
granate/- .................................................................................................. 110 375
2493 **Halfgroat**. Similar ................................................................................. 650 2000
2494 **Penny**. Similar, but M. D. G. ROSA, etc. .............................................. 475 1750

2495

2495  — As last. R. CIVITAS LONDON; no *mm.* .......................................... 475 1750
2495A— Base penny. Similar to 2474 but M.D.G. etc........................*All late 19th cent. fabrications*

The groats and smaller silver coins of this period have Mary's portrait only, but the shillings and sixpences show the bust of the queen's husband, Philip of Spain.

*Mintmarks*

Lis (105 ⚜       Half-rose and castle ▓

GOLD

2496

|  | *F* | *VF* |
|  | £ | £ |
| 2496 **Angel**. As illustration; wire line inner circles, calm sea, *mm*. lis........... | 2500 | 6000 |
| 2496A — — New-style, large wings, wire line i.c........................................... | 2650 | 6500 |
| 2496B — — As above but beaded i.c................................................................ | 2750 | 6750 |
| 2497 **Half-angel**. Similar to 2496................................................................. | 4500 | 12000 |

SILVER

2498                 2500

| 2498 **Shilling**. Busts face-to-face, full titles, undated, no *mm*. ........................ | 275 | 1100 |
| 2499   — — — also without mark of value...................................................... | 325 | 1250 |
| 2500   — — 1554............................................................................................... | 300 | 1200 |
| 2501   — English titles only 1554, 1555............................................................. | 300 | 1200 |
| 2501A — — undated .......................................................................................... | 375 | 1350 |
| 2502   — — without mark of value, 1554, 1555 (rare)................................... | 350 | 1300 |
| 2503   — — date below bust, 1554, 1555............................................................. | 1350 | 3500 |
| 2504   — — As last, but without ANG., 1555................................................. | 1500 | 4000 |

2505

|  | | *F*<br>£ | *VF*<br>£ |
|---|---|---|---|
| 2505 | **Sixpence**. Similar. Full titles, 1554 (and undated?)............................... | 275 | 1200 |

2506

| 2506 | — English titles only, 1555 (no *mm.*, rare), 1557 (*mm.* lis, rounder garnishing) | 285 | 1250 |
|---|---|---|---|
| 2506A | — As last but heavy beaded i.c. on obv. 1555. (Irish 4d. obv. mule).... | 325 | 1350 |
| 2507 | — — date below bust, 1554, 1557 (very rare)...................................... | 525 | 1500 |

2508

| 2508 | **Groat**. Crowned bust of Mary 1. R. POSVIMVS etc.; *mm.* lis ............. | 110 | 375 |
|---|---|---|---|
| 2509 | **Halfgroat**. Similar, but POSVIM, *mm.* lis............................................. | 350 | 975 |

2510

| 2510 | **Penny**. Similar to 2495, but P. Z. M. etc.; *mm.* lis................................. | 325 | 950 |
|---|---|---|---|
| 2510A | **Base penny**. Similar to 2495A, but P. Z. M . etc.; *mm.* halved rose and castle or castle/–, (used as a halfpenny)................................................ | 65 | 200 |

Elizabeth's coinage is particularly interesting on account of the large number of different denominations issued. 'Crown' gold coins were again issued as well as the 'fine' gold denominations. In 1559 the base shillings of Edward VI's second and third coinages were called in and countermarked for recirculation at reduced values. Smaller debased coins were also devalued but not countermarked. The old debased groat became a three halfpence and other coins in proportion. The normal silver coinage was initially struck at 0.916 fineness as in the previous reign but between 1560 and 1577 and after 1582 the old sterling standard of 0.925 was restored. Between 1578 and 1582 the standard was slightly reduced and the weights were reduced by 1/32nd in 1601. Gold was similarly reduced slightly in quality 1578-82, and there was a slight weight reduction in 1601.

To help alleviate the shortage of small change, and to avoid the expense of minting an impossibly small silver farthing, a threefarthing piece was introduced to provide change if a penny was tendered for a farthing purchase. The sixpence, threepence, threehalfpence and threefarthings were marked with a rose behind the queen's head to distinguish them from the shilling, groat, half-groat and penny.

Coins of exceedingly fine workmanship were produced in a screw press introduced by Eloye Mestrelle, a French moneyer, in 1561. With parts of the machinery powered by a horse-drawn mill, the coins produced came to be known as 'mill money'. Despite the superior quality of the coins produced, the machinery was slow and inefficient compared to striking by hand. Mestrelle's dismissal was engineered in 1572 and six years later he was hanged for counterfeiting.

*Mintmarks*

| First Issue | | Lis (105, milled) | 1584-6 | Escallop (79) |
|---|---|---|---|---|
| 1558-60 | Lis (106) | 1569-71 Castle (71) | 1587-9 | Crescent (72b) |
| Second Issue | | 1572-3 Ermine (77) | 1590-2 | Hand (86) |
| 1560-1 | Cross crosslet (21) | 1573-4 Acorn (65b) | 1591-5 | Tun (123) |
| | Martlet (94) | 1573-8 Eglantine (27) | 1594-6 | Woolpack (124) |
| Third Issue | | Fourth Issue | 1595-8 | Key (90) |
| 1560-6 | Star (23, milled) | 1578-9 Greek cross (7) | 1597-1600 Anchor (57) | |
| 1561-5 | Pheon (53) | 1580-1 Latin cross (14) | 1600 | **0** |
| 1565 | Rose (33) | 1582 Sword (113) | Sixth Issue | |
| 1566 | Portcullis (107) | Fifth Issue | 1601-2 | **1** |
| 1566-7 | Lion (92) | 1582-3 Bell (60) | 1602 | **2** |
| 1567-70 | Coronet (74) | 1582-4 A (54) | | |

N.B. *The dates for* mms *sometimes overlap. This is a result of using up old dies, onto which the new mark was punched.*

# GOLD

**Hammered Coinage**

**First to Third issues, 1559-78.** ('Fine' gold of 0.994. 'Crown' gold of 0 .916 fineness. Sovereigns of 240 gr.). Mintmarks; lis to eglantine.

|      |                                                                                                                                              | F £  | VF £  |
|------|----------------------------------------------------------------------------------------------------------------------------------------------|------|-------|
| 2511 | **'Fine' Sovereign** (30 s.) Queen enthroned, tressure broken by throne, reads Z not ET, no chains to portcullis. R. Arms on rose; *mm*. lis. .......... | 4500 | 12000 |

2512

| 2512   | —— Similar but ET, chains on portcullis; *mm*. crosslet ........................ | 3250 | 8500 |
|--------|----------------------------------------------------------------------------------|------|------|
| 2513   | **Angel**. St. Michael. R. Ship. Wire line inner circles; *mm*. lis. ................. | 850  | 2250 |
| 2513A  | — Similar, but beaded i.c. on *obv.*, *mm*. lis ............................................. | 825  | 2000 |
| 2514   | —— Similar, but beaded inner circles; ship to r.; *mm*. 106, 21, 74, 27,.. | 650  | 1400 |
| 2515   | ——— Similar, but ship to l.; *mm*. 77-27 ................................................ | 675  | 1500 |
| 2516   | **Half Angel**. As 2513, wire line inner circles; *mm*. lis ............................. | 1250 | 3500 |
| 2516A  | — As last, but beaded i.c.s, legend ends. Z.HIB .......................................... | 900  | 2500 |
| 2517   | — As 2514, beaded inner circles; *mm*. 106, 21, 74, 77-27 ...................... | 600  | 1350 |
| 2518   | **Quarter Angel**. Similar; *mm*. 74, 77-27................................................. | 550  | 1250 |

2513                          2520A

| 2519   | **Half Pound** (10 s.) Young crowned bust l. R. Arms. Wire line inner circles; *mm*. lis.................................................................... | 1850 | 6000 |
|--------|----------------------------------------------------------------------------------------------------------------------------------------------------|------|------|
| 2520   | — Similar, but beaded inner circles; *mm*. 21, 33-107............................. | 850  | 2250 |
| 2520A  | —— Smaller bust; *mm*. lion ........................................................ | 975  | 3000 |
| 2520B  | —— Broad bust, ear visible; *mm*. 92, 74, 71 ......................................... | 900  | 2350 |
| 2521   | **Crown**. As 2519; *mm*. lis................................................................. | 1650 | 5000 |
| 2522   | — Similar to 2520; *mm*. 21, 33-107...................................................... | 675  | 1700 |
| 2522A  | — Similar to 2520B; *mm*. 74, 71, 92 ...................................................... | 725  | 1850 |
| 2523   | **Half Crown**. As 2519; *mm*. lis................................................................ | 1500 | 4500 |
| 2524   | — Similar to 2520; *mm*. 21, 33-107 (2 busts) ........................................ | 675  | 1650 |
| 2524A  | — Similar to 2520B; *mm*. 107-71................................................................ | 700  | 1750 |

|  |  | *F* | *VF* |
|---|---|---|---|
|  |  | £ | £ |

**Fourth Issue, 1578-82** (`Fine' gold only of 0.992). *Mms* Greek cross,
Latin cross and sword.

| 2525 | **Angel**. As 2514; *mm*. 7, 14, 113 .................................................. | 650 | 1400 |
|---|---|---|---|
| 2526 | **Half Angel**. As 2517; *mm*. 7, 14, 113.......................................... | 650 | 1450 |
| 2527 | — Similar, but without E and rose above ship; *mm*. latin cross............... | 750 | 1750 |
| 2528 | **Quarter Angel**. As last; *mm*. 7, 14, 113..................................... | 575 | 1350 |

**Fifth Issue, 1583-1600** (`Fine' gold of 0.995, `crown' gold of 0.916; pound of 174.5 grs. wt.).
Mintmarks: bell to **O**.

2529

| 2529 | **Sovereign** (30 s:). As 2512, but tressure not normally broken by back of throne; *mm*. 54-123 ................................................................... | 2750 | 6500 |
|---|---|---|---|

2530

| 2530 | **Ryal** (15 s.). Queen in ship. R. Similar to 1950; *mm*. 54-86 (*rev*. only) .. | 5250 | 14500 |
|---|---|---|---|

2531

| 2531 | **Angel**. As 2514; *mm*. 60-123, 90-**O** ........................................ | 675 | 1450 |
|---|---|---|---|
| 2532 | **Half Angel**. As 2517; *mm*. 60-86, 90-57.................................... | 650 | 1400 |
| 2533 | **Quarter Angel**. As 2518; *mm*. 60-123, 90-57/– ...................................... | 525 | 1250 |

|   |   | F | VF |
|---|---|---|---|
|   |   | £ | £ |
| 2534 | **Pound** (20 s.). Old bust l., with elaborate dress and profusion of hair; *mm.*, lion and tun/tun, 123-**O**................................................................ | 1250 | 3000 |

2535

| 2535 | **Half Pound**. Similar; *mm.* tun................................................... | 1100 | 2750 |
|------|----------------------------------------------------------------------|------|------|
| 2535A | — Similar but smaller bust with less hair; *mm.* 123-**O** ........................... | 1050 | 2650 |

2536

| 2536 | **Crown**. Similar to 2534; *mm.* 123-90. **O** ............................................... | 850 | 2350 |
|------|-----------------------------------------------------------------------------------|-----|------|
| 2537 | **Half Crown**. Similar; *mm.* -/123, 123-0, **O**........................................... | 700 | 1600 |

**Sixth Issue, 1601-3** ('Fine' gold of 0.994, 'crown' gold of 0.916; Pound of 172 gr.). Mintmarks: **1** and **2**

| 2538 | **Angel**. As 2531; *mm.* **1, 2**........................................................................... | 750 | 2000 |
|------|------------------------------------------------------------------------------------------------|------|------|
| 2539 | **Pound**. As 2534; *mm.* **1, 2**......................................................................... | 1450 | 3650 |
| 2540 | **Half Pound**. As 2535A; *mm.* **1, 2**................................................................ | 1500 | 4000 |
| 2541 | **Crown**. As 2536; *mm.* **1, 2**......................................................................... | 1350 | 3500 |
| 2542 | **Half Crown**. As 2537; *mm.* **1, 2**................................................................. | 1350 | 3500 |

**Milled Coinage, 1561-70**

2543

| 2543 | **Half Pound**. Crowned bust l.; *mm.* star, lis............................................. | 1650 | 4500 |
|------|----------------------------------------------------------------------------------------|------|------|
| 2544 | **Crown**. Similar; *mm.* star, lis ..................................................................... | 1350 | 4000 |
| 2545 | **Half Crown**. Similar; *mm.* star, lis............................................................. | 1650 | 5000 |

For further details on both AV and AR milled coinage, *see* D. G. Borden *'An introduction to the milled coinage of Elizabeth I'*. BNJ 1983

## SILVER

**Hammered Coinage**

*Countermarked Edward VI base shillings* (1559)

2546             2547

|  | Fair | F |
|---|---|---|
|  | £ | £ |
| 2546   **Fourpence-halfpenny**. Edward VI 2nd period 6oz and 8oz shillings .... cmkd on obv. with a portcullis; *mm.* 66, –/33, 52, t, 111, Y and 122 | 825 | 2250 |
| 2547   **Twopence-farthing**. Edward VI 3rd period 3 oz. shillings ................... counockmarked on obverse with a seated greyhound; *mm.* 92. 105, 35 and 87 | 950 | 2750 |

N.B.   *Occasionally the wrong countermark was used*

**First Issue, 1559-60** (.916 fine, shillings of 96 grs.)

2548                           2551

|  | F | VF |
|---|---|---|
|  | £ | £ |
| 2548   **Shilling**. Without rose or date. ELIZABET(H), wire line inner circles, pearls on bodice, busts 1A, and 1B; *mm.* lis.......................................... | 375 | 1500 |
| 2549   — Similar, ELIZABETH, wire line and beaded inner circles, no pearls on bodice, busts 1D, 2A and 2B; *mm.* lis ................................................... | 125 | 525 |
| 2550   **Groat**. Without rose or date, wire line or no inner circles (two busts); *mm.* lis .................................................................................................. | 120 | 500 |

1A           1B           1D           2A           2B

| | | |
|---|---|---|
| 2551   — Similar, wire line and beaded inner circles, circles *mm.* lis ............. | 65 | 225 |
| 2551A— — Small bust and shield (from halfgroat punches); *mm.* lis ........... | 85 | 325 |

| | F | VF |
|---|---|---|
| | £ | £ |
| 2552 **Halfgroat**. Without rose or date, wire line inner circles; *mm*. lis ......... | 110 | 500 |
| 2553 **Penny**. Without rose or date, wire line inner circles; *mm*. lis ............... | 175 | 625 |
| 2554 — Similar but dated 1558 on *obv*.; *mm*. lis ......................................... | 375 | 1250 |

**Second Issue, 1560-1** (0.925 fineness, shilling of 96 gr.)

|  2555  |  2559  |  2560  |
|---|---|---|

| | F | VF |
|---|---|---|
| 2555 **Shilling**. Without rose or date, beaded inner circles. ET instead of Z busts 3A, 3B, 3C and 3J; *mm*. 21, 94 .................................................. | 100 | 350 |
| 2555A— large bust with pearls on bodice as 2548; *mm*. 21, bust 1A, 94, bust 1B | 125 | 525 |
| 2556 **Groat**. Without rose or date, bust as 2551; *mm*. 21, 94 ........................ | 50 | 175 |
| 2557 **Halfgroat**. Without rose or date; *mm*. 21, 94..................................... | 35 | 120 |
| 2558 **Penny**. Without rose or date (three bust varieties); *mm*. 21, 94............ | 25 | 65 |

|  3A  |  3B  |  3C  |  3J  |
|---|---|---|---|

**Third Issue, 1561-77** (Same fineness and weight as last)

| | F | VF |
|---|---|---|
| 2559 **Sixpence**. With rose and date, large flan (27 *mm*. or more), large bust with hair swept back, 1561; *mm*. pheon............................................................. | 125 | 550 |
| 2560 — Similar, small bust, 1561; *mm*. pheon................................................. | 65 | 225 |

|                                                                                                                      | F | VF |
|---|---|---|
|                                                                                                                      | £ | £ |
| 2561   — Smaller flan (26.5 *mm.*). Small regular bust, 1561-6; *mm.* 53-107 ......                                  | 55 | 175 |

2561                2561B                2562                2563

| 2561B — Similar, very large bust, with rose, 1563-5; *mm.* pheon ....................... | 90 | 350 |
| 2562   — Intermediate bust, ear shows, 1566-74; *mm.* 92-65b (also 1567 *mm.* 71/ 74) ................................................................................................................ | 55 | 175 |
| 2562A — Similar, without date; *mm.* lion, coronet, ermine ................................. | 300 | 850 |
| 2563   — Larger bust, 1573-7; *mm.* 77-27 .................................................. | 50 | 165 |
| 2564   **Threepence**. With rose and date 1561, large flan (20.5 *mm.*); *mm.* pheon | 40 | 125 |
| 2565   — smaller flan (19 *mm.*). Regular bust, 1561-7; *mm.* 53-92 .................... | 35 | 110 |
| 2566   — taller bust, ear shows, 1566-77; *mm.* 92-27, 27/-, 27/65b.................... | 35 | 110 |
| 2566A — Similar, without rose, 1568; *mm.* coronet ........................................... | 175 | 525 |

2567                             2571

| 2567   **Halfgroat**. Without rose or date; *mm.* 107-71 ......................................... | 50 | 165 |
| 2568   **Threehalfpence**. With rose and date 1561, large flan (17 *mm.*) *mm.* pheon | 35 | 125 |
| 2569   — — Smaller flan (16 *mm.*); 1561-2, 1564-70, 1572-8; *mm.* 53-27 ........ | 30 | 110 |
| 2570   **Penny**. Without rose or date; *mm.* 33-71, 65b, 27, 33/107, 92/107, 74/107 | 25 | 75 |
| 2571   **Threefarthings**. With rose and date 1561-2, 1564, 1567, 1568, 1572-7; *mm.* 53, 74, 77-27...................................................................................... | 50 | 135 |

**Fourth Issue, 1578-82** (0.921 fineness, "shilling" of 95.6 gr.)

2572                             2573

| 2572   **Sixpence**. As 2563, 1578-82; *mm.* 7-113, 14/113, 14/7 ........................... | 45 | 150 |
| 2573   **Threepence**. As 2566, 1578-82; *mm.* 7-113............................................. | 30 | 100 |
| 2574   **Threehalfpence**. As 2569, 1578-9, 1581-2; *mm.* 7-113........................... | 30 | 110 |
| 2575   **Penny**. As 2570; *mm.* 7-113, 7/14, 14/7 .................................................. | 25 | 70 |
| 2576   **Threefarthings**. As 2571, 1578-9, 1581-2; *mm.* 7-113............................. | 60 | 165 |

**Fifth Issue, 1582-1600** (0.925 fineness, shilling of 96 gr.)

| | | 2577 | 2578A | 2581 | |
|---|---|---|---|---|---|
| | | | | F | VF |
| | | | | £ | £ |

| | | | F £ | VF £ |
|---|---|---|---|---|
| 2577 | **Shilling**. Without rose or date, ELIZAB; ear concealed, busts 3B and 6A *mm.* 60-72b, ear shows. bust 6B *mm.* 79-**0** (mules occur) | | 90 | 275 |
| 2578 | **Sixpence**. As 2572, ELIZABETH, 1582, 1583 *mm.* bell | | 55 | 175 |
| 2578A | — Similar, ELIZAB, 1582-1600; *mm.* 60-**0**, also 1583 *mm.* 79/54 | | 45 | 150 |
| 2579 | **Halfgroat**. Without rose or date, two pellets behind bust. ℞. CIVITAS LONDON; *mm.* 60-**0** (*mm.* bell sometimes without pellets) | | 25 | 65 |
| 2580 | **Penny**. Without rose or date. ℞. CIVITAS LONDON; *mm.* 60-57, 90/-, 57/-, **0**/- | | 20 | 65 |
| 2581 | **Halfpenny**. Portcullis. ℞. Cross and pellets; *mm.* none, 54-**0** | | 20 | 65 |

6A          6B

**Sixth Issue, 1601-2** (0.925 fineness, shilling of 92.9 gr.)

2582                                    2583

| | | | F | VF |
|---|---|---|---|---|
| 2582 | **Crown**. As illustration, *mm.* **1** | | 1100 | 2750 |
| 2582A | – Similar, *mm.* **2** | | 1500 | 4500 |
| 2583 | **Halfcrown**. As illustration, *mm.* **1** | | 750 | 1750 |
| 2583A | – Similar, *mm.* **2** | | 1750 | 6000 |
| 2584 | **Shilling**. As 2577; bust 6B *mm.* **1, 2** | | 90 | 275 |
| 2585 | **Sixpence**. As 2578A, 1601-2; *mm.* **1, 2** | | 55 | 175 |
| 2586 | **Halfgroat**. As 2579, *mm.* **1, 2, 2/-** | | 25 | 70 |
| 2587 | **Penny**. As 2580, *mm.* **1, 2, 2/-** | | 25 | 70 |
| 2588 | **Halfpenny**. As 2581, *mm.* **1, 2** | | 25 | 70 |

|       |       |
|-------|-------|
| *F*   | *VF*  |
| £     | £     |

**Milled coinage**

2589 **Shilling**. Without rose or date; *mm*. star. Plain dress, large size (over 31 *mm*.)    425    1350

2590 — decorated dress, large size.................................................... 275    900

2591 — — intermediate size (30-31 *mm*.)......................................... 200    675

2592 — — small size (under 30 *mm*.) ................................................ 175    575

| 2593 | 2594 | 2595 |
|------|------|------|

2593 **Sixpence**. Small bust, large rose. ℞. Cross fourchee, 1561 *mm*. star........ 95    300

2594 Tall narrow bust with plain dress, large rose, 1561-2; *mm*. star .............. 90    275

2595 — similar, but decorated dress, 1562...................................... 90    275

| 2597 | 2598 |
|------|------|

2596 Large broad bust, elaborately decorated dress, small rose, 1562; *mm*. star    85    250

2597 — — cross pattée on *rev*., 1562, 64 *mm*. star ......................................... 90    275

2598 — similar, pellet border, 1563-4................................................. 95    325

2598A Bust with low ruff, raised rim, 1564, 1566 (both overdates) .................... 100    375

| 2599 | 2600 | 2601 |
|------|------|------|

2599 Small bust, 1567-8, ℞. As 2593; *mm*. lis.............. 85    275

2600 Large crude bust breaking legend; 1570, *mm*. lis; 1571/0, *mm*. castle
(over lis)............................................................................ 225    750

2601 **Groat**. As illustration........................................ 125    450

2602 **Threepence**. With rose, small bust with plain dress, 1561 ...................... 135    475

2603 Tall narrow decorated bust with medium rose, 1562............................ 95    300

2604 Broad bust with very small rose, 1562........................................ 100    325

2605 Cross pattee on *rev*., 1563, 1564/3........................................ 175    600

| 2606 |
|------|

2606 **Halfgroat**. As groat .......................................... 150    500

|      |      |
| ---- | ---- |
| *F*  | *VF* |
| £    | £    |

2607  **Threefarthings**. E . D . G . ROSA, etc., with rose. R. CIVITAS LONDON, shield with 1563 above ............................................................................      1350    4500

**Portcullis money**
Trade coins of 8, 4, 2, and 1 Testerns were coined at the Tower Mint in 1600/1 for the first voyage of the incorporated 'Company of Merchants of London Trading into the East Indies'. The coins bear the royal arms on the obverse and a portcullis on the reverse and have the *mm*. **O**. They were struck to the weights of the equivalent Spanish silver 8, 4, 2 and 1 reales.

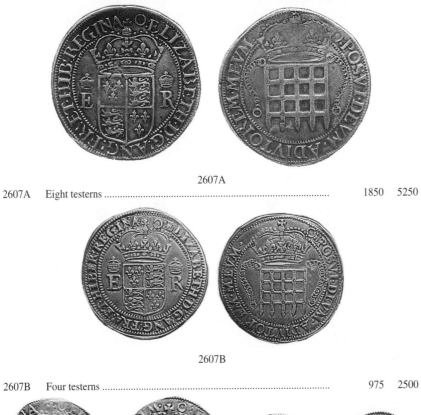

2607A

2607A    Eight testerns .............................................................................      1850    5250

2607B

2607B    Four testerns ...............................................................................       975    2500

2607C                                 2607D

2607C    Two testerns......................................................................................     750    2000
2607D    One testern........................................................................................     575    1500

# THE HOUSE OF STUART, THE COMMONWEALTH, AND THE HOUSE OF ORANGE, 1603-1714

## JAMES I, 1603-25

With the accession of James VI of Scotland to the English throne, the royal titles and coat of arms are altered on the coinage; on the latter the Scottish rampant lion and the Irish harp now appear in the second and third quarters. In 1604 the weight of the gold pound was reduced and the new coin became known as the 'Unite'. Fine gold of 0·979 and crown gold of 0·916 fineness were both issued, and a gold four-shilling piece was struck 1604-19. In 1612 all the gold coins had their values raised by 10%; but in 1619 the Unite was replaced by a new, lighter 20s. piece, the 'Laurel', and a lighter rose-ryal, spur-ryal and angel were minted.

In 1613 the king granted Lord Harington a licence to coin farthings of copper as a result of repeated public demands for a low value coinage; this was later taken over by the Duke of Lennox. Towards the end of the reign coins made from silver sent to the mint from the Welsh mines had the Prince of Wales's plumes inserted over the royal arms.

*Mintmarks*

| 125 | 105 | 33 | 79 | 84 | 74 | 90 |
|---|---|---|---|---|---|---|
| 60 | 25 | 71 | 45 | 32 | 123 | 132 |
| 72b | 7a | 16 | 24 | 125 | 105 | 46 |

First coinage
1603-4    Thistle (125)
1604-5    Lis (105)

Second coinage
1604-5    Lis (105)
1605-6    Rose (33)
1606-7    Escallop (79)
1607      Grapes (84)
1607-9    Coronet (74)

1609-10  Key (90)
1610-11  Bell (60)
1611-12  Mullet (25)
1612-13  Tower (71)
1613     Trefoil (45)
1613-15  Cinquefoil (32)
1615-16  Tun (123)
1616-17  Book on lectern (132)
1617-18  Crescent (72b, gold)
1618-19  Plain cross (7a)

1619     Saltire cross (16, gold)

Third coinage
1619-20  Spur rowel (24)
1620-1   Rose (33)
1621-3   Thistle (125)
1623-4   Lis (105)
1624     Trefoil (46)

# GOLD

**First coinage, 1603-4** (Obverse legend reads D' . G' . ANG : SCO : etc.)

|  |  | F<br>£ | VF<br>£ |
|---|---|---|---|
| 2608 | **Sovereign** (20s.). King crowned r., half-length, first bust with plain armour. R. EXVRGAT, etc.; *mm.* thistle | 975 | 2750 |
| 2609 | — second bust with decorated armour; *mm.* thistle, lis | 1000 | 2850 |

2610                                                    2612

| 2610 | **Half-sovereign.** Crowned bust r. R. EXVRGAT, etc.; *mm.* thistle | 1750 | 5500 |
|---|---|---|---|
| 2611 | **Crown.** Similar. R. TVEATVR, etc.; *mm.* 125, 105/125 | 1350 | 3500 |
| 2612 | **Halfcrown.** Similar; *mm.* thistle, lis | 675 | 1650 |

**N.B.** *The Quarter-Angel of this coinage is considered to be a pattern (possibly a later strike), although coin weights are known.*

**Second coinage, 1604-19** (Obverse legend reads D' G' MAG : BRIT : etc.)

2613                                    2614

| 2613 | **Rose-ryal** (30s., 33s. from 1612). King enthroned. R. Shield on rose; *mm.* 33-90, 25-132 | 1600 | 3750 |
|---|---|---|---|
| 2614 | **Spur ryal** (15s., 16s. 6d. from 1612). King in ship; *mm.* 33, 79, 74, 25-32, 132 | 2350 | 6750 |
| 2615 | **Angel** (10s., 11s. from 1612). Old type but larger shield; *mm.* 33-74, 60-16 | 675 | 1650 |
| 2616 | —— pierced for use as touch-piece | 425 | 850 |
| 2617 | **Half-angel** (5s., 5s. 6d. from 1612). Similar; *mm.* 71-132, 7a, 16 | 1500 | 4500 |

|      |                                                                                                      | F    | VF   |
|------|------------------------------------------------------------------------------------------------------|------|------|
|      |                                                                                                      | £    | £    |
| 2618 | **Unite** (20s., 22s. from 1612). Half-length second bust r. R. FACIAM etc.; *mm.* lis or rose ...... | 450  | 1050 |
| 2619 | — fourth bust; *mm.* rose to cinquefoil .......................                                       | 400  | 875  |

2620

2622                                    2624

| 2620 | — fifth bust; *mm.* cinquefoil to saltire ......................................                       | 400 | 875 |
| 2621 | **Double-crown**. Third bust r. R. HENRICVS, etc.; *mm.* lis or rose ........                          | 325 | 775 |
| 2622 | Fourth bust; *mm.* rose to bell .......................................                                | 300 | 725 |
| 2623 | Fifth bust; *mm.* key, mullet to saltire ...............................                               | 275 | 700 |
| 2624 | **Britain crown**. First bust r.; *mm.* lis to coronet .......................                         | 200 | 525 |
| 2625 | Third bust; *mm.* key to cinquefoil ...............................                                    | 200 | 525 |
| 2626 | Fifth bust; *mm.* cinquefoil to saltire ...........................                                    | 185 | 475 |

2627

| 2627 | **Thistle crown** (4s.). As illus.; *mm.* lis to plain cross ......................                  | 200  | 500  |
| 2628 | — IR on only one side or absent both sides; *mm.* 79, 74, 71-123 ..........                          | 210  | 525  |
| 2629 | **Halfcrown**. I' D' G' ROSA SINE SPINA. First bust; *mm.* lis to key .....                          | 175  | 375  |
| 2630 | Third bust; *mm.* key to trefoil, trefoil/tower ...........................                          | 175  | 375  |
| 2631 | Fifth bust; *mm.* cinquefoil to plain cross...............................                           | 165  | 350  |

### Third coinage, 1619-25

| 2632 | **Rose-ryal** (30s.; 196.5 grs.). King enthroned. R. XXX above shield; lis, lion and rose emblems around; *mm.* 24, 125, 105 ...................... | 1750 | 4750 |
| 2633 | Similar but plain back to throne; *mm.* trefoil...........................                            | 1850 | 5000 |

2634 2635

|  | | F £ | VF £ |
|---|---|---|---|
| 2634 | **Spur-ryal** (15s.). As illus. ℞. Somewhat like 2614, but lis are also crowned. *mm.* 24-125, 46 | 2350 | 6750 |
| 2635 | **Angel** (10s.) of new type; *mm.* 24-46 | 900 | 2650 |
| 2636 | — pierced for use as touch-piece | 475 | 1250 |
| 2637 | **Laurel** (20s.; 140.5 gr.). First (large) laur, bust l.; *mm.* 24, 24/- | 550 | 1250 |
| 2638 | Second, medium, square headed bust, `SS' tie ends; *mm.* 24, 33 | 475 | 1000 |
| 2638A | Third, small rounded head, ties wider apart; *mm.* 33, 125 | 450 | 925 |

2638B

| 2638B | Fourth head, very small ties; *mm.* 105, 46 | 400 | 825 |
|---|---|---|---|
| 2638C | Fourth head variety, tie ends form a bracket to value; *mm.* lis | 425 | 900 |
| 2639 | Fifth, small rather crude bust; *mm.* trefoil | 1350 | 4000 |

2640 2641A

| 2640 | **Half-laurel**. First bust; *mm.* spur rowel | 425 | 950 |
|---|---|---|---|
| 2641 | — As 2638A; *mm.* rose | 425 | 950 |
| 2641A | — As 2638B; *mm.* 33-46, 105/- | 350 | 700 |
| 2642 | **Quarter-laurel**. Bust with two loose tie ends; *mm.* 24-105 | 185 | 450 |
| 2642A | Bust as 2638C; *mm.* 105, 46, 105/46 | 185 | 450 |

2642B

| | F | VF |
|---|---|---|
| | £ | £ |

2642B As last but beaded, i.c. on *rev.* or both sides; *mm.* 105, 46 ..................... 200 475
*Rev. mm. on* ¹/₂ *and* ¹/₄ *laurels normally follows REGNA.*

## SILVER

2643

**First coinage, 1603-4**

| 2643 | **Crown**. King on horseback. R. EXVRGAT, etc., shield; *mm.* thistle, lis | 950 | 2750 |
| 2644 | **Halfcrown**. Similar................................................................................ | 1100 | 3500 |

2645                                                  2646

| 2645 | **Shilling**. First bust, square-cut beard. R. EXVRGAT, etc.; *mm.* thistle... | 110 | 450 |
| 2646 | — Second bust, beard appears to merge with collar; *mm.* thistle, lis ....... | 80 | 250 |
| 2647 | **Sixpence**. First bust; 1603; *mm.* thistle.................................................... | 90 | 300 |

| | | |
|---|---|---|
| 2649 | 2650 | 2651 |

| | | F | VF |
|---|---|---|---|
| | | £ | £ |
| 2648 | Second bust; 1603-4; *mm.* thistle, lis ...................................................... | 45 | 175 |
| 2649 | **Halfgroat**. Second bust, II behind head; *mm.* thistle, lis ......................... | 25 | 70 |
| 2650 | **Penny**. First bust I behind head; *mm.* thistle............................................ | 50 | 175 |
| 2650A | — Second bust; *mm.* thistle, lis................................................................ | 15 | 50 |
| 2651 | **Halfpenny**. As illustration; *mm.* thistle, lis ............................................. | 15 | 45 |

**Second coinage, 1604-19**

| | | | |
|---|---|---|---|
| 2652 | **Crown**. King on horseback. ℞. QVAE DEVS, etc. *rev.* stops; *mm.* 105-84 | 825 | 2350 |

2653

| | | | |
|---|---|---|---|
| 2653 | **Halfcrown**. Similar; *mm.* 105-79 ............................................................ | 1250 | 3750 |
| 2654 | **Shilling**. Third bust, beard cut square and stands out (*cf.* illus. 2657); *mm.* lis, rose ...................................................................................................... | 75 | 225 |
| 2655 | — Fourth bust, armour plainer (*cf.* 2658); *mm.* 33-74, 90 over 74, or 60 over 74........................................................................................................... | 75 | 250 |

2656

| | | | |
|---|---|---|---|
| 2656 | — Fifth bust, similar, but hair longer; *mm.* 74-7a (a variety has a single arched crown, *mm.* 74) ........................................................................... | 80 | 275 |

2657                                          2658

|        |                                                                                            | F | VF |
|        |                                                                                            | £ | £  |

| 2657 | **Sixpence**. Third bust; 1604-6; *mm.* lis, rose, escallop | 45 | 160 |
| 2658 | — Fourth bust; 1605-16; *mm.* rose to book, 90/60, 25/60 | 50 | 175 |
| 2658A | — Fifth bust, 1618; *mm.* plain cross | 700 | 2000 |
| 2659 | **Halfgroat**. As illus. but larger crown on *obv.*; *mm.* lis to coronet | 15 | 45 |

2660                                    2663

| 2660 | —— Similar, but smaller crown on *obv.*; *mm.* coronet to plain cross | 15 | 45 |
| 2660A | As before, but TVEATVR legend both sides; *mm.* plain cross over book | 35 | 100 |
| 2661 | **Penny**. As halfgroat but no crowns; *mm.* 105-32,7a and none, -/84, 32/- | 15 | 45 |
| 2662 | — As before but TVEATVR legend both sides; *mm.* mullet | 30 | 90 |
| 2663 | **Halfpenny**. As illus.; *mm.* 105- 25, 32; all *mms* on *rev.* only | 15 | 40 |

### Third coinage, 1619-25

| 2664 | **Crown**. As 2652, with plain or grass ground line, colon stops on *obv.*, no stops on *rev.*; *mm.* 33-46 | 625 | 1450 |

2665

| 2665 | —— plume over shield; *mm.* 125-46 | 800 | 2250 |

2666

| | F | VF |
|---|---|---|
| | £ | £ |

2666 **Halfcrown**. As 2664 but normally plain ground line only; all have bird-
headed harp; *mm*. 33-46 ............................................................ 225 | 750

2666A— — Similar but no ground line; *mm*. rose ............................................. 475 | 1350

| 2667 | | 2669 |

2667 — — Plume over shield; groundline *mm*. 125-46 .................................... 350 | 1200

2668 **Shilling**. Sixth (large) bust, hair longer and very curly; *mm*. 24-46 ........ 85 | 300

2669 — — plume over shield; *mm*. 125-46 ....................................................... 200 | 675

2670                          2672

2670 **Sixpence**. Sixth bust; 1621-4; *mm*. 33-46; 1621/0, *mm*. rose ................... 50 | 175

2671 **Halfgroat**. As 2660 but no stops on *rev*.; *mm*. 24-46 and none, 105 and 46,
46/- *mm*. 24 with *rev*. stops known .......................................................... 15 | 40

2671A Similar but no inner circles; *mm*. lis, trefoil over lis .............................. 20 | 60

2672 **Penny**. As illus.; *mm*. 24, 105, two pellets, none, trefoil, ........................ 15 | 35

2672A— Similar but without inner circles on one or both sides; *mm*. lis, two
pellets ................................................................................................. 15 | 40

2673 **Halfpenny**. As 2663, but no *mm*. ......................................................... 15 | 35

## COPPER

For further details see C. Wilson Peck, *English Copper, Tin and Bronze Coins in the British Museum, 1558-1958.*

2674                      2675                      2676

|  | F £ | VF £ |
|---|---|---|
| 2674 **Farthing**. 'Harington', small size. 1a, (originally tinned surface). Mintmark on or below cushion of crown. *mm:* A, B, C, D, F, S, Ermine, Millrind, Pellet, :< | 50 | 100 |
| 2675 — — 1b, (occasionally tinned surface). Mintmark replaces central jewel on circlet of crown. *mm:* Trefoil, Crescent, Mullet or crown unmodified | 35 | 70 |
| 2676 — 2, normal size, mintmark on reverse only; *mm.* Cinquefoil, Cross saltire, Lis, Martlet, Mullet, Trefoil | 20 | 40 |
| 2677 'Lennox'. 3a; mintmark on reverse only; *mm.* Bell, Tower | 25 | 50 |

2678                      2679                      2680

| 2678 — 3b; *mm.* mintmark both sides; *mm:* Flower, Fusil | 8 | 20 |
|---|---|---|
| 2679 — — 3c; mintmark on obverse only; *mm.* Annulet, Bell, Coronet, Crescent, Cross flory fitchée, Cross patée fourchée, Dagger, Eagle's head, Fusil, Grapes, Key, Lion passant, Mascle, Quatrefoil, Rose (double), Star, Star (pierced), Thistlehead, Trefoil, Triangle, Triangle (pellet below), Tun, Woolpack | 8 | 20 |
| 2680 — — 3d; las 3c but with larger crowns; *mm:* A, Dagger, Fusil, Lion rampant, Lis (three), Mascle, Stirrip, Trefoil, Triangle, Tun | 8 | 20 |
| 2681 — 4; oval flan, legend starts at bottom left; *mm:* Cross patée. Originally issued for use in Ireland. | 60 | 120 |

2681

Numismatically, this reign is one of the most interesting. Some outstanding machine-made coins were produced by Nicholas Briot, a French die-sinker, but they could not be struck at sufficient speed to supplant hand-hammering methods, and the weights often had to be adjusted by blank filing. In 1637 a branch mint was set up at Aberystwyth to coin silver extracted from the Welsh mines. After the king's final breach with Parliament the parliamentary government continued to issue coins at London with Charles's name and portrait until the king's trial and execution. The coinage of copper farthings continued to be manufactured privately under licences held first by the Duchess of Richmond, then by Lord Maltravers and later by various other persons. The licence was finally revoked by Parliament in 1644.

During the Civil War coins were struck at a number of towns to supply coinage for those areas of the country under Royalist control. Many of these coins have an abbreviated form of the 'Declaration' made at Wellington, Shropshire, Sept., 1642, in which Charles promised to uphold the Protestant Religion, the Laws of England and the Liberty of Parliament. Amongst the more spectacular pieces are the gold triple unites and the silver pounds and half-pounds struck at Shrewsbury and Oxford, and the emergency coins, some made from odd-shaped pieces of silver plate during the sieges of Newark, Scarborough, Carlisle and Pontefract.

*Mintmarks*

| 105 | 10 | 96 | 71 | 57 | 88 | 101 | 35 |
|-----|----|----|----|----|----|-----|----|

| 87 | 107 | 60 | 75 | 123 | 57 | 119a | 23 |
|----|-----|----|----|-----|----|------|----|

| 119b | 98 | 112 | 81 | 120 | 109 |
|------|----|----|----|-----|-----|

**Tower Mint under Charles I**

| 1625 | Lis (105) | 1633-4 | Portcullis (107) |
|------|-----------|--------|------------------|
| 1625-6 | Cross Calvary (10) | 1634-5 | Bell (60) |
| 1626-7 | Negro's head (96) | 1635-6 | Crown (75) |
| 1627-8 | Castle (71) | 1636-8 | Tun (123) |
| 1628-9 | Anchor (57) | 1638-9 | Anchor (57) |
| 1629-30 | Heart (88) | 1639-40 | Triangle (119a) |
| 1630-1 | Plume (101) | 1640-1 | Star (23) |
| 1631-2 | Rose (35) | 1641-3 | Triangle in circle |
| 1632-3 | Harp (87) | | (119b) |

**Tower Mint under Parliament**

| 1643-4 | P in brackets (98) |
|--------|---------------------|
| 1644-5 | R in brackets (112) |
| 1645 | Eye (81) |
| 1645-6 | Sun (120) |
| 1646-8 | Sceptre (109) |

Mint mark no. 57 maybe upright, inverted, or horizontal to left or right.

| 59 | B | 58 *var* | 58 |
|----|----|----------|----|

**Briot's Mint**

| 1631-2 | Flower and B (59) | 1638-9 | Anchor (57) |
|--------|-------------------|--------|-------------|
| 1632 | **B** | | Anchor and B (58) |
| | | | (B upright or on side) |
| | | | Anchor and mullet (58v) |

| | | | | | | | |
|---|---|---|---|---|---|---|---|
| 61 | 104 | 35 | 92 | 103 | 6 | 65b | 71 |

| | | | | | | | |
|---|---|---|---|---|---|---|---|
| 89 | 91 *var* | 131 | 84 | 94 *var* | 64 | 93 | 34 |

| | | | | | | | |
|---|---|---|---|---|---|---|---|
| 102 | 67 | 127 | 128 | 129 | 25 | 83 | 100 |

| | | | | |
|---|---|---|---|---|
| 134 | 71 | A | B | 75 |

**Provincial Mints**

| | |
|---|---|
| 1638-42 | Book (61, *Aberystwyth*) |
| 1642 | Plume (104, *Shrewsbury*) |
| | Pellets or pellet (*Shrewsbury*) |
| 1642-3 | Rose (35, *Truro*) |
| | Bugle (134, *Truro*) |
| 1642-4 | Lion (92, *York*) |
| 1642-6 | Plume (103, *Oxford*) |
| | Pellet or pellets (*Oxford*) |
| | Lis (105, *Oxford*) |
| 1643 | Cross pattee (6, *Bristol*) |
| | Acorn (65b, *Bristol*) |
| | Castle (71, *Worcester* or *Shrewsbury*) |
| | Helmet (89, *Worcester* and *Shrewsbury*) |
| 1643-4 | Leopard's head (91 var. *Worcester*) |
| | Two lions (131, *Worcester*) |
| | Lis (105, *Worcs.* or *Shrews.*) |
| | Bunch of grapes (84, *Worcs.* or *Shrews.*) |
| | Bird (94 var., *Worcs.* or *Shrews.*) |

| | |
|---|---|
| 1643-4 | Boar's head (64 *Worcs.* or *Shrews.*) |
| | Lion rampant (93, *Worcs.* or *Shrews.*) |
| | Rosette (34, *Worcs.* or *Shrews.*) |
| 1643-5 | Plume (102, *Bristol*) |
| | Br. (67, *Bristol*) |
| | Pellets (*Bristol*) |
| | Rose (35, *Exeter*) |
| | Rosette (34, *Oxford*) |
| 1643-6 | Floriated cross (127, *Oxford*) |
| 1644 | Cross pattee (6, *Oxford*) |
| | Lozenge (128, *Oxford*) |
| | Billet (129, *Oxford*) |
| | Mullet (25, *Oxford*) |
| 1644-5 | Gerb (83, *Chester*) |
| | Pear (100, *Worcester*) |
| | Lis (105, *Hereford?*) |
| | Castle (71, *Exeter*) |
| 1645-6 | Plume (102, *Ashby, Bridgnorth*) |
| 1645 | A (*Ashby*) |
| 1646 | B (*Bridgnorth*) |
| 1648-9 | Crown (75, *Aberystwyth Furnace*) |

# GOLD

**Tower mint, under the King, 1625-42**

**Tower Gold**

|  |  | F | VF |
|---|---|---|---|
|  |  | £ | £ |
| 2682 | **Angel**. As for James I last issue, but *rev.* reads AMOR POPVLI etc; without mark of value; *mm.* lis and cross calvary .................. | 1650 | 5000 |
| 2683 | — — pierced for use as touch-piece ...................... | 725 | 2000 |
| 2684 | — X in field to r.; *mm.* 96-88, 71 and 96/71, 57 and 71/57 ..................... | 1350 | 4500 |
| 2685 | — — — pierced for use as touch-piece .................. | 525 | 1350 |
| 2686 | — X in field to l.; *mm.* 96, 88, 35-23 .................. | 1350 | 4500 |

2687

| 2687 | — — — pierced for use as touch-piece .................. | 525 | 1350 |
|---|---|---|---|
| 2688 | **Unite** (20s.). First bust with ruff and collar of order, high double-crown. R. Square-topped shield; *mm.* lis. .................. | 450 | 1100 |
| 2688A | — Similar, but extra garnishing to shield; *mm.* lis .................. | 500 | 1200 |
| 2689 | — Similar, but flat single-arched crown; *mm.* lis, cross calvary .............. | 475 | 1150 |
| 2689A | R. As 2688A. *mm.* lis .................. | 525 | 1250 |

2690

| 2690 | Second bust with ruff and armour nearly concealed with scarf; R. Square-topped shield with slight garnishing *mm.* 10-88 .................. | 450 | 1000 |
|---|---|---|---|
| 2690A | Similar but more elongated bust, usually dividing legend. *mm.* 57-101, 88/101 .................. | 450 | 1000 |
| 2691 | — As 2690A but *mm.* anchor below bust .................. | 975 | 2750 |
| 2691A | *Obv.* as 2690A. R. As next: *mm.* plume .................. | 700 | 1650 |
| 2692 | Third bust, more armour visible. R. Oval shield with CR at sides; *mm.* 101, 35. | 475 | 1100 |
| 2693 | Fourth bust, small lace collar with large high crown usually breaking i.c., long hair. Garter ribbon on breast. R. Oval shield with crowned CR at sides; *mm.* harp, portcullis .................. | 450 | 1000 |
| 2693A | Similar, but unjewelled crown, within or touching i.c.; *mm.* 107-23 ........ | 425 | 950 |
| 2694 | Sixth (Briot's) bust, large lace collar. R. Similar; *mm.* 119a-119b .......... | 450 | 1050 |

2696                          2696A                          2697

|  | | F | VF |
|---|---|---|---|
|  | | £ | £ |
| 2696 | **Double-crown**. First bust. As 2688. R. Square-topped shield; *mm*. lis.... | 525 | 1350 |
| 2696A | Similar to last but wider flatter double-arched crown; *mm*. 105, 10......... | 425 | 950 |
| 2697* | Second bust. R. Similar to 2690; *mm*. 10-57 ........................................... | 300 | 750 |
| 2697A* | Similar to 2690A: *mm*. 57-101 ........................................... | 325 | 750 |
| 2697B | *Obv*. as last. R. As next: *mm*. plume ......................................... | 525 | 1350 |
| 2698 | Third bust. Flat or domed crown. R. Oval shield with CR at sides; *mm*. plume, rose ............................................................... | 350 | 850 |
| 2699 | Fourth bust, large head, high wide crown. R. Oval shield with crowned CR at sides; *mm*. harp, crown............................................................... | 350 | 850 |
| 2699A | — Similar to last, but flat crown, jewelled outer arch: *mm*. 87-123 ........ | 325 | 750 |
| 2699B | — Similar, but smaller head, unjewelled crown: *mm*. 60-57................... | 325 | 750 |
| 2699C | — Sim. to 2699, but bust within i.c.; *mm*. bell ........................................ | 375 | 900 |
| 2700 | Fifth bust (Early Aberystwyth style). R. Similar; *mm*. anchor ................. | 525 | 1350 |
| 2700A | — (Late Aberystwyth style). R. *mm*. anchor, triangle ............................. | 425 | 1100 |
| 2701 | Sixth bust. R. Normal; *mm*. 119a-119b.................................................. | 350 | 850 |

*For these coins inner circles are sometimes omitted on *obv*., *rev*., or both. *See also 2704, 2704A and 2707.*

2703                          2707

| 2703 | **Crown**. First bust with small round crown. R. Square-topped shield; *mm*. lis, cross calvary....................................................................................... | 200 | 450 |
|---|---|---|---|
| 2703A | As 2696A. *mm*. cross calvary.................................................................... | 225 | 575 |
| 2704 | Second bust as 2690. R. Similar; *mm*. 10-71 ........................................ | 200 | 450 |
| 2704A | As 2690A. *mm*. 57-101, 88/-, 57/-, 101/-................................................ | 185 | 400 |
| 2704B | As 2691. Wire line i.c.s on *rev*................................................................ | 525 | 1350 |
| 2705 | *Obv*. as 2690A. R. As next; 101, 35, 101/- ............................................. | 225 | 525 |
| 2706 | Third bust. R. Oval shield with CR at sides; *mm*. plume........................ | 375 | 900 |
| 2707 | Fourth bust. R. Oval shield with crowned CR at sides; *mm*. -/87, 87-119b, 23/119a, 107/60.................................................................................... | 185 | 425 |
| 2708 | Fifth (Aberystwyth style) bust. R. Similar; *mm*. anchor ......................... | 450 | 1250 |

**Tower mint, under Parliament, 1642-9.** All Charles I types

|  |  | *F* | *VF* |
|---|---|---|---|
|  |  | £ | £ |
| 2710 | **Unite**. Fourth bust, as 2693A; *mm.* (P), (P)/-............................................ | 675 | 1650 |
| 2711 | Sixth bust, as 2694 but crude style; *mm.* (P), (R), 119b........................... | 700 | 1750 |

2712

| 2712 | Seventh bust, cruder style; *mm.* eye, sun, sceptre .................................... | 725 | 1850 |
|---|---|---|---|
| 2713 | **Double-crown**. Fourth bust, as 2699B; *mm.* eye .................................... | 650 | 1850 |
| 2714 | Fifth bust, as 2700A; *mm.* sun, sceptre ...................................................... | 550 | 1350 |
| 2715 | Sixth bust, as 2701; *mm.* (P) ................................................................... | 475 | 1100 |
| 2716 | Eighth, dumpy bust with single flat-arched crown; *mm.* sun.................... | 725 | 2250 |
| 2717 | **Crown**. Fourth bust, as 2707 jewelled crown; *mm.* -/98 , 98/-, 98-120.... | 250 | 625 |
| 2717A | Sim. but unjewelled crown. R. Small crude shield; *mm.* 81-109 .............. | 250 | 650 |

**Nicholas Briot's coinage, 1631-2**

| 2718 | **Angel**. Type  somewhat as Tower but smaller and neater; *mm.* -/B ......... | 2750 | 7500 |
|---|---|---|---|

2719

| 2719 | **Unite**. As illustration. R. FLORENT etc.; *mm.* flower and B/B.............. | 2000 | 5500 |
|---|---|---|---|
| 2720 | **Double-crown**. Similar but X.  R. CVLTORES, etc. *mm.* flower and B/B | 1350 | 3500 |
| 2720A | Similar but King's crown unjewelled: *mm.* flower and B/B, B ................ | 1350 | 3500 |
| 2721 | **Crown**. Similar; *mm.* B............................................................................ | 2250 | 6500 |

**Briot's Hammered issue, 1638-9**

2695

| 2721A | **Unite**. Briot's (sixth) bust, large lace collar. R. FLORENT etc., Briot's square-topped shield dividing crowned C R; *mm.* anchor ........................ | 2750 | 8000 |
|---|---|---|---|

|                                                                                      | F | VF |
|--------------------------------------------------------------------------------------|---|----|
|                                                                                      | £ | £  |

2721B **Double-crown**. Briot's bust, similar. R. CVLTORES etc., square-topped
     shield dividing crowned C R; *mm.* anchor ............................................... 1750   5000

2721C **Crown**. Briot's bust, similar. R. CVLTORES etc., oval shield dividing
     crowned C R (a Briot hammered issue/Tower mule); *mm.* anchor ........... 1000   2750

## Provincial issues, 1638-49

### Chester mint, 1644
2722  **Unite**. As Tower. Somewhat like a crude Tower sixth bust. R. Crowned,
     oval shield, crowned CR, *mm.* plume ....................................................... 12500   37500

### Shrewsbury mint, 1642 (See also 2749)
2723  **Triple unite**, 1642. Half-length figure l holding sword and olive-branch;
     *mm.*: R. EXVRGAT, etc., around RELIG PROT, etc., in two wavy lines.
     III and three plumes above, date below ..................................................... 17500   65000

### Oxford mint, 1642-6
2724  **Triple unite**. As last, but *mm.* plume, tall narrow bust, 1642 .................. 4000   9250

2725  Similar, but 'Declaration' on continuous scroll, 1642-3 ............................ 4250   10000

2725A Large bust of fine style. King holds short olive branch; *mm.* small lis ..... 9750   32500

2726  As last, but taller bust, with scarf behind shoulder, 1643, *mm.* plume ..... 4750   10500

2727

| 2727 | Similar, but without scarf, longer olive branch, 1643 .............................. | 4250 | 9250  |
|------|------------------------------------------------------------------------------------|------|-------|
| 2728 | Similar, but OXON below 1643, rosette stops ........................................ | 5250 | 15000 |
| 2729 | Smaller size, olive branch varies, bust size varies, 1644 OXON .............. | 4750 | 10250 |
| 2730 | — Obv. as 2729, 1644 / OX .......................................................... | 5000 | 11000 |
| 2731 | **Unite**. Tall thin bust. R. 'Declaration' in two wavy lines, 1642; *no mm.*... | 1200 | 3000  |
| 2732 | — R. 'Declaration' in three lines on continuous scroll, 1642-3 ................ | 1250 | 3250  |
| 2733 | Tall, well-proportioned bust. R. Similar, 1643, no *mm.* ......................... | 1500 | 4000  |
| 2734 | Shorter bust, king's elbow not visible. R. Similar, 1643; *mm.* plume/- .... | 1100 | 2750  |
| 2735 | Similar but longer olive branch curving to l. 1644 / OX; *mm.* plume ...... | 1100 | 2750  |

2735A

|      |                                                                                  | F | VF |
|------|----------------------------------------------------------------------------------|------|------|
|      |                                                                                  | £ | £ |
| 2735A | Similar, but dumpy bust breaking lower i.c., small flan .......................... | 1350 | 3500 |
| 2736 | Tall bust to edge of coin. R. Similar, 1643 ........................................... | 2000 | 5750 |
| 2737 | As 2734. R. 'Declaration' in three straight lines, 1644 / OX ..................... | 2250 | 6000 |
| 2738 | Similar to 2734, but smaller size; small bust, low olive branch. 1645 ..... | 1650 | 4500 |
| 2739 | — R. Single plume above 'Declaration', 1645-6 / OX; *mm.* plume, rosette, none .......................................................................................... | 1350 | 3750 |
| 2740 | **Half-unite.** 'Declaration' in three straight lines, 1642 ............................. | 1500 | 4500 |
| 2741 | 'Declaration' on scroll; *mm.* plume; 1642-3 ........................................... | 1350 | 4000 |

2742

| 2742 | Bust to bottom of coin, 1643; Oxford plumes ......................................... | 1100 | 2750 |
|------|----------------------------------------------------------------------------------|------|------|
| 2743 | — 1644 / OX. Three Shrewsbury plumes (neater work) ......................... | 1500 | 4500 |
| | **Bristol mint**, 1643-5 | | |
| *2744 | **Unite.** Somewhat as 2734; Two busts known. *mm.* Br. or Br/ plumelet.; 1645............................................................................................................ | 8500 | 26500 |
| 2745 | **Half-unite.** Similar 1645 ...................................................................... | 8500 | 27500 |
| | **Truro mint**, 1642–3 | | |
| 2745A | **Half-Unite.** Crowned bust l. (similar to Tower 4th bust). R. CVLT, etc., crowned shield ........................................................................ | 8750 | 30000 |
| | **Exeter mint**, 1643–5 | | |
| 2746 | **Unite.** *obv.* sim. to early Oxford bust. R. FLORENT, etc., crowned oval shield between crowned CR, *mm.* rose ...................................................... | 13500 | 40000 |
| 2747 | — R. CVLTORES, etc., similar but no CR ............................................ | 13500 | 40000 |
| | **Worcester mint**, 1643-4 | | |
| 2748 | **Unite.** Crude bust R. FLORENT, etc., double annulet stops, crowned oval shield, lion's paws on either side of garniture, no *mm.* ............................. | 12500 | 37500 |
| | **Salopia (Shrewsbury) mint**, 1644 | | |
| 2749 | **Unite.** *Obv.* bust in armour. R. Cr. shield, crowned CR. *mm.* lis/- .......... | 12500 | 37500 |
| | **Colchester besieged**, 1648 | | |
| 2750 | **Ten Shillings** Gateway of castle between CR; below OBS COL 16 S/X 48. Uniface – now considered a later concoction ........................................... | | |

**Pontefract besieged,** 1648-9. After the death of Charles I, in the name of Charles II

| | F £ | VF £ |
|---|---|---|
| 2751 **Unite**. DVM : SPIRO : SPERO around CR crowned. CAROLVS : SECVИDVS : 16 48, castle, OBS on l., PC above.................................... | 27500 | 85000 |
| 2752 **Unite**. CAROL : II, etc., around HANC : DEVS, etc. R. POST : MORTEM, etc., around castle. *Octagonal*.......................................................................... | 25000 | 82500 |

# SILVER

### Tower mint, under the King, 1625-42

| | | |
|---|---|---|
| 2753 **Crown**. King on horseback with raised sword. 1a. Horse caparisoned with plume on head and crupper. R. Square-topped shield over long cross fourchee; *mm*. lis, cross calvary ................................................................ | 625 | 1500 |
| 2754 — 1b. Similar, but plume over shield, no cross; *mm*. 105, 10, 71 ........... | 950 | 2500 |
| 2755 — 2a. Smaller horse, plume on hd. only, cross on housings, king holds sword on shoulder. R. Oval garnished shield over cross fourchee, CR above; *mm*. harp ......................................................................................... | 550 | 1250 |
| 2756 — 2b[1]. — — plume divides CR, no cross; *mm*. plume, rose.................... | 675 | 1650 |
| 2757 — 2b[2]. — — — with cross; *mm*. harp...................................................... | 700 | 1750 |

2758

| | | |
|---|---|---|
| 2758 — 3a. Horse without caparisons. R. Oval shield without CR; *mm*. 60-23 | 575 | 1350 |
| 2759 — 3b. — — plume over shield; *mm*. 107, 75, 123 ................................... | 675 | 1650 |
| 2760 'Briot' horse with ground-line; *mm*. triangle in circle .............................. | 2750 | 7500 |
| 2761 **Halfcrown**. As 2753. 1a[1]. Rose on housings, ground-line; *mm*. lis ......... | 275 | 900 |

2761

| | | |
|---|---|---|
| 2762 — 1a[2]. Similar, but no rose or ground-line; *mm*. 105, 10 over 105.......... | 200 | 525 |
| 2762A — —, with ground-line; *mm*. lis ............................................................. | 325 | 1000 |
| 2763 — 1a[3]. As last but shield not over cross; *mm*. 10 sometimes over lis on one or both sides, 96 ...................................................................................... | 175 | 475 |
| 2763A — Similar but only slight garnishing to shield; *mm*. 10, 71 ................... | 185 | 500 |
| 2763B — As 2763, light weight (204 grains as standard) *mm* 10, (usually over lis) | 275 | 750 |

|      |                                                                                   | F | VF |
|------|-----------------------------------------------------------------------------------|---|----|
|      |                                                                                   | £ | £  |
| 2765 | — 1b. Heavy garnishing, plume over shield; *mm.* 105, 10, 96 | 525 | 1350 |
| 2765A | — Similar but only slight garnishing; *mm.* 96-57 | 525 | 1350 |
| 2766 | — 2/1b. As 2755 but rose on housings. R. As last; *mm.* heart, plume | 925 | 2250 |
| 2767 | — 2a. As 2755. R. Flattened oval garnished shield without cross; *mm.* 101/ | | |
|      | 35 plume, rose, (CR above, divided by rose (very rare), lis over rose (rare), lis) | 95 | 275 |
| 2768 | — 2b. Similar, but large plume between the CR; *mm.* plume, rose | 165 | 575 |
| 2769 | — 2c. As 2a, but differently garnished oval shield with CR at sides; *mm.* | | |
|      | harp, portcullis, portcullis/harp (rare) | 75 | 200 |
| 2770 | — 2d. Similar, but with plume over shield; *mm.* harp | 950 | 2500 |

|      |      |
|------|------|
| 2773 | 2775 |

| 2771 | — 3a¹. No caparisons on horse, upright sword, scarf flies out from waist. | | |
|------|--------------------------------------------------------------------------|---|---|
|      | R. Round garnished shield, no CR; *mm.* 60-119a, 60/75 | 65 | 185 |
| 2772 | — 3b. — — plume over shield; *mm.* 107-123 | 135 | 450 |
| 2773 | — 3a². — cloak flies from king's shoulder; R. Shields vary; *mm.* 123-23, | | |
|      | 119b, 119b over 119a/119b | 60 | 185 |
| 2774 | — — — — rough ground beneath horse; R. Shields vary; *mm.* 119a, 23, | 60 | 185 |
| 2775 | — 4. Foreshortened horse, mane before chest, tail between legs; *mm.* 23, | | |
|      | 119b | 50 | 135 |

*Most late Tower halfcrowns have irregular flans.*

|      |       |
|------|-------|
| 2776 | 2776A |

| 2776 | **Shilling**. 1. Bust in ruff, high crown, jewelled arches. R. Square-topped | | |
|------|------------------------------------------------------------------------------|---|----|
|      | shield over cross fourchee; *mm.* lis, (normal weight 92.9 gr.) | 95 | 400 |
| 2776A | — Similar but larger crown, plain inner arch; *mm.* 105, 10 over 105 | 85 | 350 |
| 2777 | Similar but light weight (81.75 grs.); *mm.* 105, 10 over 105 | 100 | 425 |
| 2778 | — 1b¹. As 2776A, but plume over shield, no cross; *mm.* 105, 10 over 105 | 475 | 1500 |
| 2779 | — 1a. Bust in ruff and armour concealed by scarf. R. As 2776; 10-71 | 85 | 300 |
| 2780 | — — — — light weight; *mm.* cross Calvary (often extremely small XII) | 90 | 325 |
| 2781 | — 1b². As 2779, but plume over shield, no cross; *mm.* 10-101 | | |
|      | (five bust varieties) | 135 | 475 |
| 2781A | — — light weight 1b² *mm.* 10 | 150 | 525 |
| 2782 | — 1b³, — — — cross; *mm.* negro's head | 1250 | 3000 |

|                                                                                 | F    | VF   |
|                                                                                 | £    | £    |
| 2783 — 2a. More armour visible. R. Oval shield, CR above; *mm.* 35, 101, 101 over 88/101, (three bust varieties) | 65   | 250  |
| 2784 — 2b. — — plume over shield; *mm.* 101, 35, 101 over 88/101, (three bust varieties) | 150  | 550  |
| 2785 — 3[1]. Bust with lace collar, (six bust varieties). R. Flattish oval shield, CR at sides; *mm.* harp, portcullis | 45   | 225  |
| 2786 — 3[2]. — — plume over shield; *mm.* harp (three bust varieties) | 750  | 2250 |

2787                                                   2793

| 2787 — 3a. — no inner circles, rounder shield without CR; *mm.* 60-123 (five bust varieties) | 35   | 165  |
| 2788 — 3b. — — plume over shield; *mm.* 60-123 (Two bust varieties) | 95   | 325  |
| 2789 — 4[1]. Large Aberystwyth bust, medium or small XII. R. Square-topped shield over cross fleury; *mm.* tun, 57 over 123 (obv.) small neat cross ends | 85   | 300  |
| 2790 — 4[1]. var. Similar, but rounder shoulders, large XII; *mm.* 57, 119a, (cross ends vary) | 40   | 175  |
| 2790A— *O* as above. R As Briot's 1st or 2nd hammered issue *mm* Δ over anchor | 250  | 850  |
| 2791 — 4[2]. Smaller Aberystwyth bust with small double-arched crown, small XII, *mm.* tun, small neat cross ends; large XII, *mm.* tun, anchor | 60   | 225  |
| 2792 — 4[3]. — single-arches, large XII; *mm.* 123, 57, 119a, 119b (cross ends vary) | 35   | 150  |
| 2793 — 4[4]. Older (Briot's style) bust, very pointed beard; *mm.* 119a-119b | 35   | 135  |
| 2793A— *Obv.* as last. R. as Briot's 2nd hammered issue. *mm.* Δ/Δ over anchor | 225  | 750  |
| 2794 **Sixpence.** 1. As 2776, but dated 1625-6; small bust *mm.* lis, large bust *mm.* lis. 10 (*rare*) | 75   | 300  |
| 2794A— Lightweight, 40.85 grains; large bust *mm* 10, 1625-6 | 95   | 375  |
| 2795 — 1a[1]. As 2779, but dated 1625-9; *mm.* 10-88 (busts vary) | 85   | 350  |
| 2795A   Lightweight, 40.85 grains, 1626 *mm* 10 | 100  | 375  |
| 2796 — 1a[2]. — no cross, 1630; *mm.* heart, plume | 200  | 675  |

2797                              2799                    2802

| 2797 — 2a. As 2783, no date; *mm.* plume, rose | 55   | 250  |
| 2798 — 2b. — plume dividing CR; *mm.* plume, rose, plume/rose | 75   | 375  |
| 2799 — 3. As 2785; *mm.* harp, portcullis (busts and crowns vary) | 40   | 150  |
| 2799A— 3. As above but no CR *mm.* portcullis | 125  | 450  |

|  | | F | VF |
|---|---|---|---|
|  | | £ | £ |
| 2800 | — 3a. no inner circles; *mm.* 60-123 (busts and crowns vary).................. | 35 | 145 |
| 2801 | — 4[1]. As first Aberystwyth sixpence, double-arch crown, small VI. R. Square-topped shield over cross; *mm.* tun | 65 | 250 |
| 2801A | — 4[1.] Similar but lyre cross ends on *rev*, *mm.* tun .......................... | 90 | 375 |
| 2802 | — 4[1]. var. — similar, but large VI; *mm.* tun, anchor.............................. | 40 | 175 |
| 2803 | — 4[2]. Second Aberystwyth bust, single-arched crown; *mm.* 123, 57, 119a | 35 | 165 |
| 2804 | — 4[2]. larger bust, *mm.* triangle ................................................................. | 45 | 185 |
| 2805 | — 4[3]. Older (Briot's style) bust; *mm.* 119a-119b (moline cross ends)..... | 40 | 175 |

2806          2808          2818

| 2806 | **Halfgroat**. 1. Crowned rose type. Beaded and/or wire line inner circles on one or both sides. *mm* 105, 105/–, 10, 96, no *mm*............................... | 25 | 75 |
|---|---|---|---|
| 2807 | — 1a. —— similar but without inner circles, *mm* 96–101 ...................... | 25 | 80 |
| 2808 | — 2a. King's 2nd bust in ruff and mantle. R. Oval shield; *mm.* plume, rose | 25 | 85 |
| 2809 | — 2b. Similar, but with plume over shield; *mm.* plume, rose, plume/-.... | 30 | 110 |
| 2809A | —— 2a Var. 3rd bust, with more armour. breaks i.c. at top. R. As last; *mm.* plume, rose ...................................................................................... | 25 | 85 |
| 2809B | —— Sim. but plume over shield; *mm.* plume................................................ | 30 | 120 |
| 2810 | — 3[1]. Bust with lace collar. R. Oval shield between CR; no inner circles; *mm.* harp, portcullis, crown............................................................... | 20 | 50 |
| 2811 | — 3[2]. —— inner circles *mm.* harp, portcullis or ··/harp ......................... | 20 | 45 |
| 2812 | — 3[3]. —— inner circle on R. *mm.* harp, portcullis ............................. | 20 | 50 |
| 2813 | — 3[4]. —— inner circle on O. *mm.* harp, portcullis ............................. | 20 | 50 |
| 2814 | — 3[5]. —— no CR, no inner circles; *mm.* portcullis ............................. | 25 | 60 |
| 2815 | — 3[6]. ——— inner circles on *obv.*; *mm.* harp, portcullis, ................... | 25 | 60 |
| 2816 | — 3a[1]. — R. Rounder shield, different garniture, no i.cs.; *mm.* 60-119a. | 20 | 45 |
| 2817 | — 3a[2]. —— inner circle on *obv.*; *mm.* triangle, anchor........................ | 25 | 65 |
| 2818 | — 3a[3]. —— inner circles both sides; *mm.* 119a-119b ........................ | 20 | 50 |
| 2819 | — 3a[4]. Aberystwyth bust, no inner circles; *mm.* anchor........................ | 40 | 90 |
| 2820 | — 3a[5]. — inner circle on *rev.*; *mm.* anchor ..................................... | 40 | 95 |
| 2821 | — 3a[6]. Very small bust, no inner circles; *mm.* anchor............................ | 50 | 125 |

2822          2828          2831

| 2822 | **Penny**. 1. Rose each side; i.cs.; *mm.* 96, :/lis, lis/:, one or two pellets, lis | 20 | 40 |
|---|---|---|---|
| 2823 | — 1a. — no i.cs.; *mm.* lis, one or two pellets, anchor ............................. | 20 | 40 |
| 2824 | — 1b. — i.c. on *rev.*; *mm.* negro's head/two pellets................................. | 40 | 100 |
| 2825 | — 2. Bust in ruff and mantle. R. Oval shield; i.cs.; *mm.* plume, plume/rose, rose | 30 | 75 |
| 2826 | — 2[1]. —— no i.cs.; *mm.* plume, rose ...................................................... | 30 | 75 |
| 2827 | — 2a[1]. More armour visible; no i.cs.; *mm.* plume, rose, plume/rose........ | 20 | 60 |
| 2828 | — 2a[2]. — i.c. on *obv.*; *mm.* plume, rose, plume over rose ...................... | 25 | 65 |
| 2829 | — 2a[3]. — i.cs. both sides; *mm.* plume, rose ............................................ | 20 | 60 |
| 2830 | — 2a[4]. — i.c. on *rev.*; *mm.* rose over plume............................................ | 30 | 75 |

|        |                                                                         | *F* | *VF* |
|--------|-------------------------------------------------------------------------|-----|------|
|        |                                                                         | £   | £    |
| 2831   | — 3¹. Bust in lace collar. R. CR at sides of shield; no i.cs.; *mm.* harp, one or two pellets. ··/harp (also *obv.* i.c. *mm.* harp) | 15 | 35 |
| 2832   | — 3². — similar but no CR; *mm.* 87, 107, 107/··, pellets, none | 15 | 35 |
| 2833   | — 3³. — — i.c. on *obv.*; *mm.* harp,··, | 15 | 40 |
| 2834   | — 3⁴. — — i.c. on *rev.*; *mm.* harp | 20 | 50 |
| 2835   | — 3a¹. — similar, but shield almost round and with scroll garniture; no i.cs.; *mm.* bell, triangle, one to four pellets, none, bell/·· | 15 | 40 |
| 2835A  | — 3a¹ variety — i.c. on *obv.*, *rev.* or both sides; *mm.* triangle/two pellets, Δ,··, | 20 | 50 |
| 2836   | — 3a³. Aberystwyth bust; i.c. on *obv.* or none; *mm.* one or two pellets or triangle or anchor or none; or a mule of these *mms.* | 20 | 45 |

2837

| 2837 | **Halfpenny**. Rose each side; no legend or *mm.* | 15 | 40 |

*Many small denominations have uneven irregular flans.*

### Tower mint, under Parliament, 1642-8. All Charles I type

| 2838 | **Crown**. 4. Foreshortened horse; *mm.* (P) to sun | 600 | 1450 |
|------|------|------|------|
| 2839 | — 5. Tall spirited horse; *mm.* sun | 725 | 1850 |
| 2840 | **Halfcrown**. 3a³. As 2773, but coarse work; *mm.* (P) to sun, 81/120 | 45 | 150 |
| 2841 | — 4. Foreshortened horse; *mm.* (P) | 150 | 575 |
| 2842 | — 5. Tall horse; *mm.* sun, sceptre | 60 | 175 |
| 2843 | **Shilling**. 4⁴. Briot style bust, *mm.* (P), (R); coarse work; *mm.* eye, sun | 35 | 145 |
| 2843A | — 4⁴ var. Narrow bust with double arched crown and pronounced nick in truncation, *mm.* sun | 275 | 650 |

2844                                 2845

| 2844 | — 4⁵. Long narrow coarse bust; *mm.* sun, sceptre | 50 | 200 |
|------|------|------|------|
| 2845 | — 4⁶. Short bust with narrow crown; *mm.* sceptre | 55 | 225 |

2845A

| 2845A | — — Short broad bust, as illus., broader crown; *mm.* sceptre | 70 | 275 |
|-------|------|------|------|
| 2846  | **Sixpence**. 4³. Briot style bust; *mm.* (P) (R) | 65 | 225 |

2847                    2848

| | F £ | VF £ |
|---|---|---|
| 2847  — $4^4$. Late Aberystwyth bust modified; *mm.* (P) to sceptre .................... | 55 | 200 |
| 2848  — $4^5$. Squat bust of crude style; *mm.* eye, sun over eye .......................... | 100 | 350 |
| 2848A— $4^5$ var., small bust with double arched crown, like the small 3a portrait, inner circle on *obv. mm.* sun over eye...................................................... | 275 | 750 |
| 2849  **Halfgroat**. $3a^3$. Sim. to 2818; *mm.* (P) to sceptre, 98/119b..................... | 20 | 65 |
| 2850  — $3a^7$. Older, shorter bust, pointed beard; *mm.* eye to sceptre................ | 20 | 65 |
| 2851  **Penny**. $3a^2$. Older bust; *mm.* pellets, i.c. on *obv.* only............................ | 20 | 75 |

## Nicholas Briot's coinage, 1631-9

### First milled issue, 1631-2

| | F £ | VF £ |
|---|---|---|
| 2852  **Crown**. King on horseback. ℞. Crowned shield between CR crowned; *mm.* flower and B / B .............................................................................. | 725 | 1750 |

2853

| | F £ | VF £ |
|---|---|---|
| 2853  **Halfcrown**. Similar................................................................................ | 375 | 1250 |
| 2854  **Shilling**. Briot's early bust with falling lace collar. ℞. Square-topped shield over long cross fourchee; ℞. Legend starts at top or bottom (extr. rare) *mm.* flower and B/B, B........................................................................ | 275 | 750 |

2855

| | F £ | VF £ |
|---|---|---|
| 2855  **Sixpence**. Similar, but VI behind bust; *mm.* flower and B/B, flower and B/- | 135 | 375 |

2856                    2856A

|      |                                                                                                           | F £ | VF £ |
|------|-----------------------------------------------------------------------------------------------------------|-----|------|
| 2856 | **Halfgroat**. Briot's bust, B below, II behind. R. IVSTITIA, etc., square-topped shield over long cross fourchee | 45  | 125  |
| 2856A| Pattern halfgroat. Uncrowned bust in ruff r. R. crowned, interlocked Cs. (North 2687). (Included because of its relatively regular appearance.) | 45  | 125  |
| 2857 | **Penny**. Similar, but I behind bust, B below bust; position of legend may vary | 50  | 135  |

**Second milled issue**, 1638-9

2859

|      |                                                                                                           | F   | VF   |
|------|-----------------------------------------------------------------------------------------------------------|-----|------|
| 2858 | **Halfcrown**. As 2853, but *mm*. anchor and B | 300 | 850  |
| 2859 | **Shilling**. Briot's late bust, the falling lace collar is plain with broad lace border, no scarf. R. As 2854 but cross only to inner circle; *mm*. anchor and B, anchor or muled | 150 | 450  |
| 2860 | **Sixpence**. Similar, but VI; *mm*. anchor, anchor and mullet/anchor | 65  | 175  |
|      | *The two last often exhibit flan reduction marks.* |     |      |

**Briot's hammered issue**, 1638-9

|      |                                                                                                           | F   | VF   |
|------|-----------------------------------------------------------------------------------------------------------|-----|------|
| 2861 | **Halfcrown**. King on Briot's style horse with ground line. R. Square-topped shield; *mm*. anchor, triangle over anchor. Also muled with Tower *rev*. | 725 | 2000 |
| 2862 | **Shilling**. Briot's first hammered issue, Sim. to 2859; R. Square-topped shield over short cross fleury, contraction stops on *obv*., pellet stops *rev. mm*. anchor | 600 | 1750 |
| 2862A| — Briot's second hammered issue. As 2862 but lozenge stops both sides. *mm*. anchor, triangle over anchor or triangle | 300 | 850  |

**Provincial and Civil War issues, 1638-49**
**York mint**, 1643-4. *Mm*. lion

|      |                                                                                                           | F   | VF   |
|------|-----------------------------------------------------------------------------------------------------------|-----|------|
| 2863 | **Halfcrown**. 1. Ground-line below horse. R. Square-topped shield between CR | 575 | 1650 |
| 2864 | — 2. — R. Oval shield as Tower 3a, groundline grass or dotted | 475 | 1350 |
| 2865 | — 3. No ground-line. R. Similar | 450 | 1250 |
| 2866 | *— 4. As last, but EBOR below horse with head held low. Base metal, often very base | 75  | 225  |
| 2867 | — 5. Tall horse, mane in front of chest, EBOR below. R. Crowned square-topped shield between CR, floral spray in legend | 300 | 850  |

*These pieces are contemporary forgeries (Besly, the York mint of Charles I, BNJ 54, 1984)

2868

| | | F | VF |
| --- | --- | --- | --- |
| | | £ | £ |
| 2868 | — 6. As last, but shield is oval, garnished (*rev.* detail variations) ........... | 250 | 700 |
| 2869 | — 7. Similar, but horse's tail shows between legs. R. Shield as last, but with lion's skin garniture, no CR or floral spray ............................................ | 225 | 650 |

2870

| 2870 | **Shilling**. 1. Bust in scalloped lace collar similar to 3¹. R. EBOR above square-topped shield over cross fleury ............................................................ | 200 | 600 |
| --- | --- | --- | --- |
| 2871 | — 2. Similar, but bust in plain armour, mantle; coarse work ................... | 225 | 650 |
| 2872 | — 3. *Obv.* as above illustration. — R. EBOR below oval shield ............. | 225 | 650 |
| 2873 | — 4. — Similar, but crowned oval shield (*obv.* finer style) ..................... | 175 | 525 |
| 2874 | — 5. — As last, but lion's skin garniture ............................................. | 175 | 525 |
| 2875 | **Sixpence**. *Obv.* Sim. to 2870. Crowned oval shield ................................ | 250 | 725 |

2876                                    2877

| 2876 | — — Crowned CR at sides................................................................. | 225 | 600 |
| --- | --- | --- | --- |
| 2877 | **Threepence**. As type 1 shilling, but III behind bust. R. As 2870............. | 55 | 150 |

**Aberystwyth mint**, 1638/9-42. *Mm.* book.
Plume 1=with coronet and band. Plume 2=with coronet only

| 2878 | **Halfcrown**. Horseman similar to 2773, but plume 2 behind. R. Oval garnished shield with large plume above. *Obv.* plume 2, *rev.* plume 1. ... | 650 | 2250 |
| --- | --- | --- | --- |
| 2879 | — Similar to 2774, plume 1 behind King, ground below horse. *Obv.* squat plume 1, *rev.* plume 1................................................................ | 750 | 2250 |

|      |                                                                        | F    | VF   |
|------|------------------------------------------------------------------------|------|------|
|      |                                                                        | £    | £    |
| 2880 | As 2773 but more spirited horse, no ground. FRAN ET HIB, plume 2/1     | 650  | 2250 |

2881

| 2881 | **Shilling**. Bust with large square lace collar, plume 2 before, small XII. R. As before. No inner circles | 375 | 1200 |
| 2882 | — inner circle on *rev*. | 325 | 975 |
| 2883 | As 2881, but large plume 1 or 2, large XII, inner circles, large or small shield | 325 | 975 |

2884

| 2884 | As last, but small narrow head, square lace collar, large or square plume | 375 | 1200 |
| 2885 | Small Briot style face, small crown, plume 2, large shield | 475 | 1500 |
| 2885A | **Sixpence**. *Obv*. as Tower bust 3a, plume before. R. as 2889; inner circles both sides, *mm*. book (*obv*. only) | 375 | 1000 |

2886

| 2886 | Somewhat as 2881, but double-arched crown, small VI; no inner circles | 275 | 800 |
| 2887 | Similar to 2886, but single arched crown, plume 2, inner circle *obv*. Large VI | 300 | 850 |
| 2888 | Similar, but with inner circles both sides | 300 | 850 |
| 2889 | — — *Rev*. with small squat-shaped plume above, sometimes no *rev*. *mm*. | 275 | 800 |
| 2890 | Bust as the first Oxford sixpence; with crown cutting inner circle | 425 | 1200 |

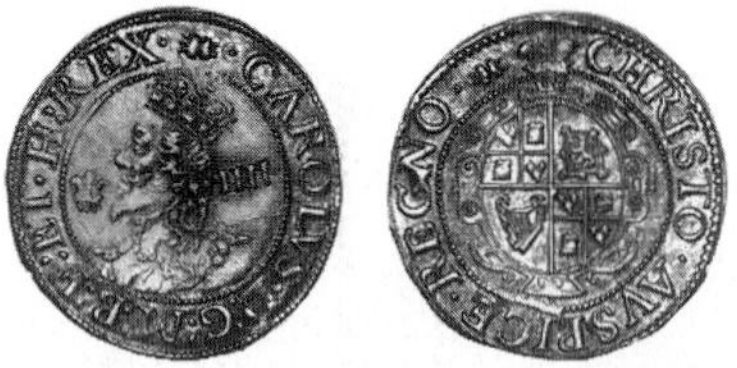

2891 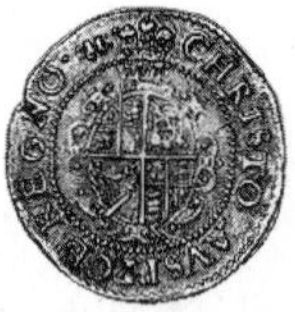      2894 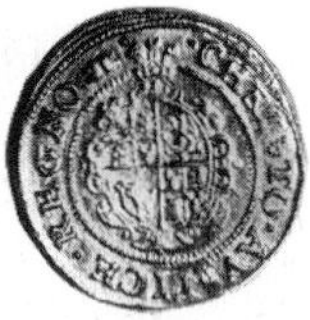      2895

| | F £ | VF £ |
|---|---|---|
| 2891 **Groat**. Large bust, lace collar, no armour on shoulder. Crown breaks or touches inner circle. R. Shield, plume 1 or 2 | 50 | 150 |
| 2892 — Similar, armour on shoulder, shorter collar. R. Similar | 55 | 165 |
| 2893 — Smaller, neater bust well within circle. R. Similar | 50 | 150 |
| 2894 **Threepence**. Small bust, plume 2 before. R. Shield, plume 1 or 2 above, *obv.* legend variations | 40 | 125 |
| 2895 — Similar, but crown cuts i.c. squat pl. on *obv.*, R. Pl. 2, *obv.* legend variations | 45 | 135 |
| 2900 **Halfgroat**. Bust as Tower type 3. R. Large plume. No inner circles, *mm.* pellet/book,book | 45 | 140 |

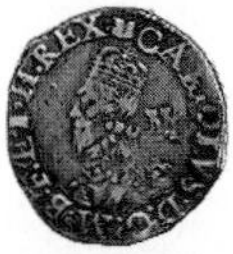

2900A 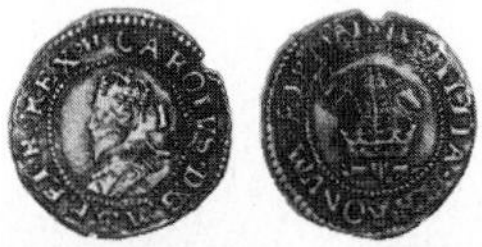      2905 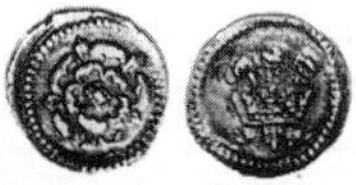      2907

| | F | VF |
|---|---|---|
| 2900A Bust as 2886. R. As last, no inner circle | 50 | 150 |
| 2901 Bust with round lace collar; single arch crown, inner circles, colon stops | 45 | 135 |
| 2902 After Briot's bust, square lace collar: inner circles | 45 | 135 |
| 2903 **Penny**. As 2901; CARO; no inner circles | 60 | 185 |
| 2904 As 2901; CARO; inner circles | 50 | 175 |
| 2905 As last but reads CAROLVS; inner circles | 65 | 225 |
| 2906 *Obv.* similar to 2890, tall narrow bust, crown touches inner circle | 70 | 235 |
| 2907 **Halfpenny**. No legend. *O*. Rose. R. Plume | 150 | 525 |

**Aberystwyth-Furnace mint**, 1648/9. *Mm.* crown

| | F | VF |
|---|---|---|
| 2908 **Halfcrown**. King on horseback. R. Sim. to 2878 | 1650 | 4500 |
| 2909 **Shilling**. Aberystwyth type, but *mm.* crown | 1750 | 5000 |
| 2910 **Sixpence**. Similar | 950 | 2500 |

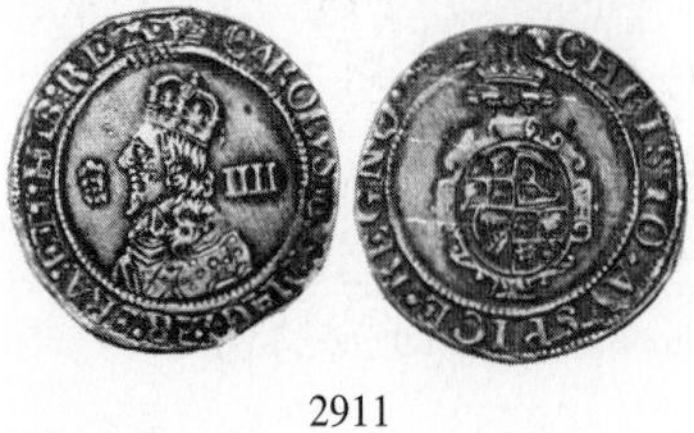

2911 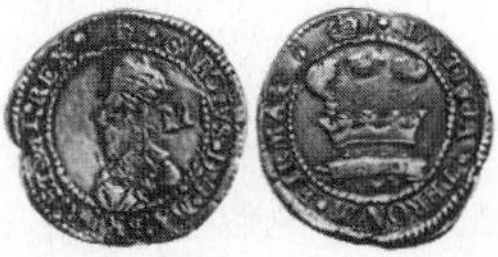      2913

| | F | VF |
|---|---|---|
| 2911 **Groat**. Similar | 200 | 500 |
| 2912 **Threepence**. Similar | 175 | 450 |
| 2913 **Halfgroat**. Similar. R. Large plume | 250 | 700 |
| 2914 **Penny**. Similar | 675 | 1750 |

**Uncertain mint (? Hereford) 1644-5**

2915                          2930/1

|  | F £ | VF £ |
|---|---|---|
| 2915 **Halfcrown**. As illustration, dated 1645 or undated ................................. | 1750 | 5000 |
| 2915A— Scarf with long sash ends. CH (Chirk castle?) below horse. R. Oval shield 1644 ...................................................................................... | 2250 | 6500 |
| 2915B — R. Crowned oval shield, lion paws ...................................................... | 2000 | 6000 |

**Shrewsbury mint**, 1642. Plume without band used as *mm.* or in field.

| 2917 **Pound**. King on horseback, plume behind, from the puncheon of Tower grp. 3 crowns. R. Declaration between two straight lines, XX and three Shrewsbury plumes above, 1642 below; *mm.* pellets, pellets/- ...................................... | 1850 | 4250 |
|---|---|---|
| 2918 Similar, but Shrewsbury horse walking over pile of arms; no *mm.*, pellets | 1650 | 3750 |
| 2919 As last, but cannon amongst arms and only single plume and XX above Declaration, no *mm.* ............................................................................... | 2000 | 4500 |
| 2920 **Half-pound**. As 2917, but X; *mm.* pellets .............................................. | 1250 | 2750 |
| 2921 Similar, but only two plumes on *rev.*; *mm.*, pellets................................... | 1650 | 4000 |
| 2922 Shrewsbury horseman with ground-line, three plumes on *rev.*; *mm.*, none, pellets/- ...................................................................................................... | 1100 | 2500 |
| 2923 — with cannon and arms or arms below horse; *mm.* pellets/- .................. | 1200 | 2650 |
| 2924 — no cannon in arms, no plume in *obv.* field; *mm.* plume/pellets, plume/- | 875 | 1850 |
| 2925 **Crown**. Aberystwyth horseman from the puncheon of a Tower halfcrown no ground line ........................................................................................... | 5500 | 17500 |

2926

| 2926 Shrewsbury horseman with ground-line; *mm.* -/pellets, pellets/-, none.... | 750 | 1750 |
|---|---|---|
| 2927 **Halfcrown**. *O*. From Aberystwyth die; (S2880); *mm.* book. R. Single plume above Declaration, 1642 ......................................................................... | 900 | 2500 |
| 2928 Sim. to Aberystwyth die, fat plume behind. R. Three plumes above Declaration; *mm.* pellets, pellets/- ............................................................. | 450 | 1250 |

|      |                                                                              | *F* | *VF* |
|------|------------------------------------------------------------------------------|-----|------|
|      |                                                                              | £   | £    |
| 2929 | Shrewsbury horseman, no ground line. R. As 2927, single plume, no *mm.*       | 575 | 1650 |
| 2929A| — — R. As 2933...............................................................| 450 | 1250 |
| 2930 | — R. 2: plume; 6, above Declaration.....................................      | 975 | 3250 |
| 2931 | — with ground-line. R. Similar ................................              | 975 | 3250 |
| 2932 | — — R. As 2927, single plume.............................                    | 575 | 1650 |
| 2933 | — — R. Three plumes above Declaration; *mm.* none or pellets ..............   | 400 | 1100 |
| 2933A| — — R. Aberystwyth die, plume over shield; *mm.* -/book......................| 950 | 2750 |
| 2934 | As 2933 but no plume behind king; *mm.* plume/pellets..........................| 375 | 1050 |
| 2935 | **Shilling**. *O*. From Aberystwyth die; S2885 *mm.* book. R. Declaration type | 900 | 2250 |
| 2936 | *O*. From Shrewsbury die. R. Similar................................          | 950 | 2500 |

**Oxford mint,** 1642-6. *Mm.* usually plume with band, except on the smaller denominations when it is lis or pellets. There were so many dies used at this mint that we can give only a selection of the more easily identifiable varieties.

For many years Oxford Halfcrowns and Shillings have been catalogued according to Morrieson obverse die varieties. In many cases, these are very small and difficult to identify. We have, therefore, simplified the obverse classification and used the available space to expand the listing of the more interesting reverse varieties.

2937

| 2937 | **Pound**. Large horseman over arms, no exergual line, fine workmanship. R. Three Shrewsbury plumes and XX above Declaration, 1642 below; *mm.* plume/pellets ............................................................ | 2500 | 6750 |
|------|-----------------------------------------------------------------------------------------------|------|-------|
| 2938 | — Similar, but three Oxford plumes, 1643; *mm.* as last............................              | 2350 | 6250 |
| 2939 | Shrewsbury horseman trampling on arms, exergual line. R. As last, 1642                         | 1750 | 3750 |
| 2940 | — — cannon amongst arms, 1642-3; *mm.* similar ..................................               | 1650 | 3500 |
| 2941 | — as last but exergue is chequered, 1642; *mm.* similar..........................               | 1850 | 4500 |
| 2942 | Briot's horseman, 1643; *mm.* similar......................................................     | 3000 | 7000 |
| 2943 | *O*. As 2937. R. Declaration in cartouche, single large plume above, 1644 OX below .................................................................................. | 4250 | 10500 |
| 2944 | **Half-pound**. Shrewsbury horseman over arms, Oxford plume behind. R. Shrewsbury die, 1642; mm. plume/- ...................................... | 900 | 2250 |
| 2945 | — R. Three Oxford plumes above, 1642; mm. plume/- ..........................                    | 800 | 1850 |
| 2945A| — — 1643; *mm.* plume/- ..........................................................            | 875 | 2000 |

|  | *F* | *VF* |
|---|---|---|
|  | £ | £ |

2946 **Crown.** Shrewsbury die with groundline. R. Three Oxford plumes,
 1642; no mm. ................................................................................ | 750 | 1850

2946A—— 1643; no *mm.* ...................................................................... | 750 | 1850

2947 Oxford horseman, grass below. R. Three Oxford plumes, 1643; *mm.*
 plume/- ........................................................................................... | 1250 | 3250

2948

2948 Rawlins' crown. King riding over a view of the city. R. Floral scrolls
 above and below Declaration, date in script, 1644 OXON; *mm.*
 floriated cross/- *(Electrotypes and copies of this coin are common)* ........ | 8500 | 27500

2949 **Halfcrown.** *O.* Shrewsbury die with groundline, plume behind. R.
 Oxford die, declaration in two lines, three Oxford plumes above,
 1642 below; no *mm.* ....................................................................... | 475 | 1350

2950 — no plume behind. R. as last, 1642; *mm.* plume/- ...................... | 375 | 950

2951 Shrewsbury horseman with groundline, Oxford plume behind. R.
 Shrewsbury die, 1642; *mm.* plume/- ............................................. | 375 | 950

2952 — R. Three Oxford plumes, 1642; *mm.* plume/- ........................ | 225 | 625

2953 —— without groundline, 1642; *mm.* plume/- ............................ | 225 | 625

2954

2954 Oxford horseman without groundline, 1643; *mm.* plume/-...................... | 210 | 600

2954A—— R. Shrewsbury die, 1642; *mm.* plume/- or no *mm.*........................ | 400 | 1000

2955 — with groundline. R. Three Oxford plumes, 1643; *mm.* plume/- .......... | 210 | 625

2956 Briot horseman, grassy, rocky or uneven ground. R. Three Oxford plumes,
 1643; *mm.* plume/-, plume & rosette/- ....................................... | 225 | 650

2957 —— 1643 OX; *mm.* plume/rosette, rosette ............................................. | 250 | 675

2958 —— 1644 OX; *mm.* plume/- ...................................................................... | 250 | 675

2958A—— lozenges by OX, 1644 OX; *mm.* plume/- ....................................... | 275 | 700

| | F | VF |
|---|---|---|
| | £ | £ |

2959 — — 1645 OX; *mm.* plume/-, plume/rosette ........................................... 225 650

2959A— — pellets by date, 1645 OX; *mm.* plume/- ........................................ 325 850

2960 — — 1646 OX; *mm.* plume/- ................................................................. 250 700

2961 — — pellets or annulets by plumes and date, 1646 OX; *mm.* plume/- ... 275 725

2962 — R. Large central plume and two Oxford plumes, 1643; *mm.* plume/- . 275 725

2963 — — 1643 OX; *mm.* plume/-, rosette/-, plume & rosette/rosette, plume
& rosette/- ............................................................................................. 250 675

2964 — — rosettes by OX, 1643 OX; *mm.* rosette/-, plume & rosette/-........... 275 750

2965                                                    2965A

2965 — — plain, pellets or lozenges by plumes and/or OX, 1644 OX; *mm.*
plume/- plume/rosette, rosette .................................................... 225 625

2965A— — date in script, 1644 OX; *mm.* plume/- ......................................... 250 675

2966 — — rosettes by plumes and date, 1644 OX; *mm.* plume & rosette/rosette 325 850

2967 — — small plumes by date, 1644 OX; *mm.* plume & rosette/-, rosette .. 375 1000

2968 — R. Large central plume and two small Shrewsbury plumes, lozenges
in field, date in script, 1644 OX; *mm.* plume/rosette .............................. 400 1050

2969 — — small plumes by date, pellets by OX, 1644 OX; *mm.* plume/- ....... 425 1100

2970 **Shilling.** *O.* Shrewsbury die. R. Declaration in three lines, three Oxford
plumes above, 1642; *mm.* plume/- ............................................................. 650 1850

2971 Oxford bust (small). R. Three Oxford plumes, 1642; *mm.* Oxford plume/-, 225 675

2972 Oxford bust (small or large). R. Three Oxford plumes, 1643; *mm.*
Oxford plume/-, Oxford plume/rosette ....................................................... 200 650

2972A— — pellets by date, 1644; *mm.* plume/- ................................................ 240 700

2972B— — 1644 OX; mm. plume/rosette ......................................................... 240 700

2973 — R. Oxford and two Shrewsbury plumes, lozenges by date, 1644 OX;
*mm.* plume/- .................................................................................................. 300 850

2974

2974 — R. Three Shrewsbury plumes, 1643; *mm.* plume/- ............................. 250 750

2975

|      |                                                                                               | F £ | VF £ |
|------|-----------------------------------------------------------------------------------------------|------|------|
| 2975 | Fine Oxford bust. R. Three Oxford plumes, lozenges in field, 1644 OX; *mm.* Shrewsbury plume/- | 250 | 750 |
| 2975A | — — large date in script, 1644 OX; *mm.* plume/- | 300 | 825 |
| 2976 | — 1645 OX; *mm.* plume/- | 875 | 2500 |
| 2976A | — R. Oxford and two Shrewsbury plumes, 1644 OX; *mm.* plume/- | 300 | 850 |
| 2977 | — R. Three Shrewsbury plumes, 1644 OX; *mm.* plume/- | 250 | 750 |
| 2978 | — — annulets or pellets at date, 1646; *mm.* plume/floriated cross, plume/- | 250 | 750 |
| 2979 | Rawlins' die. Fine bust with R. on truncation. R. Three Oxford plumes, rosettes or lozenges by plumes, lozenges by date, 1644 OX; *mm.* Shrewsbury plume/rosette, Shrewsbury plume/- | 450 | 1250 |
| 2979A | — — pellets by date, no OX, 1644; *mm.* plume/- | 475 | 1250 |
| 2979B | — R. Oxford and two Shrewsbury plumes, 1644 OX; *mm.* plume/- | 525 | 1350 |

2980

| 2980 | **Sixpence.** O. Aberystwyth die R. Three Oxford plumes, 1642; *mm.* book/- | 275 | 850 |
|------|----------------------------------------------------------------------------|-----|-----|
| 2980A | — — 1643; *mm.* book/- | 250 | 725 |
| 2981 | — R. Three Shrewsbury plumes, 1643; *mm.* book/- | 225 | 650 |
| 2982 | — R. Shrewsbury plume and two lis, 1644 OX (groat rev. die); *mm.* book/- | 575 | 1350 |
| 2983 | **Groat.** O. Aberystwyth die. R. Shrewsbury plume and two lis, 1644 OX; *mm.* book/- | 165 | 475 |
| 2984 | — R. Three Shrewsbury plumes, 1644 OX; mm. book/- | 185 | 575 |

2985

| 2985 | Oxford bust within inner circle. R. As 2983, 1644 OX; mm. floriated cross/- | 135 | 375 |
|------|-----------------------------------------------------------------------------|-----|-----|

|  | | *F* | *VF* |
|---|---|---|---|
|  | | £ | £ |
| 2985A— | R. Three Shrewsbury plumes, 1644 OX; *mm.* floriated cross/- .......... | 175 | 550 |
| 2985B— | R. Single plume, 2 scrolls and OX monogram over Decl, 1645; *mm.* floriated cross/- ................... | 200 | 600 |
| 2986 | Large bust to top of coin. R. As 2983, 1644 OX; *mm.* lis/- ................ | 225 | 650 |
| 2987 | Large bust to bottom of coin. R. As 2983, 1644 OX; no *mm.* .................. | 200 | 600 |
| 2988 | — R. Single plume, 2 scrolls and OX monogram over Decl, 1645; no *mm.* | 145 | 425 |
| 2989 | Rawlins' die, no inner circle, R on shoulder. R. As 2983, 1644 OX; no *mm.* ................... | 200 | 600 |
| 2990 | — R. Single plume, Declaration in cartouche, 1645; no *mm.* ................... | 175 | 550 |

2990

| 2991 | — — 1646/5; no mm. .................. | 175 | 550 |
|---|---|---|---|
| 2992 | **Threepence.** *O.* Aberystwyth die. R. Three lis over Declaration, 1644 OX; *mm.* book/- .................. | 135 | 375 |
| 2993 | Rawlins; die, R below shoulder. R. Aberystwyth die, oval shield; *mm.* lis/book .................. | 135 | 375 |
| 2994 | — R. Three lis over Declaration, 1644; *mm.* lis/- .................. | 100 | 250 |

2995                              3000

| 2995 | Crown breaks inner circle, no R. R. Three lis, 1646/4; *mm.* lis/-.............. | 110 | 275 |
|---|---|---|---|
| 2996 | **Halfgroat.** Small bust, beaded or wireline inner circle. R. Large plume in field; *mm.* mullet/lis, lis, -/lis .................. | 110 | 275 |
| 2997 | — R. Three lis over Delcaration, 1644 OX; *mm.* lis.................. | 125 | 300 |
| 2998 | **Penny.** *O.* Aberystwyth die, CARO. R. Small plume in field; *mm.* book/- | 135 | 400 |
| 2999 | Aberystwyth die, CAROLVS; R. Large plume; *mm.* book/- .................. | 150 | 425 |
| 3000 | Rawlins' die, CARO. R. Small plume; *mm.* lis/mullet, lis/- .................. | 275 | 750 |
| 3001 | Broad bust, CAROL. R. Small plume; *mm.* lis .................. | 275 | 750 |
| 3002 | — R. Three lis over Declaration, 1644; *mm.* lis .................. | 675 | 1750 |

**Bristol mint**, 1643-5. *Mm.* usually plume or Br., except on small denominations

| 3003 | **Halfcrown.** *O.* Oxford die with or without ground-line. R. Declaration, three Bristol plumes above, 1643 below, *mm.* plume/- or plume/cross.... | 425 | 1200 |
|---|---|---|---|
| 3004 | — Obv. as above. R as above, but *mm.* Br. 1643 .................. | 450 | 1250 |
| 3005 | King wears unusual flat crown, *obv. mm.* acorn? between four pellets. R. As 3003, 1643 .................. | 400 | 1000 |
| 3006 | — Obv. as above. R as 3004, *mm.* Br., 1643-4.................. | 350 | 850 |
| 3007 | Shrewsbury plume behind king. R. As last.................. | 300 | 750 |
| 3008 | — Obv. as above. R as 3004 but Br below date instead of as *mm* . 1644. | 325 | 800 |

3009

|  | | F<br>£ | VF<br>£ |
|---|---|---|---|
| 3009 | — Obv. as 3007 but Br below horse. Ꞃ as above but 1644-5 .................. | 300 | 750 |
| 3010 | — Obv. as above. Ꞃ as 3004, *mm.* Br. and Br. below date, 1644-5 ......... | 325 | 800 |
| 3011 | **Shilling**. *O*. Oxford die. Ꞃ. Declaration, 1643, 3 crude plumes above, no *mm.* | 325 | 950 |

3012                    3014

|  | | | |
|---|---|---|---|
| 3012 | — — Ꞃ Similar, but *mm.* Br., 1643-4, less crude plumes........................ | 300 | 850 |
| 3013 | —Obv. Coarse bust. Ꞃ. As 3011, no *mm.* ............................................... | 350 | 950 |
| 3014 | — — Coarse bust, Ꞃ. as 3012, *mm.* Br, but 1644 ..................................... | 325 | 900 |

3015                    3017

|  | | | |
|---|---|---|---|
| 3015 | Obv. Bust of good style, plumelet before face. Ꞃ. As 3012 *mm.* Br. but 1644-5 | 275 | 725 |
| 3016 | — — Ꞃ.as 3012, 1644, but Br below date instead of *mm.* ....................... | 285 | 750 |
| 3016A | — — Ꞃ as 3012, 1644 but plume and plumelet either side ...................... | 275 | 725 |
| 3017 | —Obv. Taller bust with high crown, no plumelets before, *mm.* Br. on its side. Ꞃ As 3016 Br.below 1644-5 ................................................................ | 325 | 900 |
| 3018 | —Obv. As 3017 but no *mm.* Ꞃ as above but *mm.* Br., no Br. below 1644-5 | 350 | 925 |
| 3018A | — — Ꞃ as above but plume and plumelets, 1645.................................... | 375 | 1000 |
| 3019 | **Sixpence**. Small bust, nothing before. Ꞃ. Declaration surrounded by CHRISTO etc., 1643; *mm.* ./Br................................................................. | 425 | 1250 |

3020

|      |                                                                                                      | F | VF |
|------|------------------------------------------------------------------------------------------------------|---|----|
|      |                                                                                                      | £ | £  |
| 3020 | Fine style bust. Plumelet before face, 1644; *mm.* ./Br. (on its side) ......... | 250 | 575 |
| 3021 | **Groat**. Bust l. R. Declaration, 1644............................................................ | 185 | 500 |
| 3022 | — Plumelet before face, 1644................................................................... | 175 | 475 |
| 3023 | — Br. below date, 1644 ............................................................................ | 175 | 475 |
| 3023A| — Similar, but larger bust and more spread plume before. Mm. pellet/Br; nothing below 1644.................................................................................. | 185 | 500 |

3024                            3026                          3027

|      |                                                                                               | F | VF |
|------|-----------------------------------------------------------------------------------------------|---|----|
| 3024 | **Threepence**. *O*. As 2992. Aberystwyth die; *mm.* book. R. Declaration, 1644 | 165 | 450 |
| 3025 | Bristol die, plume before face, no *mm.*, 1644 ......................................... | 225 | 600 |
| 3026 | **Halfgroat**. Br. in place of date below Declaration .................................. | 225 | 625 |
| 3027 | **Penny**. Similar bust, I behind. R. Large plume with bands..................... | 325 | 850 |

*This penny may belong to the late declaration issue. It has the same reverse plume punch as 3044.*

### Late 'Declaration' issues, 1645-6

After Bristol surrendered on 11 September 1645, many of the Royalist garrison returned unsearched to Oxford and the Bristol moneyers appear to have continued work, using altered Bristol dies and others of similar type bearing the marks A, B and plume. Ashby de la Zouch was reinforced from Oxford in September 1645 and, following its fall on 28 February 1645/6, Royalist forces marched to Bridgnorth-on-Severn, holding out until 26 April 1646. Mr Boon has suggested (cf. SCBI 33, p. xli) that Ashby and Bridgnorth are plausible mint sites and the most likely candidates for the A and B marked issues, if these do indeed represent fixed mint locations.

### Ashby de la Zouch mint (?), 1645

3028

|      |                                                                                      | F | VF |
|------|--------------------------------------------------------------------------------------|---|----|
| 3028 | **Halfcrown**. Horseman of Bristol type, A below. R. Altered Bristol die. A (over Br) below date, 1645; *mm.* plume/A (over Br) .............................. | 2000 | 6250 |

|      |                                                                                          | *F*  | *VF* |
|------|------------------------------------------------------------------------------------------|------|------|
|      |                                                                                          | £    | £    |
| 3029 | - - R. A below date (new die), 1645; *mm.* plume/A ............................           | 2000 | 6250 |
| 3030 | - - R. Nothing below date 1645; *mm.* plume/A.................................            | 1850 | 5250 |
| 3031 | **Shilling.** Crowned bust left. R. Declaration type, A below date, 1645; mm. plume/A ............................................................................ | 750 | 2250 |

3032

| 3032 | - plumelet before face, 1645; *mm.* plume/A ............................................ | 825 | 2500 |
| 3033 | **Sixpence.** Bust of Bristol style, plumelet before face. R. Declaration type, 1645; *mm.* A (on its side)/- ........................................................ | 750 | 1850 |
| 3034 | **Groat.** Similar, plumelet before face, 1645; *mm.* A (on its side)/- ........... | 675 | 1650 |
| 3035 | **Threepence.** Similar, plumelet before face. R. Single plumelet above Declaration, 1645; no *mm.* ........................................................... | 425 | 1050 |

**Bridgnorth-on-Severn mint (?), 1646**

| 3036 | **Halfcrown.** Horseman of Bristol type, A below (same die as 3028-30). R. Scroll above Declaration, B below, 1646; *mm.* plume/A ........................ | 2000 | 5750 |
| 3036A | - - R. Nothing below date, 1646; *mm.* plume/- ......................................... | 1650 | 4250 |
| 3037 | - plumelet (over A) below horse (same die as 3028-30 recut). R. Nothing below date, 1646; *mm.* plume, plume/- ................................................ | 875 | 2250 |

3038

| 3038 | - - plumelet below date, 1646; *mm.* plume ............................................... | 875 | 2250 |
| 3039 | **Shilling.** Crowned bust left, plumelet before face (same die 3032). R. Scroll above Declaration, 1646; *mm.* plume/plumelet ............................. | 350 | 950 |
| 3039A | - Bristol obverse die, nothing before face. R. Scroll above Declaration, 1646; *mm.* Br/- .............................................................................. | 475 | 1250 |
| 3040 | - - plume before face (altered die of 3039A), 1646; *mm.* plumelet (over Br)/- ................................................................................................. | 375 | 1000 |

3041

|  | | *F* | *VF* |
|  | | £ | £ |

3041 **Sixpence.** Crowned bust left, plume before face. R. Scroll above Declaration, 1646; *mm.* B/- .......................................................................................... 250 575

3042 **Groat.** Similar, plumelet before face, 1646; *mm.* plumelet, plumelet/- .......... 200 475

3043 **Threepence.** Similar, plumelet before face. R. Single plume above Declaration, 1646; *mm.* plumelet/-................................................................ 175 400

3044 **Halfgroat.** Crowned bust left, II behind. R. Large plume with bands dividing date, 1646; no *mm.* ............................................................................................. 425 1000

**Truro mint,** 1642-3. *Mm.* rose except where stated

3045 **Crown.** King on horseback, head in profile, sash flies out in two ends. R. CHRISTO, etc., round garnished shield ............................................... 285 725

3046 **Halfcrown.** King on walking horse, groundline below, R. Oblong shield, CR above, *mm.* bugle/– .................................................................................. 950 2750

3047 Galloping horse, king holds baton. R. Oblong shield, CR at sides .......... 1750 6000

3048                                        3052

3048 Walking horse, king holds sword. R. Similar ........................................ 800 2250

3049 — R. Similar, but CR above .................................................................... 825 2250

3050 Galloping horse, king holds sword. R. Similar, but CR at sides ............. 1100 3000

3051 — R. Similar, but CR above ..................................................................... 1200 3250

3052 Trotting horse. R. Similar, but CR at sides ............................................. 675 1650

3053 **Shilling.** Small bust of good style. R. Oblong shield ............................. 2250 6500

**Exeter mint,** 1643-6. Undated or dated 1644-5 *Mm.* rose except where stated

3054 **Half-pound.** King on horseback, face towards viewer, sash in large bow. R. CHRISTO, etc., round garnished shield. Struck from crown dies on a thick flan ............................................................................................................ *Extremely rare*

3055 **Crown.** King on horseback, sash in large bow. R. Round garnished shield ................................................................................................................ 300 750

|                                                                                  | *F* | *VF* |
|----------------------------------------------------------------------------------|-----|------|
|                                                                                  | £   | £    |
| 3056 — Shield garnished with twelve even scrolls ........................................ | 350 | 900  |
| 3057 As 3055, Ṙ Date divided by *mm*. 16 rose 44 ........................................... | 375 | 950  |
| 3058 — Ṙ Date to l. of *mm*. 1644 ................................................................ | 275 | 725  |
| 3059 — *mm*: rose/EX, 1645 ...................................................................... | 350 | 900  |
| 3060 King's sash flies out in two ends; *mm*. castle/rose, 1645 ...................... | 550 | 1350 |
| 3061 — *mm*. castle/EX, 1645 .................................................................. | 300 | 800  |
| 3062 — *mm*. castle, 1645 ...................................................................... | 275 | 700  |
| 3063 **Halfcrown**. King on horseback, sash tied in bow. R. Oblong shield CR at sides ..................................................................................... | 650 | 1650 |
| 3064 — R. Round shield with eight even scrolls ........................................... | 275 | 675  |

3065                          3067

| 3065 — R. Round shield with five short and two long scrolls ........................ | 235 | 550  |
| 3066 — R. Oval shield with angular garnish of triple lines ........................... | 750 | 2000 |

3071

| 3067 Briot's horseman with lumpy ground. R. As 3064 ............................... | 450  | 1050  |
| 3068 — R. As 3065 .................................................................................. | 375  | 850   |
| 3069 — R. As 3066 .................................................................................. | 750  | 2000  |
| 3070 — R. As 3065, date to l. of *mm*. 1644 .............................................. | 450  | 1050  |
| 3071 King on spirited horse galloping over arms. R. Oval garnished shield, 1642 in cartouche below ................................................... | 2750 | 8500  |
| 3072 — R. As 3070, date to l. of *mm*. 1644-5 ........................................... | 3250 | 10000 |
| 3073 — R. *mm*. castle, 1645 .................................................................. | 3500 | 10500 |
| 3074 Short portly king, leaning backwards on ill-proportioned horse, 1644, 16 rose 44 ................................................................................. | 675  | 1750  |
| 3075 Horse with twisted tail, sash flies out in two ends R. As 3064 ............... | 475  | 1100  |

3076

| | F £ | VF £ |
|---|---|---|

3076— R. As 3070, date divided by *mm.* 16 rose 44, or date to 1. of *mm.*
1644-5 ................................................................................................ 450 1050

3077 — R. *mm.* castle, 1645 ............................................................... 475 1200

3078 — R. *mm.* EX, 1645 ................................................................... 575 1350

3079 — R. Declaration type; *mm.* EX. 1644-5 .................................... 1850 4250

3080 — R. Similar, EX also below declaration, 1644 ...................... 1750 4000

3081 **Shilling.** Large Oxford style bust. R. Round shield with eight even
scrolls ............................................................................................... 850 2500

3082 — R. Oval shield with CR at sides ........................................... 825 2250

3083 Normal bust with lank hair. R. As 3081 ................................. 650 1500

3083A— R. As 3082 ............................................................................ 725 1750

3084 — R. Round shield with six scrolls ........................................ 450 1000

3085                                     3087A

3085 — R. Similar, date 1644, 45 to left of rose *mm.* 16 rose 44 (rare),
1644 to right of rose (very rare) ................................................. 325 875

3086 — R. Declaration type, 1645 .................................................... 900 2500

3087 **Sixpence.** Similar to 3085, large bust and letters 1644 rose ...... 275 675

3087A— Smaller bust and letters from punches used on 3088, small or large
VI, 16 rose 44................................................................................ 275 700

3088 **Groat.** Somewhat similar but 1644 at beginning of *obv.* legend.............. 100 275

3089                        3091                    3092

3089 **Threepence.** Similar. R. Square shield, 1644 above ............................ 100 275

3090 **Halfgroat.** Similar, but II. R. Oval shield, 1644 ................................ 225 575

3091 — R. Large rose, 1644 ...................................................................... 225 600

3092 **Penny.** As last but I behind head ....................................................... 300 900

|  | | F<br>£ | VF<br>£ |
|---|---|---|---|

**Worcester mint 1643-4**

3093 **Halfcrown**. King on horseback l., W below; *mm.* two lions. R. Declaration
type 1644 altered from 1643 Bristol die; *mm.* pellets ............................... 1250 2750
3094 — R. Square-topped shield; *mm.* helmet, castle ..................................... 750 1850
3095 — R. Oval shield; *mm.* helmet................................................................. 850 2000

3096

| | | | |
|---|---|---|---|
| 3096 | Similar but grass indicated; *mm.* castle. R. Square-topped shield; *mm.* helmet or pellets. | 650 | 1650 |
| 3097 | — R. Oval draped shield, lis or lions in legend | 700 | 1850 |
| 3098 | — R. Oval shield CR at sides, roses in legend | 725 | 1850 |
| 3099 | — R. FLORENT etc., oval garnished shield with lion's paws each side . | 750 | 2000 |
| 3100 | Tall king, no W or *mm.* R. Oval shield, lis, roses, lions or stars in legend | 600 | 1650 |
| 3101 | — R. Square-topped shield; *mm.* helmet | 700 | 1850 |
| 3102 | — R. FLORENT, etc., oval shield; no *mm.* | 750 | 2000 |
| 3103 | Briot type horse, sword slopes forward, ground-line. R. Oval shield, roses in legend; *mm.* 91v, 105, none (combinations) | 700 | 1850 |
| 3104 | — Similar, but CR at sides, 91v/- | 750 | 2000 |
| 3105 | Dumpy, portly king, crude horse. R. As 3100; *mm.* 91v, 105, none | 700 | 1850 |

3106

3106 Thin king and horse. R. Oval shield, stars in legend; *mm.* 91v, none...... 600 1650

**Worcester or Salopia (Shrewsbury) 1643-4**

3107 **Shilling**. Bust of king l., adequately rendered. R. Square-topped shield;
*mm.* castle.............................................................................................. 850 2500
3108 — R. CR above shield; *mm.* helmet and lion.......................................... 850 2500
3109 — R. Oval shield; *mm.* lion, pear.......................................................... 800 2350
3110 — Bust a somewhat crude copy of last (two varieties); *mm.* bird, lis.
R. Square-topped shield with lion's paws above and at sides; *mm.* boar's
head, helmet ........................................................................................... 950 2750

3111

|      |                                                                      | F | VF |
|------|----------------------------------------------------------------------|---|----|
|      |                                                                      | £ | £ |
| 3111 | — — CR above                                                         | 900 | 2750 |
| 3112 | — R. Oval shield, lis in legend; *mm.* lis                           | 850 | 2500 |
| 3113 | — R. Round shield; *mm.* lis, 3 lis                                  | 800 | 2250 |
| 3114 | Bust r.; *mm.* pear/-, pear/lis. R. draped oval shield with or without CR. (Halfcrown reverse dies) | 1650 | 5000 |
| 3115 | **Sixpence**. As 3110; *mm.* castle, castle/boar's hd               | 750 | 2250 |

3116                           3117

| 3116 | **Groat**. As 3112; *mm.* lis/helmet, rose/helmet | 475 | 1050 |
| 3117 | **Threepence**. Similar; *mm.* lis | 275 | 625 |
| 3118 | **Halfgroat**. Similar; *mm.* lis (*O.*) various (*R.*) | 450 | 1000 |

**Salopia (Shrewsbury) mint, 1644**

| 3119 | **Halfcrown**. King on horseback l. SA below; *mm.* lis. R. (*mm.* lis, helmet, lion rampant, none). Cr. oval shield; CHRISTO etc. *mm.* helmet | 2500 | 7500 |
| 3120 | — R. FLORENT, etc., crowned oval shield, no *mm.* | 2500 | 7500 |
| 3121 | — SA erased or replaced by large pellet or cannon ball; *mm.* lis in legend, helmet. R. As 3119 | 1250 | 3750 |
| 3122 | Tall horse and king, nothing below; *mm.* lis. R. Large round shield with crude garniture; *mm.* helmet | 725 | 1850 |
| 3123 | — R. Uncrowned square-topped shield with lion's paw above and at sides; *mm.* helmet | 800 | 2250 |
| 3124 | — R. Small crowned oval shield; *mm.* various | 625 | 1650 |

3125

|  | | F £ | VF £ |
|---|---|---|---|
| 3125 | — R. As 3120....................................................................... | 700 | 1850 |
| 3126 | Finer work with little or no mane before horse. R. Cr. round or oval shield | 800 | 2250 |
| 3127 | Grass beneath horse. R. Similar; *mm.* lis or rose ..................................... | 900 | 2500 |
| 3128 | Ground below horse. R. As 3120............................................................. | 1000 | 2750 |

**Hartlebury Castle (Worcs.) mint, 1646**

3129

| 3129 | **Halfcrown**. *O. Mm.* pear. R. HC (Hartlebury Castle) in garniture below shield; *mm.* three pears............................................................................. | 1250 | 3000 |
|---|---|---|---|

**Chester mint, 1644**

•                3130

| 3130 | **Halfcrown**. As illus. R. Oval shield; *mm.* three gerbs and sword............ | 725 | 1850 |
|---|---|---|---|
| 3131 | — Similar, but without plume or CHST; R. Cr. oval shield with lion skin; *mm.* prostrate gerb; -/cinquefoil, -/: ........................................................ | 750 | 2000 |

| | F | VF |
|---|---|---|
| | £ | £ |

3132 — R. Crowned square-topped shield with CR at sides both crowned *rev.*;
*mm.* cinquefoil (these dies were later crudely recut) .............................. 975 2650

3133 As 3130, but without plume or CHST. R. Declaration type, 1644 *rev.*; *mm.*
plume.................................................................................................... 900 2500

3133A **Shilling**. Bust l. R. Oval garnished shield; *mm.* ∴ (obv. only) ................ 850 2650

3133B — R. Square-topped shield; *mm.* as last .................................................. 900 2750

3133C — R . Shield over long cross ..................................................................... 900 2750

3134 **Threepence**. R. Square-topped shield; *mm.*-/ prostrate gerb................... 850 2500

**Welsh Marches mint?** 1644

3135

3135 **Halfcrown**. Crude horseman, l. R. Declaration of Bristol style divided by a
dotted line, 3 plumes above, 1644 below ................................................. 700 1750

**Carlisle besieged**, 1644-5

3136 **Three shillings**. Large crown above C R between rosettes III. S below. *rev.*
OBS . CARL / . 1645, rosette below........................................................ 4500 9750

3137　　　　　　　　　　　　　　　3139

3137 Similar but :- OBS :/-: CARL :./.1645, rosette above and below ............. 4250 9500

3138 **Shilling**. Large crown above C R between trefoil of pellets, XII below.
*rev.* as 3137 ......................................................................................... 3000 7000

3139 R. Legend and date in two lines................................................................ 3250 8000

**Note**. *(3136-39) Round or Octagonal pieces exist.*

**Newark besieged**, several times 1645-6, surrendered May 1646

3140                                  3144

|  | | F £ | VF £ |
|---|---|---|---|
| 3140 | **Halfcrown**. Large crown between CR ; below, XXX. *rev.* OBS / NEWARK / 1645...... | 750 | 1850 |
| 3140A | — Similar 1646.................................................. | 600 | 1350 |
| 3141 | **Shilling**. Similar but crude flat shaped crown, NEWARKE, 1645 ......... | 500 | 1200 |
| 3142 | Similar but normal arched crown, 1645.................................... | 475 | 1000 |
| 3143 | — NEWARK, 1645 or 1646................................................ | 475 | 950 |
| 3144 | **Ninepence**. As halfcrown but IX, 1645 or 1646.................................... | 450 | 950 |
| 3145 | — NEWARKE, 1645.............................................................. | 475 | 975 |

3146

| 3146 | **Sixpence**. As halfcrown but VI, 1646....................................................... | 525 | 1200 |
|---|---|---|---|

**Pontefract besieged**, June 1648-March 1648-9

| 3147 | **Two shillings** (lozenge shaped). DVM : SPIRO : SPERO around CR crowned. R. Castle surrounded by OBS, PC, sword and 1648................. | *Extremely rare* | |
|---|---|---|---|

3148

|                                                                              | F      | VF   |
|------------------------------------------------------------------------------|--------|------|
|                                                                              | £      | £    |
| 3148  **Shilling** (lozenge shaped, octagonal or round). Similar ............. | 1100   | 3000 |

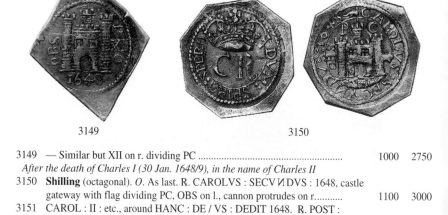

3149                                    3150

| 3149  — Similar but XII on r. dividing PC ...................................... | 1000 | 2750 |
|---|---|---|

*After the death of Charles I (30 Jan. 1648/9), in the name of Charles II*

3150  **Shilling** (octagonal). *O*. As last. ℞. CAROLVS : SECVИDVS : 1648, castle
gateway with flag dividing PC, OBS on l., cannon protrudes on r........... 1100  3000

3151   CAROL : II : etc., around HANC : DE / VS : DEDIT 1648. ℞. POST :
MORTEM : PATRIS : PRO : FILIO around gateway etc. as last............ 1250  3250

**Scarborough besieged**, July 1644-July 1645

| 3156 | 3165 | 3169 |

*VF*

Type I. Large Castle with gateway to left, SC and value Vs below

3152 **Crown.** (various weights)................................................................ 25000

Type II. Small Castle with gateway, no SC, value punched on flan

| 3153 | **Five shillings and eightpence.** ................................................ | 17500 |
| 3154 | **Crown.** Similar .......................................................................... | 22500 |
| 3155 | **Three shillings.** Similar ............................................................ | 13500 |
| 3156 | **Two shillings and tenpence.** Similar........................................ | 11000 |
| 3157 | **Two shillings and sevenpence.** Similar.................................... | 11000 |
| 3158 | **Halfcrown.** Similar ................................................................... | 17500 |
| 3159 | **Two shillings and fourpence.** Similar....................................... | 11000 |
| 3161 | **One shilling and ninepence.** *Struck from a different punch, possibly of later manufacture*.................................................. | |
| 3162 | **One shilling and sixpence.** Similar to 3159 ............................ | 9750 |
| 3163 | **One shilling and fourpence.** Similar........................................ | 9750 |
| 3164 | **One shilling and threepence.** Similar...................................... | 9750 |
| 3165 | **Shilling.** Similar....................................................................... | 13500 |
| 3166 | **Sixpence.** Similar...................................................................... | 12500 |
| 3167 | **Groat.** Similar .......................................................................... | 10000 |

Type III. Castle gateway with two turrets, value punched below

| 3168 | **Two shillings and twopence** ..................................................... | 7500 |
| 3169 | **Two shillings.** Castle punched twice........................................ | 7500 |
| 3170 | **One shilling and sixpence.** Similar to 3168 ............................ | 7000 |
| 3171 | **One shilling and fourpence.** Similar........................................ | 7000 |
| 3172 | **One shilling and threepence.** Similar...................................... | 7000 |
| 3173 | **One shilling and twopence.** Similar......................................... | 6750 |
| 3174 | **One shilling and one penny.** Similar ....................................... | 6750 |
| 3175 | **Shilling.** Similar....................................................................... | 9000 |
| 3176 | **Elevenpence.** Similar ................................................................ | 6500 |
| 3177 | **Tenpence.** Similar ..................................................................... | 6500 |
| 3178 | **Ninepence.** Similar ................................................................... | 6500 |
| 3178A | **Eightpence.** Similar................................................................. | 6000 |
| 3179 | **Sevenpence.** Similar.................................................................. | 6000 |
| 3180 | **Sixpence.** Similar...................................................................... | 8500 |

## COPPER

For further details see C. Wilson Peck, *English Copper, Tin and Bronze Coins in the British Museum, 1558-1958.*

3181                                            3183

|  | *F* | *VF* |
|---|---|---|
|  | £ | £ |

3181 **Royal farthing**. 'Richmond' 1a, colon stops, CARO over
IACO; *mm.* on *obv.* only; *mm:* Coronet, Crescent with mullet, Dagger,
Mascle............................................................................................................... 12     24

3182 — — 1b. CARA; (Contemporary forgeries manufactured from official
punches. Usually F for E in REX) *mm.* on *obv.* only; *mm:* Annulet, Coronet,
Cross patée fourchée, Dagger, Fusil, Key, Mascle, Trefoil, Tun ............. 100     200

3183 — — 1c. CARO; *mm.* on *obv.* only; *mm:* A, A with pellet, Annulet,
Annulet with pellet within, Bell, Book, Cinquefoil, Crescent (large and
small), Cross (pellets in angles), Cross calvary, Cross patée, Cross patée
fitchée, Cross patonce, Cross patonce in saltire, Cross saltire, Dagger,
Ermine, Estoile, Estoile (pierced), Eye, Fish hook, Fleece, Fusil, Fusils
(two), Gauntlet, Grapes, Halberd, Harp, Heart, Horseshoe, Leaf, Lion
passant, Lis (large), Lis (demi), Lis (three), Martlet, Mascle with pellet
within, Nautilus, Rose (single), Shield, Spearhead, Tower, Trefoil,
Woolpack, Woolpack over annulet............................................................. 8     20

3184                                            3185

3184 — — 1d, apostrophe stops, eagle-headed harp, *mm.* on *obv.* only; *mm:*
Crescent (large), Lion rampant, Rose (double), Trefoil............................ 10     20

3185 — 1e. Beaded harp, *mm* Rose (double) on *obv.* only................................. 8     20

3186 — 1f. Scroll-fronted harp, 5 jewels on circlet *mm* Rose (double) on *obv.*
only........................................................................................................................ 12     35

3187 — 1g. Scroll-fronted harp, 7 jewels on circlet *mm* Rose (double) on *obv.*
only........................................................................................................................ 6     18

3187A

| | F | VF |
| --- | --- | --- |
| | £ | £ |
| 3187A— 1g on uncut square flan | 150 | 300 |
| — Longer strips of two to nine farthings also exist | *Extremely Rare* | |

3188                                     3192

| | | F | VF |
| --- | --- | --- | --- |
| 3188 | Transitional issue 2, double-arched crowns *mm* on *obv.* only; *mm:* Harp, Quatrefoil | 18 | 45 |
| 3189 | 'Maltravers' 3a; inner circles *mm.* on *obv.* only; *mm:* Bell, Rose (double) Woolpack | 18 | 45 |
| 3190 | — 3b. *mm.* both sides; *mm:* Bell, Cross patée, Lis (large), Lis (small), Martlet, Rose (double), Woolpack | 8 | 20 |
| 3191 | — 3c. Different *mm.* on each side; *mm:* Bell/Cross patée fitchée, Cross patée fitchée/Bell, Harp/Bell, Harp/Billet, Harp/Woolpack, Lis/Portcullis Martlet/Bell, Woolpack/Portcullis, Woolpack/Rose (double). | 8 | 20 |
| 3192 | 'Richmond' oval. 4a. CARO over IACO; legend starts at bottom left, *mm:* Cross patée on both sides. | 45 | 90 |
| 3193 | — 4a, *mm.* Cross patée on *obv.* only | 45 | 90 |

                   3194                                     3200

| | | F | VF |
| --- | --- | --- | --- |
| 3194 | — 4b. CARO, colon stops; *mm.* Lis (demi) on *obv.* only | 30 | 60 |
| 3195 | — — — *mm.* on *rev.* only; *mm:* Martlet, Millrind | 30 | 60 |
| 3196 | — — — *mm.* on both sides; *mm:* Crescent/Crescent, Scroll/Scroll, 9/9, Lis (demi)/Scroll | 30 | 60 |
| 3197 | — 4c. apostrophe stops; *mm.* Rose (double) on *obv.* only | 30 | 60 |
| 3198 | — — — *mm.* Rose (double) both sides | 45 | 90 |
| 3199 | — — — *mm.* Rose (double) on *obv.*; Scroll on *rev.* | 30 | 60 |
| 3200 | 'Maltravers' oval. 5, no inner circles, legend starts bottom left, *mm.* Lis (large) on both sides | 75 | 150 |

*3192 to 3200, the oval farthings, were originally issued for use in Ireland*

|      |                                                                                  | F<br>£ | VF<br>£ |
|------|----------------------------------------------------------------------------------|--------|---------|
| 3201 | **Rose farthing**. 1a. Double-arched crowns; sceptres within inner circle, BRIT; *mm.* on *obv.* or *rev.* or both; *mm:* Lis, Cross pattée | 12 | 25 |
| 3202 | — 1b. similar but sceptres just cross inner circle, BRIT; *mm.* Lis on *obv.* or both sides or not present. | 10 | 20 |
| 3203 | — 1c. similar but sceptres almost to outer circle, BRIT; *mm.*s as 3201 ... | 12 | 25 |

3204                                              3207

|      |                                                                                  | F<br>£ | VF<br>£ |
|------|----------------------------------------------------------------------------------|--------|---------|
| 3204 | — 1d. similar but BRI; *mm.* on *obv.* or *rev.* or both sides or different each side; *mm:* Lis, Mullet, Cross pattée | 10 | 20 |
| 3205 | Transitional mules of 1d or (rarely) 1c and 2, double and single arched crowns; *mm.* as 3204; *mm:* Lis, Mullet, Crescent | 6 | 18 |
| 3206 | — 2. Single-arched crowns; *mm.* as 3204 | 4 | 12 |
| 3207 | — 3. Sceptres below crown; *mm.* Mullet on both sides | 30 | 50 |

The coins struck during the Commonwealth have inscriptions in English instead of Latin which was considered to savour of too much popery. St. George's cross and the Irish harp take the place of the royal arms. The silver halfpenny was issued for the last time. Coins with *mm.* anchor were struck during the protectorship of Richard Cromwell.

*Mintmarks*

1649-57 Sun    ☀       1658-60 Anchor   ⚓

## GOLD

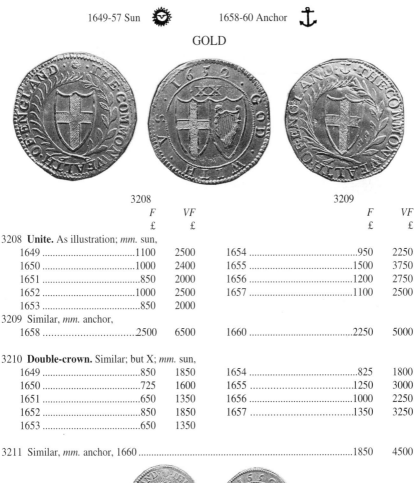

3208            3209

| | F £ | VF £ | | F £ | VF £ |
|---|---|---|---|---|---|
| **3208 Unite.** As illustration; *mm.* sun, | | | | | |
| 1649 | 1100 | 2500 | 1654 | 950 | 2250 |
| 1650 | 1000 | 2400 | 1655 | 1500 | 3750 |
| 1651 | 850 | 2000 | 1656 | 1200 | 2750 |
| 1652 | 1000 | 2500 | 1657 | 1100 | 2500 |
| 1653 | 850 | 2000 | | | |
| **3209** Similar, *mm.* anchor, | | | | | |
| 1658 | 2500 | 6500 | 1660 | 2250 | 5000 |
| | | | | | |
| **3210 Double-crown.** Similar; but X; *mm.* sun, | | | | | |
| 1649 | 850 | 1850 | 1654 | 825 | 1800 |
| 1650 | 725 | 1600 | 1655 | 1250 | 3000 |
| 1651 | 650 | 1350 | 1656 | 1000 | 2250 |
| 1652 | 850 | 1850 | 1657 | 1350 | 3250 |
| 1653 | 650 | 1350 | | | |
| | | | | | |
| **3211** Similar, *mm.* anchor, 1660 | | | | 1850 | 4500 |

3212

| | F £ | VF £ | | F £ | VF £ |
|---|---|---|---|---|---|
| **3212 Crown.** Similar, but V; *mm.* sun, | | | | | |
| 1649 | 700 | 1500 | 1654 | 675 | 1400 |
| 1650 | 625 | 1250 | 1655 | 900 | 2500 |
| 1651 | 650 | 1350 | 1656 | 850 | 2250 |
| 1652 | 625 | 1250 | 1657 | 875 | 2350 |
| 1653 | 625 | 1250 | | | |

|  | F £ | VF £ |  | F £ | VF £ |
|---|---|---|---|---|---|
| 3213 Similar *mm.* anchor, | | | | | |
| 1658 | 1600 | 4250 | 1660 | 1850 | 5250 |

## SILVER

3215

| 3214 **Crown.** Same type; *mm.* sun, | | | | | |
|---|---|---|---|---|---|
| 1649 | 1750 | 5000 | 1653 | 625 | 1250 |
| 1651 | 1100 | 3000 | 1654 | 725 | 1650 |
| 1652 | 675 | 1450 | 1656 | 650 | 1350 |

| 3215 **Halfcrown.** Similar; *mm.* sun, | | | | | |
|---|---|---|---|---|---|
| 1649 | 350 | 1050 | 1654 | 200 | 500 |
| 1651 | 225 | 625 | 1655 | 750 | 2000 |
| 1652 | 225 | 650 | 1656 | 190 | 475 |
| 1653 | 190 | 475 | 1657 | 1350 | 3000 |

| 3216 Similar, *mm.* anchor | | | | | |
|---|---|---|---|---|---|
| 1658 | 800 | 1850 | 1660 | 800 | 1850 |
| 1659 | 2000 | 5250 | | | |

| 3217 **Shilling.** Similar; *mm.* sun, | | | | | |
|---|---|---|---|---|---|
| 1649 | 175 | 475 | 1654 | 145 | 325 |
| 1651 | 135 | 300 | 1655 | 250 | 700 |
| 1652 | 140 | 325 | 1656 | 145 | 325 |
| 1653 | 135 | 300 | 1657 | 400 | 950 |

3218

| 3218 Similar, *mm.* anchor | | | | | |
|---|---|---|---|---|---|
| 1658 | 425 | 1050 | 1660 | 425 | 1050 |
| 1659 | 1750 | 4500 | | | |

|  | F £ | VF £ |  | F £ | VF £ |
|---|---|---|---|---|---|
| **3219 Sixpence.** Similar; *mm.* sun, | | | 1654 | 110 | 300 |
| 1649 | 125 | 375 | 1655 | 275 | 800 |
| 1651 | 110 | 275 | 1656 | 110 | 285 |
| 1652 | 110 | 275 | 1657 | 300 | 850 |
| 1653 | 100 | 265 | | | |
| | | | | | |
| 3220 Similar; *mm.* anchor, | | | 1660 | 375 | 925 |
| 1658 | 400 | 925 | | | |
| 1659 | 825 | 2250 | | | |

3221

3222

| | | F £ | VF £ |
|---|---|---|---|
| 3221 | **Halfgroat.** | 25 | 80 |
| 3222 | **Penny.** Similar, but I above shields | 20 | 60 |

3223

| | | F £ | VF £ |
|---|---|---|---|
| 3223 | **Halfpenny.** | 20 | 60 |

Oliver Cromwell, 'the Great Emancipator' was born on 25th April 1599 in Huntingdon. He married Elizabeth Bourchier in August 1620 and had nine children seven of whom survived infancy. The Protectorate was established on 16th December 1653, with work on the production of portrait coins authorised in 1655. Although often referred to as patterns, there is in fact nothing to suggest that the portrait coins of Oliver Cromwell were not intended for circulation. Authorised in 1656, the first full production came in 1657 and was followed by a second more plentiful one before Cromwell's death on 3rd September 1658. All coins were machine made, struck from dies by Thomas Simon in the presses of the Frenchman, Pierre Blondeau. Later, some of Simon's puncheons were sold in the Low Countries and an imitation Crown was made there. Other Dutch dies were prepared and some found their way back to the Mint, where in 1738 it was decided to strike a set of Cromwell's coins. Shillings and Sixpences were struck from the Dutch dies, and Crowns from new dies prepared by John Tanner. Thomas Simon who was born in 1618, later died in the Great Plague of 1665. Oliver was succeeded as Lord Protector by his son Richard of whom no coins were struck.

## GOLD

| | F | VF | EF |
|---|---|---|---|
| | £ | £ | £ |

**3224** **Fifty shillings.** Laur. head l. R. Crowned Shield of the Protectorate, die axis ↑↓ 1656. ........................................................ 5000 16000 35000
    Inscribed edge PROTECTOR · LITERIS · LITERÆ · NUMMIS · CORONA · ET · SALUS

3225
1656 gold Broad

**3225** **Broad.** of Twenty Shillings. Laur. head l. R. Crowned Shield of the Protectorate, but grained edge die axis ↑↓ 1656. ............................ 4000 6500 12500

## SILVER

3226
1658 Crown 8 over 7 - Die flawed drapery

**3226** **Crown.** Dr. bust l. R. Crowned shield, 1658/7. Inscribed edge ↑↓ 1750 3000 4750
**3226A** **Crown.** Dutch copy, similar with AVG legend 1658................ 1800 3500 5500
**3226B** **Crown.** Tanner's copy (struck 1738) dated 1658...................... 1800 3500 5500

|  | F | VF | EF |
|---|---|---|---|
|  | £ | £ | £ |

**3227** **Halfcrown.** Dr. bust l. R. Crowned shield 1656 HI type legend die axis ↑↓ ............................................................ | | |

1850   3250   5500

3227A
1658 Halfcrown with HIB obverse legend

**3227A Halfcrown.** Similar,1658 HIB type legend die axis ↑↓ ...............

950   1750   3000

3228
1658 Shilling

**3228** **Shilling.** Dr. bust l. R. Crowned shield, grained edge, 1658 die axis ↑↓ ............................................................................

500   950   1850

**3229** **Sixpence.** Similar 1658 die axis ↑↓ ......................................

*Extremely rare*

## COPPER

3230
Copper portrait Farthing

**3230** **Farthing.** Dr. bust l. R. CHARITIE AND CHANGE, shield ↑↓ .

3000   6000   —

*There are also other reverse types for this coin.*

For the first two years after the Restoration the same denominations, apart from the silver crown, were struck as were issued during the Commonwealth although the threepence and fourpence were soon added. Then, early in 1663, the ancient hand hammering process was finally superceded by the machinery of Blondeau.

For the emergency issues struck in the name of Charles II in 1648/9, see the siege pieces of Pontefract listed under Charles I, nos. 3150-1.

**Hammered coinage,** 1660-2

*Mintmark: Crown.*

3301             3302

## GOLD

| | F £ | VF £ |
|---|---|---|
| **First issue.** Without mark of value; *mm.* crown on *obv.* only | | |
| 3301 **Unite** (20s.). Type as illustration | 1350 | 4000 |
| 3302 **Double-crown.** As illustration | 850 | 2500 |
| 3303 **Crown.** Similar | 825 | 2350 |

3303                    3304

| | | |
|---|---|---|
| **Second issue.** With mark of value; *mm.* crown on *obv.* only | | |
| 3304 **Unite.** Type as illustration | 1000 | 2500 |
| 3305 **Double-crown.** As illustration | 750 | 2000 |
| 3306 **Crown.** Similar | 800 | 2250 |

## SILVER

3307

|  | F | VF |
|---|---|---|
|  | £ | £ |

First issue. Without inner circles or mark of value; *mm.* crown on *obv.* only

3307 **Halfcrown.** Crowned bust, as 3308 ..................................................... 850 2750

3308 3309

| 3308 | **Shilling**. Similar | 275 | 925 |
|---|---|---|---|
| 3309 | **Sixpence**. Similar | 225 | 725 |
| 3310 | **Twopence**. Similar | 35 | 100 |
| 3311 | **Penny**. Similar | 35 | 95 |
| 3312 | As last, but without mintmark | 50 | 125 |

3313 3322

Second issue. Without inner circles, but with mark of value; *mm.* crown on *obv.* only

| 3313 | **Halfcrown**. Crowned bust | 900 | 3250 |
|---|---|---|---|
| 3314 | **Shilling**. Similar | 425 | 1200 |
| 3315 | **Sixpence**. Similar | 850 | 2750 |
| 3316 | **Twopence**. Similar, but mm. on obv. only | 85 | 275 |

3310                              3317                         3326

|   |   | F<br>£ | VF<br>£ |
|---|---|---|---|
| 3317 | Similar, but mm. both sides (machine made)............................................ | 20 | 60 |
| 3318 | Bust to edge of coin, legend starts at bottom l. (machine made, single arch<br>crown)..................................................................................................... | 20 | 50 |
| 3319 | **Penny**. As 3317........................................................................................ | 25 | 70 |
| 3320 | As 3318 (single arch crown) ..................................................................... | 20 | 50 |

3321

**Third issue**. With inner circles and mark of value; *mm.* crown on both sides

| | | | |
|---|---|---|---|
| 3321 | **Halfcrown**. Crowned bust to i.c. (and rarely to edge of coin)................... | 175 | 575 |
| 3322 | **Shilling**. Similar, rarely *mm.* crown on *obv.* only ...................................... | 145 | 375 |
| 3323 | **Sixpence**. Similar...................................................................................... | 125 | 350 |
| 3324 | **Fourpence**. Similar.................................................................................... | 25 | 65 |
| 3325 | **Threepence**. Similar .................................................................................. | 25 | 60 |
| 3326 | **Twopence**. Similar..................................................................................... | 20 | 45 |
| 3327 | **Penny**. Similar .......................................................................................... | 20 | 45 |

## Grading of Early and Later Milled Coinage

Milled coinage refers to coins that are struck by dies worked in a mechanical coining press. The early period is defined from the time of the successful installation of Peter Blondeau's hand powered machinery at the mint, initiated to strike the first portrait coins of Oliver Cromwell in 1656. The early period continuing until the advent of Matthew Boulton's steam powered presses from 1790. The coinage of this early period is therefore cruder in it's execution than the latter. When pricing coins of the early peiod, we only attribute grades as high as extremely fine, and as high as uncirculated for the latter period. Most coins that occur of the early period in superior grades than those stated will command considerably higher prices, due to their rarity. We suggest the following definitions for grades of preservation:

## Milled Coinage Conditions

**Proof**  A very carefully struck coin from specially prepared dies, to give a superior definition to the design, with mirror-like fields. Occurs occasionally in the Early Milled Coinage, more frequently in the latter period. Some issues struck to a matt finish for Edward VII.

**FDC**  *Fleur-de-coin.* Absolutely flawless, untouched, without wear, scratches, marks or hairlines. Generally applied to proofs.

**UNC**  *Uncirculated.* A coin in as new condition as issued by the Mint, retaining full lustre or brilliance but, owing to modern mass-production methods of manufacture and storage, not necessarily perfect.

**EF**  *Extremely Fine.* A coin that exhibits very little sign of circulation, with only minimal marks or faint wear, which are only evident upon very close scrutiny.

**VF**  *Very Fine.* A coin that exhibits some wear on the raised surfaces of the design, but really has only had limited circulation.

**F**  *Fine.* A coin that exhibits considerable wear to the raised surfaces of the design, either through circulation, or damage perhaps due to faulty striking

**Fair**  *Fair.* A coin that exhibits wear, with the main features still distinguishable, and the legends, date and inscriptions still readable.

**Poor**  *Poor.* A coin that exhibits considerable wear, certainly with milled coinage of no value to a collector unless it is an extremely rare date or variety.

## Examples of Condition Grading

### Early Milled

Gold *N*        Silver *R*        Copper *Æ*

**Extremely Fine**

Gold **A/**          Silver **Æ**          Copper **Æ**

**Very Fine**

**Fine**

*George III*        *James II*        *George II*
*fifth bust Guinea*    *Second bust Crown*    *old head Halfpenny*

## Later Milled

Gold **A/**          Silver **Æ**          Copper **Æ**

**Uncirculated**

Gold *A͞V* Silver *Æ͞R* Copper *Æ*

**Extremely Fine**

**Very Fine**

**Fine**

*Victoria
Jubilee head Half-Sovereign*

*George IV
laureate bust Crown*

*Victoria
Young head Farthing*

Charles II was born at St James Palace on 29th May 1630. He spent a long exile in France and returned after the fall of the Protectorate in 1660. The Restoration commenced and he married Catherine of Braganza, but he bore no legitimate successor. Charles II died on 6th February 1685.

Early in 1663, the ancient hand hammering process was finally superceded by the machinery of Blondeau. John and Joseph Roettier, two brothers, engraved the dies with a safeguard against clipping, the larger coins were made with the edge inscribed DECVS ET TVTAMEN and the regnal year. The medium-sized coins were given a grained edge.

The new gold coins were current for 100s., 40s., 20s. and 10s., and they came to be called 'Guineas' as the gold from which some of them were made was imported from Guinea by the Africa Company (whose badge was the Elephant and Castle). It was not until some years later that the Guinea increased in value to 21s. and more. The Africa Co. badge is also found on some silver and so is the plume symbol indicating silver from the Welsh mines. The four smallest silver denominations, though known today as 'Maundy Money', were actually issued for general circulation: at this period the silver penny was probably the only coin distributed at the Royal Maundy ceremonies. Though never part of the original agreement, smaller coins were eventually also struck by machinery.

A good regal copper coinage was issued for the first time in 1672, but later in the reign, farthings were struck in tin (with a copper plug) in order to help the Cornish tin industry.

**Engravers and designers:** John Roettier (1631-1700), Thomas Simon (1618-1665)

## GOLD

3328
1669 First bust type Five-Guineas

**Milled coinage**

| | F | VF | EF | | F | VF | EF |
|---|---|---|---|---|---|---|---|
| | £ | £ | £ | | £ | £ | £ |

**3328 Five Guineas.** First laur. bust r., pointed trun., regnal year on edge in words, die axis ↑↓ (e.g. 1669=VICESIMO PRIMO), R. Crowned cruciform shields, sceptres in angles

| | F | VF | EF | | F | VF | EF |
|---|---|---|---|---|---|---|---|
| 1668 VICESIMO .....1250 | 3750 | 8000 | | 1674 – SEXTO...........1650 | 4250 | 9250 |
| 1669 – PRIMO.........1500 | 4000 | 9000 | | 1675 V. SEPTIMO ....1600 | 4250 | 9250 |
| 1670 – SECVNDO ..1500 | 4000 | 8750 | | 1676 – SEPTIMO ......1750 | 5000 | 9500 |
| 1670 – Similar proof FDC | Extremely rare | | | 1676 – OCTAVO.......1650 | 4250 | 9000 |
| 1671 – TERTIO .......1650 | 5250 | 10000 | | 1677 – NONO...........1350 | 3750 | 8250 |
| 1672 – QVARTO.....1650 | 5250 | 10000 | | 1678 – TRICESIMO...1500 | 4000 | 8750 |
| 1673 – QVINTO ......1500 | 4500 | 9500 | | 1678/7 – TRICESIMO ..1250 | 3750 | 8250 |

**3329 Five Guineas.** First bust with elephant below, similar die axis ↑↓

| | F | VF | EF | | F | VF | EF |
|---|---|---|---|---|---|---|---|
| 1668 VICESIMO ....1250 | 3500 | 8000 | | 1675 V. SEPTIMO ....1500 | 4000 | 8250 |
| 1669 – PRIMO.........1600 | 4250 | 9250 | | 1677/5 – NONO ................... | Extremely rare | |

**3330**
1677 Five-Guineas with elephant and castle provenance mark

|  | F | VF | EF |  | F | VF | EF |
|---|---|---|---|---|---|---|---|
|  | £ | £ | £ |  | £ | £ | £ |

**3330 Five Guineas.** First bust with elephant and castle below, similar die axis ↑↓

| 1675 – SEPTIMO ............ | *Extremely rare* | | | 1678 TRICESIMO.....1600 | 4250 | 9250 |
| 1676 – OCTAVO.....1650 | 4500 | 9250 | 1678/7– TRICESIMO..1600 | 4250 | 9250 |
| 1677 – NONO..........1500 | 4000 | 8750 | | | |

**3331 Five Guineas.** Second laur. bust r., rounded trun. similar die axis ↑↓

| 1678/7 TRICESIMO..1400 | 3750 | 8500 | 1682 T. QVARTO .....1250 | 3500 | 8250 |
| 1679 – PRIMO.........1650 | 4500 | 9250 | 1683 – QVINTO........1250 | 3500 | 8250 |
| 1680 – SECVNDO ..1650 | 4500 | 9250 | 1683/2—QVINTO .......1500 | 4000 | 8750 |
| 1681 – TERTIO .......1450 | 3800 | 8750 | 1684 – SEXTO..........1200 | 3250 | 7750 |

**3332 Five Guineas.** Second laur. bust r., with elephant and castle below, similar die axis ↑↓

| 1680 T. SECVNDO........ | *Extremely rare* | | 1683 T. QVINTO ......1600 | 4250 | 9250 |
| 1681 – TERTIO ......1500 | 4000 | 8750 | 1684 – SEXTO ..........1250 | 3500 | 8000 |
| 1682 – QVARTO ....1250 | 3500 | 8250 | | | |

**3333**
1664 First bust type Two Guineas

**3334**
1664 Two Guineas with elephant only below

**3333 Two Guineas.** First laur. bust r., pointed trun. R. Crowned cruciform shields, sceptres in angles, die axis ↑↓

| 1664 ........................1000 | 3000 | 6000 | 1669 ............................ | *Extremely rare* | |
| 1665 ............................... | *Extremely rare* | | 1671 ............................950 | 3800 | 6750 |
| | | | 1673 ............................ | *Extremely rare* | |

**3334 Two Guineas.** First bust with elephant below, similar die axis ↑↓

| 1664 ............................................................................................800 | 2500 | 5500 |

**3335 Two Guineas.** Second laur. bust r., rounded trun, similar die axis ↑↓

| 1675.........................1100 | 3850 | 6250 | 1680.........................1050 | 3250 | 6250 |
| 1676.........................1050 | 3250 | 6000 | 1681...........................850 | 2750 | 5500 |
| 1677.........................1100 | 3650 | 6250 | 1682.........................1100 | 3650 | 6250 |
| 1678/7 .......................850 | 2750 | 5250 | 1683...........................950 | 3000 | 5750 |
| 1679.........................1100 | 3650 | 6250 | 1684.........................1150 | 3800 | 6500 |

*Overstruck dates are listed only if commoner than the normal date or if no normal date is known.*

3335
1679 Two Guineas - second bust

3339
1663 Guinea first bust, elephant below

| | F | VF | EF | | F | VF | EF |
|---|---|---|---|---|---|---|---|
| | £ | £ | £ | | £ | £ | £ |

**3336 Two Guineas.** Second bust with elephant and castle below, similar die axis ↑↓

| | F | VF | EF | | F | VF | EF |
|---|---|---|---|---|---|---|---|
| 1676 | 1050 | 3250 | 6250 | 1682 | 1050 | 3500 | 6750 |
| 1677 | | *Extremely rare* | | 1683 | 950 | 3000 | 6000 |
| 1678 | 850 | 2750 | 5750 | 1684 | 1150 | 3750 | 6800 |

**3337 Two Guineas.** Second bust with elephant only below, die axis ↑↓ 1678 ...... *Extremely rare*
**3337A Broad** of 20s. Laur. and dr. bust r. R. Crowned shield of arms (approx. 3400 issued),
    die axis ↑↓ 1662 ....900     2150     3750
**3338 Guinea.** First laur. bust r., R. Crowned cruciform shields, die axis
    ↑↓ 1663 ..................800     2750     6000
**3339 Guinea.** First bust with elephant below, similar die axis ↑↓ 1663 ..........750     2500     5500
**3340 Guinea.** Second laur. bust r.,similar die axis ↑↓ 1664 ............................675     2250     5000

3341
1664 Guinea second bust elephant below

**3341 Guinea.** Second bust with elephant below, similar die axis ↑↓1664 ....4000     9500     —
**3342 Guinea.** Third laur. bust r. similar die axis ↑↓

| | F | VF | EF | | F | VF | EF |
|---|---|---|---|---|---|---|---|
| 1664 | 500 | 2000 | 4750 | 1669 | 550 | 2750 | 5500 |
| 1665 | 525 | 2250 | 5000 | 1670 | 525 | 2750 | 5500 |
| 1666 | 550 | 2750 | 5500 | 1671 | 550 | 2750 | 5000 |
| 1667 | 525 | 2250 | 5000 | 1672 | 550 | 2750 | 5000 |
| 1668 | 550 | 2750 | 5500 | 1673 | 600 | 2800 | 5250 |

 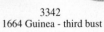  

3342
1664 Guinea - third bust

3344
Fourth bust

3345
Fourth bust -
elephant and castle below

**3343 Guinea.** Third laur. bust r., with elephant below, similar die axis ↑↓

| | F | VF | EF | | |
|---|---|---|---|---|---|
| 1664 | 600 | 2500 | 5250 | 1668 | *Extremely rare* |
| 1665 | 625 | 2750 | 5500 | | |

| | F | VF | EF | | F | VF | EF |
|---|---|---|---|---|---|---|---|
| | £ | £ | £ | | £ | £ | £ |

**3344 Guinea.** Fourth laur. bust r., rounded trun. similar die axis ↑↓

| | F | VF | EF | | F | VF | EF |
|---|---|---|---|---|---|---|---|
| 1672 ......................450 | 2000 | 4250 | | 1678 ........................375 | 1350 | 3500 |
| 1673 ......................450 | 2000 | 4250 | | 1679 ........................380 | 1250 | 3250 |
| 1674 ......................450 | 2000 | 4250 | | 1680 ........................350 | 1250 | 3250 |
| 1675 ......................450 | 2000 | 4250 | | 1681 ........................450 | 2000 | 4250 |
| 1675 CRAOLVS error.... | *Extremely rare* | | | 1682 ........................400 | 1650 | 3850 |
| 1676 ......................375 | 1350 | 3500 | | 1682 rev.@90° axis...750 | 2750 | 5500 |
| 1677 ......................375 | 1350 | 3500 | | 1683 ........................375 | 1350 | 3500 |
| 1677 Oover Oon it's side | *Extremely rare* | | | 1684 ........................400 | 1650 | 3850 |

**3345 Guinea.** Fourth laur. bust r., with elephant and castle below, similar die axis ↑↓

| | F | VF | EF | | F | VF | EF |
|---|---|---|---|---|---|---|---|
| 1674 ............................... | *Extremely rare* | | | 1679 ........................475 | 1850 | 4250 |
| 1675 ......................500 | 2000 | 4750 | | 1680 ........................600 | 2250 | 5000 |
| 1676 ......................425 | 1650 | 4000 | | 1681 ........................485 | 1900 | 4750 |
| 1677 ......................450 | 1850 | 4500 | | 1682 ........................475 | 1850 | 4500 |
| 1677 GRATIR error........ | *Extremely rare* | | | 1683 ........................600 | 2500 | 5500 |
| 1678 ......................500 | 2000 | 4750 | | 1684 ........................485 | 1900 | 4500 |

**3346 Guinea.** — — with elephant below bust, similar die axis ↑↓

| | | | | | |
|---|---|---|---|---|---|
| 1677/5 ............................ | *Extremely rare* | | 1678 ............................... | *Extremely rare* |

3347
1669 Half-Guinea, first bust

3348
1682 Half-Guinea, second bust

**3347 Half-Guinea.** First laur. bust r., pointed trun.R. Crowned cruciform shields, sceptres in angles die axis ↑↓

| | F | VF | EF | | F | VF | EF |
|---|---|---|---|---|---|---|---|
| 1669 ......................350 | 1100 | 3350 | | 1671 ........................375 | 1150 | 3600 |
| 1670 ......................300 | 950 | 3000 | | 1672 ........................375 | 1150 | 3600 |

**3348 Half-Guinea.** Second laur. bust r., rounded trun. similar die axis ↑↓

| | F | VF | EF | | F | VF | EF |
|---|---|---|---|---|---|---|---|
| 1672 ......................325 | 1000 | 3000 | | 1678/7 ......................375 | 1150 | 3850 |
| 1673 ......................425 | 1350 | 3600 | | 1679 ........................350 | 1100 | 3350 |
| 1674 ......................475 | 1450 | 3850 | | 1680 ........................425 | 1350 | 3850 |
| 1675 ......................500 | 1500 | 4250 | | 1681 ........................425 | 1350 | 3850 |
| 1676 ......................300 | 950 | 2750 | | 1682 ........................425 | 1350 | 3850 |
| 1676/4 ......................375 | 1150 | 3600 | | 1683 ........................325 | 1000 | 3000 |
| 1677 ......................350 | 1100 | 3350 | | 1684 ........................300 | 980 | 2750 |
| 1678 ......................350 | 1100 | 3350 | | | | |

**3349 Half-Guinea.** Second bust with elephant and castle below, similar die axis ↑↓

| | F | VF | EF | | F | VF | EF |
|---|---|---|---|---|---|---|---|
| 1676 ......................600 | 2250 | — | | 1681 ............................... | *Extremely rare* | |
| 1677 ......................475 | 1450 | 3850 | | 1682 ........................475 | 1450 | 3850 |
| 1678/7 ......................375 | 1150 | 3600 | | 1683 ............................... | *Extremely rare* | |
| 1680 ............................... | *Extremely rare* | | | 1684 ........................350 | 1100 | 3300 |

# SILVER

3350
1662 Crown, first type, rose below bust

|  | F £ | VF £ | EF £ |  | F £ | VF £ | EF £ |
|---|---|---|---|---|---|---|---|

**3350 Crown**. First dr. bust r., rose below, R. Crowned cruciform shields, interlinked C's in angles
edge undated, die axis ↑↓ 1662.....................120 825 3500

**3350A Crown**. — — — Similar, die axis ↑↑ 1662.........................275 1250 —

**3350B Crown**. — — — II of legend at 12 o'clock, similar die axis ↑↓ 1662 .......... *Extremely rare*

**3351 Crown**.— — edge dated,similar die axis ↑↓ 1662..............................140 950 3850

**3351A Crown**.— — edge dated struck en medaille, similar die axis ↑↑ 1662....200 1100 —

**3351B Crown**.— striped cloak struck en medaille, similar die axis ↑↑ 1662...275 1250 —

**3351C Crown**.— striped cloak to drapery, 1662 similar die axis ↑↓ .............275 1400 4750

**3352 Crown**.— no rose, edge dated, similar die axis ↑↓ 1662....................150 1000 4000

**3353 Crown**.— — edge not dated, similar die axis ↑↓ 1662.......................140 950 4000

**3353A Crown**. — — — die axis ↑↓ 1662 ......................................275 1250 —

**3354 Crown**.— — legend re-arranged shields altered, 1663, similar regnal year on edge in
Roman figures ANNO REGNI XV die axis ↑↓...................................150 1000 4000
1663 no stops on reverse ..................................................................500 — —

**3355 Crown**. Second dr. bust r., regnal year on edge in Roman figures (e.g. 1664 = XVI), die axis ↑↓

| 1664 edge XVI........ 110 | 675 | 3250 | 1666 XVIII ...............110 | 750 | 3500 |
|---|---|---|---|---|---|
| 1665 XVI ...................... | *Extremely rare* | | 1666 XVIII RE·X........... | *Extremely rare* | |
| 1665/4 XVII..............725 | 1900 | — | 1667 XVIII .............2250 | — | — |
| 1665 XVII.................725 | 1900 | — | | | |

3356 – RE•X variety

3356
Elephant provenance mark

**3356 Crown**. Second bust elephant below, similar, die axis ↑↓
1666 XVIII ...............325 1250 — 1666 XVIII RE·X.....450 1500 —

3357
1669 Crown - second bust

| | F £ | VF £ | EF £ | | F £ | VF £ | EF £ |
|---|---|---|---|---|---|---|---|

**3357 Crown.** Second bust, similar Regnal year on edge in words (e.g. 1667= DECIMO NONO) die axis ↑↓

| | F | VF | EF | | F | VF | EF |
|---|---|---|---|---|---|---|---|
| 1667 D. NONO ..........100 | 600 | 3000 | | 1669/8 V· PRIMO..........350 | 1100 | — | |
| 1667 — AN.· REG.· ..100 | 675 | 3300 | | 1670 V. SECVNDO ......125 | 725 | 3650 | |
| 1668 VICESIMO ........90 | 550 | 2850 | | 1670/69 V. SECVND......150 | 825 | 4000 | |
| 1668 — error edge ........ | *Extremely rare* | | | 1671 V· TERTIO ..........100 | 725 | 3650 | |
| 1668/7 VICESIMO ....100 | 600 | 3000 | | 1671 — T/R in ET ........950 | 2500 | — | |
| 1668/5 VICESIMO ........ | *Extremely rare* | | | 1671 — ET over FR ....1200 | 3300 | — | |
| 1669 V· PRIMO ........325 | 1000 | — | | | | | |

3358
Third bust Crown

3359
Fourth bust Crown

**3358 Crown.** Third dr. bust r. R.Similar die axis ↑↓

| | F | VF | EF | | F | VF | EF |
|---|---|---|---|---|---|---|---|
| 1671 V. TERTIO ........ 95 | 600 | 3300 | | 1675 — EGNI error........800 | — | — | |
| 1671 V. QVARTO.......... | *Extremely rare* | | | 1676 V. OCTAVO ..........95 | 600 | 3300 | |
| 1672 V. QVARTO ...... 95 | 600 | 3300 | | 1676 OCCTAVO............100 | 775 | 3650 | |
| 1673 V. QVARTO ......... | *Extremely rare* | | | 1677 V. NONO ..............120 | 775 | 3650 | |
| 1673 V. QVINTO ...... 95 | 600 | 3300 | | 1677/6 V. NONO ..........140 | 900 | — | |
| 1673 B/R in BR..........200 | 1100 | — | | 1678/7 TRICESIMO ......140 | 900 | — | |
| 1673/2 V. QVINTO ..150 | 825 | 3850 | | 1679 T. PRIMO..............100 | 675 | 3300 | |
| 1674 V. SEXTO ............. | *Extremely rare* | | | 1680/79 T. SECVNDO ......120 | 725 | 3650 | |
| 1675/3 V. SEPTIMO..725 | 2500 | — | | 1680 T. SECVNDO .......125 | 775 | 4250 | |
| 1675 — ...................1150 | 4250 | — | | | | | |

**3359 Crown.** Fourth dr. bust r. R.Similar die axis ↑↓

| | F | VF | EF | | F | VF | EF |
|---|---|---|---|---|---|---|---|
| 1679 T. PRIMO............95 | 600 | 3000 | | 1682/1 T. QVARTO ........95 | 600 | 3300 | |
| 1679 HIBR·EX ..........150 | 900 | — | | 1682 T. QVARTO..........650 | 2250 | 5250 | |
| 1680 T. SECVNDO ..100 | 600 | 3300 | | 1682/1 QVRRTO error ....450 | 1400 | — | |
| 1680/79 T. SECVNDO 140 | 825 | — | | 1683 T. QVINTO ..........500 | 1650 | — | |
| 1681 T. TERTIO........100 | 600 | 3300 | | 1684 T. SEXTO..............400 | 1150 | — | |

**3360 Crown.**— elephant and castle below bust, die axis ↑↓ 1681 T. TERTIO ........2750 | 5250 | —

3361 - First bust Halfcrown 3362 - Second bust Halfcrown

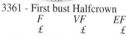

|  | F £ | VF £ | EF £ |  | F £ | VF £ | EF £ |
|---|---|---|---|---|---|---|---|

**3361 Halfcrown.** First dr. bust r. R. Crowned cruciform shields, interlinked C's in angles, regnal year on edge in Roman figures die axis ↑↓

| | F | VF | EF |
|---|---|---|---|
| 1663 XV ............. | 95 | 600 | 3000 |
| 1663 XV V/S in CAROLVS ............. | 200 | 875 | — |
| 1663 XV A/T in GRATIA ............. | 200 | 875 | — |
| 1663 XV no stops on obverse ............. | 175 | 800 | — |
| 1663 XV different die axis to usual ............. | 275 | 950 | — |

**3362 Halfcrown.** Second dr. bust r., similar die axis ↑↓ 1664 XVI ............. 200 1100 3750
**3363 Halfcrown.** Third dr. bust r., similar die axis ↑↓ 1666/4 XVIII ............. 1050 3500 —
**3364 Halfcrown.** Third bust elephant below, die axis ↑↓ 1666 XVIII ............. 900 2000 —

3364
Third bust, elephant below Halfcrown

3365
1670 Halfcrown, third bust

**3365 Halfcrown.** Third dr. bust r. regnal date on edge in words (eg. 1667=DECIMO NONO) ↑↓

| | | | | | | | |
|---|---|---|---|---|---|---|---|
| 1667/4 D. NONO............. | *Extremely rare* | | 1669 — R/I in PRIMO ... | | *Extremely rare* | |
| 1668/4 VICESIMO...225 | 950 | — | 1670 V. SECVNDO ........85 | 500 | 3000 |
| 1668/4 CAROLVS....350 | 1250 | — | 1670 – MRG for MAG ....350 | 1250 | — |
| 1669/4 V. PRIMO.....225 | 850 | — | 1670 V/S CAROLVS ....300 | 1100 | — |
| 1669 V. PRIMO........450 | 1400 | — | 1670 E/R in ET ..............350 | 1250 | — |

3366
1671 Halfcrown third bust variety

3367
Fourth bust Halfcrown

**3366 Halfcrown.** Third bust variety r. R. Similar die axis ↑↓

| | | | | | | |
|---|---|---|---|---|---|---|
| 1671 V. TERTIO........80 | 500 | 2250 | 1672 V. TERTIO............. | *Extremely rare* | |
| 1671 A/R in MAG ....175 | 900 | — | 1672 V. QVARTO ..........80 | 500 | 2250 |
| 1671/0 V. TERTIO...100 | 600 | 3350 | | | |

|  | F £ | VF £ | EF £ |  | F £ | VF £ | EF £ |
|---|---|---|---|---|---|---|---|

**3367 Halfcrown.** Fourth dr. bust r. R. Similar die axis ↑↓

| | F | VF | EF | | F | VF | EF |
|---|---|---|---|---|---|---|---|
| 1672 V. QVARTO ....120 | | 500 | 3000 | 1679 T. PRIMO................80 | | 400 | 2250 |
| 1673 V. QVINTO ........80 | | 400 | 2250 | 1679 — GRATTA error . | | *Extremely rare* | |
| 1673 —A/R in FRA........ | | *Extremely rare* | | 1679 — REGᴚI error..... | | *Extremely rare* | |
| 1673 — B/R in BR ......... | | *Extremely rare* | | 1679 —DECNS error......225 | | 775 | — |
| 1673 — FR/M in FRA.... | | *Extremely rare* | | 1679 — DNCVS error ....350 | | — | — |
| 1674 V. SEXTO ........125 | | 450 | 3000 | 1679 — PRICESIMO ......250 | | 825 | — |
| 1674/3 V. SEXTO......275 | | — | — | 1679 — inverted A's for | | | |
| 1675 V. SEPTIMO ......90 | | 450 | 2750 | V's on edge............350 | | — | — |
| 1675 — Retrograde 1 100 | | 500 | 3000 | 1680 T. SECVNDO........150 | | 725 | — |
| 1676 V. OCTAVO ......75 | | 350 | 1950 | 1680 T. SECVNDꝊ error | | *Extremely rare* | |
| 1676 R/T in BR.............. | | *Extremely rare* | | 1681 T. TERTIO ..............90 | | 450 | 2750 |
| 1676 — Retrograde 1 ..85 | | 400 | 2250 | 1681/0 —.....................225 | | — | — |
| 1677 F/H in FRA ............ | | *Extremely rare* | | 1682 T. QVARTO..........100 | | 500 | 3000 |
| 1676 F/H in FRA ............ | | *Extremely rare* | | 1682/79 T. QVARTO..... | | *Extremely rare* | |
| 1677 V. NONO ............80 | | 400 | 2500 | 1683 T. QVINTO ............80 | | 400 | 2250 |
| 1678 TRICESIMO ....200 | | 725 | — | 1684/3 T. SEXTO ..........200 | | 775 | — |

3369 - Plume in centre      3370 - Elephant and Castle below bust

**3368 Halfcrown.** Fourth bust plume below, R. Similar die axis ↑↓

| 1673 V. QVINTO ....2000 | — | — | 1683 T. QVINTO ........... | *Extremely rare* |

**3369 Halfcrown.**— plume below bust and in centre of *rev.*, die axis ↑↓ 1673 V. QVINTO  *Extremely rare*

**3370 Halfcrown.**— elephant and castle below bust, die axis ↑↓ 1681 T. TERTIO ..2000  6000  22500

## SHILLINGS

First bust        First bust variety        Second bust        Third bust

First bust        First bust var.        First bust and        Second bust
                                         first bust variety    single top leaf

3371 - First bust  3371 – Transposed Irish and Scottish shields

| | F | VF | EF | | F | VF | EF |
|---|---|---|---|---|---|---|---|
| | £ | £ | £ | | £ | £ | £ |

**3371  Shilling.** First dr. bust r.R. Crowned cruciform shields interlinked C's in angles edge milled,

| | | | |
|---|---|---|---|
| 1663 die axis ↑↑ (en medaille) | 125 | 550 | 1750 |
| 1663 die axis ↑↓ as usual | 85 | 350 | 850 |
| 1663 GARTIA error, die axis ↑↓ | 1000 | — | — |
| 1663 Transposed shields of Scotland and Ireland, die axis ↑↓ | 150 | 825 | 2000 |
| 1663 A over G in FRA, die axis ↑↓ | 950 | — | — |

3372
1663 Shilling - first bust variety

3374
1666 'Guinea' head shilling

**3372  Shilling.** First bust variety r. similar die axis ↑↓

| | | | | | | | |
|---|---|---|---|---|---|---|---|
| 1663 | 80 | 350 | 825 | 1668 | 450 | 1500 | — |
| 1666 | | *Extremely rare* | | 1669/6 | | *Extremely rare* | |

**3373  Shilling.** First bust variety r. elephant below bust, die axis ↑↓ 1666 ..400  1400  3500

**3374  Shilling.** Guinea head, elephant below bust, die axis ↑↓ 1666..........1750  4000  —

3375 - Second bust shilling  3376 - Plume both sides shilling of 1676

**3375  Shilling.** Second dr. bust r. similar die axis ↑↓

| | | | | | | | |
|---|---|---|---|---|---|---|---|
| 1666 | 1650 | 5000 | — | 1676 | 75 | 450 | 1000 |
| 1668 | 60 | 350 | 825 | 1676 higher bust | | *Extremely rare* | |
| 1668/7 | 75 | 450 | 1050 | 1676/5 | 85 | 475 | 1100 |
| 1669 | | *Extremely rare* | | 1677 | 75 | 450 | 1000 |
| 1670 | 90 | 500 | 1200 | 1678 | 90 | 500 | 1200 |
| 1671 | 110 | 550 | 1400 | 1678/7 | 90 | 500 | 1200 |
| 1672 | 75 | 450 | 1050 | 1679 | 75 | 450 | 1000 |
| 1673 | 110 | 725 | 1400 | 1679/7 | 90 | 500 | 1200 |
| 1673/2 | 160 | 725 | 1650 | 1680 | | *Extremely rare* | |
| 1674 | 135 | 600 | 1500 | 1681 | 110 | 550 | 1400 |
| 1674/3 | 110 | 550 | 1300 | 1681/0 | 110 | 550 | 1400 |
| 1675 | 160 | 725 | 1650 | 1682/1 | 550 | 1400 | — |
| 1675/4 | 160 | 725 | 1650 | 1683 | | *Extremely rare* | |

|     | F | VF | EF |     | F | VF | EF |
| --- | £ | £ | £ | --- | £ | £ | £ |

**3376 Shilling.** Second Bust — plume below bust and in centre of *rev.* similar die axis ↑↓

| 1671 | 200 | 725 | 2250 | 1676 | 225 | 775 | 2500 |
| 1673 | 225 | 775 | 2500 | 1679 | 250 | 950 | 2750 |
| 1674 | 200 | 725 | 2250 | 1680 | 325 | 1100 | 3000 |
| 1675 | 225 | 775 | 2500 | 1680/79 | 325 | 1100 | 3000 |

3377
1674 Shilling - plume on reverse only

3378
1679 Shilling - plume on obverse only

**3377 Shilling.** — Plume *rev.* only, similar die axis ↑↓ 1674 ........300  1400  3300

**3378 Shilling.** — Plume *obv.* only similar die axis ↑↓

| 1677 | 500 | 1900 | 3850 | 1679 | 400 | 1650 | 3600 |

**3379 Shilling.** — elephant and castle below bust, die axis ↑↓ 1681/0.......2250  —  —

3380
Third bust Shilling

3381
1683 Shilling - fourth bust

**3380 Shilling.** Third dr. (large) bust r. similar die axis ↑↓

| 1674 | 250 | 1050 | 3000 | 1675/3 | 200 | 775 | 2500 |
| 1675 | 200 | 775 | 2500 | | | | |

**3381 Shilling.** Fourth dr. (large) bust r., older features, similar die axis ↑↓

| 1683 | 150 | 600 | 1650 | 1684 | 125 | 500 | 1400 |

3382
1676 Sixpence

**3382 Sixpence.** Dr. bust r. R. Crowned cruciform shields, interlinked C's in angles die axis ↑↓

| 1674 | 50 | 300 | 700 | 1679 | 65 | 350 | 800 |
| 1675 | 50 | 300 | 700 | 1680 | 90 | 400 | 950 |
| 1675/4 | 65 | 375 | 850 | 1681 | 50 | 275 | 600 |
| 1676 | 90 | 400 | 950 | 1682 | 90 | 400 | 950 |
| 1676/5 | 90 | 400 | 950 | 1682/1 | 65 | 350 | 750 |
| 1677 | 50 | 300 | 700 | 1683 | 50 | 300 | 700 |
| 1678/7 | 65 | 350 | 750 | 1684 | 75 | 350 | 750 |

3383 - Undated Fourpence

|  | F | VF | EF |  | F | VF | EF |
|---|---|---|---|---|---|---|---|
|  | £ | £ | £ |  | £ | £ | £ |

**3383 Fourpence.** Undated. Crowned dr. bust l. to edge of coin, value behind. R. Shield, die axis ↑↓ .................................................................15  45  100

3384 - 1678 Fourpence          3386 - 1678 Threepence

**3384 Fourpence.** Dated. Dr. bust r. R. Crowned four interlinked Cs quartered emblems die axis ↑↓

| | | | | | | |
|---|---|---|---|---|---|---|
| 1670 ............................12 | 35 | 95 | 1678................................10 | 25 | 75 |
| 1671 ............................10 | 30 | 90 | 1678/6 ............................10 | 30 | 90 |
| 1672/1 ..........................10 | 25 | 80 | 1678/7 ............................10 | 30 | 90 |
| 1673 ............................10 | 25 | 80 | 1679................................10 | 25 | 75 |
| 1674 ............................10 | 25 | 80 | 1680................................10 | 25 | 75 |
| 1674/4 sideways .........12 | 35 | 165 | 1681................................10 | 25 | 75 |
| 1674 7 over 6 ..............10 | 30 | 90 | 1681 B/R in HIB ..............12 | 35 | 165 |
| 1675 ............................10 | 25 | 80 | 1681/0 ............................10 | 30 | 90 |
| 1675/4 ..........................10 | 30 | 90 | 1682................................10 | 25 | 75 |
| 1676 ............................10 | 25 | 80 | 1682/1 ............................10 | 30 | 90 |
| 1676 7 over 6 ..............10 | 30 | 90 | 1683................................10 | 25 | 75 |
| 1676/5 ..........................10 | 30 | 90 | 1684................................10 | 30 | 90 |
| 1677 ............................10 | 25 | 75 | 1684/3 ............................10 | 25 | 75 |

**3385 Threepence.** Undated. As 3383, die axis ↑↓ ..............................................10  30  90

**3386 Threepence.** Dated. Dr. bust r. R. Crowned three interlinked C's, die axis ↑↓

| | | | | | | |
|---|---|---|---|---|---|---|
| 1670 ..............................6 | 25 | 75 | 1678................................6 | 20 | 65 |
| 1671 ..............................6 | 20 | 65 | 1678 on 4d flan ..............6 | 20 | 80 |
| 1671 GRΛTIA ............10 | 35 | 165 | 1679................................6 | 20 | 65 |
| 1671 GRΛTIA ..............8 | 25 | 105 | 1679 O/A in CAROLVS ....10 | 35 | 165 |
| 1672/1 ............................6 | 20 | 65 | 1680................................6 | 20 | 65 |
| 1673 ..............................6 | 20 | 65 | 1681................................6 | 20 | 65 |
| 1674 ..............................6 | 20 | 65 | 1681/0 ............................7 | 25 | 75 |
| 1675 ..............................6 | 25 | 75 | 1682................................6 | 20 | 65 |
| 1676 ..............................6 | 20 | 65 | 1682/1 ............................7 | 25 | 75 |
| 1676/5 ............................7 | 25 | 75 | 1683................................6 | 20 | 65 |
| 1676 ERA for FRA.....10 | 35 | 165 | 1684................................6 | 20 | 65 |
| 1677 ..............................6 | 25 | 75 | 1684/3 ............................7 | 25 | 75 |

**3387 Twopence.** Undated. As 3383 (double arch crown) die axis ↑↓ ..................6  25  65

3388 - 1678 Twopence          3390 - 1678 Penny

| | F | VF | EF | | F | VF | EF |
|---|---|---|---|---|---|---|---|
| | £ | £ | £ | | £ | £ | £ |

**3388  Twopence.** Dated. Dr. bust r. R. Crowned pair of linked C's, die axis ↑↓

| | F | VF | EF | | F | VF | EF |
|---|---|---|---|---|---|---|---|
| 1668 die axis ↑↑ | 8 | 25 | 75 | 1678/6 | 8 | 25 | 75 |
| 1670 | 6 | 20 | 65 | 1679 | 6 | 20 | 65 |
| 1671 | 6 | 20 | 65 | 1679 HIB over FRA | 10 | 35 | 165 |
| 1672/1 | 6 | 20 | 65 | 1680 | 6 | 20 | 65 |
| 1672/1 GRΛTIΛ | 10 | 35 | 135 | 1680/79 | 8 | 25 | 75 |
| 1673 | 8 | 25 | 75 | 1681 | 6 | 20 | 65 |
| 1674 | 6 | 20 | 65 | 1682/1 | 8 | 25 | 75 |
| 1675 | 6 | 20 | 65 | 1682/1 ERA for FRA | 10 | 35 | 165 |
| 1676 | 6 | 20 | 65 | 1683 | 6 | 20 | 65 |
| 1677 | 8 | 25 | 75 | 1683/2 | 8 | 25 | 75 |
| 1678 | 6 | 25 | 65 | 1684 | 8 | 25 | 75 |

**3389  Penny.** Undated. As 3383 (double arch crown) die axis ↑↓ .................... 6    30    100

**3390  Penny.** Dated. Dr. bust r. R. Crowned C die axis ↑↓

| | F | VF | EF | | F | VF | EF |
|---|---|---|---|---|---|---|---|
| 1670 | 8 | 25 | 90 | 1678 ƆRATIA error | 10 | 35 | 165 |
| 1671 | 8 | 25 | 90 | 1678 | 9 | 30 | 110 |
| 1672/1 | 8 | 25 | 90 | 1679 | 9 | 30 | 110 |
| 1673 | 8 | 25 | 90 | 1680 | 8 | 25 | 90 |
| 1674 | 8 | 25 | 90 | 1680 on 2d flan | | *Extremely rare* | |
| 1674 ƆRATIA error | 10 | 35 | 165 | 1681 | 10 | 35 | 135 |
| 1675 | 8 | 25 | 90 | 1682 | 9 | 30 | 100 |
| 1675 ƆRATIA error | 10 | 35 | 165 | 1682/1 | 10 | 35 | 135 |
| 1676 | 9 | 30 | 110 | 1682 ERA for FRA | 10 | 35 | 165 |
| 1676 ƆRATIA error | 10 | 35 | 165 | 1683/1 | 8 | 25 | 90 |
| 1677 | 8 | 25 | 90 | 1684 | 9 | 30 | 110 |
| 1677 ƆRATIA error | 10 | 35 | 165 | 1684/3 | 10 | 35 | 135 |

**3391  Maundy Set.** Undated. The four coins .................................................. 85    350    600

**3392  Maundy Set.** Dated. The four denominations.  Uniform dates

| | F | VF | EF | | F | VF | EF |
|---|---|---|---|---|---|---|---|
| 1670 | 70 | 250 | 500 | 1678 | 70 | 300 | 600 |
| 1671 | 60 | 200 | 500 | 1679 | 65 | 225 | 550 |
| 1672 | 70 | 225 | 550 | 1680 | 60 | 200 | 525 |
| 1673 | 60 | 200 | 500 | 1681 | 70 | 300 | 600 |
| 1674 | 60 | 200 | 500 | 1682 | 65 | 225 | 550 |
| 1675 | 65 | 225 | 550 | 1683 | 60 | 200 | 500 |
| 1676 | 65 | 225 | 550 | 1684 | 65 | 225 | 550 |
| 1677 | 65 | 225 | 550 | | | | |

## COPPER AND TIN

3393 - 1675 Halfpenny

| | F | VF | EF | | F | VF | EF |
|---|---|---|---|---|---|---|---|
| | £ | £ | £ | | £ | £ | £ |

**3393** Copper **Halfpenny** Cuir. bust l. R. Britannia seated l. date in ex., die axis ↑↓

| | F | VF | EF | | F | VF | EF |
|---|---|---|---|---|---|---|---|
| 1672 | 50 | 300 | 950 | 1673 no stops on obv. | | *Extremely rare* | |
| 1672 CRAOLVS error | | *Extremely rare* | | 1673 no rev. stop | 85 | 450 | — |
| 1673 | 40 | 275 | 850 | 1675 | 45 | 275 | 900 |
| 1673 CRAOLVS error | | *Extremely rare* | | 1675 no stops on obv. | 75 | 400 | — |
| | | | | 1675/3 | 175 | 550 | — |

3394 - 1675 Farthing                          3395 - Tin Farthing

**3394** Copper **Farthing.** Cuir. bust l. R. Britannia sealed l. date in ex., die axis ↑↓

| | F | VF | EF | | F | VF | EF |
|---|---|---|---|---|---|---|---|
| 1672 | 40 | 225 | 600 | 1673 BRITINNIA error | | *Extremely rare* | |
| 1672 Rev. | | | | 1673 no stops on obv. | | *Extremely rare* | |
| loose drapery | 50 | 275 | 800 | 1673 no rev. stop | | *Extremely rare* | |
| 1672 no stops on obv. | 60 | 300 | 900 | 1674 | 50 | 250 | 650 |
| 1672 RO/OL on obv. | 75 | 400 | — | 1675 | 40 | 225 | 600 |
| 1672 die axis ↑↑ | 60 | 300 | 900 | 1675 no stop after CAROLVS | | *Extremely rare* | |
| 1673 | 40 | 225 | 600 | 1679 | 50 | 250 | 650 |
| 1673 CAROLA error | 75 | 400 | — | 1679 no rev. stop | 60 | 300 | 900 |
| 1673 O/sideways O | | *Extremely rare* | | | | | |

| | Fair | F | VF | EF |
|---|---|---|---|---|
| | £ | £ | £ | £ |

Prices for tin coinage based on corrosion free examples, and in the top grades with some lustre

**3395** Tin **Farthing.** Somewhat similar, but with copper plug, edge inscribed NUMMORVM FAMVLVS, and date on edge only die axis ↑↓

| | | Fair | F | VF | EF |
|---|---|---|---|---|---|
| 1684 | various varieties of edge | 50 | 225 | 750 | 2750 |
| 1685 | | | | *Extremely rare* | |

James II, brother of Charles II, was born on 14th October 1633, he married Anne Hyde with whom he produced 8 children. He lost control of his reign when the loyalist Tories moved against him over his many Catholic appointments. Parliament invited his protestant daughter Mary with husband William of Orange to be joint rulers. James II abdicated and died in exile in France.

During this reign the dies continued to be engraved by John Roettier (1631-1700), the only major difference in the silver coinage being the ommission of the interlinked C's in the angles of the shields on the reverses. The only provenance marked silver coin of this reign is the extremely rare plume on reverse 1685 Shilling. The elephant and castle provenance mark continues to appear on some of the gold coins of this reign. Tin halfpence and farthings provided the only base metal coinage during this short reign. All genuine tin coins of this period have a copper plug.

## GOLD

|  | F | VF | EF |  | F | VF | EF |
|---|---|---|---|---|---|---|---|
|  | £ | £ | £ |  | £ | £ | £ |

**3396 Five Guineas.** First laur. bust l., R. Crowned cruciform shields sceptres misplaced in angles date on edge in words (e.g. 1686 = SECVNDO)

die axis ↑↓ 1686 SECVNDO .......................................................... 1500     5500     12500

**3397 Five Guineas.** First laur bust l. R. similar bust sceptres normal. die axis ↑↓

1687 TERTIO ......... 1250    4500    9750     1688 QVARTO ...... 1350    4750    10500

3397A
1687 Five Guineas, second bust

**3397A Five Guineas.** Second laur. bust l. R. similar die axis ↑↓

1687 TERTIO ......... 1250    4500    9750     1688 QVARTO ...... 1350    4750    10500

3398
1687 Five Guineas, first bust, elephant and castle below

|  | F | VF | EF |  | F | VF | EF |
|---|---|---|---|---|---|---|---|
|  | £ | £ | £ |  | £ | £ | £ |

**3398   Five Guineas.** First laur. bust l. Elephant and castle below R. Similar die axis ↑↓

| 1687 TERTIO | 1500 | 4250 | 11000 | 1688 QVARTO | 1600 | 5000 | 12000 |

3399
1688 Two Guineas 8 over 7

**3399   Two Guineas.** Laur. bust l. R. Crowned cruciform shields, sceptres in angles, edge milled, die axis ↑↓

| 1687 | 950 | 3000 | 5750 | 1688/7 | 1000 | 3500 | 6500 |

**3400   Guinea.** First laur. bust l. R. Crowned cruciform shields, sceptres in angles, edge milled, die axis ↑↓

| 1685 | 400 | 1850 | 4500 | 1686 | 450 | 2000 | 4750 |

**3401   Guinea.** First bust elephant and castle below R. similar die axis ↑↓

| 1685 | 500 | 2250 | 5000 | 1686 | | *Extremely rare* | |

3402
1688 Guinea, second bust

**3402   Guinea.** Second laur. bust l. R. similar die axis ↑↓

| 1686 | 325 | 1650 | 3750 | 1687/6 | 400 | 1850 | 4250 |
| 1687 | 325 | 1650 | 3750 | 1688 | 350 | 1750 | 4250 |

| 3403 | 3404 |
|---|---|
| 1686 Guinea, second bust, elephant and castle below | 1688 Half-Guinea |

|  | F | VF | EF |  | F | VF | EF |
|---|---|---|---|---|---|---|---|
|  | £ | £ | £ |  | £ | £ | £ |

**3403 Guinea.** Second bust elephant and castle below R. similar die axis ↑↓

| 1686 | ..........................525 | 2500 | 5500 | 1688 | ..........................375 | 2000 | 5000 |
| 1687 | ..........................375 | 1750 | 4500 |

**3404 Half-Guinea.** Laur. bust l. R. Crowned cruciform shields sceptres in angles, edge milled
die axis ↑↓

| 1686 | ..........................300 | 1100 | 3250 | 1687 | ..........................400 | 1400 | 3750 |
| 1686 OBV/BVS | .............. | *Extremely rare* | | 1688 | ..........................350 | 1500 | 4000 |

**3405 Half-Guinea.** Laur bust with elephant and castle below, R. similar die axis ↑↓

| 1686 | ..........................700 | 3500 | — |

# SILVER

3406
1686 Crown, first bust, no stops on obverse

**3406 Crown.** First dr. bust, l. regnal year on edge in words (e.g. 1686 = SECVNDO) die axis ↑↓

| 1686 SECVNDO | ................................................................250 | 1000 | 4500 |
| 1686 — No stops on obverse | ................................................................400 | 1200 | — |

3407
1687 Crown, second bust

**3407 Crown.** Second dr. bust l. R. Crowned cruciform shields edge inscribed in raised letters
die axis ↑↓

| 1687 TERTIO | ...........150 | 675 | 2250 | 1688/7 QVARTO | .....175 | 825 | 3250 |
| 1688 QVARTO | .........150 | 775 | 3000 |

Halfcrown hair ties

3408
1685 Halfcrown, first bust

1st bust            2nd bust

| | F | VF | EF | | | F | VF | EF |
|---|---|---|---|---|---|---|---|---|
| | £ | £ | £ | | | £ | £ | £ |

**3408  Halfcrown.** First laur and dr. bust, l. regnal year on edge in words
(e.g. 1685 = PRIMO) die axis ↑↓

| | | | | | | | | |
|---|---|---|---|---|---|---|---|---|
| 1685 PRIMO | 125 | 600 | 2000 | 1686 TERTIO | 150 | 675 | 2250 |
| 1686 SECVNDO | 125 | 600 | 2000 | 1687 TERTIO | 125 | 600 | 200 |
| 1686/5 — | 275 | 950 | — | 1687/6 — | 150 | 675 | 2250 |
| 1686 TERTIO Vover S or B | | | | 1687 — 6 over 8 | | *Extremely rare* | |
| in JACOBVS | 300 | 950 | — | | | | |

**3409  Halfcrown.** Second laur and dr. bust l. R. Crowned cruciform shields
edge inscribed in raised letters die axis ↑↓

| | | | | | | | | |
|---|---|---|---|---|---|---|---|---|
| 1687 TERTIO | 180 | 675 | 2250 | 1688 QVARTO | 125 | 600 | 2000 |

3410
1687 Shilling

**3410  Shilling.** Laur and Dr. bust l. R. Crowned cruciform shields die axis ↑↓

| | | | | | | | | |
|---|---|---|---|---|---|---|---|---|
| 1685 | 100 | 400 | 1100 | 1686 G/A in MAG | 125 | 500 | 1250 |
| 1685 no stops on rev. | 175 | 725 | 1950 | 1687 | 150 | 550 | 1350 |
| 1686 | 125 | 500 | 1250 | 1687/6 | 100 | 400 | 1100 |
| 1686/5 | 125 | 500 | 1250 | 1687 G/A in MAG | 175 | 600 | 1750 |
| 1686 V/S in JACOBVS | 125 | 500 | 1250 | 1688 | 125 | 500 | 1250 |
| | | | | 1688/7 | 150 | 550 | 1350 |

**3411  Shilling.** Similar, plume in centre of *rev.,* die axis ↑↓ 1685 ......Fair £5500

3412                              3413
1686 Sixpence, early shields, indented tops   1688 Sixpence, later shields

**3412  Sixpence.** Laur and dr. bust l. R. Early type crowned cruciform shields die axis ↑↓

| | | | | | | | | |
|---|---|---|---|---|---|---|---|---|
| 1686 | 90 | 400 | 825 | 1687/6 | 100 | 475 | 925 |
| 1687 | 100 | 450 | 925 | | | | |

**3413  Sixpence.** Similar R. Late type shields die axis ↑↓

| | | | | | | | | |
|---|---|---|---|---|---|---|---|---|
| 1687 | 90 | 400 | 825 | 1687 Later/early shields | 100 | 475 | 925 |
| 1687/6 | 90 | 450 | 925 | 1688 | 90 | 450 | 925 |

3414 - 1686 Fourpence          3415 - 1687 Threepence

|  | F £ | VF £ | EF £ |  | F £ | VF £ | EF £ |
|---|---|---|---|---|---|---|---|
| **3414  Fourpence.** Laur. head l. R. IIII Crowned die axis ↑↓ |  |  |  |  |  |  |  |
| 1686 | 10 | 30 | 100 | 1688 | 8 | 30 | 100 |
| 1686 Date over crown. | 10 | 30 | 100 | 1688 1 over 8 | 20 | 55 | 165 |
| 1687/6 | 8 | 25 | 90 | 1688/7 | 8 | 30 | 100 |
| 1687 8 over 7 | 10 | 30 | 100 |  |  |  |  |
| **3415  Threepence.** Laur. head l. R. III Crowned die axis ↑↓ |  |  |  |  |  |  |  |
| 1685 | 8 | 30 | 90 | 1687 | 10 | 35 | 100 |
| 1685 Groat flan | 30 | 80 | 165 | 1687/6 | 8 | 30 | 90 |
| 1686 | 8 | 30 | 90 | 1688 | 8 | 30 | 90 |
| 1686 4d obv. die | 10 | 35 | 110 | 1688/7 | 10 | 35 | 100 |
| **3416  Twopence.** Laur. head l. R. II Crowned die axis ↑↓ |  |  |  |  |  |  |  |
| 1686 | 10 | 25 | 90 | 1687 ERA for FRA | 20 | 45 | 140 |
| 1686 IΛCOBVS | 15 | 35 | 110 | 1688 | 10 | 30 | 100 |
| 1687 | 10 | 25 | 90 | 1688/7 | 10 | 30 | 100 |

3416 - 1686 Twopence     3417 - 1688 Penny

|  | F | VF | EF |  | F | VF | EF |
|---|---|---|---|---|---|---|---|
| **3417  Penny.** Laur. head l. R. I Crowned die axis ↑↓ |  |  |  |  |  |  |  |
| 1685 | 10 | 30 | 100 | 1687/8 | 15 | 35 | 110 |
| 1686 | 10 | 30 | 100 | 1688 | 10 | 30 | 100 |
| 1687 | 10 | 30 | 100 | 1688/7 | 10 | 30 | 100 |
| 1687/6 | 10 | 30 | 100 |  |  |  |  |
| **3418  Maundy Set.** As last four. Uniform dates |  |  |  |  |  |  |  |
| 1686 | 75 | 325 | 600 | 1688 | 75 | 325 | 600 |
| 1687 | 75 | 325 | 600 |  |  |  |  |

# TIN

3419 Tin Halfpenny

|  | *Fair*<br>£ | *F*<br>£ | *VF*<br>£ | *EF*<br>£ |
|---|---|---|---|---|

Prices for tin coinage based on corrosion free examples, and in the top grades with some lustre

**3419 Halfpenny.** Laur. and dr. bust r. R. Britannia seated l. date on edge die axis ↑↓

| | | | | |
|---|---|---|---|---|
| 1685 various varieties of edge | 75 | 200 | 650 | 3000 |
| 1686 | 95 | 225 | 700 | 3500 |
| 1687 | 75 | 200 | 650 | 3000 |

3420
Cuirassed bust Tin Farthing

**3420 Farthing.** Laur. and Cuir. bust r. R. Britannia seated l. date on edge die axis ↑↓

| | | | | |
|---|---|---|---|---|
| 1684 | | | *Extremely rare* | |
| 1685 various varieties of edge | 60 | 175 | 550 | 2000 |
| 1686 two varieties of edge | 75 | 200 | 600 | 2500 |
| 1687 | | | *Extremely rare* | |

3421
Draped bust Tin Farthing

**3421 Farthing.** Dr. bust r.; date on edge, 1687 various varieties of edge ↑↓

| | | | | |
|---|---|---|---|---|
| | 90 | 225 | 750 | 3000 |

Mary Stuart was born on 30 April 1662, and married William of Orange as part of Charles II's foreign policy. She eventually became William's loyal servant but bore him no children. The Bill and the Claim of Rights were both passed in 1689 and forbade the Royal and Prerogative rights of Monarchs. Mary died from smallpox on 28 December 1694.

Due to the poor state of the silver coinage, much of it worn hammered coin, the Guinea, which was valued at 21s. 6d. at the beginning of the reign, circulated for as much as 30s. by 1694. The elephant and elephant and castle provenance marks continue on some gold coin. The tin Halfpennies and Farthings were replaced by copper coins in 1694. The rampant Lion of Nassau is now placed as an inescutcheon on the centre of the royal arms. The WM monogram appears in the angles of the silver coins of this reign.

**Engravers and designers:** George Bower (d.1689), Henry Harris (d.1704), John Roettier (1631-1700), James Roettier (1663-1698), Norbert Roettier (b.1665)

3422
1691 Five Guineas

| | F £ | VF £ | EF £ | | F £ | VF £ | EF £ |
|---|---|---|---|---|---|---|---|
| **3422 Five Guineas.** Conjoined busts r. regnal year on edge in words (e.g. 1691 = TERTIO) ↑↓ | | | | | | | |
| 1691 TERTIO | 1250 | 3750 | 9500 | 1693 QVINTO | 1250 | 3750 | 9500 |
| 1692 QVARTO | 1250 | 3750 | 9500 | 1694/2 SEXTO | 1350 | 4000 | 10000 |
| 1692 QVINTO | | *Extremely rare* | | 1694 SEXTO | 1500 | 4500 | 11000 |

3423

Elephant and castle below busts

3424

1694 Two Guineas 4 over 3

**3423 Five Guineas.** Conjoined busts, elephant and castle below, R. Crowned shield of arms die axis ↑↓

| | F | VF | EF | | F | VF | EF |
|---|---|---|---|---|---|---|---|
| 1691 TERTIO | 1350 | 4000 | 10000 | 1694/2 SEXTO | 1350 | 4250 | 10500 |
| 1692 QVARTO | 1350 | 4000 | 11000 | 1694 SEXTO | 1500 | 4500 | 11000 |
| 1693 QVINTO | 1500 | 4500 | 11000 | | | | |

**3424 Two Guineas.** Conjoined busts r. R. Crowned shield of arms, Lion of Nassau at centre die axis ↑↓

| | F | VF | EF | | F | VF | EF |
|---|---|---|---|---|---|---|---|
| 1693 | 800 | 2500 | 5250 | 1694/3 | 800 | 2500 | 5250 |

**3425 Two Guineas.** Conjoined busts, elephant and castle below, R. similar die axis ↑↓

| | F | VF | EF | | F | VF | EF |
|---|---|---|---|---|---|---|---|
| 1691 | | *Extremely rare* | | 1694/3 | 900 | 2750 | 5500 |
| 1693 | 900 | 2750 | 5500 | | | | |

3426

1689 Guinea

3427

1689 Elephant and castle below busts

| | F £ | VF £ | EF £ | | F £ | VF £ | EF £ |
|---|---|---|---|---|---|---|---|

**3426 Guinea.** Conjoined busts r. R. Crowned shield of arms Lion of Nassau at centre die axis ↑↓

| 1689 | 350 | 2000 | 4750 | 1692 | 375 | 2250 | 5250 |
|---|---|---|---|---|---|---|---|
| 1690 | 375 | 2500 | 5500 | 1693 | 375 | 2500 | 5500 |
| 1690 GVLIFLMVS | *Extremely rare* | | | 1694 | 350 | 2000 | 5000 |
| 1691 | 375 | 2000 | 5000 | 1694/3 | 375 | 2250 | 5250 |

**3427 Guinea.** Conjoined busts elephant and castle below R. Similar die axis ↑↓

| 1689 | 375 | 2000 | 5000 | 1692 | 375 | 2250 | 4750 |
|---|---|---|---|---|---|---|---|
| 1690 | 450 | 2250 | 5500 | 1693 | | *Extremely rare* | |
| 1691 | 375 | 2250 | 5250 | 1694 | 375 | 2250 | 5250 |
| | | | | 1694/3 | 400 | 2250 | 5250 |

**3428 Guinea.** Conjoined busts elephant only below, R. Similar die axis ↑↓

| 1692 | 450 | 2250 | 5500 | 1693 | | *Extremely rare* | |
|---|---|---|---|---|---|---|---|

*Overstruck dates are listed only if commoner than the normal date or if no normal date is known.*

3429

1689 Half-Guinea, first busts, first shield

3430

1690 Half-Guinea, second busts, second shield

**3429 Half-Guinea.** First busts r. R. First Crowned shield of arms die axis ↑↓

| 1689 | 425 | 1850 | 4000 |
|---|---|---|---|

**3430 Half-Guinea.** Second busts r. R. Second Crowned shield of arms die axis ↑↓

| 1690 | 325 | 2000 | 4500 | 1693 | | *Extremely rare* | |
|---|---|---|---|---|---|---|---|
| 1691 | 350 | 1850 | 4000 | 1693/2 | | *Extremely rare* | |
| 1692 | 375 | 1600 | 3500 | 1694 | 325 | 1600 | 3500 |

**3431 Half-Guinea.** Second busts elephant and castle below, R. Second shield of arms die axis ↑↓

| 1691 | 325 | 1600 | 3500 | 1692 | 350 | 1750 | 4000 |
|---|---|---|---|---|---|---|---|

**3432 Half-Guinea.** Second busts elephant only below, R. Second shield of arms die axis ↑↓

| 1692 | | *Extremely rare* | |
|---|---|---|---|

## SILVER

3433

1691 Crown

**3433 Crown.** Conjoined busts r. regnal year on edge in words (e.g. 1691 = TERTIO) die axis ↑↓

| 1691 TERTIO | 275 | 1000 | 4000 | 1692 QVARTO | 275 | 1000 | 4000 |
|---|---|---|---|---|---|---|---|
| 1691 I/E in legend | 500 | 1350 | — | 1692/2 QVARTO | 425 | 1600 | — |
| 1691 TERTTIO | | *Extremely rare* | | 1692/2 QVINTO | 275 | 1000 | 4000 |

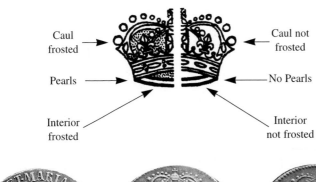

Caul frosted →
Caul not ← frosted
Pearls →
← No Pearls
Interior frosted
Interior not frosted

3434
1689 Halfcrown - first reverse

3435
1689 Halfcrown - second reverse

|  | F £ | VF £ | EF £ |  | F £ | VF £ | EF £ |
|---|---|---|---|---|---|---|---|

**3434 Halfcrown.** First busts, r. R. First crowned shield, 1689 PRIMO R. Crown with caul
and interior frosted, with pearls edge inscribed die axis ↑↓ .........................75    350    1400
1689— 2nd L/M in GVLIELMVS ..................................................................95    425    1550
1689 — 1st V/A in GVLIELMVS, only caul frosted .........................................90    400    1500
1689 — — interior also frosted, no pearls .........................................................90    400    1500
1689 Caul only frosted, pearls................................................................................80    350    1400
1689 — no pearls.....................................................................................................90    400    1500
1689 No frosting, pearls . .......................................................................................95    425    1550
1689 No stops on obverse ...................................................................................110    450    1650
1689 FRA for FR.....................................................................................................125    650    2200

**3435 Halfcrown.** First busts r. R. Second crowned shield die axis ↑↓

| | F | VF | EF | | F | VF | EF |
|---|---|---|---|---|---|---|---|
| 1689 PRIMO R. Caul ..90 | 375 | 1400 | | 1689 Caul only frosted, | | | |
| and interior frosted with pearls | | | | no pearls ................90 | 375 | 1400 |
| 1689 — — no pearls ...100 | 400 | 1500 | | 1689 no frosting, pearls ......85 | 350 | 1400 |
| 1689 — — — ЕT for ET error *Extremely rare* | | | | 1689 no frosting, no | | | |
| 1689 GVLI ЕMVS error . | *Extremely rare* | | | pearls .....................85 | 350 | 1400 |
| 1689 Caul only | | | | 1690 SECVNDO — ......100 | 425 | 1650 |
| frosted pearls ......85 | 350 | 1400 | | 1690 — GRETIA error ....200 | 800 | 2650 |
| 1689 interior frosted, | | | | 1690 TERTIO ................125 | 550 | 1900 |
| no pearls .............90 | 375 | 1400 | | | | |

3436
1691 Halfcrown, second busts, third reverse

|  | F | VF | EF |  | F | VF | EF |
|---|---|---|---|---|---|---|---|
|  | £ | £ | £ |  | £ | £ | £ |

**3436  Halfcrown.** Second busts r. ℞. Crowned cruciform shields, WM monogram in angles
die axis ↑↓

| 1691 TERTIO | 90 | 475 | 1600 | 1693 QVINTO | 90 | 400 | 1400 |
|---|---|---|---|---|---|---|---|
| 1692 QVARTO | 90 | 475 | 1600 | 1693 3/inverted 3 | 100 | 475 | 1600 |
| 1692 R/G in REGINA | | *Extremely rare* | | 1693 inverted 3 | 200 | 700 | 2250 |
| 1692 QVINTO | 200 | 825 | — | | | | |

3437                                           3438
1692 Shilling-inverted 1                     1693 Sixpence

**3437  Shilling.** Conjoined busts r. ℞. Crowned cruciform shields, WM monogram in angles die axis ↑↓

| 1692 | 110 | 600 | 1400 | 1693 9/0 | 150 | 650 | 1400 |
|---|---|---|---|---|---|---|---|
| 1692 inverted 1 | 150 | 700 | 1650 | 1693 | 100 | 550 | 1200 |
| 1692 RE/ET on ℞. | | *extremely rare* | | | | | |

**3438  Sixpence.** Conjoined busts r. R. Crowned cruciform shields, WM monogram in angles die axis ↑↓

| 1693 | 100 | 450 | 850 | 1694 | 110 | 500 | 1000 |
|---|---|---|---|---|---|---|---|
| 1693 inverted 3 | 125 | 550 | 1100 | | | | |

3439                                           3440
1690 Groat, first busts                      1692 Groat, second busts

**3439  Fourpence.** First busts, r. no tie to wreath. R. Crowned 4 die axis ↑↓

| 1689 GV below bust | 8 | 25 | 90 | 1690 | 10 | 30 | 100 |
|---|---|---|---|---|---|---|---|
| 1689 G below bust | 8 | 25 | 90 | 1690 6 over 5 | 10 | 35 | 110 |
| 1689 stop befor G | 10 | 30 | 100 | 1691 | 12 | 35 | 120 |
| 1689 berries in wreath | 10 | 30 | 100 | 1691/0 | 11 | 30 | 105 |
| 1689 GVLEELMVS | 55 | 165 | – | 1694 | 12 | 35 | 120 |

|  | F £ | VF £ | EF £ |  | F £ | VF £ | EF £ |
|---|---|---|---|---|---|---|---|

**3440  Fourpence.** Second busts r. tie to wreath. R. Crowned 4 die axis ↑↓

| 1692 | 11 | 40 | 105 | 1693/2 | 12 | 40 | 120 |
|---|---|---|---|---|---|---|---|
| 1692/1 | 12 | 40 | 120 | 1694 | 12 | 40 | 120 |
| 1692 MAR•IA | *Extremely rare* | | | 1694 small lettering | 12 | 40 | 120 |
| 1693 | 12 | 40 | 120 | | | | |

**3441  Threepence.** First busts, r. no tie to wreath. R. Crowned 3 die axis ↑↓

| 1689 | 7 | 25 | 80 | 1690 6 over 5 | 8 | 30 | 90 |
|---|---|---|---|---|---|---|---|
| 1689 No stops on rev. | 10 | 35 | 100 | 1690 Large lettering | 8 | 30 | 90 |
| 1689 LMV over MVS | 10 | 35 | 100 | 1690 9 over 6 | 8 | 30 | 90 |
| 1689 Hyphen stops on rev. | 8 | 30 | 90 | 1691 | 30 | 90 | 225 |
| 1690 | 8 | 30 | 90 | | | | |

**3442  Threepence.** Second busts, r. tie to wreath R. Crowned 3 die axis ↑↓

| 1691 | 10 | 35 | 110 | 1693 GV below bust | 9 | 30 | 100 |
|---|---|---|---|---|---|---|---|
| 1692 G below bust | 10 | 35 | 110 | 1694 G below bust | 9 | 30 | 100 |
| 1692 GV below bust | 10 | 35 | 110 | 1694 — MARIΛ error | 10 | 45 | 165 |
| 1692 GVL below bust | 10 | 35 | 110 | 1694 GV below bust | 9 | 30 | 100 |
| 1693 G below bust | 9 | 30 | 100 | 1694 GVL below bust | 9 | 30 | 100 |
| 1693/2 G below bust | 9 | 30 | 100 | | | | |

**3443  Twopence.** Conjoined busts r. R. Crowned 2 die axis ↑↓

| 1689 | 8 | 25 | 90 | 1694/3 | 10 | 35 | 110 |
|---|---|---|---|---|---|---|---|
| 1691 | 8 | 25 | 90 | 1694/3 no stop after DG | 10 | 35 | 110 |
| 1692 | 9 | 30 | 100 | 1694 MARLA error | 25 | 55 | 275 |
| 1693 | 9 | 30 | 100 | 1694 HI for HIB | 10 | 35 | 110 |
| 1693/2 | 10 | 35 | 110 | 1694 GVLI below bust | 10 | 35 | 110 |
| 1693 GV below bust | 10 | 35 | 110 | 1694 GVL below bust | 10 | 35 | 110 |
| 1694 | 10 | 35 | 110 | | | | |

3444 - 1689 Penny                    3445 - Legend intruded

**3444  Penny.** Legend continuous over busts, R. Crowned 1 die axis ↑↓

| 1689 | 150 | 350 | 600 | 1689 MARIΛ | 175 | 350 | 650 |
|---|---|---|---|---|---|---|---|
| 1689 GVIELMVS error | 250 | 450 | 850 | | | | |

**3445  Penny.** Legend broken by busts, R. Crowned 1 die axis ↑↓

| 1690 | 14 | 45 | 155 | 1694 date spread | 12 | 40 | 135 |
|---|---|---|---|---|---|---|---|
| 1691/0 | 12 | 40 | 135 | 1694 no stops on obv. | 15 | 45 | 155 |
| 1692 | 14 | 45 | 155 | 1694 HI for HIB | 20 | 55 | 195 |
| 1692/1 | 15 | 45 | 165 | 1694 — 9/6 | 15 | 45 | 155 |
| 1693 | 12 | 40 | 135 | | | | |

3446 - Maundy Set

**3446  Maundy Set.** The four denominations. Uniform dates

| 1689 | 250 | 600 | 1000 | 1693 | 150 | 300 | 750 |
|---|---|---|---|---|---|---|---|
| 1691 | 95 | 225 | 650 | 1694 | 95 | 225 | 650 |
| 1692 | 150 | 300 | 750 | | | | |

## TIN AND COPPER

3447

Tin Halfpenny first busts

| | Fair £ | F £ | VF £ | EF £ |
|---|---|---|---|---|

Prices for tin coinage based on corrosion free examples, and in the top grades with some lustre

**3447** Tin **Halfpenny.** Small dr. busts r.; date on edge ↑↓ 1689....850　1500　—　—

— — — obv. with star stops 1689 ............................................. *Extremely rare*

3448

Tin Halfpenny cuirasssed busts

**3448** Tin **Halfpenny.** — Large cuir. busts r.; R. Britannia seated L. date only on edge, die axis ↑↓

1690 various edge varieties.............................................75　175　650　2500

**3449** Tin **Halfpenny.** Similar date in ex. and on edge die axis ↑↓

1691 various edge varieties.............................................60　150　600　2000

1691 in ex. 1692 on edge ........................................ *Extremely rare*

1692............................................................60　150　600　2000

**3450** Tin **Farthing.** Small dr. busts r. R. Britannia seated l. die axis ↑↓

1689..........................................................250　650　1850　—

1689, in ex. 1690 on edge............................................. *Extremely rare*

3451

1690 Tin Farthing

**3451** Tin **Farthing.** Large cuir. busts r. R. Britannia seated l.die axis ↑↓

1690, in ex. 1689 on edge............................................. *Extremely rare*

1690 various edge varieties.............................................50　150　550　2000

1691 various edge varieties.............................................50　150　550　2000

1692............................................................65　175　600　2250

3452
1694 Halfpenny

| | F £ | VF £ | EF £ |
|---|---|---|---|
| **3452** Copper **Halfpenny,** Conjoined busts r. R. Britannia die axis ↑↓ | | | |
| 1694 ............................................................................................ | 60 | 250 | 750 |
| 1694 GVLIEMVS error ........................................................... | 225 | 500 | – |
| 1694 MVRIA error ................................................................. | 275 | 550 | – |
| 1694 MΛRIΛ error ................................................................. | 175 | 450 | – |
| 1694 BRITΛNNI/Λ .................................................................. | 200 | 475 | – |
| 1694 no rev. stop .................................................................. | 175 | 450 | – |
| 1694 GVLEELMVS ................................................................. | 250 | 525 | – |

3453
1694 Farthing

| | F £ | VF £ | EF £ |
|---|---|---|---|
| **3453** Copper **Farthing,** Conjoined busts r. R. Britannia die axis ↑↓ | | | |
| 1694 ............................................................................................ | 60 | 250 | 675 |
| 1694 MΛRIΛ error ................................................................. | 200 | 450 | – |
| 1694 no stop after MΛRIΛ .................................................... | 150 | 325 | – |
| 1694 — BRITΛNNIΛ .............................................................. | 175 | 350 | – |
| 1694 no stop on rev. .............................................................. | 150 | 325 | – |
| 1694 no stop on obv. .............................................................. | 150 | 325 | – |
| 1694 GVLIELMS, BRITΛNNIΛ errors .................................... | 275 | 500 | – |
| 1694 BRITΛNNIΛ .................................................................. | 200 | 400 | – |
| 1694 Broad heavier flan 25.5mm ......................................... | 250 | 450 | – |

William of Orange was born on 4th November 1650. He married Mary Stuart under Charles II's foreign policy and was invited to England by Parliament, where he proceeded to supress the Jacobite rebellion. The Bank of England was founded during this reign, and William ruled alone and without issue after Mary's death until his own demise on 8th March 1702 following a serious fall from his horse.

In 1696 a great re-coinage was undertaken to replace the hammered silver that made up most of the coinage in circulation, much of it being clipped and badly worn. Branch mints were set up at Bristol, Chester, Exeter, Norwich and York to help with the re-coinage. For a short time before they were finally demonetized, unclipped hammered coins were allowed to circulate freely provided they were officially pierced in the centre. Silver coins with roses between the coats of arms were made from silver obtained from the West of England mines. The elephant and castle provenance mark continues on some guineas and half-guineas.

**Engravers and designers:** Samuel Bull (d.c.1720), John Croker (1670-1740), Henry Harris (d.1704), John Roettier (1663-1698).

## GOLD

| | | |
|---|---|---|
| **3454** | | **3455** |
| 1699 Five Guineas, first bust | | Elephant and castle below first bust |

| F | VF | EF | | F | VF | EF |
|---|---|---|---|---|---|---|
| £ | £ | £ | | £ | £ | £ |

**3454  Five Guineas.** First laur. bust r. regnal year on edge in words (e.g. 1699 = UNDECIMO) ↑↓
1699 UNDECIMO ..1250    4250    9500        1700 DVODECIMO ......1450    5500    12000
**3455  Five Guineas.** First bust elephant and castle below, 1699 UNDECIMO ......1500    5250    12500

| | | |
|---|---|---|
| **3456** | | **3457** |
| 1701 Five Guineas 'fine work' | | 'Fine work' Two Guineas |

**3456  Five Guineas.** Second laur. bust r. ('fine work'), R. Crowned cruciform shields Plain or ornamental sceptres DECIMO TERTIO die axis ↑↓ 1701 ........................................1250    4750    10000
**3457  Two Guineas.** ('fine work'), Laur. bust r. similar die axis ↑↓ 1701 ........1250    3750    5750

3458
1695 Guinea, first bust

| | F | VF | EF | | F | VF | EF |
|---|---|---|---|---|---|---|---|
| | £ | £ | £ | | £ | £ | £ |

**3458  Guinea.** First laur. bust r. R. Crowned cruciform shields, sceptres in angles die axis ↑↓

1695 ..........................250    1750    4000     1697................................300    1850    4750
1696 ..........................300    2000    5250

**3459  Guinea.** First bust elephant and castle below R. Similar die axis ↑↓

1695 ..........................325    1850    4500     1696 ..............................    *Extremely rare*

| 3460 | 3463 | 3463 |
|---|---|---|
| Second bust | 1701 Guinea, plain sceptres | Ornamental sceptres |

**3460  Guinea.** Second laur. bust r. R. Similar with human-headed harp in Irish arms. die axis ↑↓

1697 ..........................275    1850    4750     1699................................300    2000    5500
1698 ..........................250    1500    3500     1700................................250    1500    3500

**3461  Guinea.** Second bust elephant and castle below. R. Similar die axis ↑↓

1697 ........................1000    3750      —       1699......................................    *Extremely rare*
1698 ..........................350    1850    4500     1700............................1000    3750      —

**3462  Guinea.** Second laur. bust. r. R. Similar with Human headed harp. Large lettering and
large date, die axis ↑↓ 1698 ................................................250    1750    3750

**3463  Guinea.** — R. Narrow crowns, plain or ornamented sceptres, axis ↑↓ 1701 .........250    1750    3750

**3464  Guinea.** Second bust elephant and castle below, die axis ↑↓ 1701 ................    *Extremely rare*

**3465  Guinea.** Third laur. bust r. ('fine work'), R. Similar die axis ↑↓1701........400    2250    5250

| 3466 | 3468 |
|---|---|
| 1695 Half-Guinea, early harp | Later harp |

**3466  Half-Guinea.** Laur. bust r. R. With early harp, die axis ↑↓ 1695 ............225    750    2750

**3467  Half-Guinea.** Laur. bust elephant and castle below. R. With early harp, die axis ↑↓

1695 ..........................325    1250    3250     1696................................250    950    3000

**3468  Half-Guinea.** Laur. bust r. R. Crowned cruciform shields, sceptres in angles with late harp, die axis ↑↓

1697 ..........................300    1400    3750     1700................................200    650    2500
1698 ..........................200    650    2500     1701................................200    650    2500
1699 ..............................    *Extremely rare*

**3469  Half-Guinea.** Laur. bust elephant and castle below, die axis ↑↓ 1698 ....275    950    3250

## SILVER

3470
1695 Crown - first bust - round collar

| | F | VF | EF | | F | VF | EF |
|---|---|---|---|---|---|---|---|
| | £ | £ | £ | | £ | £ | £ |

**3470 Crown**. First dr. bust, r. R.First harp, regnal year on edge in words (e.g. 1696 = OCTAVO) ↑↓

| | F | VF | EF | | F | VF | EF |
|---|---|---|---|---|---|---|---|
| 1695 SEPTIMO | 70 | 300 | 1250 | 1696 G/D IN GRA | 400 | 750 | — |
| 1695 OCTAVO | 75 | 350 | 1400 | 1696 — no stops | 425 | 850 | — |
| 1695 OCTAⱯO error | 150 | 600 | — | 1696/5 | 425 | 850 | — |
| 1695 TVTA·EN error | | *Extremely rare* | | 1696 GEI for DEI | 450 | 950 | — |
| 1695 plain edge proof *FDC* £6750 | | | | | | | |
| 1696 OCTAVO | 60 | 275 | 1150 | 1696 — no stops | 475 | 1000 | — |
| 1696 No stops on | | | | 1696 plain edge proof *FDC* £6750 | | | |
| obverse | 300 | 750 | — | | | | |

3471
1696 Crown, second bust - hair across breast

**3471 Crown**. Second dr. bust r. R. Second harp (hair across breast), 1696 (two varieties) die axis ↑↓
OCTAVO ................................................................................................ *Each unique*

3472
Third bust, straight breastplate

**3472 Crown**. Third dr. bust, r. R. First harp, die axis ↑↓ 1696 OCTAVO ....70    300    1250
1696 TRICESIMO ...................................................................................... *Extremely rare*
1696 plain edge proof............................................................................... *FDC* £7500

|   | F | VF | EF |
|---|---|----|----|
|   | £ | £ | £ |

**3473** **Crown.** Similar, R. Second harp, die axis ↑↓ 1697 NONO....................850   3000   13500

3474

1700 Crown, third bust variety

**3474** **Crown.** Third bust variety r. R. Third harp, ↑↓ 1700 DVODECIMO .......75   350   1250
  1700 DECIMO. TERTIO................................................................................90   450   1500
  1700 ANN · error on edge..........................................................................500   —   —
  1700 ECIMO error on edge................................................................*Extremely rare*
**3475** **Halfcrown.** First bust r. R. Small shields, 1696 die axis ↑↓ OCTAVO .....55   275   800
  — — 1696 DECⱯS error ............................................................................150   650   —
**3476** **Halfcrown.** B (*Bristol*) below First bust, die axis ↑↓ 1696 OCTAVO ......60   300   950
  — 1696 B Similar proof *FDC* £11000

3477                                3478
Chester Mint                      Exeter Mint

**3477** **Halfcrown.** C (*Chester*) below first bust, die axis ↑↓ 1696 OCTAVO....125   500   1250
**3478** **Halfcrown.** E (*Exeter*) below first bust, die axis ↑↓ 1696 OCTAVO......250   650   1750
**3479** **Halfcrown.** N (*Norwich*) below first bust, die axis ↑↓ 1696 OCTAVO ....85   350   950
**3480** **Halfcrown.** y (*York*) below first bust, die axis ↑↓ 1696 OCTAVO ........125   500   1250

3480                              3481
1696 Halfcrown - York Mint       1696 Halfcrown, large sheild
                                 reverse with early harp

**3481** **Halfcrown.** First bust r. R. Large shield, early harp,
  die axis ↑↓ 1696 OCTAVO.........................................................................60   300   850
  1696 Proof plain edge....................................................................*Extremely rare*

|   | F | VF | EF |   | F | VF | EF |
|---|---|----|----|---|---|----|----|
|   | £ | £  | £  |   | £ | £  | £  |

**3482 Halfcrown.** — B *(Bristol)* below bust, die axis ↑↓ 1696 OCTAVO......60 · 300 · 850

**3483 Halfcrown.** — C *(Chester)* below bust, die axis ↑↓ 1696 OCTAVO.......70 · 350 · 950

**3484 Halfcrown.** — E *(Exeter)* below bust, die axis ↑↓ 1696 OCTAVO........80 · 450 · 1050

**3485 Halfcrown.** — N *(Norwich)* below bust, die axis ↑↓ 1696 OCTAVO....175 · 700 · 1650

**3486 Halfcrown.** — y *(York)* below bust, die axis ↑↓ 1696 OCTAVO.........75 · 350 · 950

— — die axis ↑↓ 1696 y *(York)*, Scots Arms at date................................ *Extremely rare*

— die axis ↑↓ y over E 1696.......................................................... *Extremely rare*

3487
Large shields, ordinary harp

3488
Bristol Mint

**3487 Halfcrown.** First bust r. ℞. Large shields, ordinary harp die axis ↑↓

| 1696 OCTAVO.........150 | 600 | 1400 | 1697 G/A in MAG.......... | *Extremely rare* |
| 1697 NONO................50 | 250 | 800 | 1697/6 —.................120 | 450 · 1250 |
| 1697 — GRR for GRA .................*Fair* £1000 | | | | |

**3488 Halfcrown.** — B *(Bristol)* below first bust, die axis ↑↓ 1697 NONO ..55 · 275 · 850

1697 proof on thick flan *FDC* .......................................................... *Extremely rare*

1697 — no stops on reverse.........................................................70 · 350 · 1000

3489
1696 Chester Mint Halfcrown, large shields

**3489 Halfcrown.** — C *(Chester)* below first bust, similar die axis ↑↓

1696 OCTAVO .........120 · 585 · 1450 · 1697 NONO................60 · 325 · 750

3490

1697 Exeter Mint Halfcrown, large shields

| | F | VF | EF | | | F | VF | EF |
| | £ | £ | £ | | | £ | £ | £ |

**3490 Halfcrown.** — E (*Exeter*) below first bust, similar die axis ↑↓

| | F | VF | EF | | F | VF | EF |
|---|---|---|---|---|---|---|---|
| 1696 OCTAVO | 125 | 525 | 1400 | 1697 NONO | 50 | 275 | 800 |
| 1696 NONO | *Extremely rare* | | | 1697 — TѴTAMEN error | *Extremely rare* | | |
| 1697 OCTAVO | *Extremely rare* | | | 1697 E over C or B under bust | *Extremely rare* | | |

3491

1697 Norwich Mint Halfcrown, large shields

**3491 Halfcrown.** — N (*Norwich*) below first bust, similar die axis ↑↓

| | F | VF | EF | | F | VF | EF |
|---|---|---|---|---|---|---|---|
| 1696 OCTAVO | 150 | 600 | 1750 | 1697 NONO | 60 | 325 | 900 |
| 1697 OCTAVO | *Extremely rare* | | | 1697 — Scots Arms at date | *Fair* £1000 | | |

**3492 Halfcrown.** — — y (*York*) below first bust, similar die axis ↑↓

| | F | VF | EF | | | |
|---|---|---|---|---|---|---|
| 1697 NONO | 50 | 300 | 800 | 1697 OCTAVO | *Extremely rare* | |

**3493 Halfcrown.** Second dr. bust r. (hair across breast), die axis ↑↓ 1696 OCTAVO    *Unique*

3494
1700 Halfcrown, modified large shields

| | F £ | VF £ | EF £ | | F £ | VF £ | EF £ |
|---|---|---|---|---|---|---|---|

**3494  Halfcrown.** First dr. bust R. Modified large shields die axis ↑↓

| | F | VF | EF | | F | VF | EF |
|---|---|---|---|---|---|---|---|
| 1698 OCTAVO | *Extremely rare* | | | 1699 — Lion of | | | |
| 1698 DECIMO | 50 | 275 | 800 | Nassau inverted | 650 | 1400 | — |
| 1698/7 — | *Extremely rare* | | | 1700 DVODECIMO | 50 | 250 | 750 |
| 1698 UNDECIMO | *Extremely rare* | | | 1700 D. TERTIO | 60 | 325 | 850 |
| 1699 UNDECIMO | 80 | 350 | 1000 | 1700 — DECѴS error | 100 | 400 | 1000 |
| 1699 — Inverted A's for | | | | 1701 D. TERTIO | 60 | 325 | 850 |
| V's on edge | 200 | 650 | — | 1701 — no stops | | | |
| 1699 — Scots Arms at date | *Extremely rare* | | | on reverse | 95 | 400 | 1000 |

3495
1701 Halfcrown, elephant and castle below bust

**3495  Halfcrown.** – elephant and castle below bust, die axis ↑↓ 1701 D. TERTIO *Fair* 1400

3496
1701 Halfcrown, plumes on reverse

**3496  Halfcrown.** – R. Plumes in angles, die axis ↑↓ 1701 D. TERTIO ........... 150    600    1500

# SHILLINGS

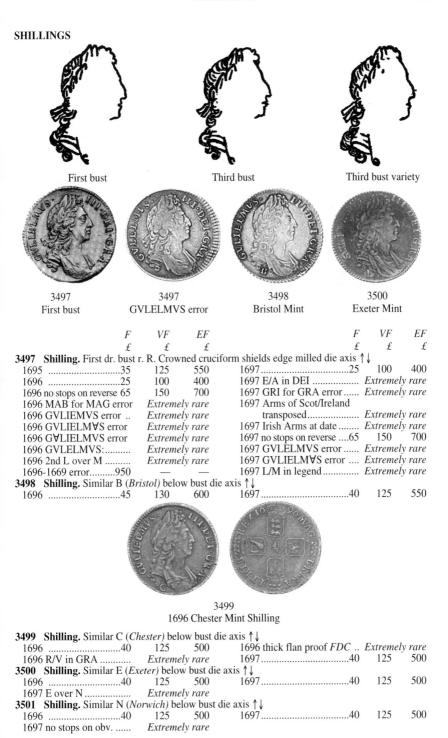

| First bust | Third bust | Third bust variety |
|---|---|---|

| 3497 | 3497 | 3498 | 3500 |
|---|---|---|---|
| First bust | GVLELMVS error | Bristol Mint | Exeter Mint |

|  | F | VF | EF |  | F | VF | EF |
|---|---|---|---|---|---|---|---|
|  | £ | £ | £ |  | £ | £ | £ |

**3497  Shilling.** First dr. bust r. R. Crowned cruciform shields edge milled die axis ↑↓

| 1695 .............................35 | 125 | 550 | 1697 ..................................25 | 100 | 400 |
|---|---|---|---|---|---|
| 1696 .............................25 | 100 | 400 | 1697 E/A in DEI ................. | *Extremely rare* | |
| 1696 no stops on reverse 65 | 150 | 700 | 1697 GRI for GRA error ...... | *Extremely rare* | |
| 1696 MAB for MAG error | *Extremely rare* | | 1697 Arms of Scot/Ireland | | |
| 1696 GVLIEMVS error .. | *Extremely rare* | | transposed.................... | *Extremely rare* | |
| 1696 GVLIELMⱯS error | *Extremely rare* | | 1697 Irish Arms at date ........ | *Extremely rare* | |
| 1696 GⱯLIELMVS error | *Extremely rare* | | 1697 no stops on reverse ....65 | 150 | 700 |
| 1696 GVLELMVS:.......... | *Extremely rare* | | 1697 GVLELMVS error ...... | *Extremely rare* | |
| 1696 2nd L over M .......... | *Extremely rare* | | 1697 GVLELMⱯS error .... | *Extremely rare* | |
| 1696-1669 error..........950 | — | — | 1697 L/M in legend.............. | *Extremely rare* | |

**3498  Shilling.** Similar B (*Bristol*) below bust die axis ↑↓

| 1696 .............................45 | 130 | 600 | 1697................................40 | 125 | 550 |
|---|---|---|---|---|---|

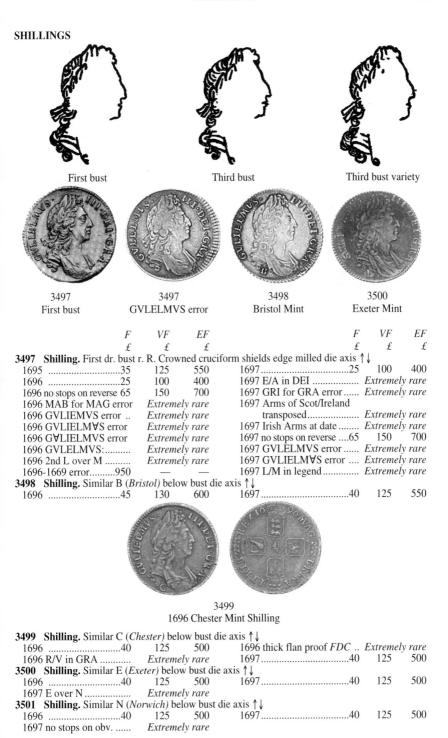

3499
1696 Chester Mint Shilling

**3499  Shilling.** Similar C (*Chester*) below bust die axis ↑↓

| 1696 .............................40 | 125 | 500 | 1696 thick flan proof *FDC* .. | *Extremely rare* | |
|---|---|---|---|---|---|
| 1696 R/V in GRA ............ | *Extremely rare* | | 1697................................40 | 125 | 500 |

**3500  Shilling.** Similar E (*Exeter*) below bust die axis ↑↓

| 1696 .............................40 | 125 | 500 | 1697................................40 | 125 | 500 |
|---|---|---|---|---|---|
| 1697 E over N ................. | *Extremely rare* | | | | |

**3501  Shilling.** Similar N (*Norwich*) below bust die axis ↑↓

| 1696 .............................40 | 125 | 500 | 1697................................40 | 125 | 500 |
|---|---|---|---|---|---|
| 1697 no stops on obv. ...... | *Extremely rare* | | | | |

|  | F | VF | EF |  | F | VF | EF |
|---|---|---|---|---|---|---|---|
|  | £ | £ | £ |  | £ | £ | £ |

**3502 Shilling.** Similar y (*York*) below bust die axis ↑↓

| 1696 | .40 | 125 | 500 | 1697 Arms of Scot/Ireland |
|---|---|---|---|---|
| 1697 | .40 | 125 | 500 | transposed.................. *Extremely rare* |

1697 Arms of France/Ireland
transposed ...................... *Extremely rare*

**3503 Shilling.** Similar Y (*York*) below bust die axis ↑↓

| 1696 | .85 | 175 | 725 | 1697 | .65 | 150 | 575 |
|---|---|---|---|---|---|---|---|

1697 Y over ⅄ ................. *Extremely rare*

3504           3503
Second bust     York Mint – Y

**3504 Shilling.** Second dr. bust r. (hair across breast), similar die axis ↑↓ 1696       *Unique*

3505             3507             3511
Third bust       Chester Mint      Third bust var.

**3505 Shilling.** Third dr. bust r., similar die axis ↑↓ 1697 .....................................30   100   375

**3506 Shilling.** Similar B (*Bristol*) below bust, die axis ↑↓ 1697 ........................65   150   575

**3507 Shilling.** Similar C (*Chester*) below bust die axis ↑↓

| 1696 | .175 | 425 | 1050 | 1697 no stops on reverse ....80 | 175 | 725 |
|---|---|---|---|---|---|---|
| 1697 | .40 | 125 | 475 | 1697 Arms of Scotland |  |  |
| 1697 FR.A error | .80 | 175 | 725 | at date .......................... *Extremely rare* |  |  |

**3508 Shilling.** Similar E (*Exeter*) below bust, die axis ↑↓

| 1696 | .......................... *Extremely rare* | 1697 | .65 | 150 | 575 |
|---|---|---|---|---|---|

**3509 Shilling.** Similar N (*Norwich*) below bust, die axis ↑↓ 1697 .....................65   150   575

**3510 Shilling.** Similar y (*York*) below bust die axis ↑↓

| 1696 | .......................... *Extremely rare* | 1697 | .65 | 150 | 575 |
|---|---|---|---|---|---|

**3511 Shilling.** Third bust variety r. similar die axis ↑↓

1697 GⱯLIELMVS error    *Extremely rare*      1697 GVLIELMⱯS error .... *Extremely rare*

| 1697 | .25 | 100 | 375 | 1698 | .40 | 125 | 500 |
|---|---|---|---|---|---|---|---|

1698 plain edge proof *FDC* £3000

**3512 Shilling.** Similar B (*Bristol*) below bust, die axis ↑↓ 1697 ........................65   150   575

**3513 Shilling.** Similar C (*Chester*) below bust, die axis ↑↓ 1697 ...................150   375   1000

**3514 Shilling.** Similar R. Plumes in angles, die axis ↑↓ 1698 ..........................200   475   1150

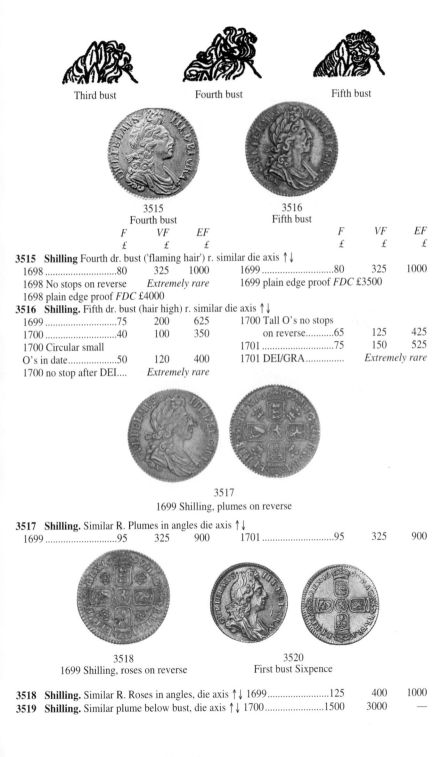

Third bust         Fourth bust         Fifth bust

3515
Fourth bust

3516
Fifth bust

| | F | VF | EF | | F | VF | EF |
|---|---|---|---|---|---|---|---|
| | £ | £ | £ | | £ | £ | £ |

**3515 Shilling** Fourth dr. bust ('flaming hair') r. similar die axis ↑↓

| 1698 ............................80 | 325 | 1000 | 1699 ............................80 | 325 | 1000 |
|---|---|---|---|---|---|
| 1698 No stops on reverse | *Extremely rare* | | 1699 plain edge proof *FDC* £3500 | | |
| 1698 plain edge proof *FDC* £4000 | | | | | |

**3516 Shilling.** Fifth dr. bust (hair high) r. similar die axis ↑↓

| 1699 ............................75 | 200 | 625 | 1700 Tall O's no stops | | |
|---|---|---|---|---|---|
| 1700 ............................40 | 100 | 350 | on reverse...........65 | 125 | 425 |
| 1700 Circular small | | | 1701 ............................75 | 150 | 525 |
| O's in date...................50 | 120 | 400 | 1701 DEI/GRA............... | *Extremely rare* | |
| 1700 no stop after DEI.... | *Extremely rare* | | | | |

3517
1699 Shilling, plumes on reverse

**3517 Shilling.** Similar R. Plumes in angles die axis ↑↓

| 1699 ............................95 | 325 | 900 | 1701 ............................95 | 325 | 900 |
|---|---|---|---|---|---|

3518
1699 Shilling, roses on reverse

3520
First bust Sixpence

**3518 Shilling.** Similar R. Roses in angles, die axis ↑↓ 1699......................125    400    1000

**3519 Shilling.** Similar plume below bust, die axis ↑↓ 1700......................1500    3000    —

## SIXPENCES

| First bust | Third bust | Early harp. large crown. | Later harp, small crown. |
|---|---|---|---|

| | F | VF | EF | | F | VF | EF |
|---|---|---|---|---|---|---|---|
| | £ | £ | £ | | £ | £ | £ |

**3520 Sixpence.** First dr. bust r. R. Crowned cruciform shields, edge milled early harp die axis ↑↓

| | F | VF | EF | | F | VF | EF |
|---|---|---|---|---|---|---|---|
| 1695 ............................40 | 120 | 425 | | 1696 ..Scots Arms at date | *Extremely rare* | | |
| 1696 ............................20 | 75 | 225 | | 1696/5 .........................45 | 120 | 425 | |
| 1696 Heavy flan.............. | *Extremely rare* | | | 1696 no stops on | | | |
| 1696 French Arms at date | *Extremely rare* | | | obverse...............35 | 100 | 375 | |
| 1696 GVLIELMⱯS ........ | *Extremely rare* | | | 1696 DFI for DEI .......... | *Extremely rare* | | |

**3521 Sixpence.** Similar B *(Bristol)* below bust, die axis ↑↓ 1696...................25 · 75 · 275

— — 1696 B over E................................................................................ *Extremely rare*

**3522 Sixpence.** Similar C *(Chester)* below bust, die axis ↑↓ 1696 ................30 · 85 · 375

**3523 Sixpence.** Similar E *(Exeter)* below bust, die axis ↑↓ 1696 ..................40 · 100 · 425

**3524 Sixpence.** Similar N *(Norwich)* below bust, die axis ↑↓ 1696...............50 · 120 · 375

3525
1696 York Mint Sixpence, early harp, first bust

| | | F | VF | EF |
|---|---|---|---|---|
| **3525 Sixpence.** Similar y *(York)* below bust, die axis ↑↓ 1696......................20 | | | 75 | 275 |
| **3526 Sixpence.** Similar Y *(York)* below bust, die axis ↑↓ 1696.....................40 | | | 125 | 425 |
| — — — 1696 no stops on obverse .......................................................75 | | | 275 | — |
| **3527 Sixpence.** Similar R. Later harp, large crowns, die axis ↑↓ 1696..........75 | | | 225 | 475 |
| — — — 1696 no stops on obverse .......................................................100 | | | 275 | 525 |

**3528 Sixpence.** — — — B *(Bristol)* below bust, similar die axis ↑↓

| | F | VF | EF | | F | VF | EF |
|---|---|---|---|---|---|---|---|
| 1696 ............................75 | 225 | 475 | | 1697 ............................40 | 120 | 425 | |
| 1696 no stops on | | | | | | | |
| obv. ...................80 | 250 | 500 | | | | | |

**3529 Sixpence.** — — — C *(Chester)* below bust, similar die axis ↑↓ 1697..75 · 225 · 475

**3530 Sixpence.** — — — E *(Exeter)* below bust, similar die axis ↑↓ 1697 ....40 · 125 · 425

**3531 Sixpence.** — — R. small crowns, similar die axis ↑↓

| | F | VF | EF | | F | VF | EF |
|---|---|---|---|---|---|---|---|
| 1696 ............................75 | 225 | 475 | | 1697 Arms of France/Ireland | | | |
| 1697 ............................20 | 75 | 275 | | transposed.............. | *Extremely rare* | | |
| 1697 GVLIELMⱯS .....75 | 225 | 475 | | | | | |

3532
Bristol Mint Sixpence, small crowns

|  | F £ | VF £ | EF £ |  | F £ | VF £ | EF £ |
|---|---|---|---|---|---|---|---|
| **3532 Sixpence.** — — — B *(Bristol)* below bust, similar die axis ↑↓ | | | | | | | |
| 1696 | 75 | 225 | 475 | 1697 | 30 | 75 | 300 |
| 1696 no stops on O. | 85 | 250 | 500 | 1697 B over E | 40 | 125 | 325 |
| **3533 Sixpence.** — — — C *(Chester)* below bust, similar die axis ↑↓ | | | | | | | |
| 1696 | 100 | 275 | 575 | 1697 Irish shield at date.. | *Extremely rare* | | |
| 1697 | 30 | 75 | 300 | 1697 Plain edge | 125 | 300 | 625 |
| **3534 Sixpence.** — — — E *(Exeter)* below bust, similar die axis ↑↓ | | | | | | | |
| 1697 | 35 | 85 | 325 | 1697 E over B | *Extremely rare* | | |
| **3535 Sixpence.** — — — N *(Norwich)* below bust, similar die axis ↑↓ | | | | | | | |
| 1696 | 75 | 225 | 475 | 1697 | 30 | 75 | 300 |
| 1697 GVLIEMVS | *Extremely rare* | | | | | | |

3536
York Mint Sixpence

| | F £ | VF £ | EF £ | | F £ | VF £ | EF £ |
|---|---|---|---|---|---|---|---|
| **3536 Sixpence.** — — — y *(York)* below bust, similar die axis ↑↓ | | | | | | | |
| 1697 | 45 | 125 | 425 | 1697 Irish shield at date.. | *Extremely rare* | | |

| 3537 | | | | 3540 | | | |
|---|---|---|---|---|---|---|---|
| Second bust Sixpence | | | | Chester Mint Sixpence, third bust | | | |

| | F £ | VF £ | EF £ | | F £ | VF £ | EF £ |
|---|---|---|---|---|---|---|---|
| **3537 Sixpence.** Second dr. bust r. R. Similar die axis ↑↓ | | | | | | | |
| 1696 | 200 | 550 | 1400 | 1696 GVLELMVS | 250 | 650 | 1400 |
| 1697 GVLIELMⱯS | *Extremely rare* | | | 1697 | 95 | 275 | 950 |
| 1697 G/I in GRA | *Extremely rare* | | | 1697 GR/DE in GRA | *Extremely rare* | | |
| 1697 GVLIEMVS | *Extremely rare* | | | | | | |
| **3537A Sixpence.** Third dr. bust, r. early harp, large crowns. E *(Exeter)* below bust, 1696 | *Extremely rare* | | | | | | |
| **3537B Sixpence.** — — — --- Y *(York)* below bust, similar die axis ↑↓ 1696 | *Extremely rare* | | | | | | |

3538
1699 Sixpence, third bust, later harp, large crowns

|  | F | VF | EF |  | F | VF | EF |
|---|---|---|---|---|---|---|---|
|  | £ | £ | £ |  | £ | £ | £ |

**3538 Sixpence.** Third dr. bust, r., R. Later harp, large crowns, similar die axis ↑↓

| 1697 GVLIEIMVS | .....50 | 200 | 450 |  |  |  |  |
| 1697 | .............20 | 75 | 250 | 1699 | ..............75 | 225 | 475 |
| 1697 GⱯLIELMVS | ..100 | 250 | 525 | 1700 | ..............30 | 75 | 300 |
| 1698 | .............30 | 75 | 300 | 1701 | ..............35 | 85 | 325 |

**3539 Sixpence.**— — B *(Bristol)* below bust, similar die axis ↑↓

| 1697 | .............45 | 125 | 425 | 1697 IRA for FRA | .......... | *Extremely rare* | |

**3540 Sixpence.**— — C *(Chester)* below bust, similar die axis ↑↓ 1697........75 225 475
**3541 Sixpence.**— — E *(Exeter)* below bust, similar die axis ↑↓ 1697 ..........75 225 475
**3542 Sixpence.** Third dr. bust, r. R. Small crowns, similar die axis ↑↓

| 1697 | .............25 | 100 | 350 | 1697 G/D for GRA | ......... | *Extremely rare* | |
| 1697 D/F in DEI | ............. | *Extremely rare* | | | | | |

**3543 Sixpence.**— — C *(Chester)* below bust, similar die axis ↑↓ 1697........75 225 475
**3544 Sixpence.**— — E *(Exeter)* below bust, similar die axis ↑↓ 1697 ..........35 100 375

3545
1699 York Mint Sixpence - Y provenance mark

3547
1699 Sixpence, roses on reverse

**3545 Sixpence.**— — Y *(York)* below bust, similar die axis ↑↓ 1697 ............75 225 475
**3546 Sixpence.**— — ℞. Plumes in angles, similar die axis ↑↓

| 1698 | .............35 | 85 | 325 | 1699 | ..............35 | 85 | 325 |

**3547 Sixpence.**— ℞. Roses in angles, similar die axis ↑↓

| 1699 | .............75 | 225 | 475 | 1699 GⱯLIELMVS | ........ | *Extremely rare* | |

3548
1700 Sixpence, plume below bust

3549
1698 Groat or Fourpence

**3548 Sixpence.**— plume below bust, R. Similar die axis ↑↓ 1700 ............1250 — —
**3549 Fourpence.** Laur. and dr. bust r. R. 4 Crowned die axis ↑↓

| 1697 | ............................... |  | *Unique* | 1700 | ..............11 | 30 | 110 |
| 1698 | .............14 | 35 | 140 | 1701 | ..............14 | 35 | 140 |
| 1699 | .............11 | 30 | 110 | 1702 | ..............10 | 30 | 100 |

3550 - 1695 Threepence         3551 - 1695 Twopence

|  | F | VF | EF |  | F | VF | EF |
|---|---|---|---|---|---|---|---|
|  | £ | £ | £ |  | £ | £ | £ |

**3550 Threepence.** Laur. and dr. bust r. R. 3 Crowned die axis ↑↓

| 1698 | 11 | 30 | 100 | 1701 GBA for GRA ....15 | 40 | 140 |
| 1699 | 12 | 35 | 110 | 1701 small lettering......11 | 30 | 100 |
| 1700 | 11 | 30 | 100 | 1701 large lettering ......12 | 35 | 100 |

**3551 Twopence.** Laur. and dr. bust r. R. Crown to edge of coin, large figure 2 die axis ↑↓

| 1698 | 15 | 45 | 110 |

**3551A Twopence.** Laur. and dr. bust r. R Crown within inner circle of legend, smaller figure 2, die axis ↑↓

| 1698 | 10 | 35 | 100 | 1700............................9 | 30 | 90 |
| 1699 | 9 | 30 | 90 | 1701............................9 | 30 | 90 |

**3552 Penny.** Laur. and dr. bust r. R. 1 Crowned die axis ↑↓

| 1698 | 10 | 30 | 90 | 1699............................10 | 30 | 100 |
| 1698 IRA for FRA error..12 | 40 | 110 | 1700............................10 | 30 | 100 |
| 1698 HI.BREX error ....12 | 40 | 110 | 1701............................10 | 30 | 100 |

3553 - 1701 Maundy Set

**3553 Maundy Set.** The four denominations. Uniform dates

| 1698 | 75 | 250 | 600 | 1700............................90 | 275 | 650 |
| 1699 | 90 | 275 | 650 | 1701............................75 | 250 | 600 |

## COPPER

3554 - 1696 Halfpenny

**3554 Halfpenny.** First issue. Laur. and cuir. bust r. R. Britannia with r. hand raised die axis ↑↓

| 1695 | 35 | 150 | 650 | 1697............................25 | 150 | 600 |
| 1695 BRITANNIA error ..150 | — | — | 1697 all stops omitted..200 | — | — |
| 1695 no stop on rev.......65 | 225 | — | 1697 I/E in TERTIVS..200 | — | — |
| 1695 no stops on obv. ..65 | 225 | — | 1697 GVLILMVS, no rev. stop *Extremely rare* |
| 1696 | 25 | 150 | 600 | 1697 no stop |
| 1696 GVLIEMVS, no rev. stop *Extremely rare* | | | after TERTIVS....50 | 225 | — |
| 1696 TERTVS error ....225 | — | — | 1698............................35 | 175 | 700 |

|   | F | VF | EF |   |   | F | VF | EF |
|---|---|----|----|---|---|---|----|----|
|   | £ | £  | £  |   |   | £ | £  | £  |

**3555  Halfpenny.** Second issue. Laur. and cuir. bust r. R. Britannia Date in legend die axis ↑↓

| | F | VF | EF | | F | VF | EF |
|---|---|---|---|---|---|---|---|
| 1698 Stop after date | 30 | 150 | 650 | 1699 BRITANNIA error ......200 | — | — |
| 1699 no stop after date | 25 | 140 | 600 | 1699 GVLIEMVS error ......200 | — | — |
| | | | | 1699 BRITAN IA error ......200 | — | — |

**3556  Halfpenny.** Third issue. Laur. and cuir. bust r. R. Britannia with r. hand on knee die axis ↑↓

| | F | VF | EF | | F | VF | EF |
|---|---|---|---|---|---|---|---|
| 1699 | 25 | 140 | 600 | 1700 BRITANNIA error ....35 | 150 | 650 |
| 1699 stop after date | 200 | — | — | 1700 — no stop after ......50 | 200 | 700 |
| 1699 BRITANNIA error | 95 | 300 | — | 1700 BRIVANNIA error.....*Extremely rare* | | |
| 1699 GVILELMVS error | 225 | — | — | 1700 GVLIELMS ............95 | 275 | — |
| 1699 TERTVS error | 225 | — | — | 1700 GVLIEEMVS .........50 | 200 | 700 |
| 1699 — no rev. stop | 200 | — | — | 1700 TER TIVS ...............40 | 175 | 675 |
| 1699 no stops on obv. | 95 | 300 | — | 1700 I/V in TERTIVS ......175 | — | — |
| 1699 no stop after | | | | 1701 ................................30 | 140 | 600 |
| GVLIELMVS | 95 | 275 | — | 1701 BRITANNIA ............50 | 200 | 700 |
| 1700 | 25 | 140 | 600 | 1701 — no stops on obv. .....225 | — | — |
| 1700 no stops on obv. | 95 | 275 | — | 1701 — inverted A's | | |
| 1700 no stop after | | | | for V's .....................60 | 225 | 750 |
| GVLIELMVS | 95 | 275 | — | | | |

3557
1695 Farthing date in exergue

3558
1699 Farthing date in legend

**3557  Farthing.** First issue Laur. and cuir. bust r. R. Britannia l. die axis ↑↓

| | F | VF | EF | | F | VF | EF |
|---|---|---|---|---|---|---|---|
| 1695 | 35 | 200 | 625 | 1698 ................................200 | 525 | — |
| 1695 GVLIELMV error | 225 | — | — | 1698 B/G on rev. ............225 | — | — |
| 1696 | 30 | 175 | 575 | 1699 ................................35 | 200 | 600 |
| 1697 | 25 | 150 | 525 | 1699 GVLILEMVS• ......125 | 250 | — |
| 1697 GVLIELMS error | 225 | — | — | 1700 ................................25 | 125 | 550 |
| 1697 TERTIV error | 200 | — | — | 1700 RRITANNIA .........225 | — | — |

**3558  Farthing.** Second issue. Laur. and cuir. bust r. R. Britannia date at end of legend die axis ↑↓

| | F | VF | EF | | |
|---|---|---|---|---|---|
| 1698 Stop after date | 40 | 225 | 750 | 1699 — No stop before or after*Extremely rare* | |
| 1699 no stop after date | 45 | 250 | 800 | 1699 BRITANNIA .........200 | — — |
| 1699 no stop after | | | | 1699 BRITANNIA ........200 | — — |
| GVLIELMVS .........*Extremely rare* | | | | | |

Anne, the second daughter of James II, was born on 6th February 1665 and as a protestant succeeded to the throne on William III's death. Anne married Prince George of Denmark and produced 17 children, sadly none surviving to succeed to the throne. Anne died on 1st August 1714.

The Act of Union of 1707, which effected the unification of the ancient kingdoms of England and Scotland into a single realm, resulted in a change in the royal arms—on the Post-Union coinage the English lions and Scottish lion are emblazoned per pale on the top and bottom shields. After the Union the rose in the centre of the reverse of the gold coins is replaced by the Garter star.

Following a successful Anglo-Dutch expedition against Spain, bullion seized in Vigo Bay was sent to be minted into coin, and the coins made from this metal had the word VIGO placed below the Queen's bust. The elephant and castle provenance mark continues on some guineas in the Post-Union period.

**Engravers and designers:** Samuel Bull (d.c1720), Joseph Cave (d.c1760), James Clerk, John Croker (1670-1741), Godfrey Kneller (1646-1723)

## GOLD

3560
1705 Pre-Union Five Guineas
**Before Union with Scotland. The shields on the reverse are Pre-Union type.**

|  | F | VF | EF |  | F | VF | EF |
|---|---|---|---|---|---|---|---|
|  | £ | £ | £ |  | £ | £ | £ |

**3560 Five Guineas.** Dr. bust l, regnal year on edge in words (e.g. 1705 = QVARTO) die axis ↑↓

| 1705 QVARTO | 1500 | 4500 | 12000 | 1706 QVINTO | 1250 | 3500 | 10000 |
|---|---|---|---|---|---|---|---|

**3561 Five Guineas.** Similar VIGO below bust, die axis ↑↓ 1703 (Three varieties)

| SECVNDO | | | | | 12500 | 25000 | 50000 |
|---|---|---|---|---|---|---|---|

3562
1706 Pre-Union Guinea

3563
1703 VIGO Guinea

**3562 Guinea.** Dr. bust l. R. Crowned cruciform shields sceptres in angles die axis ↑↓

| 1702 | 400 | 1750 | 4000 | 1706 | 600 | 2250 | 4750 |
|---|---|---|---|---|---|---|---|
| 1702 proof *FDC* | | *Extremely rare* | | 1707 | 550 | 2000 | 4500 |
| 1705 | 625 | 2500 | 5000 | | | | |

3565
1703 VIGO Half-Guinea

3564
1702 Pre-Union Half-Guinea

|  | F | VF | EF |  | F | VF | EF |
|--|---|----|----|--|---|----|----|
|  | £ | £ | £ |  | £ | £ | £ |

**3563  Guinea.** Similar with VIGO below bust, die axis ↑↓ 1703 ....................4500  10000  22500

**3564  Half-Guinea.** Dr bust l. R. Crowned cruciform shields sceptres in angles die axis ↑↓
1702 ..........................525      1950      4750        1705..............................500      1750      4500

**3565  Half-Guinea.** Similar with VIGO below bust, 1703 ..............................3750    9000    15000

3566
1706 Post-Union Five Guineas

**After Union with Scotland.** The shields on the reverse are changed to Post-Union type die axis ↑↓

**3566  Five Guineas.** Dr. bust l., regnal year on edge in words 1706 QVINTO ......1750    3750    10000

3567
1709 - Narrow shields

3568
1713 - Broad shields

**3567  Five Guineas.** Similar R. Narrower shields, tall narrow crowns, larger rev. lettering, die axis ↑↓
1709 OCTAVO ..............................................................................................1500    4000    11000

**3568  Five Guineas.** Similar R. Broader shields edge inscribed die axis ↑↓
1711 DECIMO ........1500      3750      10000        1714/3 D. TERTIO ......1500    4500    12000
1713 DVODECIMO 1500      4000      11000        1714 D. TERTIO..........1650    4750    12500

3569
1713 Two Guineas

|  | F | VF | EF |  | F | VF | EF |
|---|---|---|---|---|---|---|---|
|  | £ | £ | £ |  | £ | £ | £ |

**3569** **Two Guineas.** Dr. bust l.R. Crowned cruciform shields sceptres in angles edge milled die axis ↑↓

| 1709 | 600 | 1750 | 4250 | 1713 | 600 | 1650 | 4000 |
| 1711 | 600 | 1650 | 4000 | 1714/3 | 700 | 2000 | 4750 |

**3570** **Guinea.** First dr. bust l. R. Crowned cruciform shields sceptres in angles edge milled die axis ↑↓

| 1707 | 350 | 1250 | 3000 | 1708 | | *Extremely rare* | |

| 3571 | 3574 |
| 1707 Guinea, first bust, elephant and castle below | 1713 Guinea, third bust |

**3571** **Guinea.** First dr. bust l. elephant and castle below, R. Similar die axis ↑↓

| 1707 | 550 | 1650 | 4250 | 1708 | | *Extremely rare* | |

**3572** **Guinea.** Second dr. bust l. R. Similar die axis ↑↓

| 1707 | | *Extremely rare* | | 1709 | 350 | 1100 | 3000 |
| 1708 | 300 | 1250 | 3000 | | | | |

**3573** **Guinea.** Second bust elephant and castle below R. Similar die axis ↑↓

| 1708 | 550 | 1750 | 2250 | 1709 | 500 | 1850 | 4000 |

**3574** **Guinea.** Third dr. bust l. R. Similar die axis ↑↓

| 1710 | 325 | 900 | 2500 | 1713/1 | 500 | 1000 | 2500 |
| 1711 | 350 | 1000 | 2500 | 1713 | 300 | 750 | 1500 |
| 1712 | 350 | 1000 | 2500 | 1714 | 300 | 750 | 1500 |
| | | | | 1714 GRΛTIΛ | 600 | 1250 | 3000 |

3575
1713 Half-Guinea

**3575** **Half-Guinea.** Dr. bust l. R. Crowned cruciform shields, sceptres in angles, edge milled die axis ↑↓

| 1707 | 325 | 950 | 2500 | 1711 | 300 | 900 | 2250 |
| 1708 | 350 | 1000 | 2750 | 1712 | 275 | 850 | 2000 |
| 1709 | 325 | 950 | 2500 | 1713 | 250 | 750 | 1850 |
| 1710 | 250 | 750 | 1850 | 1714 | 275 | 850 | 2000 |

# SILVER

3576
1703 VIGO Crown

| | F | VF | EF | | F | VF | EF |
|---|---|---|---|---|---|---|---|
| | £ | £ | £ | | £ | £ | £ |

**Before Union with Scotland. The shields on the reverse are Pre-Union type.**

**3576  Crown.** VIGO below dr. bust, l., regnal year on edge in words (e.g. 1703 = TERTIO) die axis↑↓
1703 TERTIO ............................................................................................325      1200      3750

3577                                                            3578
1705 Crown, plumes on reverse                1707 Pre-Union crown, roses and plumes

**3577  Crown.** Dr bust l. R. Plumes in angles, die axis ↑↓ 1705 QVINTO...500      1750      4750
**3578  Crown.** R. Similar Crowned cruciform shields Roses and plumes in angles die axis ↑↓
1706 QVINTO ..........150        650      1950      1707 SEXTO ............175        700      2250

3579
1703 Halfcrown, plain below bust

**3579  Halfcrown** . Dr. bust l. R. Similar Regnal year on edge in words die axis ↑↓
1703 TERTIO...................................................................................650      2500      9500

| | 3580 | | | | 3581 | |
|---|---|---|---|---|---|---|
| | 1703 VIGO Halfcrown | | | | 1705 Halfcrown, plumes on reverse | |
| | *F* | *VF* | *EF* | | *F* | *VF* | *EF* |
| | £ | £ | £ | | £ | £ | £ |

**3580  Halfcrown.** Similar VIGO below bust, die axis ↑↓ 1703 TERTIO ....120      375      1100

**3581  Halfcrown.** Dr. bust l. R. Plumes in angles, similar die axis ↑↓

1704 TERTIO...........140      625      1750      1705 QVINTO..........120      500      1350

| 3582 | 3583 |
|---|---|
| 1707 Halfcrown, Pre-Union, roses and plumes | 1702 Shilling |

**3582  Halfcrown.** Dr. bust l. R. Roses and plumes in angles, similar die axis ↑↓

1706 QVINTO ............95      375      1000      1707 SEXTO .............85      325      900

First bust                  Second bust

**3583  Shilling.** First dr. bust l. R. Similar die axis↑↓ 1702.............................75      325      600

3584

1702 Shilling, plumes on reverse

**3584  Shilling.** Similar R. Plumes in angles, die axis ↑↓ 1702 ......................85      350      650

**3585  Shilling.** First dr. bust VIGO below , die axis ↑↓

1702 ...........................80      300      600      1702 :ANNA ..................      *Extremely rare*

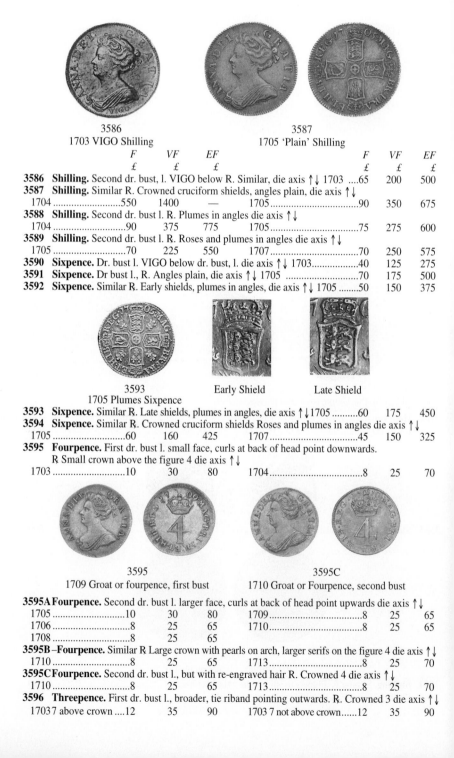

3586                                    3587
1703 VIGO Shilling                    1705 'Plain' Shilling

|  | F | VF | EF |  | F | VF | EF |
|---|---|---|---|---|---|---|---|
|  | £ | £ | £ |  | £ | £ | £ |

**3586  Shilling.** Second dr. bust, l. VIGO below R. Similar, die axis ↑↓ 1703 ....65    200    500
**3587  Shilling.** Similar R. Crowned cruciform shields, angles plain, die axis ↑↓
1704 ........................550    1400    —    1705 ..............................90    350    675
**3588  Shilling.** Second dr. bust l. R. Plumes in angles die axis ↑↓
1704 ........................90    375    775    1705 ..............................75    275    600
**3589  Shilling.** Second dr. bust l. R. Roses and plumes in angles die axis ↑↓
1705 ........................70    225    550    1707 ..............................70    250    575
**3590  Sixpence.** Dr. bust l. VIGO below dr. bust, l. die axis ↑↓ 1703 ................40    125    275
**3591  Sixpence.** Dr bust l., R. Angles plain, die axis ↑↓ 1705 ........................70    175    500
**3592  Sixpence.** Similar R. Early shields, plumes in angles, die axis ↑↓ 1705 ........50    150    375

3593                  Early Shield              Late Shield
1705 Plumes Sixpence

**3593  Sixpence.** Similar R. Late shields, plumes in angles, die axis ↑↓1705 ..........60    175    450
**3594  Sixpence.** Similar R. Crowned cruciform shields Roses and plumes in angles die axis ↑↓
1705 ........................60    160    425    1707 ..............................45    150    325
**3595  Fourpence.** First dr. bust l. small face, curls at back of head point downwards.
R Small crown above the figure 4 die axis ↑↓
1703 ........................10    30    80    1704 ..............................8    25    70

3595                                   3595C
1709 Groat or fourpence, first bust   1710 Groat or Fourpence, second bust

**3595A Fourpence.** Second dr. bust l. larger face, curls at back of head point upwards die axis ↑↓
1705 ........................10    30    80    1709 ..............................8    25    65
1706 ........................8    25    65    1710 ..............................8    25    65
1708 ........................8    25    65
**3595B –Fourpence.** Similar R Large crown with pearls on arch, larger serifs on the figure 4 die axis ↑↓
1710 ........................8    25    65    1713 ..............................8    25    70
**3595C Fourpence.** Second dr. bust l., but with re-engraved hair R. Crowned 4 die axis ↑↓
1710 ........................8    25    65    1713 ..............................8    25    70
**3596  Threepence.** First dr. bust l., broader, tie riband pointing outwards. R. Crowned 3 die axis ↑↓
1703 7 above crown ....12    35    90    1703 7 not above crown ......12    35    90

|  | F £ | VF £ | EF £ |  | F £ | VF £ | EF £ |
|---|---|---|---|---|---|---|---|

**3596A Threepence.** Second dr. bust l., taller and narrow, tie riband pointing inwards die axis ↑↓

| 1704 | 10 | 30 | 80 | 1706 | 8 | 25 | 65 |
| 1705 | 10 | 30 | 80 |  |  |  |  |

3596B
1707 Threepence, third bust

**3596B Threepence.** Third larger more finely engraved dr. bust l. R. Crowned 3, die axis ↑↓

| 1707 | 8 | 25 | 65 | 1710 | 8 | 25 | 65 |
| 1708 | 8 | 25 | 65 | 1713 | 8 | 25 | 65 |
| 1708/7 | 8 | 25 | 65 | 1713 mule with 4d obv. |  |  |  |
| 1709 | 8 | 25 | 65 | die | 12 | 35 | 120 |

**3597 Twopence.** First dr. bust l., as fourpence, R. Crown to edge of coin, small figure 2 die axis ↑↓

| 1703 | 12 | 30 | 80 | 1705 | 8 | 25 | 55 |
| 1704 | 8 | 25 | 55 | 1706 | 10 | 25 | 65 |
| 1704 No stops on obv. | 12 | 30 | 80 | 1707 | 10 | 25 | 65 |

**3597A Twopence.** Second dr. bust l., as fourpence, R Crown within inner circle of legend, large figure 2 die axis ↑↓

| 1708 | 8 | 25 | 55 | 1710 | 8 | 25 | 55 |
| 1709 | 10 | 30 | 65 | 1713 | 8 | 25 | 55 |

**3598 Penny.** Dr. bust l. R. Crowned 1 die axis ↑↓

| 1703 | 12 | 30 | 90 | 1709 | 10 | 30 | 75 |
| 1705 | 10 | 30 | 75 | 1710 | 14 | 35 | 100 |
| 1706 | 10 | 30 | 75 | 1713/0 | 12 | 30 | 90 |
| 1708 | 14 | 35 | 100 |  |  |  |  |

3599
1713 Maundy Set

|  | F £ | VF £ | EF £ |  | F £ | VF £ | EF £ |
|---|---|---|---|---|---|---|---|

**3599 Maundy Set.** The four denominations. Uniform dates

| 1703 | 75 | 175 | 625 | 1709 | 75 | 175 | 525 |
| 1705 | 75 | 175 | 625 | 1710 | 80 | 200 | 625 |
| 1706 | 65 | 150 | 500 | 1713 | 70 | 175 | 550 |
| 1708 | 80 | 200 | 625 |  |  |  |  |

**After Union with Scotland**

The shields on the reverse are changed to the Post-Union types. The Edinburgh coins have been included here as they are now coins of Great Britain.

3600
1708E Edinburgh Mint Crown

| | F £ | VF £ | EF £ | | F £ | VF £ | EF £ |
|---|---|---|---|---|---|---|---|
| **3600** | **Crown.** Second dr. bust, l. E (Edinburgh) below, R. Crowned cruciform shields regnal year on edge in words, die axis ↑↓ (e.g. 1708 = SEPTIMO) | | | | | | |
| | 1707 SEXTO .................100 | 500 | 1000 | 1708/7 SEPTIMO ..........150 | 600 | 1350 |
| | 1708 SEPTIMO ............120 | 550 | 1150 | 1708/7 M/E on edge ......175 | 700 | 1650 |

3601
1708 Crown, second bust, plain reverse

**3601** **Crown.** Second dr. bust l. R. Crowned cruciform shields, angles plain die axis ↑↓
1707 SEPTIMO .............120      550      1150      1708 SEPTIMO .............200      750      —
**3602** **Crown.** Similar R. Plumes in angles, die axis ↑↓
1708 SEPTIMO .............150      600      1350      1708 — BR for BRI ...........*Extremely rare*

3603
1713 Crown, third bust, roses and plumes

**3603** **Crown.** Third dr. bust. l. R. Roses and plumes, 1713 DVODECIMO .....120      600      1250

3604

1708 Halfcrown, Post-Union

| | F | VF | EF | | F | VF | EF |
|---|---|---|---|---|---|---|---|
| | £ | £ | £ | | £ | £ | £ |

**3604  Halfcrown.** Dr. bust R. Plain, regnal year on edge in words (e.g. 1709 = OCTAVO), die axis ↑↓

| 1707 SEPTIMO ...............60 | 275 | 800 | 1709 OCTAVO ...............60 | 275 | 800 |
|---|---|---|---|---|---|
| 1707 no stops on reverse ..125 | 400 | — | 1708 SEPTIMO ...............70 | 325 | 900 |
| 1713 DVODECIMO .......70 | 325 | 900 | | | |

**3605  Halfcrown.** Dr. bust E below R. Crowned cruciform shields die axis ↑↓

| 1707 SEXTO ..................40 | 175 | 625 | 1708 SEPTIMO ...............70 | 325 | 900 |
|---|---|---|---|---|---|
| 1707 SEPTIMO ..................*Extremely rare* | | | 1709 OCTAVO .............325 | 900 | — |

| 3606 | 3609 |
|---|---|
| 1708 Halfcrown, plumes on reverse | 1707 Edinburgh Mint Shilling |

**3606  Halfcrown.** Similar R. Plumes in angles, die axis ↑↓ 1708 SEPTIMO .....80    375    1100

3607

1714 Halfcrown, roses and plumes

**3607  Halfcrown.** Similar R. Roses and plumes in angles die axis ↑↓

| 1710 NONO ....................70 | 325 | 900 | 1714 D. TERTIO ..............60 | 275 | 800 |
|---|---|---|---|---|---|
| 1712 UNDECIMO ..........60 | 225 | 700 | 1714/3 D. TERTIO ........100 | 450 | 1150 |
| 1713 DVODECIMO ........70 | 325 | 900 | | | |

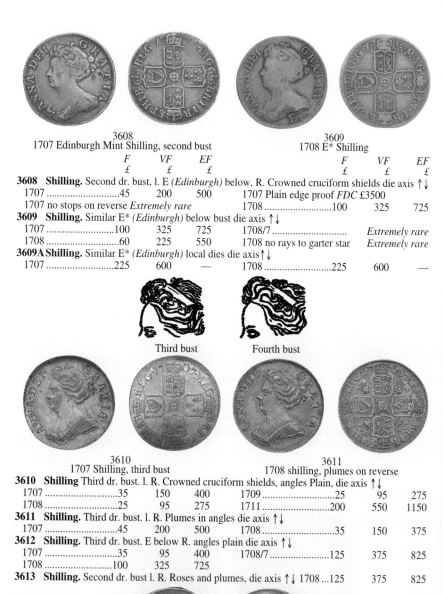

3608
1707 Edinburgh Mint Shilling, second bust

3609
1708 E* Shilling

|  | F | VF | EF |  |  | F | VF | EF |
|---|---|---|---|---|---|---|---|---|
|  | £ | £ | £ |  |  | £ | £ | £ |

**3608  Shilling.** Second dr. bust, l. E *(Edinburgh)* below, R. Crowned cruciform shields die axis ↑↓

| 1707 | ............................45 | 200 | 500 | 1707 Plain edge proof *FDC* £3500 |  |  |  |
|---|---|---|---|---|---|---|---|
| 1707 no stops on reverse *Extremely rare* |  |  |  | 1708 | .........................100 | 325 | 725 |

**3609  Shilling.** Similar E* *(Edinburgh)* below bust die axis ↑↓

| 1707 | .........................100 | 325 | 725 | 1708/7 | ............................. | *Extremely rare* |  |
|---|---|---|---|---|---|---|---|
| 1708 | ...........................60 | 225 | 550 | 1708 no rays to garter star |  | *Extremely rare* |  |

**3609A Shilling.** Similar E* *(Edinburgh)* local dies die axis ↑↓

| 1707 | .........................225 | 600 | — | 1708 | .........................225 | 600 | — |
|---|---|---|---|---|---|---|---|

Third bust                Fourth bust

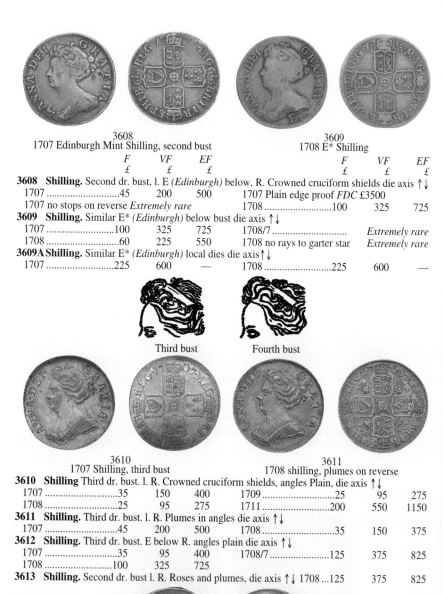

3610
1707 Shilling, third bust

3611
1708 shilling, plumes on reverse

**3610  Shilling** Third dr. bust. l. R. Crowned cruciform shields, angles Plain, die axis ↑↓

| 1707 | ............................35 | 150 | 400 | 1709 | ............................25 | 95 | 275 |
|---|---|---|---|---|---|---|---|
| 1708 | ............................25 | 95 | 275 | 1711 | .........................200 | 550 | 1150 |

**3611  Shilling.** Third dr. bust. l. R. Plumes in angles die axis ↑↓

| 1707 | ............................45 | 200 | 500 | 1708 | ............................35 | 150 | 375 |
|---|---|---|---|---|---|---|---|

**3612  Shilling.** Third dr. bust. E below R. angles plain die axis ↑↓

| 1707 | ............................35 | 95 | 400 | 1708/7 | .....................125 | 375 | 825 |
|---|---|---|---|---|---|---|---|
| 1708 | .........................100 | 325 | 725 |  |  |  |  |

**3613  Shilling.** Second dr. bust l. R. Roses and plumes, die axis ↑↓ 1708 ...125    375    825

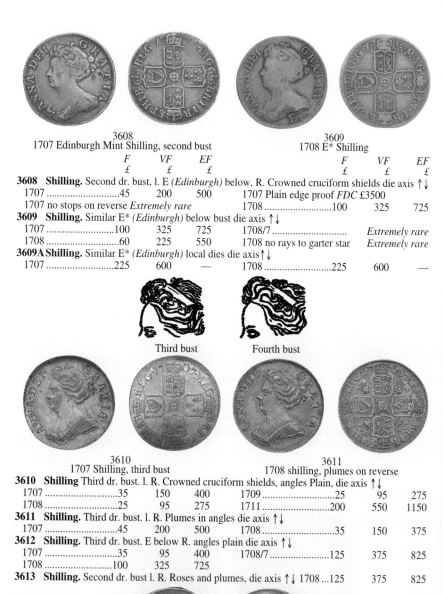

3614
1708 Shilling, roses and plumes

**3614  Shilling.** Third dr. bust l. R. Crowned cruciform shields Roses and plumes die axis ↑↓

| 1708 | .........................100 | 350 | 725 | 1710 | ............................35 | 150 | 400 |
|---|---|---|---|---|---|---|---|

| 3615 | 3620 | 3623 |
|------|------|------|
| Edinburgh bust – E* Shilling | Edinburgh Mint Sixpence | 1707 Sixpence, plumes on reverse |

|  | F | VF | EF |  | F | VF | EF |
|--|---|----|----|--|---|----|----|
|  | £ | £ | £ |  | £ | £ | £ |

**3615 Shilling.** 'Edinburgh' bust, E* below, R. Crowned cruciform shields die axis ↑↓
1707 ............................... *Extremely rare*  1709 .........................100  325  725
1708 ..........................100  275  600

**3616 Shilling.** — E below, R. Similar die axis ↑↓ 1709 .............................275  900  —

**3617 Shilling.** Fourth dr. bust. l. R. Roses and plumes die axis ↑↓
1710 ............................50  200  450  1713/2 .........................50  200  450
1710 plain edge proof *FDC.*  *Extremely rare*  1714 ............................35  150  400
1712 ............................35  150  400  1714/3 ............................  *Extremely rare*

**3618 Shilling.** Similar, R. angles plain, die axis ↑↓
1711 ..............20  80  175  1711 plain edge proof *FDC*  *Extremely rare*

**3619 Sixpence.** Normal dr. bust. l. R. angles plain die axis ↑↓
1707 ............................30  85  225  1711 ............................30  65  185
1707 BR. FRA error........  *Extremely rare*  1711 Large Lis............25  60  175
1708 ............................35  100  275

**3620 Sixpence.** Normal dr. bust E *(Edinburgh)* below R. Similar die axis ↑↓
1707 ............................35  100  275  1708/7 .........................60  175  425
1707 Proof FDC £3000  1708 .........................45  140  325

**3621 Sixpence.** Normal dr. bust E* *(Edinburgh)* below, R. Similar die axis ↑↓
1708 ............................45  140  350  1708/7 .........................55  175  400

**3622 Sixpence.** 'Edinburgh' bust, l. E* below, R. Similar die axis ↑↓ 1708 ..45  140  325

**3623 Sixpence.** Normal dr. bust. l. R. Plumes in angles die axis ↑↓
1707 ............................35  100  275  1708 .........................45  140  325

**3624 Sixpence.** Similar R. Roses and plumes in angles, die axis ↑↓ 1710 ....45  140  325

# COPPER

3625
1714 Farthing

**3625 Farthing.** Dr. bust l. R. Britannia 1714 pattern only, die axis ↑↓ .......250  425  800

## GEORGE I, 1714-27

George I was born on 28th May 1660 son of Ernest, Elector of Hanover and Sophia grandaughter of James I, and inherited the English Throne on a technicality, Parliament considered him a better alternative than James Edward Stuart – Anne's half-brother. He was however, thoroughly German, did not want to learn English and spent over half his reign in Germany. He brought two mistresses with him to England while his wife ironically languished in a German prison on a charge of adultery. His reign created a government that could run independently of the King. The office of Prime Minister was created in 1721. He also kept England out of war for his entire reign, and he died on 11 June 1727.

    The coins of the first of the Hanoverian kings have the arms of the Duchy of Brunswick and Luneberg on one of the four shields, the object in the centre of the shield being the Crown of Charlemagne. The King's German titles also appear, in abbreviated form, and name him 'Duke of Brunswick and Luneberg. Arch-treasurer of the Holy Roman Empire, and Elector', and on the Guinea of 1714, 'Prince Elector'. A Quarter-Guinea was struck for the first time in 1718, but it was of an inconvenient size, and the issue was discontinued. The elephant and castle provenance mark continues on some guineas and half-guineas, but today are rarely seen.

    Silver coined from bullion supplied to the mint by the South Sea Company in 1723 shows the Company's initials S.S.C.; similarly Welsh Copper Company bullion has the letters W.C.C. below the King's bust; and plumes and an interlinked CC in the reverse angles. Roses and plumes together on the reverse indicate silver supplied by the Company for Smelting Pit Coale and Sea Coale.

    **Engravers and Designers:** Samuel Bull (d.c.1720), John Croker (1670-1741), John Rudulf Ochs Snr, (1673-c.1748), Norbert Roettier (b.1665)

    **Prime Minister:** Sir Robert Walpole (1676 – 1745) –Whig, 1721-42

## GOLD

3626
1717 Five Guineas

| | F | VF | EF | | F | VF | EF |
|---|---|---|---|---|---|---|---|
| | £ | £ | £ | | £ | £ | £ |

**3626 Five Guineas.** Laur. head r. regnal year on edge in words (e.g. 1717 = TERTIO) die axis↑↓

| | F | VF | EF | | F | VF | EF |
|---|---|---|---|---|---|---|---|
| 1716 SECVNDO | 1600 | 4000 | 9500 | 1720 SEXTO | 1750 | 5500 | 13000 |
| 1717 TERTIO | 1750 | 4750 | 11000 | 1726 D. TERTIO | 1600 | 4250 | 10000 |
| 1717 Ɑ edge error | 2250 | 5250 | 12500 | | | | |

3627
1717 Two Guineas

|  | F £ | VF £ | EF £ |  |  | F £ | VF £ | EF £ |
|---|---|---|---|---|---|---|---|---|

**3627 Two Guineas.** Laur. head r. R. Crowned cruciform shields, sceptres in angles, edge milled, die axis ↑↓

| 1717 | 650 | 1850 | 4250 | 1720/17 | 750 | 1950 | 4500 |
| 1720 | 600 | 1800 | 4250 | 1726 | 550 | 1600 | 3750 |

3628
1714 'Prince Elector' Guinea

3630
Third bust

3631
Fourth bust

**3628 Guinea.** First laur. head r. R. Legend ends ET PR . EL (Prince Elector), die axis ↑↓

| 1714 | | | | 1000 | 2750 | 5000 |

**3629 Guinea.** Second laur. head, r. tie with two ends, R. Crowned cruciform shields, sceptres in angles normal legend ↑↓ 1715 ............................................ 350 1500 3500

**3630 Guinea.** Third laur. head, r. no hair below truncation R. Similar die axis ↑↓

| 1715 | 325 | 1300 | 3250 | 1716 | 350 | 1450 | 3500 |

**3631 Guinea.** Fourth laur. head, r. tie with loop at one end R. Similar die axis ↑↓

| 1716 | 325 | 1350 | 3250 | 1720 | 375 | 1600 | 3750 |
| 1717 | 375 | 1600 | 3750 | 1721 | 325 | 1350 | 3250 |
| 1718 | | *Extremely rare* | | 1722 | 300 | 1250 | 3000 |
| 1718/7 | | *Extremely rare* | | 1722/0 | 400 | 1650 | 4000 |
| 1719 | 325 | 1350 | 3250 | 1723 | 325 | 1350 | 3250 |
| 1719/6 | | *Extremely rare* | | | | | |

**3632 Guinea.** Fourth Laur. head, elephant and castle below R. Similar die axis ↑↓

| 1721 | | *Extremely rare* | | 1722 | | *Extremely rare* | |

3633
1724 Guinea, fifth bust

3635
1724 Half Guinea, first bust

**3633 Guinea.** Fifth (older) laur. head, r. tie with two ends R. Similar die axis ↑↓

| 1723 | 300 | 1250 | 3000 | 1726 | 250 | 1100 | 2650 |
| 1724 | 400 | 1750 | 4000 | 1727 | 375 | 1600 | 3750 |
| 1725 | 375 | 1600 | 3750 | | | | |

**3634 Guinea.** Fifth laur. head, elephant and castle below, die axis ↑↓ 1726 ...... 1250 3750 8750

| | F | VF | EF | | F | VF | EF |
|---|---|---|---|---|---|---|---|
| | £ | £ | £ | | £ | £ | £ |

**3635 Half-Guinea.** First laur. head r. R. Crowned cruciform shields, sceptres in angles die axis ↑↓

| | | | | | | | |
|---|---|---|---|---|---|---|---|
| 1715 | 350 | 800 | 2000 | 1721 | | *Extremely rare* | |
| 1717 | 275 | 650 | 1500 | 1722 | 250 | 600 | 1400 |
| 1718 | 200 | 525 | 1200 | 1722/0 | 300 | 850 | 1600 |
| 1718/7 | 250 | 600 | 1400 | 1723 | 750 | — | — |
| 1719 | 275 | 650 | 1500 | 1724 | 325 | 700 | 1750 |
| 1720 | 275 | 650 | 1500 | | | | |

**3636 Half-Guinea.** First laur. head elephant and castle below, die axis ↑↓ 1721 *Extremely rare*

3637
Half-Guinea, second bust

3638
1718 Quarter Guinea

**3637 Half-Guinea.** Second (older) laur. head r. R. Crowned cruciform shields, sceptres in angles die axis ↑↓

| | | | | | | | |
|---|---|---|---|---|---|---|---|
| 1725 | 200 | 400 | 925 | 1727 | 250 | 600 | 1400 |
| 1726 | 250 | 500 | 1250 | | | | |

**3638 Quarter-Guinea.** Laur. head R. Similar die axis ↑↓ 1718 ... 120 | 225 | 400

# SILVER

3639A
1726 Crown - small roses and plumes

**3639 Crown.** Laur and dr. bust r. R. Roses and plumes in angles, regnal year on edge in words (e.g. 1716 = SECVNDO) die axis ↑↓

| | | | | | | | |
|---|---|---|---|---|---|---|---|
| 1716 SECVNDO | 225 | 750 | 2850 | 1720/18 SEXTO | 250 | 850 | 3150 |
| 1718/6 QUINTO | 250 | 800 | 3150 | | | | |

**3639A Crown.** Similar R. small roses and plumes in angles

| | | | | | | | |
|---|---|---|---|---|---|---|---|
| 1720 SEXTO | 300 | 1000 | 4250 | 1726 D. TERTIO | 300 | 900 | 3950 |

**3640 Crown.** Similar R. SSC (South Sea Company) in angles, die axis ↑↓

1723 DECIMO ... 250 | 800 | 2750

3641
1715 Pattern Halfcrown

**3641 Halfcrown.** Laur and dr. bust r. R. Angles plain (pattern only), die axis ↑↓ 1715 *FDC* £4250

3642
1720 Halfcrown, roses and plumes

3643
1723 SSC Halfcrown

|  | F £ | VF £ | EF £ |  | F £ | VF £ | EF £ |
|---|---|---|---|---|---|---|---|

**3642 Halfcrown.** — R. Roses and plumes in angles, regnal year on edge in words (e.g. 1717 = TIRTIO)

| 1715 SECVNDO | 125 | 525 | 1650 | 1717 TIRTIO | 150 | 575 | 1750 |
|---|---|---|---|---|---|---|---|
| 1715 Edge wording out | | | | 1720/17 SEXTO | 125 | 525 | 1650 |
| of order | 250 | 700 | 1900 | 1720 SEXTO | 300 | 1050 | 2650 |
| 1715 Plain edge | *Extremely rare* | | | | | | |

**3643 Halfcrown.** Similar R. SSC in angles, die axis ↑↓ 1723 DECIMO ........120   575   1650

3644
1726 Halfcrown small roses and plumes

**3644 Halfcrown.** — R. Small roses and plumes, die axis ↑↓ 1726 D. TERTIO ..2250   5500   10000

3645
1716 Shilling, roses and plumes

3646
1721 Shilling, plain reverse

**3645 Shilling.** First laur. and dr. bust. r. R. Roses and plumes in angles, die axis ↑↓

| 1715 | 45 | 175 | 600 | 1721 | 50 | 250 | 700 |
|---|---|---|---|---|---|---|---|
| 1716 | 85 | 350 | 950 | 1721/0 | 45 | 175 | 600 |
| 1717 | 45 | 175 | 600 | 1721/19 | 45 | 225 | 700 |
| 1718 | 40 | 150 | 525 | 1721/18 plumes and roses error | *Extremely rare* | | |
| 1719 | 75 | 300 | 850 | 1722 | 45 | 175 | 600 |
| 1720 | 45 | 175 | 600 | 1723 | 45 | 175 | 600 |
| 1720/18 | 110 | 400 | 1150 | | | | |

**3646 Shilling.** First laur. and dr. bust r. R. angles plain (i.e. no marks either side) die axis ↑↓

| 1720 | 35 | 125 | 475 | 1721 | 100 | 375 | 1100 |
|---|---|---|---|---|---|---|---|
| 1720 large O | 40 | 150 | 525 | | | | |

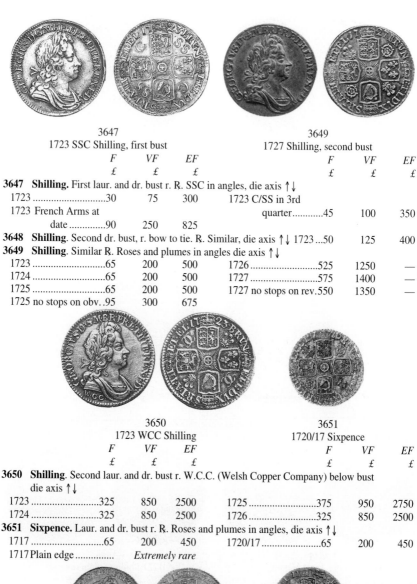

3647
1723 SSC Shilling, first bust

3649
1727 Shilling, second bust

| | F | VF | EF | | F | VF | EF |
|---|---|---|---|---|---|---|---|
| | £ | £ | £ | | £ | £ | £ |

**3647 Shilling.** First laur. and dr. bust r. ℞. SSC in angles, die axis ↑↓

| 1723 | 30 | 75 | 300 | 1723 C/SS in 3rd | | | |
|---|---|---|---|---|---|---|---|
| 1723 French Arms at | | | | quarter | 45 | 100 | 350 |
| date | 90 | 250 | 825 | | | | |

**3648 Shilling.** Second dr. bust, r. bow to tie. ℞. Similar, die axis ↑↓ 1723 ...50 | 125 | 400

**3649 Shilling.** Similar ℞. Roses and plumes in angles die axis ↑↓

| 1723 | 65 | 200 | 500 | 1726 | 525 | 1250 | — |
|---|---|---|---|---|---|---|---|
| 1724 | 65 | 200 | 500 | 1727 | 575 | 1400 | — |
| 1725 | 65 | 200 | 500 | 1727 no stops on rev. | 550 | 1350 | — |
| 1725 no stops on obv. | 95 | 300 | 675 | | | | |

3650
1723 WCC Shilling

3651
1720/17 Sixpence

| | F | VF | EF | | F | VF | EF |
|---|---|---|---|---|---|---|---|
| | £ | £ | £ | | £ | £ | £ |

**3650 Shilling.** Second laur. and dr. bust r. W.C.C. (Welsh Copper Company) below bust die axis ↑↓

| 1723 | 325 | 850 | 2500 | 1725 | 375 | 950 | 2750 |
|---|---|---|---|---|---|---|---|
| 1724 | 325 | 850 | 2500 | 1726 | 325 | 850 | 2500 |

**3651 Sixpence.** Laur. and dr. bust r. ℞. Roses and plumes in angles, die axis ↑↓

| 1717 | 65 | 200 | 450 | 1720/17 | 65 | 200 | 450 |
|---|---|---|---|---|---|---|---|
| 1717 Plain edge | | *Extremely rare* | | | | | |

3652
1723 SSC Sixpence

3653
1726 Sixpence, small roses and plumes

**3652 Sixpence.** Laur. and dr. bust r. ℞. SSC in angles, die axis ↑↓

| 1723 | 25 | 85 | 200 | 1723 larger lettering | 30 | 95 | 225 |
|---|---|---|---|---|---|---|---|

**3653 Sixpence.** Similar ℞. Small roses and plumes, die axis ↑↓ 1726 | 45 | 165 | 450

|        | 3654 |      |      |                    | 3655 |      |      |
|--------|------|------|------|--------------------|------|------|------|
|        | F    | VF   | EF   |                    | F    | VF   | EF   |
|        | £    | £    | £    |                    | £    | £    | £    |

**3654 Fourpence.** Laur. and dr. bust r. R. Crowned 4, die axis ↑↓

| 1717 | 9 | 30 | 90 | 1723 | 9 | 30 | 90 |
| 1721 | 9 | 30 | 90 | 1727 | 12 | 35 | 100 |

**3655 Threepence.** Laur. and dr. bust r. R. Crowned 3, die axis ↑↓

| 1717 | 8 | 30 | 80 | 1723 | 9 | 30 | 90 |
| 1721 | 9 | 30 | 90 | 1727 small lettering | 9 | 30 | 90 |

**3656 Twopence.** Laur. and dr. bust r. R. Crowned 2, die axis ↑↓

| 1717 | 6 | 25 | 50 | 1726 | 5 | 20 | 45 |
| 1721 | 5 | 20 | 45 | 1727 small lettering | 8 | 25 | 55 |
| 1723 | 9 | 30 | 65 | | | | |

**3657 Penny.** Laur. and dr. bust r. R. Crowned 1, die axis ↑↓

| 1716 | 5 | 25 | 45 | 1723 | 6 | 25 | 50 |
| 1718 | 5 | 25 | 45 | 1725 | 5 | 22 | 45 |
| 1720 | 5 | 25 | 45 | 1726 | 8 | 30 | 55 |
| 1720 HIPEX error | 10 | 65 | 110 | 1727 BRI·FR | 10 | 45 | 75 |

3658

**3658 Maundy Set.** As last four. Uniform dates

| 1723 | 80 | 200 | 625 | 1727 | 75 | 175 | 550 |

# COPPER

3659

**3659 Halfpenny.** 'Dump' issue obv. legend continuous over bust, plain edge, die axis ↑↓

| 1717 | 25 | 150 | 450 | 1718 no stops on obv | 125 | 400 | — |
| 1717 no stops on obv | 95 | 400 | — | 1719 | 600 | — | — |
| 1718 | 25 | 150 | 450 | 1719 grained edge | 850 | — | — |
| 1718 R/B on rev | 50 | 175 | 700 | | | | |

3660A

| | F<br>£ | VF<br>£ | EF<br>£ | | F<br>£ | VF<br>£ | EF<br>£ |
|---|---|---|---|---|---|---|---|

**3660 Halfpenny.** Second issue, second obverse, plain left shoulder strap, less hair to the right of tie knot, R. Britannia plain edge, die axis ↑↓

| | | | | | | | |
|---|---|---|---|---|---|---|---|
| 1719 ..........................35 | 150 | 550 | | 1722..................................30 | 125 | 500 |
| 1719 grained edge ......850 | — | — | | 1722 Ɐ for V on obv. ....100 | 375 | — |
| 1720 ..........................25 | 120 | 475 | | 1723..................................25 | 120 | 475 |
| 1721 ..........................30 | 125 | 500 | | 1723 Thin Flan ................... *Extremely rare* | | |
| 1721 stop after date ......40 | 160 | 550 | | 1723 no stop on rev. ......100 | 400 | — |
| 1721/0 ..........................40 | 160 | 550 | | 1724..................................25 | 120 | 475 |

**3660A Halfpenny.** Second issue, second obverse, ornate shoulder straps, die axis ↑↓

| | | | |
|---|---|---|---|
| 1719 ............................40 | 150 | 600 |

3661                    3662

**3661 Farthing.** 'Dump' issue, Similar die axis ↑↓ 1717 ....................................175    500    850

**3662 Farthing.** Second issue laur. and cuir. bust r. R. Britannia, date in ex. die axis ↑↓

| | | | | | | | |
|---|---|---|---|---|---|---|---|
| 1719 ..........................25 | 125 | 400 | | 1721..................................25 | 100 | 400 |
| 1719 no stop on rev. ....60 | 300 | — | | 1721/0 ..........................35 | 140 | 450 |
| 1719 large lettering | | | | 1721 stop after date ..........35 | 125 | 425 |
|   on obv. ..............85 | 350 | — | | 1722..................................30 | 120 | 425 |
| 1719— no stops on | | | | 1722 obv. large letters ......40 | 175 | 500 |
|   obv. ......................70 | 325 | — | | 1723 R/⋈ in REX ..........200 | — | — |
| 1719— no stops on rev..85 | 350 | — | | 1723..................................30 | 120 | 425 |
| 1720 ..........................25 | 125 | 400 | | 1724..................................30 | 120 | 425 |
| 1720 obv. large letters ..85 | 325 | — | | | | |
| 1719 last A/I on rev. ....85 | 325 | — | | | | |

George II was born on 30 October 1683 and was raised in Hanover, but upon his succession to the throne as George I's only child, he adapted himself to English society. His passions were the military, music and his wife – Caroline of Anspach, though he despised his eldest son Frederick as his own father despised him. George declared war on Spain in 1739 and he was the last King to have personally led his troops at the battle of Dettingen on 17 June 1743. Upon his death on 25 October 1760 the throne passed to his grandson George as Frederick had already died.

Silver was coined only spasmodically by the Mint during this reign; and no copper was struck after 1754. Gold coins made from bullion supplied by the East India Company bear the Company's E.I.C. initials. Some of the treasure seized by Admiral Anson during his circumnavigation of the globe, 1740-4, and by other privateers, was made into coin, which had the word LIMA below the king's bust to celebrate the expedition's successful harassment of the Spanish Colonies in the New World. Hammered gold was finally demonetized in 1733.

**Engravers and designers:** John Croker (1670-1741), John Rudolf Ochs Snr (1673-1748) and jnr (1704-88), Johann Sigismund Tanner (c.1706-75)

**Prime Ministers:** Sir Robert Walpole (1676-1745) Whig, 1721-43; Spencer Compton (1673-1743) Whig 1742-3; Henry Pelham (c.1695-1754) Whig 1743-54; William Cavendish (1720-1764) Whig 1756-7; Thomas Pelham-Holles (1693-1768) Whig 1754-6; 1757-62.

## GOLD

3663A
1741 Five Guineas - revised shield

|  | F | VF | EF |  | F | VF | EF |
|---|---|---|---|---|---|---|---|
|  | £ | £ | £ |  | £ | £ | £ |

**3663  Five Guineas.** Young laur. head l. R. Crowned shield of arms, die axis ↑↓ regnal year
on edge in words (e.g. 1729 = TERTIO)    1729 TERTIO..............1250    3750    9000
1729 Plain edge proof *FDC* £30000
**3663A Five Guineas.** Similar R. Revised shield garnish die axis ↑↓
1731 QVARTO.............200    5500   11500    1738 DVODECIMO.....1650    4750   10500
1731 QVARTO proof *FDC* £35000                1741/38 D. QVARTO....1500    4500   10000
1735 NONO................1850    5000   11000    1741 D. QVARTO.......1350    4000    9500
**3664  Five Guineas.** Young laur. head, E.I.C. (East India Company) below, die axis ↑↓
1729 TERTIO N's of ANNO inverted .........................................................1250    3750    9000

3665
1746 LIMA Five Guineas

| | F | VF | EF | | F | VF | EF |
|---|---|---|---|---|---|---|---|
| | £ | £ | £ | | £ | £ | £ |

**3665** **Five Guineas.** Old laur. head, l. LIMA below, ↑↓1746 D. NONO ..1350 4000 9500

**3666** **Five Guineas.** Old laur. head plain below, R. Crowned shield, edge inscribed die axis ↑↓
1748 V. SECVNDO 1350 4000 9500 1753 V. SEXTO .....1500 4500 10000

3667B
Repositioned legend

3667A
1735 Two Guineas - new reverse

**3667** **Two Guineas.** Young laur. head l. R Crowned shield with rounded arches, die axis ↑↓
1733 Proof *FDC* £20,000 1734/3 ....................1650 3500 —

**3667A\*** **Two Guineas.** – R. Crown with pointed arches, new type of shield garnishing die axis ↑↓
1735 ..........................................................................................550 1500 3250

**3667B\*** **Two Guineas.** Repositioned legend on obverse R. Similar
1738 ..........................425 800 1850 1739 ..........................400 750 1750

*\* Beware recent forgeries*

3668
1740 Two Guineas - Intermediate head

**3668\*** **Two Guineas.** Intermediate laur. head l. R. Crowned shield of arms die axis ↑↓
1739 ..........................450 850 2000 1740 ..........................425 800 2000
1740/39 ....................550 1100 2250

**3669\*** **Two Guineas.** Old laur. head l. R. Crowned shield of arms die axis ↑↓ ..
1748 ..........................425 1000 3000 1753 ..........................575 1400 3750

*\*Beware recent forgeries.*
*Overstruck dates are listed only if commoner than normal date or if no normal date is known.*

|   | F £ | VF £ | EF £ |   | F £ | VF £ | EF £ |
|---|---|---|---|---|---|---|---|

**3670  Guinea.** First young laur. head, l. small lettering, die axis ↑↓ 1727 ...825    2250    4750

|   |   |
|---|---|
| 3671 | 3674 |
| 1727 Guinea - small reverse shield | 1738 Guinea - second young head |

|   | F £ | VF £ | EF £ |   | F £ | VF £ | EF £ |
|---|---|---|---|---|---|---|---|

**3671  Guinea.** Similar larger lettering, smaller shield, die axis ↑↓

| 1727 | 400 | 1500 | 3500 | 1728 | 550 | 2000 | 4250 |

**3672  Guinea.** Second (narrower) young laur. head l. die axis ↑↓

| 1729 Proof *FDC* £7500 | | | | 1731 | 425 | 1650 | 3750 |
| 1730 | 450 | 1750 | 4000 | 1732 | 375 | 1400 | 3000 |

**3673  Guinea.** Second young laur. head, E.I.C. below R. Crowned shield of arms die axis ↑↓

| 1729 | 550 | 2000 | 4250 | 1732 | 425 | 1650 | 3750 |
| 1731 | 475 | 1750 | 4000 | | | | |

**3674  Guinea.** Second young laur. head l. larger lettering R. Crowned shield of arms die axis ↑↓

| 1732 | 375 | 1350 | 2750 | 1736 | 375 | 1400 | 3000 |
| 1733 | 350 | 1000 | 2500 | 1737 | 450 | 1750 | 4000 |
| 1734 | 375 | 1400 | 3000 | 1738 | 425 | 1650 | 3750 |
| 1735 | 395 | 1400 | 3000 | | | | |

**3675  Guinea.** — — E.I.C. below, die axis ↑↓ 1732 ...425    1650    3750

**3676  Guinea.** Intermediate laur. head l. r. Crowned shield of arms die axis ↑↓

| 1739 | 350 | 1000 | 2500 | 1741/39 | | *Extremely rare* | |
| 1740 | 400 | 1500 | 3250 | 1743 | | *Extremely rare* | |

**3677  Guinea.** Similar E.I.C. below, R. Similar die axis ↑↓ 1739 ...425    1650    3750

**3678  Guinea.** Similar larger lettering on *obv.,* GEORGIUS die axis ↑↓

| 1745 | | | | | 400 | 1250 | 3250 |

|   |   |   |
|---|---|---|
| 3678A | 3679 | 3680 |
| 1746 Guinea - GEORGIVS legend | LIMA Guinea | Old head Guinea |

**3678A Guinea.** Similar as last but reads GEORGIVS die axis ↑↓

| 1746 | | | | | 375 | 1350 | 2750 |

**3679  Guinea.** Intermediate laur. head LIMA below, die axis ↑↓ 1745 ...900    2250    4750

**3680  Guinea.** Old laur. head l. R. Crowned shield of arms die axis ↑↓

| 1747 | 300 | 750 | 1750 | 1753 | 325 | 775 | 1950 |
| 1748 | 250 | 575 | 1400 | 1755 | 325 | 750 | 1850 |
| 1749 | 325 | 775 | 1850 | 1756 | 325 | 750 | 1850 |
| 1750 | 300 | 750 | 1750 | 1758 | 275 | 650 | 1650 |
| 1751 | 375 | 800 | 2000 | 1759 | 275 | 600 | 1450 |
| 1752 | 275 | 600 | 1500 | 1760 | 275 | 600 | 1500 |

|  | F £ | VF £ | EF £ |  | F £ | VF £ | EF £ |
|---|---|---|---|---|---|---|---|

**3681  Half-Guinea**. Young laur. head. l. ℞ First shield of arms, die axis ↑↓

| 1728 | 275 | 750 | 2250 | 1729 | 350 | 950 | 3000 |

1728 Proof *FDC* £6000

3681A
1730 Half-Guinea - modified shield

**3681A  Half-Guinea**. Young laur. head l. ℞. Modified garnished shield die axis ↑↓

| 1730 | 600 | 1950 | — | 1735 | | | *?exists* |
| 1731 | 325 | 900 | 2750 | 1736 | 325 | 325 | 2850 |
| 1732 | 350 | 950 | 3000 | 1737 | | | *Extremely rare* |
| 1733 | | | *?exists* | 1738 | 300 | 775 | 2400 |
| 1734 | 325 | 900 | 2750 | 1739 | 350 | 950 | 3000 |

**3682  Half-Guinea**. Young laur. head l. E.I.C. below ℞. Similar die axis ↑↓

| 1729 | 375 | 1000 | 3250 | 1732 | | | *Extremely rare* |
| 1730 | 650 | 2000 | — | 1739 | | | *Extremely rare* |
| 1731 | | *Extremely rare* | | | | | |

3676                                        3683A
1740 Guinea - Intermediate head            1746 Half-guinea - GEORGIVS legend

**3683  Half-Guinea**. Intermediate laur. head l. ℞. Similar die axis ↑↓

| 1740 | 375 | 1000 | 3250 | 1745 | 325 | 925 | 2750 |
| 1743 | | *Extremely rare* | | | | | |

**3683A Half-Guinea**. Similar, but reads GEORGIVS, die axis ↑↓ 1746 ....300    800    2500

3684                                        3685
1745 LIMA Half-Guinea                      1760 Half-Guinea, old head

**3684  Half-Guinea**. Intermediate laur. head LIMA below, die axis ↑↓ 1745 ..800    2750    5000

**3685  Half-Guinea**. Old laur. head l. ℞. Similar die axis ↑↓

| 1747 | 225 | 625 | 1600 | 1753 | 200 | 600 | 1450 |
| 1748 | 225 | 625 | 1600 | 1755 | 200 | 575 | 1350 |
| 1749 | 225 | 625 | 1600 | 1756 | 175 | 550 | 1250 |
| 1750 | 200 | 600 | 1450 | 1758 | 250 | 650 | 1750 |
| 1751 | 225 | 625 | 1600 | 1759 | 150 | 500 | 1000 |
| 1751/0 | 350 | 1100 | 2250 | 1759/8 | 225 | 750 | 1750 |
| 1752 | 225 | 625 | 1600 | 1760 | 175 | 550 | 1250 |

# SILVER

3686
1735 Crown, young head

| | F | VF | EF | | F | VF | EF |
|---|---|---|---|---|---|---|---|
| | £ | £ | £ | | £ | £ | £ |

**3686** **Crown.** Young laur. and dr. bust. l. R. Crowned cruciform shields Roses and plumes
in angles, regnal year on edge in words (e.g. 1736 = NONO), die axis ↑↓

| | F | VF | EF | | F | VF | EF |
|---|---|---|---|---|---|---|---|
| 1732 SEXTO .............. | 150 | 675 | 1750 | 1734 No A in ANNO .... | 225 | 950 | 2250 |
| 1732 Proof, plain edge  *FDC* £4750 | | | | 1735 OCTAVO .............. | 150 | 675 | 1750 |
| 1734 SEPTIMO .......... | 175 | 725 | 2000 | 1735 E/B on edge .......... | 175 | 800 | 2000 |
| | | | | 1736 NONO .................. | 125 | 675 | 1750 |

**3687** **Crown.** Similar R. Roses in angles die axis ↑↓

| | F | VF | EF | | F | VF | EF |
|---|---|---|---|---|---|---|---|
| 1739 DVODECIMO .. | 150 | 625 | 1750 | 1741 D. QVARTO ........ | 125 | 625 | 1500 |

3688
1743 Crown, old head

**3688** **Crown.** Old laur. and dr. bust l. R. Crowned cruciform shields Roses in angles, die axis ↑↓
1743 D. SEPTIMO ................................................................. 125   625   1500

**3689** **Crown.** — LIMA below, die axis ↑↓ 1746 D. NONO ............................ 125   625   1500

3690
Plain reverse

3691
1731 Pattern Halfcrown

**3690** **Crown.** Old laur. and dr. bust l. R. angles Plain (i.e. no marks either side) die axis ↑↓
1746 Proof only, VICESIMO  *FDC* £3750

| 1750 V. QVARTO...... | 175 | 675 | 1750 | 1751 V. QVARTO ........ | 200 | 725 | 2000 |
|---|---|---|---|---|---|---|---|

**3691** **Halfcrown.** Young dr. bust l. R. angles plain (pattern only), 1731 *FDC* £4250

3692
1736 Halfcrown, roses and plumes

3693
1741 Halfcrown, roses on reverse

| | F | VF | EF | | | F | VF | EF |
|---|---|---|---|---|---|---|---|---|
| | £ | £ | £ | | | £ | £ | £ |

**3692 Halfcrown.** Young laur. and dr. bust l. R. Roses and plumes, regnal year on edge in words (e.g. 1732 = SEXTO), die axis ↑↓

| | | | | | | | | |
|---|---|---|---|---|---|---|---|---|
| 1731 QVINTO | ..............75 | 375 | 1100 | | 1735 OCTAVO | ............85 | 425 | 1200 |
| 1732 SEXTO | ..................75 | 375 | 1100 | | 1736 NONO | ................120 | 475 | 1250 |
| 1734 SEPTIMO | ............85 | 425 | 1200 | | | | | |

**3693 Halfcrown.** Young laur. and dr. bust l. R. Roses in angles die axis ↑↓

| | | | | | | | | |
|---|---|---|---|---|---|---|---|---|
| 1739 DVODECIMO | ......60 | 200 | 900 | | 1741 D. QVARTO | ........70 | 325 | 950 |
| 1741 Large *obv.* letters | ..85 | 275 | 1000 | | 1741/39 D. QVARTO | ..150 | 475 | 1200 |

**3694 Halfcrown.** Old dr. bust. l. GEORGIUS R. Roses in angles die axis ↑↓

| | | | | | | | | |
|---|---|---|---|---|---|---|---|---|
| 1743 D. SEPTIMO | ........55 | 225 | 850 | | 1745/3 D. NONO | ..........75 | 275 | 900 |
| 1745 D. NONO | ..............55 | 225 | 850 | | | | | |

**3695 Halfcrown.** Old laur. and dr. bust LIMA below die axis ↑↓

| | | | | | | | | |
|---|---|---|---|---|---|---|---|---|
| 1745 D. NONO | ...................45 | 175 | 575 | | 1745/3 | .........................75 | 275 | 850 |

**3695A Halfcrown.** Old laur. and dr. bust as last but reads GEORGIVS die axis ↑↓

| | | | | | | | | |
|---|---|---|---|---|---|---|---|---|
| 1746 D. NONO | .............45 | 175 | 575 | | 1746/5 D. NONO | ..........60 | 225 | 850 |

3696
1746 Proof Halfcrown

**3696 Halfcrown.** Old laur. and dr. bust l. R. Plain angles die axis ↑↓
1746 proof only VICESIMO *FDC* £1650

| | | | | | | | | |
|---|---|---|---|---|---|---|---|---|
| 1750 V. QVARTO | ........85 | 400 | 1100 | | 1751 V. QVARTO | ......100 | 450 | 1400 |

3697
1731 Plumes Shilling

**3697 Shilling.** Young laur. dr. bust. l. R. Plumes in angles, die axis ↑↓

| | | | | | | | | |
|---|---|---|---|---|---|---|---|---|
| 1727 | ..............................60 | 375 | 950 | | 1731 | ..............................75 | 425 | 1200 |

3698        3699
1727 Shilling, young bust, small letters    Young bust Shilling, large letters

| | F | VF | EF | | F | VF | EF |
|---|---|---|---|---|---|---|---|
| | £ | £ | £ | | £ | £ | £ |

**3698 Shilling.** Young laur. and dr. bust l. R. Roses and plumes in angles, die axis ↑↓

| | F | VF | EF | | F | VF | EF |
|---|---|---|---|---|---|---|---|
| 1727 | 40 | 175 | 600 | 1731 | 40 | 175 | 600 |
| 1728 | 50 | 200 | 700 | 1732 | 50 | 200 | 700 |
| 1729 | 50 | 200 | 700 | | | | |

**3699 Shilling.** Similar larger lettering. R. Roses and plumes in angles die axis ↑↓

| | F | VF | EF | | F | VF | EF |
|---|---|---|---|---|---|---|---|
| 1734 | 35 | 150 | 550 | 1736/5 | 55 | 225 | 750 |
| 1735 | 35 | 150 | 550 | 1737 | 35 | 150 | 550 |
| 1736 | 35 | 150 | 550 | | | | |

3700        3701
1728 Shilling, plain reverse    1739 Shilling, roses reverse

**3700 Shilling.** Young laur. and dr. bust l. R. Plain, die axis ↑↓ 1728..........175    450    1000

**3701 Shilling.** Young laur. and dr. bust l. R. Roses in angles die axis ↑↓

| | F | VF | EF | | F | VF | EF |
|---|---|---|---|---|---|---|---|
| 1739 | 30 | 120 | 500 | 1741 | 30 | 120 | 500 |
| 1739/7 | | *Extremely rare* | | 1741/39 | 350 | 850 | — |
| 1739 smaller garter star | 100 | 350 | 950 | | | | |

3702        3703A
1747 Shilling, old bust, roses    LIMA Shilling, GEORGIVS legend

**3702 Shilling.** Old laur. and dr. bust, l. GEORGIUS R. Roses in angles die axis ↑↓

| | F | VF | EF | | F | VF | EF |
|---|---|---|---|---|---|---|---|
| 1743 | 25 | 85 | 425 | 1745/3 | 60 | 225 | 575 |
| 1743/1 | 55 | 175 | 625 | 1747 | 30 | 95 | 425 |
| 1745 | 35 | 120 | 475 | | | | |

**3703 Shilling.** Old laur. and dr. bust LIMA below die axis ↑↓ 1745............20    85    375

**3703A Shilling.** Similar as last but reads GEORGIVS die axis ↑↓

| | F | VF | EF | | F | VF | EF |
|---|---|---|---|---|---|---|---|
| 1746 | 95 | 275 | 775 | 1746/5 | 125 | 325 | 825 |

3704
1746 Proof shilling

|  | F<br>£ | VF<br>£ | EF<br>£ |  | F<br>£ | VF<br>£ | EF<br>£ |
|---|---|---|---|---|---|---|---|

**3704  Shilling.** Old laur. and dr. bust R. plain angles die axis ↑↓

| 1746 Proof only *FDC* £1150 |  |  |  | 1750 Wide O..............60 | 175 | 600 |
| 1750 ..........................40 | 150 | 550 | 1751 ......................100 | 275 | 750 |
| 1750/6 ......................60 | 175 | 600 | 1758 ........................20 | 50 | 110 |

3705                              3706                              3707
1728 Sixpence, young bust    1728 Sixpence, plumes on reverse  1728 Sixpence, roses and plumes

**3705  Sixpence.** Young laur. and dr. bust. l. R. Angles plain, die axis ↑↓  1728 ..75   275   575
1728 Proof *FDC* £2750

**3706  Sixpence.** Similar R. Plumes in angles  die axis ↑↓ 1728 ....................50   175   425

**3707  Sixpence.** Young laur. and dr. bust l. R. Roses and plumes in angles die axis ↑↓

| 1728 ..........................25 | 120 | 300 | 1735 ..........................35 | 175 | 425 |
| 1731 ..........................25 | 120 | 300 | 1735/4 ........................40 | 200 | 475 |
| 1732 ..........................25 | 120 | 300 | 1736 ..........................30 | 150 | 375 |
| 1734 ..........................35 | 175 | 425 |  |  |  |

3708                                            3711
1739 Sixpence, roses                       1746 Proof Sixpence

**3708  Sixpence.** Young laur. and dr. bust l., R. Roses in angles, die axis ↑↓

| 1739 ..........................25 | 120 | 300 | 1741 ..........................25 | 120 | 300 |
| 1739 O/R in legend .....65 | 200 | 475 |  |  |  |

3709
1743 Sixpence, old bust, roses

**3709  Sixpence.** Old laur. and dr. bust. l. R. Roses in angles die axis ↑↓

| 1743 ..........................20 | 85 | 250 | 1745/3 ........................35 | 150 | 375 |
| 1745 ..........................20 | 85 | 250 |  |  |  |

|  | F | VF | EF |  | F | VF | EF |
|---|---|---|---|---|---|---|---|
|  | £ | £ | £ |  | £ | £ | £ |

**3710 Sixpence.** Old laur. and dr. bust LIMA below bust R. angle plain die axis ↑↓

| 1745 | 20 | 85 | 185 |

**3710A Sixpence.** Similar as last but reads GEORGIVS die axis ↑↓

| 1746 | 15 | 75 | 150 | 1746/5 | 25 | 120 | 300 |

**3711 Sixpence.** Old laur. and dr. bust l. R. angles plain die axis ↑↓

1746 *proof only FDC* £800

| 1750 | 35 | 150 | 350 | 1758 | 10 | 30 | 60 |
| 1751 | 40 | 200 | 475 | 1758 ĐEI error | 35 | 90 | 175 |
| 1757 | 10 | 30 | 60 | 1758/7 | 20 | 50 | 95 |

**3712 Fourpence.** Young laur. and dr. bust l. R. Small dome-shaped crown without pearls on arch, figure 4

| 1729 | 8 | 25 | 60 | 1731 | 8 | 25 | 60 |

**3712A Fourpence.** Similar R. Double arched crown with pearls, large figure 4, die axis ↑↓

| 1732 | 8 | 25 | 60 | 1740 | 8 | 25 | 60 |
| 1735 | 8 | 25 | 60 | 1743 | 8 | 25 | 60 |
| 1737 | 8 | 25 | 60 | 1743/0 | 15 | 65 | 130 |
| 1739 | 8 | 25 | 60 | 1746 | 6 | 20 | 50 |
|  |  |  |  | 1760 | 8 | 25 | 55 |

**3713 Threepence.** Young laur. and dr. bust l. R. Crowned 3, pearls on arch, die axis ↑↓

| 1729 | | | | | 8 | 25 | 55 |

**3713A Threepence.** Similar R. Ornate arch die axis ↑↓

| 1731 Smaller lettering | 8 | 25 | 55 | 1731 | 8 | 25 | 55 |

**3713B Threepence.** Similar R. Double arched crown with pearls, die axis ↑↓

| 1732 | 8 | 25 | 55 | 1743 Large lettering | 6 | 20 | 50 |
| 1732 with stop over head | 10 | 30 | 65 | 1743 Small lettering | 6 | 20 | 50 |
| 1735 | 8 | 25 | 55 | 1743 — stop over head | 7 | 25 | 55 |
| 1737 | 6 | 20 | 50 | 1746 | 6 | 20 | 50 |
| 1739 | 6 | 20 | 50 | 1746/3 | 7 | 25 | 55 |
| 1740 | 6 | 20 | 50 | 1760 | 6 | 20 | 50 |

**3714 Twopence.** Young laur. and dr. bust l. R. Small crown and figure 2, die axis ↑↓

| 1729 | 4 | 20 | 40 | 1731 | 4 | 20 | 40 |

**3714A Twopence.** Young laur. and dr. bust l. R. Large crown and figure 2 die axis ↑↓

| 1732 | 4 | 20 | 40 | 1743/0 | 5 | 20 | 45 |
| 1735 | 4 | 20 | 40 | 1746 | 4 | 20 | 40 |
| 1737 | 4 | 20 | 40 | 1756 | 4 | 20 | 40 |
| 1739 | 5 | 20 | 45 | 1759 | 4 | 20 | 40 |
| 1740 | 8 | 25 | 55 | 1760 | 4 | 20 | 40 |
| 1743 | 4 | 20 | 40 |  |  |  |  |

**3715 Penny.** Young laur. and dr. bust l. head. R. Date over small crown and figure 1, die axis ↑↓

| 1729 | 6 | 25 | 45 | 1731 | 5 | 20 | 40 |

**3715A Penny.** Young laur. and dr. bust l. R. Large crown dividing date die axis ↑↓

| 1732 | 5 | 20 | 40 | 1753/2 | 6 | 25 | 50 |
| 1735 | 6 | 25 | 50 | 1753 | 4 | 20 | 40 |
| 1737 | 6 | 25 | 45 | 1754 | 4 | 20 | 40 |
| 1739 | 5 | 20 | 40 | 1755 | 4 | 20 | 40 |
| 1740 | 5 | 20 | 40 | 1756 | 4 | 20 | 40 |
| 1743 | 5 | 20 | 40 | 1757 | 4 | 20 | 40 |
| 1746 | 5 | 20 | 40 | 1757 GRATIA: | 6 | 30 | 60 |
| 1746/3 | 6 | 25 | 50 | 1758 | 4 | 20 | 40 |
| 1750 | 4 | 20 | 40 | 1759 | 4 | 20 | 40 |
| 1752 | 4 | 20 | 40 | 1760 | 6 | 25 | 50 |
| 1752/0 | 6 | 25 | 50 |  |  |  |  |

3716

|  | F | VF | EF |  | F | VF | EF |
|---|---|---|---|---|---|---|---|
|  | £ | £ | £ |  | £ | £ | £ |

**3716 Maundy Set.** The four denominations. Uniform dates

| 1729 | 60 | 175 | 400 | 1739 | 50 | 150 | 350 |
| 1731 | 60 | 175 | 400 | 1740 | 50 | 150 | 350 |
| 1732 | 50 | 150 | 350 | 1743 | 60 | 175 | 400 |
| 1735 | 50 | 150 | 350 | 1746 | 45 | 150 | 350 |
| 1737 | 50 | 150 | 350 | 1760 | 75 | 225 | 400 |

## COPPER

3717

**3717 Halfpenny.** Young laur. and cuir. bust l. R. Britannia, date in ex. die axis ↑↓

| 1729 | 15 | 85 | 300 | 1733 | 12 | 75 | 275 |
| 1729 rev. no stop | 20 | 95 | 325 | 1734 | 12 | 75 | 275 |
| 1730 | 12 | 85 | 275 | 1734 R/O on obv | 20 | 120 | 350 |
| 1730 GEOGIVS error | 20 | 125 | 350 | 1734/3 | 30 | 175 | — |
| 1730 stop after date | 20 | 95 | 325 | 1734 no stops on obv | 30 | 175 | — |
| 1730 no stop after |  |  |  | 1735 | 12 | 75 | 275 |
| REX on rev | 25 | 140 | 400 | 1736 | 15 | 95 | 300 |
| 1731 | 12 | 75 | 275 | 1736/0 | 20 | 120 | 350 |
| 1731 rev. no stop | 20 | 120 | 350 | 1737 | 15 | 95 | 300 |
| 1732 | 12 | 85 | 275 | 1738 | 10 | 70 | 275 |
| 1732 rev. no stop | 20 | 120 | 350 | 1738 V/S on obv | 20 | 120 | 350 |
|  |  |  |  | 1739 | 12 | 75 | 275 |

**3718 Halfpenny.** Old laur. and cuir. bust l., GEORGIUS R. Britannia, date in ex. die axis ↑↓

| 1740 | 10 | 70 | 250 | 1743 | 10 | 70 | 250 |
| 1742 | 10 | 70 | 250 | 1744 | 10 | 70 | 250 |
| 1742/0 | 20 | 110 | 350 | 1745 | 10 | 70 | 250 |

3719

|  | F<br>£ | VF<br>£ | EF<br>£ |  | F<br>£ | VF<br>£ | EF<br>£ |
|---|---|---|---|---|---|---|---|

**3719 Halfpenny.** Old laur. and cuir. bust l. GEORGIVS, R. Britannia, date in ex. die axis ↑↓

| 1746 | 10 | 60 | 250 | 1751 | 10 | 60 | 250 |
| 1747 | 10 | 65 | 275 | 1752 | 10 | 60 | 250 |
| 1748 | 10 | 65 | 275 | 1753 | 10 | 60 | 250 |
| 1749 | 10 | 60 | 250 | 1754 | 10 | 65 | 275 |
| 1750 | 10 | 65 | 275 |  |  |  |  |

3720        3722

**3720 Farthing.** Young laur. and cuir. bust l. R. Britannia, date in ex. die axis ↑↓

| 1730 | 12 | 65 | 225 | 1735 3 over 5 | 20 | 110 | 300 |
| 1731 | 12 | 65 | 225 | 1736 | 12 | 65 | 225 |
| 1732 | 15 | 70 | 250 | 1736 triple tie ribands | 30 | 110 | 300 |
| 1732/1 | 20 | 95 | 275 | 1737 small date | 10 | 60 | 200 |
| 1733 | 12 | 65 | 225 | 1737 large date | 10 | 60 | 200 |
| 1734 | 15 | 70 | 250 | 1739 | 10 | 60 | 200 |
| 1734 no stop on obv. | 30 | 110 | 300 | 1739/5 | | *Extremely rare* | |
| 1735 | 10 | 60 | 200 |  |  |  |  |

**3721 Farthing.** Old laur. and cuir. bust. GEORGIUS R. Britannia, date in ex. die axis ↑↓

| 1741 | 15 | 70 | 225 | 1744 | 10 | 55 | 200 |

**3722 Farthing.** Similar 55 R. Britannia, date in ex. die axis ↑↓

| 1746 | 8 | 55 | 175 | 1750 | 15 | 70 | 225 |
| 1746 V over U | | *Extremely rare* | | 1754 | 5 | 35 | 95 |
| 1749 | 15 | 70 | 225 | 1754/0 | 25 | 110 | 275 |

George III, grandson of George II was born on 4 June 1738. He married Charlotte of Mecklenburg and they had nine sons and six daughters. The French Revolution and the American War of Independence both happened in his long reign, the longest yet of any King. The naval battle of Trafalgar and the Battle of Waterloo also took place during his reign. Later in his reign, he was affected by what seems to be the mental disease porphyria, and the future George IV was appointed as regent. George III died at Windsor Castle on 29 January 1820.

During the second half of the 18th century very little silver or copper was minted. In 1797 Matthew Boulton's 'cartwheels', the first copper Pennies and Twopences, demonstrated the improvement gleaned from the application of steam power to the coining press.

During the Napoleonic Wars bank notes came into general use when the issue of Guineas was stopped between 1799 and 1813, but gold 7s. pieces, Third-Guineas; were minted to relieve the shortage of smaller money. As an emergency measure Spanish 'Dollars' were put into circulation for a short period after being countermarked, and in 1804 Spanish Eight Reales were overstruck and issued as Bank of England Dollars.

The transition to a 'token' silver coinage began in 1811 when the Bank of England had 3s and 1s. 6d. tokens made for general circulation. Private issues of token money in the years 1788-95 and 1811-15 helped to alleviate the shortage of regal coinage. A change over to a gold standard and a regular 'token' silver coinage came in 1816 when the Mint, which was moved from its old quarters in the Tower of London to a new site on Tower Hill, began a complete re-coinage. The Guinea was replaced by a 20s. Sovereign, and silver coins were made which had an intrinsic value lower than their face value. The St. George design used on the Sovereign and Crown was the work of Benedetto Pistrucci.

**Engravers and Designers:**– Conrad Heinrich Kuchler (c.1740-1810), Nathaniel Marchant (1739-1816), John Rudulf Ochs Jnr. (1704-88), Lewis Pingo (1743-1830), Thomas Pingo (d.1776) Benedetto Pistrucci (1784-1855), Johann Sigismond Tanner (c.1706-75), Thomas Wyon (1792-1817), William Wyon (1795-1851), Richard Yeo (d.1779).

**Prime Ministers:**– Duke of Newcastle, (1693-1768) Whig, 1757-62; Earl of Bute, (1713-1792) Tory 1762-3; George Grenville, (1712-1770), Whig 1763-5; William Pitt 'The Elder', Earl of Chatham (1708-1778), Whig 1766-8; Duke of Gratton, (1735-1811), Whig 1767-70; Lord North, (1732-1790), Tory 1770-82; Marquis of Rockingham, (1730-1782), Whig 1765-6, 1782; Earl of Shelbourne, (1737-1805), Whig 1782-3; Henry Addington, (1757-1844) Tory, 1801-4; William Pitt 'The Younger' (1759-1806), Tory 1783-1801, 1804-6; Lord Grenville, (1759-1854), Whig, 1806-7; Duke of Portland, (1738-1809) Tory 1783, 1807-9; Spencer Perceval, (1762-1812) Tory 1809-12; Earl of Liverpool, (1770-1828) Tory 1812-27 .

# GOLD

**Early Coinages**

3723
1770 Pattern Five Guineas

**3723A Five Guineas.** Pattern only, young long haired bust r. R. crowned shield of
arms, die axis ↑↑ (en medaille)
1770 *FDC* £45,000                      1773 *FDC* £45,000
**3723B Five Guineas.** Pattern only, young bust right, hair extends under bust similar
1777 *FDC* £40,000

3724
1768 Pattern Two Guineas

3724A
1777 Pattern Two Guineas

**3724A Two Guineas.** Pattern only, young long haired bust r. R. crowned shield of arms, die axis ↑↑
(en medaille)

1768 *FDC* £22,500                1773 *FDC* £20,000

**3724B Two Guineas.** Pattern only, young bust right, hair extends under bust similar

1777 *FDC* £16,500

*There are six different bust varieties for 3723 and 3724, for further details see select bibliography*

3725
1761 Guinea first head, two leaf wreath

|  | F | VF | EF |  | F | VF | EF |
|---|---|---|---|---|---|---|---|
|  | £ | £ | £ |  | £ | £ | £ |

**3725 Guinea.** First laur. head r., 1761 (varieties with two or three leaves at top
of wreath). R. Crowned shield of arms die axis ↑↓ ...........................950    2750    4750

3726
1763 Guinea second head

**3726 Guinea.** Second laur. head r. R. Crowned shield of arms die axis ↑↓

1763 ..........................900    2250    4750        1764 ..........................850    2000    4500

3727                          3728                          3729
Guinea, third head          Guinea, fourth head          1794 Guinea, fifth head, 'spade' type

| | F £ | VF £ | EF £ | | F £ | VF £ | EF £ |
|---|---|---|---|---|---|---|---|
| **3727 Guinea.** Third laur. head r. R. Crowned shield of arms die axis ↑↓ | | | | | | | |
| 1765 | 200 | 425 | 850 | 1770 | 300 | 525 | 1000 |
| 1766 | 200 | 400 | 825 | 1771 | 250 | 450 | 900 |
| 1767 | 350 | 600 | 1250 | 1772 | 225 | 425 | 875 |
| 1768 | 225 | 425 | 875 | 1773 | 175 | 375 | 800 |
| 1769 | 275 | 475 | 925 | 1773 7 over 1 | 300 | 750 | — |
| **3728 Guinea.** Fourth laur. head r. Crowned shield of arms die axis ↑↓ | | | | | | | |
| 1774 | 150 | 350 | 600 | 1781 | 185 | 425 | 750 |
| 1774 Proof *FDC* £3750 | | | | 1782 | 165 | 375 | 625 |
| 1775 | 125 | 325 | 575 | 1783 | 200 | 450 | 850 |
| 1776 | 150 | 350 | 600 | 1784 | 175 | 400 | 700 |
| 1777 | 175 | 400 | 700 | 1785 | 125 | 325 | 575 |
| 1778 | 200 | 450 | 850 | 1786 | 165 | 375 | 625 |
| 1779 | 175 | 400 | 700 | | | | |
| **3729 Guinea.** Fifth laur. head r. R. 'Spade'-shaped shield, die axis ↑↑ | | | | | | | |
| 1787 | 125 | 300 | 550 | 1794 | 140 | 325 | 575 |
| 1787 Proof *FDC* £2500 | | | | 1795 | 150 | 350 | 600 |
| 1788 | 140 | 325 | 575 | 1796 | 180 | 400 | 750 |
| 1789 | 150 | 350 | 600 | 1797 | 180 | 400 | 750 |
| 1790 | 150 | 350 | 600 | 1798* | 120 | 275 | 500 |
| 1791 | 125 | 300 | 550 | 1798/7 | 200 | 450 | 850 |
| 1792 | 150 | 350 | 600 | 1799 | 175 | 375 | 700 |
| 1793 | 140 | 325 | 575 | * *Beware counterfeits* | | | |

3730                                    3731
1813 Guinea "Military type"            1763 Half-Guinea, first head

**3730 Guinea.** Sixth laur. head. r. R. Shield in Garter, known as the Military guinea, die axis ↑↑
1813 ................................................................................................................425    1050    1950
**3731 Half-Guinea.** First laur. head r. R. Crowned shield of arms die axis ↑↓
1762 ..........................425    1150    2950    1763 ..........................550    1650    3750

3732
1764 Half-Guinea, second head

3733
1775 Half-Guinea, third head

| | F | VF | EF | | F | VF | EF |
|---|---|---|---|---|---|---|---|
| | £ | £ | £ | | £ | £ | £ |

**3732 Half-Guinea.** Second laur. head r. R. Crowned shield of arms die axis ↑↓

| | | | | | | | |
|---|---|---|---|---|---|---|---|
| 1764 | 140 | 375 | 800 | 1772 | | *Extremely rare* | |
| 1765 | 450 | 900 | — | 1773 | 225 | 575 | 1200 |
| 1766 | 150 | 425 | 950 | 1774 | 275 | 625 | 1500 |
| 1768 | 175 | 475 | 950 | 1775 | 325 | 750 | 1850 |
| 1769 | 175 | 475 | 1000 | | | | |

3734
1785 Half-Guinea, fourth head

3735
1787 Proof Half-Guinea, fifth head

**3733 Half-Guinea** Third laur. head (less fine style) r. R. Crowned shield of arms die axis ↑↓

| | | | | | | | |
|---|---|---|---|---|---|---|---|
| 1774 | | *Extremely rare* | | 1775 | 775 | 1850 | 3950 |

**3734 Half-Guinea** Fourth laur. head r. R. Crowned shield of arms die axis ↑↓

| | | | | | | | |
|---|---|---|---|---|---|---|---|
| 1775 | 110 | 275 | 500 | 1781 | 165 | 400 | 700 |
| 1775 Proof *FDC* £3750 | | | | 1783 | 425 | 1200 | — |
| 1776 | 140 | 325 | 575 | 1784 | 150 | 375 | 650 |
| 1777 | 125 | 300 | 550 | 1785 | 140 | 325 | 575 |
| 1778 | 150 | 375 | 650 | 1786 | 110 | 275 | 500 |
| 1779 | 150 | 375 | 650 | | | | |

**3735 Half-Guinea** Fifth laur. head. r. R. 'Spade' shaped shield, date below, die axis ↑↑

| | | | | | | | |
|---|---|---|---|---|---|---|---|
| 1787 | 95 | 200 | 400 | 1794 | 145 | 350 | 575 |
| 1787 Proof *FDC* £2000 | | | | 1795 | 150 | 375 | 650 |
| 1788 | 110 | 250 | 475 | 1796 | 120 | 275 | 500 |
| 1789 | 150 | 375 | 650 | 1797 | 110 | 250 | 475 |
| 1790 | 140 | 325 | 550 | 1798 | 125 | 300 | 525 |
| 1791 | 140 | 325 | 550 | 1798/7 | 200 | 350 | 650 |
| 1792 | 500 | 1500 | — | 1800 | 250 | 650 | — |
| 1793 | 110 | 250 | 475 | | | | |

3736
1801 Half-Guinea, sixth head

**3736 Half-Guinea** Sixth laur. head. r. R. Shield in Garter, date below die axis ↑↑

| | | | | | | | |
|---|---|---|---|---|---|---|---|
| 1801 | 70 | 140 | 300 | 1803 | 75 | 165 | 325 |
| 1802 | 75 | 165 | 325 | | | | |

3737
1813 Half-Guinea, seventh head

3738
1798 Third-Guinea, first type

3739
1803 Third-Guinea, second reverse

| | F | VF | EF | | F | VF | EF |
|---|---|---|---|---|---|---|---|
| | £ | £ | £ | | £ | £ | £ |

**3737 Half-Guinea** Seventh laur. head. r. with short hair. R. Shield in garter, date below die axis ↑↑

| 1804 | 70 | 140 | 300 | 1809 | 90 | 165 | 375 |
|---|---|---|---|---|---|---|---|
| 1805 | | *Extremely rare* | | 1810 | 90 | 165 | 375 |
| 1806 | 120 | 225 | 475 | 1811 | 150 | 350 | 700 |
| 1808 | 100 | 180 | 400 | 1813 | 100 | 250 | 500 |

**3738 Third-Guinea.** First laur. head r. R. Crown, date in legend, die axis ↑↑

| 1797 | 60 | 120 | 300 | 1799 | 65 | 150 | 325 |
|---|---|---|---|---|---|---|---|
| 1798 | 60 | 120 | 300 | 1800 | 60 | 120 | 300 |

**3739 Third-Guinea.** First laur. head r. R. Similar but date below crown, die axis ↑↑

| 1801 | 60 | 120 | 300 | 1803 | 60 | 120 | 300 |
|---|---|---|---|---|---|---|---|
| 1802 | 60 | 120 | 300 | | | | |

3740
1804 Third Guinea, second head

3741
1762 Quarter-Guinea

**3740 Third-Guinea.** Second laur. head r. with short hair, R. Similar, die axis ↑↑

| 1804 | 65 | 110 | 275 | 1810 | 65 | 110 | 275 |
|---|---|---|---|---|---|---|---|
| 1806 | 70 | 125 | 300 | 1811 | 200 | 450 | 950 |
| 1808 | 70 | 125 | 300 | 1813 | 125 | 300 | 650 |
| 1809 | 70 | 125 | 300 | | | | |

**3741 Quarter-Guinea.** Laur. head r. R. Crowned shield die axis ↑↓ 1762 .....75   225   375

*For gold of the 'new coinage', 1817-20, see page 389.*

# SILVER

3742
1763 Northumberland shilling

3746
1787 Proof Shilling

**3742 Shilling.** Young laur. and dr. bust, r. known as the 'Northumberland' shilling, die axis ↑↓

| 1763 | | 275 | 525 | 1000 |
|---|---|---|---|---|

**3743 Shilling.** Older laur. and dr. bust, R. No semée of hearts in Hanoverian shield, die axis ↑↑

| 1787 | | 20 | 40 | 90 |
|---|---|---|---|---|
| 1787 Proof *FDC* | | | *Extremely rare* | |
| 1787 plain edge proof *FDC* | | | *Extremely rare* | |

**3744 Shilling.** — No stop over head, die axis ↑↑ 1787.....30   60   120

**3745 Shilling.** — No stops at date, die axis ↑↑ 1787.....35   80   175

**3745A Shilling.** — No stops on *obv.*, die axis ↑↑ 1787.....250   675   1350

**3746 Shilling.** — R. With semée of hearts, die axis ↑↑ 1787.....20   40   90

| 1787 1/1 retrograde | 40 | 110 | 275 |
|---|---|---|---|
| 1787 plain edge proof *FDC* | | *Extremely rare* | |

Hanoverian Arms

| No semée of hearts | With semée of hearts | | | 3747 - 1798 Shilling | | |
|---|---|---|---|---|---|---|
| | *F* | *VF* | *EF* | | *F* | *VF* | *EF* |
| | £ | £ | £ | | £ | £ | £ |

**3747  Shilling** No stop over head, 1798: known as the 'Dorrien and Magens' shilling *UNC* £8500

**3748  Sixpence.** Laur. and dr. bust r. R. Without semée of hearts, die axis ↑↑

   1787...................10     35     75     1787 Proof *FDC* ............*Extremely rare*

**3749  Sixpence.** Similar R. With semée of hearts, die axis ↑↑ 1787 ..............10     35     75

          3749                          3750

   1787 Sixpence, with hearts

**3750  Fourpence.** Young laur. and dr. bust r. R. Crowned 4, die axis ↑↓

| 1763 ..............4 | 15 | 30 | 1772/0 ...................5 | 20 | 35 |
|---|---|---|---|---|---|
| 1763 Proof *FDC of highest rarity* | | | 1776 ....................4 | 18 | 30 |
| 1765 .................200 | 450 | 800 | 1780 ....................4 | 18 | 30 |
| 1766 ...................5 | 20 | 35 | 1784 ....................5 | 20 | 35 |
| 1770 ...................5 | 20 | 35 | 1786 ....................6 | 25 | 40 |
| 1772 ...................5 | 20 | 35 | | | |

      3751                3753                3755

**3751  Fourpence.** Older laur. and dr. bust. R. Thin 4 ('Wire Money'), die axis ↑↑

   1792 ..............10     35     65

**3752  Fourpence.** Older laur. and dr. bust r. R. Normal Crowned 4, die axis ↑↑

   1795 ................5     18     35     1800 ....................5     18     35

**3753  Threepence.** Young laur. dr. bust r. R. Crowned 3, die axis ↑↓

| 1762 ................3 | 12 | 25 | 1772 small III ...........4 | 18 | 30 |
|---|---|---|---|---|---|
| 1763 ................3 | 12 | 25 | 1772 very large III........4 | 18 | 30 |
| 1763 Proof *FDC of highest rarity* | | | 1780 ....................4 | 18 | 30 |
| 1765 .................150 | 325 | 700 | 1784 ....................5 | 20 | 35 |
| 1766 ................5 | 20 | 35 | 1786 ....................4 | 18 | 30 |
| 1770 ................5 | 20 | 35 | | | |

**3754  Threepence.** Older laur. dr. bust. r. R. Thin 3 ('Wire Money'), die axis ↑↑

   1792 ...............10     35     65

**3755  Threepence.** Older laur. and dr. bust r. R. Normal Crowned 3, die axis ↑↑

   1795 ................5     18     35     1800 ....................5     18     35

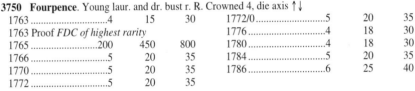

|  | F £ | VF £ | EF £ |
|---|---|---|---|

**3756  Twopence.** Young laur. and dr. bust r. ℞. Crowned 2, die axis ↑↓

| 1763 ..................6 | 25 | 35 | 1776 ....................4 | 18 | 30 |
|---|---|---|---|---|---|
| 1763 Proof *FDC of highest rarity* | | | 1780 ....................4 | 18 | 30 |
| 1765 ..................100 | 275 | 600 | 1784 ....................4 | 18 | 30 |
| 1766 ....................4 | 18 | 30 | 1786 ....................3 | 15 | 30 |
| 1772 ....................4 | 18 | 30 | 1786 large obv. lettering .3 | 15 | 30 |
| 1772 second 7/6 ..........5 | 20 | 35 | | | |

3756

**3757  Twopence** Older laur. and dr. bust. r. ℞. Thin 2 ('Wire Money'), die axis ↑↑
1792 ..................10    30    65

**3758  Twopence** Older laur. and dr. bust r. ℞. Normal Crowned 2, die axis ↑↑

| 1795 ..................3 | 15 | 30 | 1800 ....................3 | 15 | 30 |
|---|---|---|---|---|---|

**3759  Penny.** Young laur. and dr. bust r. ℞. Crowned 1, die axis ↑↓

| 1763 ..................5 | 20 | 35 | 1779 ....................4 | 18 | 30 |
|---|---|---|---|---|---|
| 1763 Proof *FDC of highest rarity* | | | 1780 ....................5 | 20 | 35 |
| 1766 ..................4 | 18 | 30 | 1781 ....................3 | 12 | 25 |
| 1770 ..................3 | 12 | 25 | 1784 ....................3 | 12 | 25 |
| 1772 ..................4 | 18 | 30 | 1786 ....................3 | 12 | 25 |
| 1776 ..................4 | 18 | 30 | | | |

**3760  Penny.** Older laur. and dr. bust. r. ℞. Thin 1 ('Wire Money'), die axis ↑↑
1792 ..................8    30    55

**3761  Penny.** Older laur. and dr. bust r. ℞. Normal Crowned 1, die axis ↑↑

| 1795 ..................3 | 12 | 30 | 1800 ....................3 | 12 | 30 |
|---|---|---|---|---|---|

**3762  Maundy Set.** Young laur. and dr. bust. r. Uniform dates

| 1763 ..................50 | 150 | 300 | 1780 ....................50 | 150 | 300 |
|---|---|---|---|---|---|
| 1763 Proof set *FDC* ........ | *Extremely rare* | | 1784 ....................50 | 150 | 300 |
| 1766 ..................50 | 150 | 300 | 1786 ....................50 | 150 | 300 |
| 1772 ..................50 | 150 | 300 | | | |

**3763  Maundy Set.** — Older laur. and dr. bust. r. ℞. Thin numerals ('Wire Money'),
1792 ..................125    275    550

**3764  Maundy Set.** Older laur. and dr. bust r. ℞. Normal numerals. Uniform dates

| 1795 ..................40 | 140 | 275 | 1800 ....................35 | 125 | 250 |
|---|---|---|---|---|---|

**Emergency Issue, die axis ↑↑**

3765A
Portrait type Dollar with oval countermark

**3765  Dollar.** Pillar type (current for 4s 9d). Spanish American 8 Reales,

oval countermark with head of George III.

| Mexico City Mint — m .....................................................375 | 850 | 1850 |
|---|---|---|
| Bolivia, Potosi Mint – PTS monogram ...............................750 | 1850 | — |
| Peru, Lima Mint – LIMÆ monogram .................................700 | 1500 | — |

|  | F £ | VF £ | EF £ |
|---|---|---|---|
| **3765A Dollar.** Portrait type, oval countermark. | | | |
| Mexico City Mint — m̥ | .95 | 275 | 500 |
| Bolivia, Potosi Mint — PTS monogram | .150 | 475 | — |
| Chile, Santiago Mint — ş | .550 | 1500 | — |
| Guatemala Mint — NG | .450 | 1250 | — |
| Spain, Madrid Mint | .275 | 675 | 1750 |
| Spain, Seville Mint | .225 | 550 | 1500 |
| Peru, Lima Mint — LIMÆ monogram | .125 | 350 | 700 |
| **3765B Dollar.** — Oval countermark on French Ecu | | *Extremely rare* | |
| **3765C Dollar.** — Oval countermark on USA Dollar | | *Of highest rarity* | |

3766
Portrait Dollar with octagonal countermark

3767
Half-Dollar with oval countermark

|  | F | VF | EF |
|---|---|---|---|
| **3766 Dollar** octagonal countermarks with head of George III | | | |
| Mexico City Mint — m̥ | .200 | 500 | 875 |
| Bolivia, Potosi Mint — PTS monogram | .600 | — | — |
| Guatamala Mint — NG | .825 | 1750 | — |
| Peru, Lima Mint — LIME monogram | .275 | 625 | 1500 |
| Spain, Madrid Mint | .450 | 950 | — |
| Spain, Seville Mint | .500 | 1200 | — |
| **3766A Dollar.** — Octagonal countermark on French Ecu | | *Of highest rarity* | |
| **3766B Dollar.** — Octagonal countermark on USA Dollar | | *Extremely rare* | |
| **3767 Half-Dollar.** With similar oval countermark. Mints of Potosi, Santiago, Madrid & Seville | *from* 100 | 275 | 575 |

**Bank of England Issue**

3768
Top leaf top left side of E in DEI

|  | F £ | VF £ | EF £ |
|---|---|---|---|
| **3768 Dollar.** (current for 5s.). laur. and dr. bust of king. r. ℞. Britannia seated l., several varieties occur, die axis ↑↑ |  |  |  |
| 1804 O. Top leaf to left side of E, R. Upright K to left of shield | 100 | 275 | 500 |
| 1804 ——no stops in CHK on truncation | 125 | 325 | 550 |
| 1804 O. Top leaf to centre of E R. Similar | 100 | 275 | 500 |
| 1804 ——no stop after REX | 110 | 300 | 525 |
| 1804 —R. K inverted to left of shield | 150 | 375 | 600 |
| 1804 —R. K inverted and incuse | 150 | 375 | 600 |
| 1804 O. Top leaf to right side of E, R. normal K | 110 | 300 | 525 |
| 1804 —R. K inverted to left of shield | 150 | 375 | 600 |
| 1804 Proof striking of all varieties above *FDC from £950* |  |  |  |

*These dollars were re-struck from Spanish-American 8-Reales until at least 1811. Dollars that show dates and Mint marks of original coin are worth rather more.*

3769
1811 Three Shillings, first bust

3770
Three Shillings, second head

|  | F £ | VF £ | EF £ |  | F £ | VF £ | EF £ |
|---|---|---|---|---|---|---|---|
| **3769 Three Shillings.** Dr and laur. bust in armour r. ℞. BANK / TOKEN / 3 SHILL. / date (in oak wreath), die axis ↑↑ |  |  |  |  |  |  |  |
| 1811 | 15 | 60 | 125 | 1812 Proof *FDC* £500 |  |  |  |
| 1811 Proof *FDC* £450 |  |  |  | 1812 Proof in gold *FDC.* | *Extremely rare* |  |  |
| 1812 | 15 | 70 | 150 | 1812 Proof in platinum *FDC* | *Extremely rare* |  |  |
| **3770 Three Shillings.** — Laureate head r. Top leaf between I/G ℞. As before but wreath of oak and olive, die axis ↑↑ |  |  |  |  |  |  |  |
| 1812 | 15 | 60 | 125 | 1815 | 15 | 70 | 150 |
| 1813 | 15 | 70 | 150 | 1816 | 175 | 600 | 1250 |
| 1814 | 15 | 70 | 150 |  |  |  |  |

3771
1811 Eighteenpence, first bust

3772
Eighteenpence, second head

| | F | VF | EF | | F | VF | EF |
|---|---|---|---|---|---|---|---|
| | £ | £ | £ | | £ | £ | £ |

**3771 Eighteenpence.** Dr. and laur. bust r. in armour R BANK/TOKEN/ls. 6D./date (in oak wreath) ↑↑

| | F | VF | EF | | F | VF | EF |
|---|---|---|---|---|---|---|---|
| 1811 ............................10 | | 35 | 100 | 1812 ............................10 | | 35 | 110 |

1811 Proof *FDC* £400

**3772 Eighteenpence.** Laureate head r. die axis ↑↑

| 1812 ............................10 | 35 | 100 | 1813 Platinum proof *FDC* £12500 | | |
|---|---|---|---|---|---|
| 1812 Proof *FDC* £350 .... | | | 1814 ............................10 | 40 | 120 |
| 1812 Platinum proof *FDC* £12500 | | | 1815 ............................10 | 40 | 120 |
| 1812 Proof R. Small letters *FDC* £2000 | | | 1816 ............................10 | 40 | 120 |
| 1813 ............................10 | 40 | 120 | | | |

3773
1812 Pattern Ninepence, 9D type

3773A
1812 Pattern Ninepence, PENCE type

**3773 Ninepence.** Similar, Laur. head 1812, R. 9D type (pattern only) die axis ↑↑ *FDC* £1000

**3773A Ninepence.** — — 1812, R. 9 pence type (pattern only) die axis ↑↑ FDC. *Extremely rare*

# COPPER

**First Issue** — Tower Mint, London

3774

3775

REV.C, leaves point between A and N

| | F | VF | EF | | F | VF | EF |
|---|---|---|---|---|---|---|---|
| | £ | £ | £ | | £ | £ | £ |

**3774 Halfpenny.** Laur. and Cuir. bust r. R. Britannia l. date in ex., die axis ↑↓

| | F | VF | EF | | F | VF | EF |
|---|---|---|---|---|---|---|---|
| 1770 ...............................12 | 50 | 225 | | 1772 ball below | | | |
| 1770 Proof *FDC* £1100 | | | | spear blade ..........10 | 45 | 225 | |
| 1770 Proof die axis ↑↑ *FDC* £1200 | | | | 1772 no incuse | | | |
| 1770 Proof in silver *FDC* | *Extremely rare* | | | hair coil ................10 | 45 | 200 | |
| 1770 no stop on rev. ......20 | 65 | 250 | | 1772 — no stop on rev. ..20 | 65 | 225 | |
| 1771 ...............................10 | 45 | 225 | | 1773 ...............................10 | 45 | 200 | |
| 1771 no stop on rev. ......20 | 65 | 250 | | 1773 no stop after | | | |
| 1771 ball below | | | | REX ....................18 | 60 | 225 | |
| spear blade ............10 | 45 | 225 | | 1773 no stop on rev.......20 | 65 | 225 | |
| 1772 incuse hair coil | | | | 1774 different obv. | | | |
| on rev. ..................10 | 45 | 225 | | profile .................18 | 60 | 225 | |
| 1772 GEORIVS error ....35 | 90 | 300 | | 1775 — ........................10 | 45 | 200 | |

**3775 Farthing.** Laur. and cuir. bust r. R. Britannia l. date in ex., die axis ↑↓

| | F | VF | EF | | F | VF | EF |
|---|---|---|---|---|---|---|---|
| 1771 REV A. leaf to r. ..20 | 65 | 225 | | 1773 no stop after REX ..25 | 75 | 225 | |
| 1771 REV B. leaf to N ..20 | 65 | 225 | | 1774 ...............................12 | 45 | 150 | |
| 1771 REV C. ................20 | 65 | 225 | | 1775 ...............................12 | 45 | 150 | |
| 1771 1st 7/1 ..................30 | 175 | — | | 1775 struck en | | | |
| 1773 ...............................10 | 40 | 150 | | medaille ↑↑ ........25 | 75 | 225 | |
| 1773 no stop on rev. ......15 | 50 | 175 | | 1775 GEORIVS ........40 | 200 | — | |

**Second Issue**—Soho Mint. Birmingham 'Cartwheel' coinage, die axis ↑↓

3776

**3776 Twopence.** Legends incuse on raised rim, 1797 .....................................25   140   325

| 1797 Copper proof *FDC* £650 | 1797 Gold proof *FDC* £12500 |
|---|---|
| 1797 Bronzed proof *FDC* £600 | 1797 Gilt copper *FDC* £1000 |
| 1797 Silver proof *FDC* £3750 | |

3777

| | VF | EF | UNC | | F | VF | EF | UNC |
|---|---|---|---|---|---|---|---|---|
| | £ | £ | £ | | £ | £ | £ | £ |

**3777 Penny.** 1797. Similar, 10 leaves in wreath on obv. ...........................10 50 225 950
1797 11 leaves in wreath on obv. ........................................10 60 275 1000
1797 Gilt copper proof *FDC* £800
1797 Copper proof *FDC* £550
1797 Bronzed proof *FDC* £500
1797 Silver proof *FDC* £3000
1797 Gold proof *FDC* £10000

*Halfpence and Farthings of this issue are patterns.*

**Third Issue**—Soho Mint, Birmingham, die axis ↑↓

3778                                     3779

**3778  Halfpenny.** Laur. and dr. bust r., R. Britannia l. date below

| 1799 Ship on rev. with | | | | 1799 Ship with | | | |
|---|---|---|---|---|---|---|---|
| 5 incuse gunports ........10 | 60 | 125 | | plain hull............ | 15 | 75 | 150 |
| 1799 Ship with 6 | | | | 1799 — raised line | | | |
| relief gunports.............12 | 65 | 135 | | on hull................ | 15 | 75 | 150 |
| 1799 Ship with 9 relief | | | | 1799 Copper proof *FDC* £300 | | | |
| gunports ......................15 | 75 | 150 | | 1799 Bronzed proof *FDC* £250 | | | |
| | | | | 1799 Gilt copper proof *FDC* £400 | | | |

**3779  Farthing.** Laur. and dr. bust r. date below R. Britannia l.

| 1799 Obv. with 3 berries | | | | 1799 Obv. with 4 berries | | | |
|---|---|---|---|---|---|---|---|
| in wreath ......................8 | 50 | 100 | | in wreath ............ | 8 | 50 | 100 |
| 1799 Copper *FDC* £225 | | | | 1799 Gold proof *FDC* £7500 | | | |
| 1799 Bronzed proof *FDC* £200 | | | | 1799 Silver proof *FDC* £2750 | | | |
| 1799 Copper gilt proof *FDC* £325 | | | | | | | |

**Fourth Issue**—Soho Mint, Birmingham, die axis ↑↓

3780

| | VF | EF | UNC | | VF | EF | UNC |
|---|---|---|---|---|---|---|---|
| | £ | £ | £ | | £ | £ | £ |

**3780   Penny.** Shorter haired, laur. and dr. bust r. date below. R. Britannia l. date below

| 1806 incuse hair curl ....10 | 60 | 225 | 1807 ............................10 | 70 | 240 |
|---|---|---|---|---|---|
| by tie knot | | | 1807 Copper proof *FDC* £375 | | |
| 1806 no incuse hair curl ..15 | 75 | 250 | 1807 Bronzed proof *FDC* £350 | | |
| 1806 Copper proof *FDC*  £300 | | | 1807 Gilt copper proof *FDC* £500 | | |
| 1806 Bronzed proof *FDC*  £300 | | | 1807 Silver proof *FDC* £3000 | | |
| 1806 Gilt copper proof *FDC*  £475 | | | 1807 Gold proof *FDC*    *Extremely rare* | | |
| 1806 Silver proof *FDC*  £3500 | | | 1807 Platinum proof *FDC*    *Extremely rare* | | |
| | | | 1808 Proof *FDC*    *Unique* | | |

3781                                          3782

**3781   Halfpenny.** Shorter haired laur. and dr. bust r. date below, R. Britannia l.

| 1806 rev. no berries..........6 | 35 | 120 | 1807 ..............................8 | 40 | 140 |
|---|---|---|---|---|---|
| 1806 rev. 3 berries..........10 | 60 | 150 | 1807 Copper proof *FDC*  £275 | | |
| 1806 Copper proof *FDC* £250 | | | 1807 Bronzed proof *FDC*  £250 | | |
| 1806 Bronzed proof *FDC* £225 | | | 1807 Gilt copper *FDC* £375 | | |
| 1806 Gilt proof *FDC* £350 | | | 1807 Silver proof *FDC* £2500 | | |
| 1806 Silver proof *FDC* £2750 | | | 1807 Gold proof *FDC*    *Extremely rare* | | |

**3782   Farthing.** Shorter haired laur. and dr. bust r. date below, R. Britannia l.

| 1806 K. on tr. .................6 | 70 | 100 | 1807 ..............................8 | 45 | 125 |
|---|---|---|---|---|---|
| 1806 incuse dot on tr......35 | 100 | 275 | 1807 Copper proof *FDC* £250 | | |
| 1806 Copper proof *FDC* £225 | | | 1807 Bronzed proof *FDC* £225 | | |
| 1806 Bronzed proof *FDC* £200 | | | 1807 Gilt copper proof *FDC* £375 | | |
| 1806 Gilt copper proof *FDC* £350 | | | 1807 Silver proof *FDC* £3000 | | |
| 1806 Silver proof *FDC* £2500 | | | 1807 Gold proof *FDC*    *Extremely rare* | | |
| 1806 Gold proof *FDC*    *Extremely rare* | | | | | |

**Last or new coinage, 1816-20**

The year 1816 is a landmark in the history of our coinage. For some years at the beginning of the 19th century Mint production was virtually confined to small gold denominations, regular full production being resumed only after the Mint had been moved from the Tower of London to a new site on Tower Hill. Steam powered minting machinery made by Boulton and Watt replaced the old hand-operated presses and these produced coins which were technically much superior to the older milled coins.

In 1816 for the first time British silver coins were produced with an intrinsic value substantially below their face value, the first official token coinage. The old Guinea was replaced by a Sovereign of twenty shillings in 1817, the standard of 22 carat (0.916) fineness still being retained.

**Mint Master or Engraver's**
**and/or designer's initials:**          WWP (William Wellesley Pole)
B.P. (Benedetto Pistrucci 1784-1855)

## GOLD

3783

**3783  Five Pounds.** 1820 LX (Pattern only) laur. head r. date below R. St George and dragon, edge inscribed die axis ↑↓ *FDC*..... £45,000
1820 Similar plain edge proof *FDC Extremely rare*

3784

**3784  Two Pounds.** 1820 LX (Pattern only) laur. head r. date below R. St George and dragon, edge inscribed die axis ↑↓ *FDC*..... £16500
1820 Similar plain edge proof *FDC Extremely rare*

| 3785 | | | | | 3785A | | | |
|---|---|---|---|---|---|---|---|---|
| | F | VF | EF | UNC | | F | VF | EF | UNC |
| | £ | £ | £ | £ | | £ | £ | £ | £ |

**3785  Sovereign.** laur. head r. coarse hair, legend type A (Descending colon after BRITANNIAR, no space between REX and F:D:). R. St. George and dragon, die axis ↑↓

| | | | | | | | | | |
|---|---|---|---|---|---|---|---|---|---|
| 1817 | 200 | 350 | 875 | 1500 | 1818 | 225 | 400 | 1050 | 1750 |
| 1817 Proof *FDC* £6000 | | | | | 1819 | | | | *Extremely rare* |

**3785A Sovereign.** Similar legend type B (Ascending colon after BRITANNIAR, space between REX and F:D:) ↑↓

| | | | | | | |
|---|---|---|---|---|---|---|
| 1817 no top serif on 2nd 1 | *Extremely rare* | | | 1818 Proof *FDC* £8000 | | |
| 1818 | 225 | 400 | 1050 | 1750 | | |

|  | F £ | VF £ | EF £ | UNC £ |  | F £ | VF £ | EF £ | UNC £ |
|---|---|---|---|---|---|---|---|---|---|

**3785B Sovereign.** laur head r. hair with tighter curls, legend type A. (as above) R. Similar die axis ↑↓
1818 ........................... *Extremely rare*

3785C
Large date, open 2 variety

3785C
Closed 2 variety

**3785C Sovereign.** Similar legend type B. (as above) die axis ↑↓

| | F | VF | EF | UNC |
|---|---|---|---|---|
| 1818 ........................... *Extremely rare* | | | | |
| 1820 Roman I........450 | 1000 | 2000 | — | |
| 1820 Small O, closed | | | | |
|    2 thin date ....275 | 550 | 1100 | 1750 | |
| 1820 Proof *FDC* £6500 | | | | |
| 1820 Slender date Proof *FDC Extremely rare* | | | | |

| | F | VF | EF | UNC |
|---|---|---|---|---|
| 1820 large date open | | | | |
|   2 close to 8 ...225 | 400 | 950 | 1500 | |
| 1820 short date 2 | | | | |
|   nearly closed ..275 | 525 | 1050 | — | |
| 1820 closed 2 ........300 | 650 | 1650 | — | |
| 1820 spread 18 and 20 | | | | |
|   short date .......... | *Extremely rare* | | | |

3786
1817 Half-Sovereign

**3786 Half-Sovereign.** laur head r. date below R. Crowned shield, edge milled die axis ↑↓

| | F | VF | EF | UNC |
|---|---|---|---|---|
| 1817 ........................85 | 175 | 300 | 500 | |
| 1817 Proof *FDC* £3750 | | | | |
| 1818/7 ....................275 | 550 | 1400 | — | |

| | F | VF | EF | UNC |
|---|---|---|---|---|
| 1818 Proof *FDC* £4500 | | | | |
| 1818.......................95 | 200 | 350 | 575 | |
| 1820.......................95 | 200 | 350 | 575 | |

3787
1818 George III Crown

**3787 Crown.** Laur. head r. R. Pistrucci's St. George and dragon within Garter edge inscribed, die axis ↑↓

| | | F | VF | EF | UNC |
|---|---|---|---|---|---|
| 1818, edge LVIII | ........................................................................ | .25 | 60 | 300 | 750 |
| 1818 | LVIII error edge inscription................................................ | *Extremely rare* | | | |
| 1818 | LVIII Proof *FDC* ........................................................... | *Extremely rare* | | | |
| 1818 | LIX....................................................................... | .25 | 60 | 300 | 750 |
| 1818 | LIX TUT∧MEN error ......................................................... | .50 | 175 | — | — |
| 1819 | LIX....................................................................... | .20 | 50 | 275 | 700 |
| 1819 | LIX no stops on edge ...................................................... | .45 | 100 | 450 | 1100 |
| 1819 | LIX R. Thicker ruled garter ............................................... | .75 | 225 | 550 | — |
| 1819/8 | LIX..................................................................... | .50 | 175 | 550 | — |
| 1819 | LX........................................................................ | .30 | 70 | 325 | 800 |
| 1819 | LX no stop after TUTAMEN.................................................. | .50 | 175 | 500 | — |
| 1820 | LX........................................................................ | .25 | 60 | 300 | 750 |
| 1820 | LX R.S/T in SOIT ......................................................... | .75 | 225 | 550 | — |
| 1820/19 | LX.................................................................... | .75 | 225 | 550 | — |

3788

1816 Halfcrown, large bust

|  | F | VF | EF | UNC |  | F | VF | EF | UNC |
|---|---|---|---|---|---|---|---|---|---|
|  | £ | £ | £ | £ |  | £ | £ | £ | £ |

**3788 Halfcrown.** Large laur. bust or 'bull' head r. date below R. Crowned garter and shield die axis ↑↑

| 1816 | 20 | 60 | 225 | 400 |
|---|---|---|---|---|
| 1816 Proof *FDC* £1750 | | | | |
| 1816 Plain proof *FDC* £1750 | | | | |
| 1817 | 20 | 60 | 225 | 400 |
| 1817 D/T in DEI | 45 | 150 | 500 | — |

| 1817 E/R in DEI | *Extremely rare* |
| 1817 S/I in PENSE | *Extremely rare* |
| 1817 Proof *FDC* £1750 | |
| 1817 Plain edge proof *FDC* £2000 | |

3789

1817 Halfcrown, small head

|  | F | VF | EF | UNC |  | F | VF | EF | UNC |
|---|---|---|---|---|---|---|---|---|---|
|  | £ | £ | £ | £ |  | £ | £ | £ | £ |

**3789 Halfcrown.** Small laur. head r. date below, R. Crowned garter and shield die axis ↑↑

| 1817 | 20 | 60 | 180 | 400 |
|---|---|---|---|---|
| 1817 Proof *FDC* £1750 | | | | |
| 1817 Plain edge proof *FDC* £1750 | | | | |
| 1817 Reversed s's in garter | *Extremely rare* | | | |
| 1818 Reversed s's in garter | *Extremely rare* | | | |
| 1818 | 25 | 70 | 250 | 475 |

| 1818 Proof *FDC* £2200 | | | | |
| 1819 Proof *FDC* £2000 | | | | |
| 1819 | 20 | 60 | 225 | 400 |
| 1819/8 | | *Extremely rare* | | |
| 1820 | 30 | 85 | 275 | 500 |
| 1820 Proof *FDC* £2200 | | | | |
| 1820 Plain edge proof *FDC* £1750 | | | | |

3790

1817 Shilling

**3790 Shilling.** laur head r. date below R. Crowned Shield in Garter edge milled, die axis ↑↑

| 1816 | 10 | 15 | 45 | 85 |
|---|---|---|---|---|
| 1816 Proof *FDC* £500 | | | | |
| 1816 Plain edge proof *FDC* £500 | | | | |
| 1816 Proof in gold *FDC* | *Extremely rare* | | | |
| 1817 | 10 | 18 | 50 | 90 |
| 1817 RRITT flaw | 15 | 25 | 90 | — |
| 1817 Proof plain edge *FDC* £400 | | | | |
| 1817 GEOE error | 100 | 225 | 450 | — |

| 1818 | 20 | 40 | 180 | 275 |
| 1818 High 8 | 30 | 75 | 175 | 350 |
| 1819/8 | 20 | 40 | 100 | 225 |
| 1819 | 10 | 20 | 55 | 125 |
| 1820 | 10 | 20 | 55 | 125 |
| 1820 I/S in HONI | 40 | 80 | 225 | 450 |
| 1820 Proof *FDC* £400 | | | | |

3791
1819 Sixpence

| | F | VF | EF | UNC | | F | VF | EF | UNC |
|---|---|---|---|---|---|---|---|---|---|
| | £ | £ | £ | £ | | £ | £ | £ | £ |

**3791**  **Sixpence.** laur head r. date below R. Crowned Shield in Garter edge milled, die axis ↑↑

| | F | VF | EF | UNC | | F | VF | EF | UNC |
|---|---|---|---|---|---|---|---|---|---|
| 1816 ..........................6 | 12 | 35 | 65 | | 1819/8 ........................12 | 25 | 50 | 85 |
| 1816 Proof plain edge *FDC* £500 | | | | | 1819 ............................10 | 20 | 45 | 75 |
| 1816 Proof in gold *FDC* | | *Extremely rare* | | | 1819 small 8 ..............10 | 20 | 45 | 75 |
| 1817 ..........................8 | 15 | 40 | 70 | | 1820 ............................10 | 20 | 45 | 75 |
| 1817 Proof plain edge *FDC* £500 | | | | | 1820 inverted 1 ..........75 | 275 | 425 | — |
| 1817 Proof milled edge *FDC* £950 | | | | | 1820 I/S in HONI ......75 | 275 | 425 | — |
| 1818 ........................10 | 20 | 45 | 75 | | 1820 obv. no colons ..100 | 375 | 525 | — |
| 1818 Proof milled edge *FDC* £900 | | | | | 1820 Proof *FDC* £900 | | | |

3792

**3792**  **Maundy Set.** (4d., 3d., 2d. and 1d.) laur. head, date below die axis ↑↑

| | | F | VF | UNC | | | F | VF | UNC |
|---|---|---|---|---|---|---|---|---|---|
| 1817 ............................ | | 60 | 150 | 300 | 1820 .............................. | | 60 | 150 | 300 |
| 1818 ............................ | | 60 | 150 | 300 | | | | | |

| | | | | EF | UNC |
|---|---|---|---|---|---|
| **3793** | — **Fourpence.** 1817, 1818, 1820 ...................................................*from* | | | 15 | 35 |
| **3794** | — **Threepence.** 1817, 1818, 1820 ................................................*from* | | | 15 | 35 |
| **3795** | — **Twopence.** 1817, 1818, 1820 ...................................................*from* | | | 10 | 25 |
| **3796** | — **Penny.** 1817, 1818, 1820 .............................................................*from* | | | 10 | 20 |

George IV, eldest son of George III, was born on 12 August 1762 and was almost a complete opposite to his father. He was very extravagant and lived in the height of luxury. He especially influenced fashion of the time which has become known as the 'Regency' style. He had numerous mistresses, and had an arranged marriage with Caroline of Brunswick. She later moved to Italy with their only daughter, but returned to claim her place as Queen upon George's accession. George banned her from ever being crowned, and he died without ever conceiving a son on 26 June 1830, when his younger brother William ascended the throne.

The Mint resumed the coinage of copper farthings in 1821, and pennies and halfpennies in 1825. A gold Two Pound piece was first issued for general circulation in 1823. A full cased proof set of the new bare head coinage was issued in limited quantities in 1826.

**Engraver's and/or designer's initials on the coins:**
B. P. (Benedetto Pistrucci)          W.W. P. (William Wellesley Pole) – Master of the Mint
J. B. M. (Jean Baptiste Merlen)

**Engravers and Designers:**– Francis Legett Chantrey (1781-1842) Jean Baptiste Merlen (1769-c.1850) Benedetto Pistrucci (1784-1855) William Wyon (1795-1851)
**Prime Ministers:**– Earl of Liverpool, (1770-1828) Tory, 1812-27; George Canning, (1770-1827) Tory, 1827; Viscount Goderich, (1782-1859), Tory 1827-8; Duke of Wellington, (1769-1852), Tory, 1828-30.

# GOLD

3797

**3797 Five Pounds.** 1826 Bare head l. date below R. Crowned shield and mantle, inscribed edge, die axis ↑↓    Proof *FDC* £10500
1826 Piedfort proof *FDC*..........................................................*Extremely rare*

3798

|  | VF £ | EF £ | UNC £ |
|---|---|---|---|

**3798 Two Pounds.** 1823 Proof *FDC* £4750
1823 Proof no JBM below truncation *FDC* ....................................................*Extremely rare*
1823 Large bare head. l. R. St. George, inscribed edge ↑↓ .......................... 600   1200   2000
**3799 Two Pounds.** Bare head l. date below R. Crowned shield and mantle inscribed edge die axis ↑↓
1824 Proof *FDC*          *Extremely rare*          1826. Piedfort proof *FDC*          *Extremely rare*
1825 Proof plain edge *FDC* £6500          1826. Proof *FDC* £4250

3800
1822 Sovereign, first type

3801
1826 Sovereign, second type

|  | F £ | VF £ | EF £ | UNC £ |  | F £ | VF £ | EF £ | UNC £ |
|---|---|---|---|---|---|---|---|---|---|

**3800  Sovereign.** Laur. head. l. R. St. George and dragon date in ex., die axis ↑↓

| 1821 | 200 | 325 | 900 | 1500 | 1823 | 325 | 1250 | 3500 | — |
|---|---|---|---|---|---|---|---|---|---|
| 1821 Proof *FDC* £3500 | | | | | 1824 | 225 | 375 | 950 | 1600 |
| 1822* | 225 | 325 | 950 | 1600 | 1825 | 300 | 950 | 2750 | — |

*Beware counterfeits.*

**3801  Sovereign.** Bare head. date below l. R. Crowned shield, die axis ↑↓

| 1825 | 200 | 325 | 750 | 1200 | 1827* | 225 | 375 | 800 | 1350 |
|---|---|---|---|---|---|---|---|---|---|
| 1825 Proof *FDC* £3500 | | | | | 1828 | 1500 | 3500 | 8000 | — |
| 1825 Plain edge proof *FDC* £3500 | | | | | 1829 | 250 | 400 | 900 | 1500 |
| 1826 | 200 | 325 | 750 | 1200 | 1830 | 250 | 400 | 900 | 1500 |
| 1826 Proof *FDC* £2750 | | | | | | | | | |

*Beware counterfeits*

3802
1821 Proof Half-Sovereign

3803
1825 Half-Sovereign, second reverse

**3802 Half-Sovereign.** Laur. head. l. R. Ornately garnished Crowned shield. die axis ↑↓

| 1821 | | | | 400 | 1000 | 2000 | 3250 |
|---|---|---|---|---|---|---|---|
| 1821 Proof *FDC* £3500 | | | | | | | |

**3803 Half-Sovereign.** Laur. head l. R. Plain Crowned shield die axis ↑↓

| 1823 | 80 | 200 | 425 | 650 | 1825 | 70 | 150 | 375 | 550 |
|---|---|---|---|---|---|---|---|---|---|
| 1824 | 75 | 175 | 400 | 600 | | | | | |

3804
1825 Half Sovereign, bare head

3804A
Extra tuft of hair to left of ear

**3804 Half-Sovereign.** Bare head. date below l. R. Crowned garnished shield die axis ↑↓

| 1826 | 80 | 150 | 350 | 600 | 1827 | 80 | 150 | 375 | 600 |
|---|---|---|---|---|---|---|---|---|---|
| 1826 Proof *FDC* £1300 | | | | | 1828 | 80 | 150 | 375 | 650 |

**3804A Half-Sovereign.** Similar with extra tuft of hair to l. ear, much heavier border, die axis ↑↓

| 1826 | 70 | 120 | 325 | 550 | 1827 | 70 | 120 | 325 | 550 |
|---|---|---|---|---|---|---|---|---|---|
| 1826 Proof *FDC* £1250 | | | | | 1828 | 75 | 140 | 350 | 600 |

# SILVER

3805
1821 Laureate bust Crown

| | F | VF | EF | UNC | | F | VF | EF | UNC |
|---|---|---|---|---|---|---|---|---|---|
| | £ | £ | £ | £ | | £ | £ | £ | £ |

**3805 Crown.** Laur. head. l. R. St. George, date in exergue, B.P. to upper right, WWP under lance,
  die axis ↑↓

| 1821, edge | SECUNDO | 30 | 185 | 1000 | 2250 |
|---|---|---|---|---|---|
| 1821 | SECUNDO WWP inverted under lance | | | *Extremely rare* | |
| 1821 | SECUNDO Proof *FDC* £3000 | | | | |
| 1821 | SECUNDO Proof in copper *FDC* £3000 | | | | |
| 1821 | TERTIO Proof *FDC* £4000 | | | | |
| 1822 | SECUNDO | 45 | 250 | 1150 | 2500 |
| 1822 | TERTIO | 30 | 185 | 1000 | 2250 |

3806
1826 Proof Crown, bare head

**3806 Crown.** Bare head. l. R. Shield with crest inscribed edge, die axis ↑↓

1825  Proof *FDC*  £6000                  1826  Proof *FDC*  £3750

| 3807 | | 3807 |
|---|---|---|
| 1820 Halfcrown, lightly garnished shield | | Heavier garnishing |

**3807 Halfcrown.** Laur. head. l. R. Crowned Garnished shield, die axis ↑↓

| 1820 | 20 | 50 | 250 | 450 | 1821 Heavier shield garnishing | | | | |
|---|---|---|---|---|---|---|---|---|---|
| 1820 Proof *FDC*  £900 | | | | | | 25 | 60 | 300 | 500 |
| 1820 Plain edge proof  *FDC* £1400 | | | | | 1823 — | 650 | 1650 | 4500 | — |
| 1821 | 20 | 50 | 250 | 450 | | | | | |

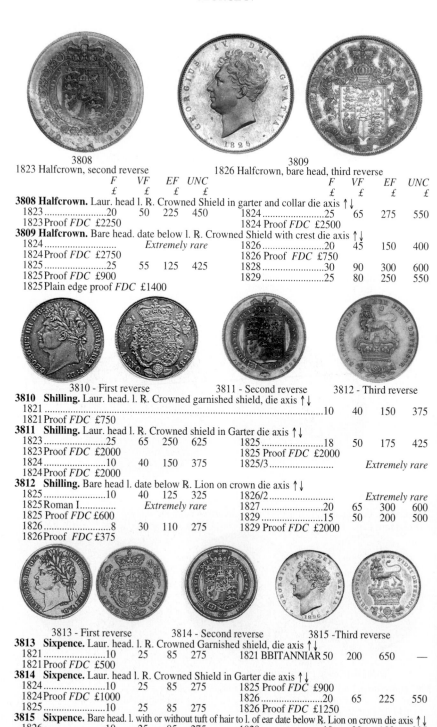

3808                                          3809
1823 Halfcrown, second reverse      1826 Halfcrown, bare head, third reverse

|  | F | VF | EF | UNC |  | F | VF | EF | UNC |
|---|---|---|---|---|---|---|---|---|---|
|  | £ | £ | £ | £ |  | £ | £ | £ | £ |

**3808 Halfcrown.** Laur. head l. R. Crowned Shield in garter and collar die axis ↑↓
1823 ......................20      50      225      450      1824 ......................25      65      275      550
1823 Proof *FDC* £2250                           1824 Proof *FDC* £2500

**3809 Halfcrown.** Bare head. date below l. R. Crowned Shield with crest die axis ↑↓
1824 ...................... *Extremely rare*      1826 ......................20      45      150      400
1824 Proof *FDC* £2750                           1826 Proof *FDC* £750
1825 ......................25      55      125      425      1828 ......................30      90      300      600
1825 Proof *FDC* £900                            1829 ......................25      80      250      550
1825 Plain edge proof *FDC* £1400

3810 - First reverse          3811 - Second reverse      3812 - Third reverse

**3810 Shilling.** Laur. head. l. R. Crowned garnished shield, die axis ↑↓
1821 ...................................................................................10      40      150      375
1821 Proof *FDC* £750

**3811 Shilling.** Laur. head l. R. Crowned shield in Garter die axis ↑↓
1823 ......................25      65      250      625      1825 ......................18      50      175      425
1823 Proof *FDC* £2000                           1825 Proof *FDC* £2000
1824 ......................10      40      150      375      1825/3 ...................... *Extremely rare*
1824 Proof *FDC* £2000

**3812 Shilling.** Bare head l. date below R. Lion on crown die axis ↑↓
1825 ......................10      40      125      325      1826/2 ...................... *Extremely rare*
1825 Roman I.............. *Extremely rare*      1827 ......................20      65      300      600
1825 Proof *FDC* £600                            1829 ......................15      50      200      500
1826 ......................8      30      110      275      1829 Proof *FDC* £2000
1826 Proof *FDC* £375

3813 - First reverse          3814 - Second reverse      3815 -Third reverse

**3813 Sixpence.** Laur. head. l. R. Crowned Garnished shield, die axis ↑↓
1821 ......................10      25      85      275      1821 BBITANNIAR 50      200      650      —
1821 Proof *FDC* £500

**3814 Sixpence.** Laur. head l. R. Crowned Shield in Garter die axis ↑↓
1824 ......................10      25      85      275      1825 Proof *FDC* £900
1824 Proof *FDC* £1000                           1826 ......................20      65      225      550
1825 ......................10      25      85      275      1826 Proof *FDC* £1250

**3815 Sixpence.** Bare head. l. with or without tuft of hair to l. of ear date below R. Lion on crown die axis ↑↓
1826 ......................10      25      85      275      1828 ......................10      30      120      325
1826 Proof *FDC* £250                            1829 ......................10      25      85      275
1827 ......................18      55      225      550      1829 Proof *FDC* £1000

3816

| | EF £ | FDC £ | | EF £ | FDC £ |
|---|---|---|---|---|---|
| **3816 Maundy Set.** (4d., 3d., 2d. and 1d.) laur head l. die axis ↑↓ | | | | | |
| 1822 | 120 | 250 | 1827 | 100 | 225 |
| 1822 Proof set *FDC* | *Extremely rare* | | 1828 | 100 | 225 |
| 1823 | 100 | 225 | 1828 Proof set *FDC* | *Extremely rare* | |
| 1824 | 120 | 250 | 1829 | 100 | 225 |
| 1825 | 100 | 225 | 1830 | 100 | 225 |
| 1826 | 100 | 225 | | | |

| | | EF | FDC |
|---|---|---|---|
| **3817 Maundy Fourpence.** 1822-30 | *from* | 15 | 25 |
| **3818 — Threepence.** small head, 1822 | | 30 | 45 |
| **3819 — Threepence.** normal head, 1823-30 | *from* | 14 | 20 |
| **3820 — Twopence.** 1822-30 | *from* | 12 | 18 |
| **3821 — Penny.** 1822-30 | *from* | 10 | 15 |

# COPPER

**First Issue, 1821-6**

3822                                           3824

| | F £ | VF £ | EF £ | UNC £ | | F £ | VF £ | EF £ | UNC £ |
|---|---|---|---|---|---|---|---|---|---|
| **3822 Farthing.** Laur. and dr. bust l. R. Britannia r. date in ex. die axis ↑↓ | | | | | | | | | |
| 1821 | 2 | 10 | 60 | 110 | 1823 — I for 1 in date | ..25 | 85 | 250 | — |
| 1822 leaf ribs incuse | 2 | 10 | 55 | 90 | 1825 — | 2 | 10 | 60 | 100 |
| 1822—inv. A's legend | .25 | 95 | 250 | — | 1825 — D/U in DEI | 20 | 75 | 225 | — |
| 1822 leaf ribs raised | 2 | 10 | 55 | 100 | 1825 leaf ribs raised | 4 | 15 | 65 | 120 |
| 1822 Proof *FDC* £600 | | | | | 1825 gold proof *FDC* | *Extremely rare* | | | |
| 1822 Proof die axis ↑↑ *FDC* £750 | | | | | 1826 — | 5 | 15 | 70 | 140 |
| 1823 — | 3 | 12 | 65 | 110 | 1826 R/E in GRATIA | 20 | 75 | 225 | — |

3823

**Second issue, 1825-30**

|        | F £ | VF £ | EF £ | UNC £ |        | F £ | VF £ | EF £ | UNC £ |
|--------|-----|------|------|-------|--------|-----|------|------|-------|

**3823  Penny.** Laur. head. l. R. Britannia, with shield bearing saltire of arms die axis ↑↑

| 1825 ......................12 | 40 | 200 | 450 | 1826-Proof *FDC* ...425 |     |     |     |     |
| 1825 Proof *FDC*£1000 |     |     |     | 1826 thick line on |     |     |     |     |
| 1826 plain saltire ........ |     |     |     |    saltire .............15 | 60 | 225 | 500 |
|   on rev. ...........10 | 40 | 175 | 450 | 1826-Proof *FDC*.£400 |     |     |     |     |
| 1826-Proof *FDC*.£375 |     |     |     | 1827 plain saltire ..150 | 500 | 1750 | — |
| 1826 thin line on |     |     |     |     |     |     |     |     |
|   saltire ..............10 | 40 | 200 | 450 |     |     |     |     |     |

**3824  Halfpenny.** die axis ↑↑ Laur. head. l. R. Britannia, with shield bearing saltire of arms

| 1825 ......................12 | 45 | 175 | 350 | 1826 rev. raised line |     |     |     |     |
| 1826 rev. two incuse |     |     |     |   on saltire ........10 | 30 | 125 | 250 |
|   lines on saltire ..8 | 20 | 100 | 200 | 1827 rev. two incuse lines |     |     |     |     |
| 1826 Proof *FDC*..£275 |     |     |     |   on saltire .........10 | 25 | 110 | 225 |

3825

**3825  Farthing.** die axis ↑↑ Laur. head. l. R. Britannia, with shield bearing saltire of arms

| 1826 ......................2 | 10 | 55 | 100 | 1828 ......................2 | 10 | 60 | 110 |
| 1826 Proof *FDC* £200 |     |     |     | 1829 ......................3 | 15 | 75 | 175 |
| 1826 Roman I ........20 | 60 | 225 | – | 1830 ......................2 | 10 | 60 | 110 |
| 1827 ......................3 | 10 | 65 | 125 |     |     |     |     |

3826                                   3827

**3826  Half-Farthing.** (for use in Ceylon). Laur. head. l. date below R.Britannia die axis ↑↑

| 1828 rev. helmet intrudes |     |     |     | 1830 — ...................25 | 75 | 225 | — |
|   legend .............10 | 25 | 110 | 275 | 1830 rev. helmet intrudes |     |     |     |     |
| 1828 rev. helmet to base |     |     |     |   legend ...........10 | 25 | 110 | 275 |
|   of legend .........10 | 25 | 100 | 225 |     |     |     |     |

**3827  Third-Farthing.** (for use in Malta). Laur. head. l. date below R.Britannia die axis ↑↑

| 1827 ................................................................................................ |     | 15 | 65 | 150 |
| 1827 Proof *FDC* £375 |     |     |     |     |

*Copper coins graded in this catalogue as UNC have full mint lustre.*

**PSI  Proof Set,** new issue, 1826. Five pounds to Farthing (11 coins) *FDC* £20000
**PSIA** — — Similar, including Maundy Set (15 coins) *FDC* £21000

William IV was born on 21 August 1765, and ascended the throne on his elder brother's death. From c.1791-1811 while Duke of Clarence, he was cohabiting with the actress Dorothea Jordan (1762-1816) who bore him ten illegitimate children. After the death of George IV's daughter, William was forced into a legitimate marriage with Adelaide of Saxe-Coburg and Meinigen. She bore him two daughters who both died in childhood. His reign was most notable for the introduction of the Reform bill and abolition of slavery. William was the last King of Hanover, and died on 20 June 1837 when the throne passed to his niece Victoria.

In order to prevent confusion between the Sixpence and Half-Sovereign the size of the latter was reduced in 1834, although the weight remained the same. The smaller gold piece was not acceptable to the public and in the following year it was made to the normal size. In 1836 the silver Groat was again issued for general circulation: it is the only British silver coin which has a seated Britannia as the type and was revised upon the suggestion of Mr Joseph Hume thus rendering the nickname "Joey". Crowns were not struck during this reign for general circulation; but proofs or patterns of this denomination were made and are greatly sought after. Silver Threepences and Three-Halfpence were minted for use in the Colonies.

**Engraver's and/or designer's initials on the coins:**
W. W. (William Wyon).
**Engravers and Designers:–** Francis Legett Chantry (1781-1842) Jean Baptiste Merlen (1769-c.1850) William Wyon (1795-1851).
**Prime Ministers:–** Earl Grey, (1764-1845), Whig, 1830-34; William Lamb, Viscount Melbourne (1779-1848) Whig, 1834, 1835-41; Sir Robert Peel, (1788-1850), Tory, 1834-5.

## GOLD

3828
1831 Proof Two Pounds

**3828 Two Pounds.** bare head r. R. crowned shield and mantle, date below, edge plain. die axis ↑↓
1831 (proof only). .................................................................................. *FDC* £5250

| | | | | | | | | |
|---|---|---|---|---|---|---|---|---|
| 3829A | | | | | 3829B | | | |
| 1831 Sovereign, no stops on trun. first bust | | | | | Second bust with broad ear top | | | |
| | F | VF | EF | UNC | | F | VF | EF | UNC |
| | £ | £ | £ | £ | | £ | £ | £ | £ |

**3829 Sovereign.** First bust. r. top of ear narrow and rounded, nose to 2nd N of BRITANNIAR, fine obv. beading. R. Crowned shield. Die axis ↑↓

| | F | VF | EF | UNC | | F | VF | EF | UNC |
|---|---|---|---|---|---|---|---|---|---|
| 1831 | 250 | 400 | 1050 | 1750 | 1832 | 225 | 375 | 1000 | 1650 |
| | | | | | 1832 Proof *FDC* £5500 | | | | |

**3829A Sovereign.** Similar, WW without stops die axis ↑↓

| | F | VF | EF | UNC |
|---|---|---|---|---|
| 1831 | 500 | 1000 | 2000 | 3000 |

**3829B Sovereign.** Second bust. r. top of ear broad and flat, nose to 2nd I in BRITANNIAR, coarser obv. beading. ↑↓

| | F | VF | EF | UNC | | F | VF | EF | UNC |
|---|---|---|---|---|---|---|---|---|---|
| 1830 plain edge proof *FDC* £6500 | | | | | | | | | |
| 1831 Proof plain edge *FDC* £2750 | | | | | | | | | |
| 1832 * | 225 | 350 | 950 | 1400 | 1836 | 250 | 375 | 975 | 1500 |
| 1833 | 250 | 375 | 1000 | 1550 | 1836 N ofANNO struck in shield*Extremely rare* | | | | |
| 1835 | 250 | 375 | 1050 | 1600 | 1837 | 275 | 400 | 1050 | 1600 |
| | | | | | 1837 Tailed 8 | 325 | 600 | 1250 | — |

*\* Beware of counterfeits*

3830  
1831 Proof Half-sovereign

3831  
Large size Half-Sovereign

| | F | VF | EF | UNC | | | F | VF | EF | UNC |
|---|---|---|---|---|---|---|---|---|---|---|
| | £ | £ | £ | £ | | | £ | £ | £ | £ |

**3830 Half-Sovereign.** Small size, bare head r.R. Crowned shield and mantle. die axis ↑↓
1831 Proof plain edge *FDC* £2000                1834 ...................... 125   250   700   1000
1831 Proof milled edge *FDC* £4000
**3831 Half-Sovereign.** Large size, bare head r.R. Crowned shield and mantle.die axis ↑↓
1835 ...................... 125   250   600   900        1837 ...................... 125   275   650   950
1836 ...................... 150   300   675   950
**3832 Half-Sovereign.** *Obv.* struck from Sixpence. die in error, 1836 ......1100  2250   3750   —

## SILVER

3832                                            3833
Half-Sovereign - Sixpence obverse die

**3833 Crown.** R. Shield on mantle, 1831 Proof only W.W. on trun. struck ↑↓ ....*FDC* £10000
1831 Proof struck in gold *FDC* £65000
1831 Bare head r. W. WYON on trun. struck ↑↑ en medaille (medal die axis)*FDC* £12500
1831 Bare head r. similar die axis ↑↓ *FDC* £13000
1834 Bare head r. W.W. on trun. struck die axis ↑↓ ........................................*FDC* £16500
**3834 Halfcrown.** Bare head.WW in script on trun. R. Shield on mantle, die axis ↑↓

WW script

WW block

3834

| 1831 Plain edge proof *FDC* £850 | | | | 1835 ........................30 | 100 | 350 | 725 |
|---|---|---|---|---|---|---|---|
| 1831 Milled edge proof *FDC* £1650 | | | | 1836/5 ....................40 | 100 | 450 | 875 |
| 1834 ........................20 | 60 | 225 | 475 | 1836 ........................20 | 60 | 225 | 475 |
| 1834 Plain edge proof *FDC* £2750 | | | | 1836 Proof *FDC* £2000 | | | |
| 1834 Milled edge proof *FDC* £1250 | | | | 1837 ........................35 | 125 | 400 | 825 |

**3834A Halfcrown.** Bare head r. block WW on trun. R. Similar. die axis ↑↓
1831 Proof *FDC* £750
1834 ..............................................................................................40   150   500   925

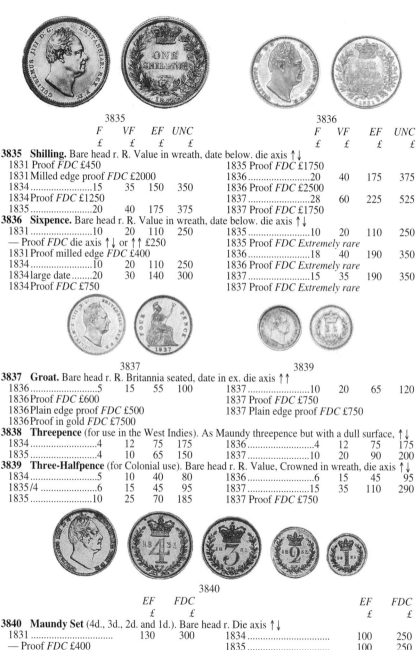

3835

| | F | VF | EF | UNC |
| --- | --- | --- | --- | --- |
| | £ | £ | £ | £ |

3836

| | F | VF | EF | UNC |
| --- | --- | --- | --- | --- |
| | £ | £ | £ | £ |

**3835  Shilling.** Bare head r. R. Value in wreath, date below. die axis ↑↓

| | | | | |
| --- | --- | --- | --- | --- |
| 1831 Proof *FDC* £450 | | | | |
| 1831 Milled edge proof *FDC* £2000 | | | | |
| 1834 ........................15 | 35 | 150 | 350 | |
| 1834 Proof *FDC* £1250 | | | | |
| 1835 ........................20 | 40 | 175 | 375 | |

| | | | | |
| --- | --- | --- | --- | --- |
| 1835 Proof *FDC* £1750 | | | | |
| 1836 ........................20 | 40 | 175 | 375 | |
| 1836 Proof *FDC* £2500 | | | | |
| 1837 ........................28 | 60 | 225 | 525 | |
| 1837 Proof *FDC* £1750 | | | | |

**3836  Sixpence.** Bare head r. R. Value in wreath, date below. die axis ↑↓

| | | | | |
| --- | --- | --- | --- | --- |
| 1831 ........................10 | 20 | 110 | 250 | |
| — Proof *FDC* die axis ↑↓ or ↑↑ £250 | | | | |
| 1831 Proof milled edge *FDC* £400 | | | | |
| 1834 ........................10 | 20 | 110 | 250 | |
| 1834 large date ........20 | 30 | 140 | 300 | |
| 1834 Proof *FDC* £750 | | | | |

| | | | | |
| --- | --- | --- | --- | --- |
| 1835 ........................10 | 20 | 110 | 250 | |
| 1835 Proof *FDC Extremely rare* | | | | |
| 1836 ........................18 | 40 | 190 | 350 | |
| 1836 Proof *FDC Extremely rare* | | | | |
| 1837 ........................15 | 35 | 190 | 350 | |
| 1837 Proof *FDC Extremely rare* | | | | |

3837

3839

**3837  Groat.** Bare head r. R. Britannia seated, date in ex. die axis ↑↑

| | | | | |
| --- | --- | --- | --- | --- |
| 1836 ........................5 | 15 | 55 | 100 | |
| 1836 Proof *FDC* £600 | | | | |
| 1836 Plain edge proof *FDC* £500 | | | | |
| 1836 Proof in gold *FDC* £7500 | | | | |

| | | | | |
| --- | --- | --- | --- | --- |
| 1837 ........................10 | 20 | 65 | 120 | |
| 1837 Proof *FDC* £750 | | | | |
| 1837 Plain edge proof *FDC* £750 | | | | |

**3838  Threepence** (for use in the West Indies). As Maundy threepence but with a dull surface, ↑↓

| | | | | |
| --- | --- | --- | --- | --- |
| 1834 ........................4 | 12 | 75 | 175 | |
| 1835 ........................4 | 10 | 65 | 150 | |

| | | | | |
| --- | --- | --- | --- | --- |
| 1836 ........................4 | 12 | 75 | 175 | |
| 1837 ........................10 | 20 | 90 | 200 | |

**3839  Three-Halfpence** (for Colonial use). Bare head r. R. Value, Crowned in wreath, die axis ↑↓

| | | | | |
| --- | --- | --- | --- | --- |
| 1834 ........................5 | 10 | 40 | 80 | |
| 1835/4 ........................6 | 15 | 45 | 95 | |
| 1835 ........................10 | 25 | 70 | 185 | |

| | | | | |
| --- | --- | --- | --- | --- |
| 1836 ........................6 | 15 | 45 | 95 | |
| 1837 ........................15 | 35 | 110 | 290 | |
| 1837 Proof *FDC* £750 | | | | |

3840

| | EF | FDC | | EF | FDC |
| --- | --- | --- | --- | --- | --- |
| | £ | £ | | £ | £ |

**3840  Maundy Set** (4d., 3d., 2d. and 1d.). Bare head r. Die axis ↑↓

| | EF | FDC | | EF | FDC |
| --- | --- | --- | --- | --- | --- |
| 1831 ................................ | 130 | 300 | 1834 ................................ | 100 | 250 |
| — Proof *FDC* £400 | | | 1835 ................................ | 100 | 250 |
| 1831 Proof struck in gold *FDC* £12500 | | | 1836 ................................ | 130 | 300 |
| 1832 ................................ | 110 | 275 | 1837 ................................ | 130 | 300 |
| 1833 ................................ | 100 | 250 | | | |

| | | | EF | FDC |
| --- | --- | --- | --- | --- |
| **3841** | — **Fourpence**, 1831-7 ............................................................*from* | | 12 | 25 |
| **3842** | — **Threepence**, 1831-7 ......................................................*from* | | 20 | 35 |
| **3843** | — **Twopence**, 1831-7 .........................................................*from* | | 10 | 20 |
| **3844** | — **Penny**, 1831-7 .................................................................*from* | | 10 | 18 |

## COPPER

3845

| | F | VF | EF | UNC | | F | VF | EF | UNC |
|---|---|---|---|---|---|---|---|---|---|
| | £ | £ | £ | £ | | £ | £ | £ | £ |

**3845 Penny.** Bare head r. No initials on trun. date below. R. Britannia r. die axis ↑↑

| 1831 | 18 | 50 | 225 | 600 | 1834 | 20 | 60 | 275 | 650 |
|---|---|---|---|---|---|---|---|---|---|
| 1831 Proof *FDC* ↑↓ £400 | | | | | 1837 | 45 | 110 | 425 | 1100 |
| 1831 Proof *FDC* ↑↑ £450 | | | | | | | | | |

**3846 Penny.** Bare head r. date below. incuse initials on trun. R. Britannia r. die axis ↑↑

| 1831 W.W on trun | *Extremely rare* | 1831 .W.W on trun. | 30 | 85 | 325 | 650 |
|---|---|---|---|---|---|---|

**3847 Halfpenny.** Bare head r. date below. R. Britannia r. die axis ↑↑

| 1831 | 12 | 25 | 95 | 225 | 1834 | 12 | 25 | 95 | 225 |
|---|---|---|---|---|---|---|---|---|---|
| 1831 Proof *FDC* ↑↓ £275 | | | | | 1837 | 10 | 20 | 85 | 200 |
| 1831 Proof *FDC* ↑↑ £375 | | | | | | | | | |

3847             3848

**3848 Farthing.** Bare head r. date below. R. Britannia r. die axis ↑↑

| 1831 rev. incuse line | | | | | 1835 die axis ↑↓ | 5 | 20 | 95 | 165 |
|---|---|---|---|---|---|---|---|---|---|
| on saltire | 2 | 10 | 60 | 100 | 1835 die axis ↑↑ | 2 | 10 | 60 | 100 |
| 1831 Proof *FDC* ↑↓ £250 | | | | | 1835 rev. incuse line | | | | |
| 1831 Proof *FDC* ↑↑ £300 | | | | | on saltire | 2 | 10 | 60 | 100 |
| 1834 incuse saltire | 2 | 10 | 60 | 100 | 1836 rev. raised line | | | | |
| 1834 rev. raised line | | | | | on saltire | 2 | 10 | 60 | 100 |
| on saltire | 2 | 10 | 60 | 100 | 1837 — | 2 | 10 | 60 | 100 |

**3849 Half-Farthing** (for use in Ceylon). Bare head r. date below. R. Britannia r. die axis ↑↑

| 1837 | 50 | 160 | 300 | — |
|---|---|---|---|---|

3849             3850

**3850 Third-Farthing** (for use in Malta). Bare head r. date below. R. Britannia r. die axis ↑↑

| 1835 | 5 | 15 | 80 | 200 |
|---|---|---|---|---|
| 1835 Proof *FDC* £400 | | | | |

Copper coins graded in this catalogue as UNC have full mint lustre

**PS2 Proof set**. Coronation, 1831. Two pounds to farthing (14 coins). *FDC* £19500

Victoria was born on 24 May 1819, and enjoyed the longest reign of any Monarch so far. She marrried the German, Prince Albert with whom she enjoyed 17 years of Marriage. Upon Albert's death she became the 'Widow of Windsor' descending into a 25 year period of mourning. She skillfully avoided conflict with other European powers, and produced connections with many Royal houses all over Europe. The Great Exhibition of 1851 was a sign of the power of the largest Empire in the world. Victoria died on 22 January 1901 at the age of 81.

In 1849, as a first step towards decimalization, a silver Florin ($^1/_{10}$ th pound) was introduced, but the coins of 1849 omitted the usual *Dei Gratia* and these so-called 'Godless' Florins were replaced in 1851 by the 'Gothic' issue. The Halfcrown was temporarily discontinued but was minted again from 1874 onwards. Between 1863 and 1880 reverse dies of the gold and silver coins were numbered in the course of Mint experiments into the wear of dies. The exception was the Florin where the die number is on the obverse below the bust.

The gold and silver coins were redesigned for the Queen's Golden Jubilee in 1887. The Double-Florin which was then issued was abandoned after only four years; the Jubilee Sixpence of 1887, known as the 'withdrawn' type, was changed to avoid confusion with the Half-Sovereign. Gold and silver were again redesigned in 1893 with an older portrait of the Queen, but the 'old head' was not used on the bronze coinage until 1895. The heavy copper Penny had been replaced by the lighter bronze 'bun' Penny in 1860. In 1874-6 and 1881-2 some of the bronze was made by Heaton in Birmingham, and these have a letter H below the date. From 1897 Farthings were issued with a dark surface.

Early Sovereigns had a shield-type reverse, but Pistrucci's St. George design was used again from 1871. In order to increase the output of gold coinage, branches of the Royal Mint were set up in Australia at Sydney and Melbourne and, later, at Perth for coining gold of imperial type.

**Engraver's and/or designer's initials on the coins:**

W. W. (William Wyon 1795-1851)    T. B. (Thomas Brock 1847-1922)
L. C. W. (Leonard Charles Wyon 1826-91)    B. P. (Benedetto Pistrucci, 1784-1855)
J. E. B. (Joseph Edgar Boehm 1834-90)

**Engravers and Designers:** George William De Saulle, (1862-1903) William Dyce (1806-64), Jean Baptiste Merlen (1769-c.1850) Edward Poynter (1836-1919)

**Prime Ministers:** Viscount Melbourne, (1779-1848), Whig, 1835-41; Sir Robert Peel, (1788-1850), Tory, 1841-6; Earl of Aberdeen, (1784-1860), Tory 1852-5, Viscount Palmerston, (1784-1865), Liberal, 1855-8 1859-65; Lord John Russell, (1792-1878), Whig, 1846-52 1865-6; Earl of Derby, (1799-1869), Conservative, 1852, 1858-9 1866-8; Benjamin Disraeli, Earl of Beaconsfield (1804-1881), Conservative, 1868, 1874-80; William Ewart Gladstone (1809-1898), 1868-74, 1880-85, 1886, 1892-94 ; Earl of Salisbury, (1830-1903), Conservative, 1885-6. 1886-92, 1895-1902; Earl of Rosebery, (1847-1929), Liberal, 1894-5.

**Young Head Coinage, 1838-87**

# GOLD

3851
1839 Five Pounds - DIRIGE reverse

**3851  Five Pounds.** 1839. Young filleted bust l. plain rear fillet R̃. 'Una and the lion' (proof only)
DIRIGIT legend, inscribed edge, die axis ↑↑                                    *FDC* £27,500
– 1839 Similar – DIRIGIT legend, struck on thick flan                          *FDC* £35,000
– 1839 Similar – DIRIGIT legend, plain edge die axis ↑↑                        *FDC* £26,500
– 1839 –13 leaves to rear fillet, R. DIRIGE legend–proof                       *FDC* £25,000
– 1839 Similar – DIRIGE legend edge letters off-centre                         *FDC* £27,500
– 1839 Similar – DIRIGE legend edge plain proof                                *FDC* £27,500
– 1839 –9 leaves to rear fillet, DIRIGE legend                                 *FDC* £22,500
– 1839 Similar – DIRIGE legend edge plain                                      *FDC* £30,000
– 1839 Similar – DIRIGE legend edge letters off-centre                         *FDC* £27,500
– 1839 Similar – DIRIGIT legend edge plain proof                               *FDC* £30,000

3852

Sovereign - first young head

**3852 Sovereign.** First (small) young head. l. date below. R̃. First shield. London mint, die axis ↑↓

| | F £ | VF £ | EF £ | UNC £ | | F £ | VF £ | EF £ | UNC £ |
|---|---|---|---|---|---|---|---|---|---|
| 1838 | 175 | 575 | 1250 | 2500 | 1844 large 44 | 85 | 110 | 225 | 400 |
| 1838 Plain edge proof *FDC* £5000 | | | | | 1844 small 44 | 120 | 225 | 500 | 1100 |
| 1839 | 225 | 650 | 1450 | 2750 | 1844 4/ ↤ | | *Extremely rare* | | |
| 1839 die axis ↑↓ Proof *FDC* £3500 | | | | | 1845 4/ ↤ | | *Extremely rare* | | |
| 1839 die axis ↑↑ Proof *FDC* £3750 | | | | | 1845 | 85 | 110 | 225 | 400 |
| 1839 Milled edge proof *FDC* £7500 | | | | | 1845 Roman I | | *Extremely rare* | | |
| 1841 | 1000 | 2000 | 5000 | — | 1846 | 85 | 110 | 225 | 400 |
| 1842 | 85 | 110 | 225 | 400 | 1846 4/ ↤ | | *Extremely rare* | | |
| 1843 | 85 | 110 | 225 | 400 | 1847 | 85 | 110 | 225 | 400 |
| 1843/2 | 175 | 250 | 650 | 1500 | 1848 | 350 | 750 | 2500 | — |

3852A                          3852B                                      3852C

Leaves differently arranged    Narrow shield                    Second large head

**3852A Sovereign.** Similar R̃ similar but leaves of the wreath arranged differently with tops of leaves closer to crown.

| | | | | | |
|---|---|---|---|---|---|
| 1838 | | | | 2250 | 4250 — — |

**3852B Sovereign.** Similar narrower shield. Considerably modified floral emblems, different leaf arrangement ↑↓

| | | | | | |
|---|---|---|---|---|---|
| 1843 | | | | 2500 | 4750 — — |

**3852C Sovereign.** Second (large) head. l. W W still in relief. date below R̃. Shield with repositioned legend die axis ↑↓

| | F | VF | EF | UNC | | F | VF | EF | UNC |
|---|---|---|---|---|---|---|---|---|---|
| 1848 | BV | 90 | 200 | 375 | 1852 | BV | 85 | 175 | 350 |
| 1849 | BV | 90 | 200 | 375 | 1853 | BV | 85 | 175 | 350 |
| 1849 Roman I | 200 | 500 | 1250 | — | 1854 | 125 | 250 | 650 | — |
| 1850 | BV | 100 | 225 | 400 | 1855 | 110 | 175 | 300 | — |
| 1851 | BV | 85 | 175 | 350 | 1872 | BV | 85 | 150 | 325 |

3852D                                3852E

WW Incuse            Extra line in ribbon - Ansell

3852F/3853A

827 on truncation

**3852D Sovereign.** Similar — WW incuse on trun. die axis ↑↓

| | F | VF | EF | UNC | | F | VF | EF | UNC |
|---|---|---|---|---|---|---|---|---|---|
| 1853 | 95 | 175 | 350 | — | 1860 | BV | 85 | 175 | 350 |
| — Proof *FDC* £6500 | | | | | 1860 large 0 | 85 | 125 | 300 | 650 |
| 1854 | BV | 85 | 175 | 350 | 1861 | BV | 85 | 175 | 350 |
| 1855 | BV | 85 | 175 | 350 | 1861 Roman I | 175 | 350 | 750 | — |
| 1856 | BV | 85 | 175 | 350 | 1862 wide date | BV | 85 | 175 | 350 |
| 1857 | BV | 85 | 175 | 350 | 1862 R/ Я in VICTORIA | | *Extremely rare* | | |
| 1858 | BV | 85 | 225 | 375 | 1862 F/ V in DEF narrow date | | *Extremely rare* | | |
| 1859 | BV | 85 | 175 | 350 | 1863 | BV | 85 | 175 | 350 |
| 1860 O over C in obverse leg. | | *Extremely rare* | | | 1863 Roman I (1/1) | 200 | 500 | | |

**3852E Sovereign.** Similar — As 3852D 'Ansell' ribbon. Additional raised line on the lower part of the ribbon ↑↓

| | | | | | |
|---|---|---|---|---|---|
| 1859 | | | | 250 | 800 3000 — |

**3852F Sovereign.** Similar — As 3852D with die number 827 on trun. die axis ↑↓

| | | | | | |
|---|---|---|---|---|---|
| 1863 | | | | 2500 | 4250 — — |

3853
Die number location

3853B
WW in relief on truncation

|  | F | VF | EF | UNC |  | F | VF | EF | UNC |
|---|---|---|---|---|---|---|---|---|---|
|  | £ | £ | £ | £ |  | £ | £ | £ | £ |

**3853 Sovereign.** Similar As 3852D R. die number in space below wreath, above floral emblem, die axis ↑↓

| 1863 | BV | 90 | 175 | 300 | 1866/5 DIE 17 only | 85 | 175 | 350 | 750 |
|---|---|---|---|---|---|---|---|---|---|
| 1864 | BV | 85 | 150 | 275 | 1868 | BV | 90 | 175 | 300 |
| 1865 | BV | 90 | 175 | 325 | 1869 | BV | 85 | 150 | 275 |
| 1866 | BV | 85 | 150 | 275 | 1870 | BV | 100 | 200 | 350 |

**3853A Sovereign.** Similar — As 3853 with die number 827 on trun. R. die number is always no. 22 die axis ↑↓

| 1863 | 2250 | 3750 | — | — |
|---|---|---|---|---|

**3853B Sovereign.** Similar — WW in relief on trun. R. die number below wreath, above floral emblem die axis ↑↓

| 1870 | BV | 90 | 175 | 325 | 1873 | BV | 90 | 175 | 300 |
|---|---|---|---|---|---|---|---|---|---|
| 1871 | BV | 80 | 140 | 275 | 1874 | 950 | 2000 | 4500 | — |
| 1872 | BV | 80 | 140 | 275 |  |  |  |  |  |

Melbourne Mint mark
3854

Sydney Mint mark
3855

**3854 Sovereign** Second (large) head. l. WW in relief date below R. M below wreath for Melbourne Mint, Australia ↑↓

| 1872 M | BV | 75 | 135 | 700 | 1883 M | 85 | 200 | 500 | 1500 |
|---|---|---|---|---|---|---|---|---|---|
| 1872/1 M | 125 | 250 | 750 | 2000 | 1884 M | BV | 75 | 110 | 500 |
| 1874 M | BV | 75 | 165 | 1000 | 1885 M | BV | 75 | 110 | 500 |
| 1880 M | 300 | 600 | 1600 | 3600 | 1886 M | 600 | 2000 | 3000 | 5600 |
| 1881 M | BV | 85 | 180 | 1250 | 181887 M | 325 | 600 | 2000 | 3750 |
| 1882 M | BV | 75 | 135 | 600 |  |  |  |  |  |

**3855 Sovereign.** Similar — As 3854 R. with S below wreath for Sydney Mint, Australia die axis ↑↓

| 1871 S | BV | 75 | 110 | 600 | 1880 S .... VICTORIA | | *Extremely rare* | | |
|---|---|---|---|---|---|---|---|---|---|
| 1872 S | BV | 75 | 135 | 900 | 1881 S | BV | 75 | 135 | 750 |
| 1873 S | BV | 75 | 130 | 750 | 1882 S | BV | 75 | 110 | 550 |
| 1875 S | BV | 75 | 135 | 750 | 1883 S | BV | 75 | 110 | 550 |
| 1877 S | BV | 75 | 110 | 500 | 1884 S | BV | 75 | 100 | 500 |
| 1878 S | BV | 75 | 110 | 500 | 1885 S | BV | 75 | 100 | 500 |
| 1879 S | BV | 75 | 110 | 500 | 1886 S | BV | 75 | 100 | 500 |
| 1880 S | BV | 75 | 120 | 750 | 1887 S | BV | 75 | 165 | 825 |

**3855A Sovereign.** Second (large) head WW incuse on trun. date below R. with S below wreath for Sydney Mint die axis ↑↓

| 1871 S | 75 | 95 | 140 | 650 |
|---|---|---|---|---|

| | 3856A |
|---|---|
| | Horse with long tail |
| | Small BP in exergue |

3856C
Horse with short tail
No BP in exergue

| | F | VF | EF | UNC | | F | VF | EF | UNC |
|---|---|---|---|---|---|---|---|---|---|
| | £ | £ | £ | £ | | £ | £ | £ | £ |

**3856 Sovereign.** First young head. l. WW buried in narrow trun. R. St. George.
London mint. Horse with short tail. Large BP and date in ex. die axis ↑↓

| | F | VF | EF | UNC |
|---|---|---|---|---|
| 1871..........................................................................................BV | | 85 | 125 | 300 |

1871 Proof milled edge*FDC* £9500
1871 Plain edge proof *FDC* £5000

**3856A Sovereign.** — — As 3856 R. Horse with long tail. Small BP and date in ex.die axis ↑↓

| 1871 ......................BV | 75 | 100 | 250 | 1876 ......................BV | 75 | 100 | 250 |
|---|---|---|---|---|---|---|---|
| 1871 Proof *FDC* plain edge £6500 | | | | 1878 ......................BV | 75 | 100 | 250 |
| 1872 ......................BV | 75 | 110 | 275 | 1879 ......................125 | 300 | 1250 | — |
| 1873 ......................BV | 75 | 100 | 250 | 1880 ......................BV | 75 | 100 | 250 |
| 1874 ......................BV | 75 | 110 | 275 | | | | |

**3856B Sovereign.** — — As 3856 R. Horse with short tail, small BP and date in ex.die axis ↑↓

| 1880 ......................BV | 75 | 100 | 250 | 1884 ......................BV | 75 | 100 | 250 |
|---|---|---|---|---|---|---|---|
| 1880 8/7..................60 | 95 | 140 | 300 | 1885 ......................BV | 75 | 125 | 275 |

**3856C Sovereign.** — — As 3856 R. Horse with short tail, date but no BP in ex.die axis ↑↓

| | F | VF | EF | UNC |
|---|---|---|---|---|
| 1880 Second 8/7............................................................................BV | | 95 | 140 | 300 |

**3856D Sovereign.** Second head. l. WW complete, on broad trun. R.
Horse with long tail, small BP and date in ex.die axis ↑↓

| 1880 8/7 ..........................................................................................60 | 95 | 140 | 300 |
|---|---|---|---|
| 1880..............................................................................................BV | 75 | 100 | 250 |

**3856E Sovereign.** — — As 3856D R. Horse with short tail. Date but no BP in ex. die axis ↑↓

| 1880..............................................................................................BV | 75 | 100 | 250 |
|---|---|---|---|

**3856F Sovereign.** — — As 3856E R. Horse with short tail, small BP and date in ex. die axis ↑↓

| 1880.......................65 | 95 | 140 | 300 | 1885 ......................BV | 75 | 110 | 275 |
|---|---|---|---|---|---|---|---|
| 1884 ......................BV | 75 | 110 | 275 | | | | |

| 3857 | 3857A |
|---|---|
| Melbourne Mint | Horse with short tail |
| WW buried in truncation | No BP in exergue |

**3857 Sovereign.** — — First head. l. WW buried in trun. M below head for Melbourne Mint,
Australia. R. Horse with long tail, small BP and date in ex. die axis ↑↓

| 1872 M ..................110 | 185 | 625 | 2500 | 1877 M..................BV | 75 | 135 | 550 |
|---|---|---|---|---|---|---|---|
| 1873 M..................BV | 80 | 165 | 900 | 1878 M..................BV | 75 | 135 | 550 |
| 1874 M..................BV | 80 | 165 | 900 | 1879 M..................BV | 70 | 100 | 550 |
| 1875 M..................BV | 75 | 135 | 650 | 1880 M..................BV | 75 | 110 | 550 |
| 1876 M..................BV | 75 | 130 | 550 | 1881 M..................BV | 75 | 110 | 550 |

**3857A Sovereign.** — — As 3857 R. horse with short tail, date but no BP in ex die axis ↑↓

| 1881 M .................BV | 70 | 110 | 550 | 1884 M .................65 | 100 | 250 | — |
|---|---|---|---|---|---|---|---|
| 1882 M..................BV | 75 | 110 | 525 | | | | |

|  | F £ | VF £ | EF £ | UNC £ |  | F £ | VF £ | EF £ | UNC £ |
|---|---|---|---|---|---|---|---|---|---|

**3857B Sovereign.** First head l. WW buried in trun. M below head for Melbourne Mint, Australia R.
Horse with short tail, small BP and date in ex. die axis ↑↓

| 1879 M | | *Extremely rare* | | | 1883 M | BV | 65 | 100 | 500 |
|---|---|---|---|---|---|---|---|---|---|
| 1880 M | | *Extremely rare* | | | 1884 M | BV | 65 | 100 | 425 |
| 1882 M | BV | 75 | 110 | 550 | 1885 M | BV | 65 | 100 | 450 |

**3857C Sovereign.** — — Second head. l. WW complete on broad truncation. R. Horse with short tail, small BP in ex.

| 1882 M | BV | 75 | 110 | 550 | 1885 M | BV | 65 | 100 | 450 |
|---|---|---|---|---|---|---|---|---|---|
| 1883 M | BV | 65 | 100 | 500 | 1886 M | BV | 65 | 100 | 425 |
| 1884 M | BV | 65 | 100 | 425 | 1887 M | BV | 75 | 110 | 550 |

**3858 Sovereign** First head. l. WW buried in narrow trun. S below head for Sydney Mint, Australia,
R. Horse with short tail, large BP and date in ex. die axis ↑↓

| 1871 S | | | | | | 70 | 135 | 500 | 1600 |
|---|---|---|---|---|---|---|---|---|---|

**3858A Sovereign.** — — As 3858 R. Horse with long tail, small BP and date in ex. die axis ↑↓

| 1871 S | BV | 100 | 400 | 1250 | 1875 S | BV | 85 | 165 | 900 |
|---|---|---|---|---|---|---|---|---|---|
| 1872 S | BV | 85 | 165 | 900 | 1876 S | BV | 85 | 165 | 750 |
| 1873 S | BV | 90 | 180 | 1150 | 1879 S | | 60 | 120 | 750 | 2150 |
| 1874 S | BV | 85 | 165 | 1250 | 1880 S | BV | 80 | 125 | 650 |

**3858B Sovereign.** — — As 3858 R. Horse with short tail, date but no BP in ex. die axis ↑↓

| 1880 S | BV | 75 | 125 | 650 | 1881 S | BV | 70 | 110 | 650 |
|---|---|---|---|---|---|---|---|---|---|

| 3858C | 3859 | 3859A |
|---|---|---|
| Sydney Mint WW on broad truncation | Type A1 | Type A2 |

**3858C Sovereign.** Second head. l. WW complete on broad trun. R.
Horse with long tail, small BP and date in ex. die axis ↑↓

| 1880 S | | | | | | BV | 80 | 125 | 650 |
|---|---|---|---|---|---|---|---|---|---|

**3858D Sovereign.** — — As 3858C R. Horse with short tail, date but no BP in ex. die axis ↑↓

| 1881 S | | 75 | 110 | 650 | 1882 S | BV | 65 | 100 | 350 |
|---|---|---|---|---|---|---|---|---|---|

**3858E Sovereign.** — — As 3858D R. Horse with short tail small BP and date in ex. die axis ↑↓

| 1882 S | BV | 65 | 100 | 350 | 1885 S | BV | 65 | 100 | 500 |
|---|---|---|---|---|---|---|---|---|---|
| 1883 S | BV | 80 | 140 | 1000 | 1886 S | BV | 65 | 100 | 500 |
| 1884 S | BV | 65 | 100 | 500 | 1887 S | BV | 65 | 100 | 550 |

**3859 Half-Sovereign.** Type A1. First (smallest) young head. date below l. R. First shield, die axis ↑↓

| 1838 | 75 | 125 | 325 | 650 | 1849 | 45 | 95 | 275 | 450 |
|---|---|---|---|---|---|---|---|---|---|
| 1839 die axis ↑↓ or ↑↑ Proof only *FDC* £1750 | | | | | 1850 | 125 | 300 | 950 | — |
| 1839 Milled edge proof *FDC* Extremely rare | | | | | 1851 | 45 | 80 | 225 | 375 |
| 1841 | 80 | 125 | 350 | 675 | 1852 | 65 | 95 | 275 | 475 |
| 1842 | 45 | 95 | 275 | 500 | 1853 | 45 | 80 | 225 | 375 |
| 1843 | 70 | 135 | 375 | 600 | 1853 Proof *FDC* £3750 | | | | |
| 1844 | 65 | 110 | 325 | 550 | 1854 | | *Extremely rare* | | |
| 1845 | 125 | 375 | 1150 | — | 1855 | 45 | 80 | 225 | 375 |
| 1846 | 65 | 110 | 325 | 550 | 1856 | 45 | 80 | 225 | 375 |
| 1847 | 65 | 110 | 325 | 550 | 1856/5 | 85 | 140 | 325 | 550 |
| 1848 Close date | 65 | 110 | 325 | 550 | 1857 | 65 | 95 | 275 | 475 |
| 1848/7 | 110 | 200 | 450 | 750 | 1858 | 65 | 95 | 275 | 475 |
| 1848 Wide date | 80 | 135 | 375 | 650 | | | | | |

**3859A Half-Sovereign.** Type A2, Second (larger) young head. date below. R. First shield die axis ↑↓

| 1858 | 45 | 80 | 225 | 375 | 1861 | 45 | 80 | 225 | 375 |
|---|---|---|---|---|---|---|---|---|---|
| 1859 | 45 | 80 | 225 | 375 | 1862 | 325 | 1000 | 3250 | — |
| 1860 | 45 | 80 | 225 | 375 | 1863 | 45 | 80 | 225 | 375 |

| 3860 | 3860C | 3860D | 3860E | 3860F |
|---|---|---|---|---|
| Die number location | Repositioned legend | Type A3 | Type A4 | Type A5 |

|  | F | VF | EF | UNC |  | F | VF | EF | UNC |
|---|---|---|---|---|---|---|---|---|---|
|  | £ | £ | £ | £ |  | £ | £ | £ | £ |

**3860 Half-Sovereign.** Type A2, second head, date below R. die number below shield, die axis ↑↓

| 1863 | 65 | 95 | 300 | 500 | 1867 | 45 | 80 | 225 | 375 |
|---|---|---|---|---|---|---|---|---|---|
| 1864 | 45 | 80 | 225 | 375 | 1869 | 45 | 80 | 225 | 375 |
| 1865 | 45 | 80 | 225 | 375 | 1870 | 45 | 80 | 225 | 375 |
| 1866 | 45 | 80 | 225 | 375 | 1871 | 45 | 80 | 225 | 375 |

**3860A Half-Sovereign.** Second head, date below R. Re-engraved shield legend and rosettes closer to border, coarse boarder teeth both sides, with die number below shield die axis ↑↓

| 1870 | 100 | 225 | 675 | — | 1871 | 100 | 225 | 675 | — |
|---|---|---|---|---|---|---|---|---|---|

**3860B Half-Sovereign.** Second head, date below R. As last but with normal border teeth and no die number below shield die axis ↑↓

| 1871 | 200 | 425 | 1000 | — |
|---|---|---|---|---|

**3860C Half-Sovereign.** Second head, date below obv. with repositioned legend, nose now points to T in VICTORIA. R. Similar to last but with die number below shield die axis ↑↓

| 1871 | 125 | 275 | 800 | — | 1872 | 100 | 225 | 675 | — |
|---|---|---|---|---|---|---|---|---|---|

**3860DHalf-Sovereign.** Type A3, Third (larger still) young head l, date below. R. As 3860A, with die number below shield die axis ↑↓

| 1872 | 45 | 80 | 225 | 375 | 1875 | 45 | 75 | 225 | 325 |
|---|---|---|---|---|---|---|---|---|---|
| 1873 | 45 | 80 | 225 | 375 | 1876 | 45 | 75 | 225 | 325 |
| 1874 | 45 | 85 | 225 | 375 | 1877 | 45 | 75 | 225 | 325 |

**3860E Half-Sovereign.** Type A4. Fourth young head l. hair ribbon now narrow, date below. R. As last with die number below shield die axis ↑↓

| 1876 | 45 | 75 | 175 | 325 | 1878 | 45 | 75 | 175 | 325 |
|---|---|---|---|---|---|---|---|---|---|
| 1877 | 45 | 75 | 175 | 325 | 1879 | 60 | 100 | 325 | 550 |

**3860F Half-Sovereign.** Type A5. Fifth young head l. in very low relief, date below. R. As last with die number below shield die axis ↑↓

| 1880 | 50 | 95 | 325 | 550 |
|---|---|---|---|---|

| 3861 | 3862 |
|---|---|
| Type A5 | Sydney Mint |

**3861 Half-Sovereign.** Fifth head, date below. R. Cross on crown buried in border. Legend and rosettes very close to heavy border, no die number below shield die axis ↑↓

| 1880 | 45 | 85 | 200 | 375 | 1885 | 45 | 75 | 175 | 275 |
|---|---|---|---|---|---|---|---|---|---|
| 1883 | 45 | 75 | 175 | 275 | 1885/3 | 80 | 140 | 300 | 600 |
| 1884 | 45 | 75 | 175 | 275 |  |  |  |  |  |

**3862 Half-Sovereign.** Type A2, Second (larger) young head l. nose points between T and O. Date below R. First crowned shield cross clear of border with S below shield for Sydney Mint, Australia, die axis ↑↓

| 1871 S | 45 | 100 | 600 | 2150 |
|---|---|---|---|---|

|   | F | VF | EF | UNC |   |   | F | VF | EF | UNC |
|---|---|----|----|-----|---|---|---|----|----|-----|
|   | £ | £ | £ | £ |   |   | £ | £ | £ | £ |

**3862A Half-Sovereign.** Similar obv. with repositioned legend, nose now points to T in VICTORIA.
Date below Ɍ Re-engraved shield cross touches border, S below shield die axis ↑↓

1872 S .............................................................................................45    100    600    2150

**3862B Half-Sovereign.** Type A3. Third (larger still) young head l. I of DEI points to rear fillet.
Date below Ɍ. As last die axis ↑↓

1875 S .............................................................................................45    100    600    2150

**3862C Half-Sovereign.** Type A4. Fourth young head l. front hair fillet now narrow. Ɍ. As last, die axis ↑↓

1879 S .............................................................................................45    110    525    2150

**3862D Half-Sovereign.** Type A5. Fifth young head l. in low relief wider tr. no front ear lobe. Date
below Ɍ as last. die axis ↑↓

1882 S...................140    475    2650    6850        1883 S....................55    110    500    3000

**3862E Half-Sovereign.** Fifth head, date below Ɍ. Cross on crown buried in border. Legend and
rosettes very close to heavy border, S below shield die axis ↑↓

1880 S....................45    120    650    2650        1883 S....................45    110    500    3000
1881 S....................45    135    800    2900        1886 S....................45    120    800    2400
1882 S...................120    475    2650    6850        1887 S....................55    120    650    2000

3863
Melbourne Mint

**3863 Half-Sovereign.** Type A3. Third (larger still) young head l. Date below Ɍ. Re-engraved shield
with M below shield for Melbourne Mint, Australia die axis ↑↓

1873 M ...................45    120    650    2350        1877 M ..................45    110    580    2150

**3863A Half-Sovereign.** Type A4, fourth young head l. hair ribbon now narrow. Ɍ. As last die axis ↑↓

1877 M ...................45    110    600    2150        1882 M ..................45    110    500    1650

**3863B Half-Sovereign.** Type A5. Fifth young head l. in low relief.Date below Ɍ. As last die axis ↑↓

1881 M ...................70    150    1250    3650        1885 M ................140    350    1850    5150
1882 M ...................45    110    500    1650        1886 M ..................75    175    1350    3650
1884 M ...................55    220    1350    3850        1887 M ................100    275    1850    5150

## Jubilee Coinage, 1887-93, die axis ↑↑

3864
1887 Five Pounds

**3864* Five Pounds.** Jubilee bust 1. Ɍ. St. George date in ex. 1887...........425    600    775    975
— Proof *FDC* £2750
— Proof no B.P. in exergue £3250

**3864A* Five Pounds.** Jubilee bust 1. Ɍ. St George, S on ground for Sydney Mint, Australia 1887 S
*Extremely rare*

* *Beware recent forgeries*

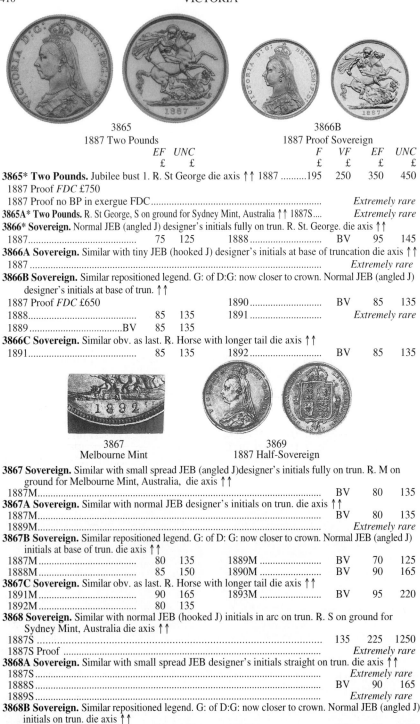

3865
1887 Two Pounds

3866B
1887 Proof Sovereign

|  | EF | UNC |  | F | VF | EF | UNC |
|---|---|---|---|---|---|---|---|
|  | £ | £ |  | £ | £ | £ | £ |

**3865\* Two Pounds.** Jubilee bust 1. R. St George die axis ↑↑ 1887 ..........195   250   350   450
   1887 Proof *FDC* £750
   1887 Proof no BP in exergue FDC................................................................. *Extremely rare*
**3865A\* Two Pounds.** R. St George, S on ground for Sydney Mint, Australia ↑↑ 1887S.... *Extremely rare*
**3866\* Sovereign.** Normal JEB (angled J) designer's initials fully on trun. R. St. George. die axis ↑↑
   1887..........................................   75   125       1888 ..........................   BV   95   145
**3866A Sovereign.** Similar with tiny JEB (hooked J) designer's initials at base of truncation die axis ↑↑
   1887 ...................................................................................................... *Extremely rare*
**3866B Sovereign.** Similar repositioned legend. G: of D:G: now closer to crown. Normal JEB (angled J)
   designer's initials at base of trun. ↑↑
   1887 Proof *FDC* £650                      1890 ..........................   BV   85   135
   1888.......................................   85   135       1891 ..........................   *Extremely rare*
   1889...................................BV   85   135
**3866C Sovereign.** Similar obv. as last. R. Horse with longer tail die axis ↑↑
   1891.......................................   85   135       1892 ..........................   BV   85   135

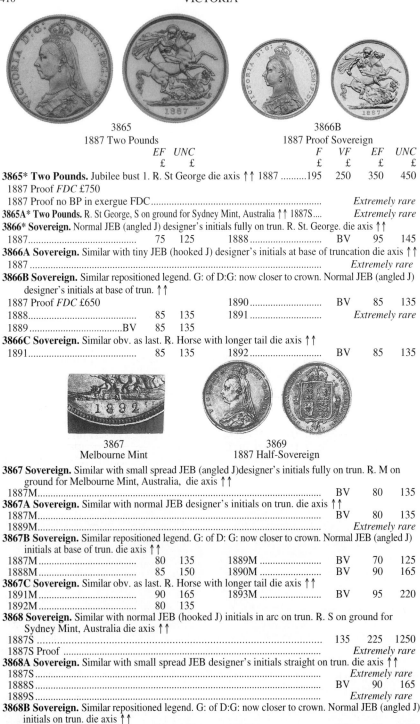

3867
Melbourne Mint

3869
1887 Half-Sovereign

**3867 Sovereign.** Similar with small spread JEB (angled J)designer's initials fully on trun. R. M on
   ground for Melbourne Mint, Australia,  die axis ↑↑
   1887M.................................................................................................   BV   80   135
**3867A Sovereign.** Similar with normal JEB designer's initials on trun. die axis ↑↑
   1887M.................................................................................................   BV   80   135
   1889M.................................................................................................   *Extremely rare*
**3867B Sovereign.** Similar repositioned legend. G: of D: G: now closer to crown. Normal JEB (angled J)
   initials at base of trun. die axis ↑↑
   1887M..........................   80   135       1889M ..........................   BV   70   125
   1888M..........................   85   150       1890M ..........................   BV   90   165
**3867C Sovereign.** Similar obv. as last. R. Horse with longer tail die axis ↑↑
   1891M..........................   90   165       1893M ..........................   BV   95   220
   1892M..........................   80   135
**3868 Sovereign.** Similar with normal JEB (hooked J) initials in arc on trun. R. S on ground for
   Sydney Mint, Australia die axis ↑↑
   1887S ..............................................................................   135   225   1250
   1887S Proof ..............................................................................   *Extremely rare*
**3868A Sovereign.** Similar with small spread JEB designer's initials straight on trun. die axis ↑↑
   1887S..................................................................................   *Extremely rare*
   1888S..................................................................................   BV   90   165
   1889S..................................................................................   *Extremely rare*
**3868B Sovereign.** Similar repositioned legend. G: of D:G: now closer to crown. Normal JEB (angled J)
   initials on trun. die axis ↑↑
   1888S..........................   90   165       1890S..........................   BV   90   165
   1889S..........................   70   125       *\* Beware recent forgeries*

|  | VF | EF | UNC |  | F | VF | EF | UNC |
|---|---|---|---|---|---|---|---|---|
|  | £ | £ | £ |  | £ | £ | £ | £ |

**3868C Sovereign.** Similar obv. as last. R. Horse with longer tail die axis ↑↑

1891S ..................................... 90 165    1893S......................... BV 100 195

1892S ..................................... 70 125

**3869 Half-Sovereign.** Similar obv. normal JEB designer's initials. on trun. R. High shield die axis ↑↑

1887............................. 60 95    1890 .......................... 120 225 —

— Proof *FDC* £350

3869A           3869B - Lower shield

3869C

Plain trun., higher shield

**3869A Half-Sovereign.** Similar small close JEB intitials. on trun. R. High shield die axis ↑↑

1887............................. 120 225 —

**3869B Half-Sovereign.** Similar normal JEB initials. on trun. R. Lower shield, date therefore spread apart, complete cross at top, die axis ↑↑

1890............................. 120 225 —    1892........................... 120 225 —

**3869C Half-Sovereign.** Similar no JEB initials on trun. R. High Shield die axis ↑↑

1887............................. 120 225 —    1891 .......................... 120 225 —

1890............................. BV 60 95    1892........................... 120 225 —

**3869D Half-Sovereign.** Jubilee bust 1. R. Lower shield, date therefore spread apart die axis ↑↑

1890............................. BV 60 95    1892 .......................... BV 60 95

1891............................. BV 75 110    1893 .......................... BV 85 120

3870           3870A

**3870 Half-Sovereign.** Similar small very spread JEB initials on trun. R. High shield, M below for Melbourne Mint, Australia, die axis ↑↑

1887M...................................................................................40 75 225 800

**3870A Half-Sovereign.** Similar small close JEB initials on trun. R. As last die axis ↑↑

1887M...................................................................................40 75 225 800

**3870B Half-Sovereign.** Similar normal JEB initials on trun. R. Lower shield, date therefore spread part die axis ↑↑

1893M...................................................................................40 120 450 1650

**3871 Half-Sovereign.** Similar small very spread JEB initials on trun. R. High shield S below for Sydney Mint, Australia ↑↑

1887S......................................................................................40 75 225 825

**3871A Half-Sovereign.** Similar small close JEB initials on trun. R As last. die axis ↑↑

1887S......................................................................................40 75 225 825

|  | F | VF | EF | UNC |
|---|---|---|---|---|
|  | £ | £ | £ | £ |

**3871B Half-Sovereign.** Jubilee bust 1. Normal JEB initials on trun. R̶. Lower shield, date therefore spread apart, S below for Sydney Mint, Australia die axis ↑↑

1889S ...................................................................................................45    125    450    1650

**3871C Half-Sovereign.** Jubilee bust 1. Normal JEB initials on trun. R̶. High shield, S below for Sydney Mint, Australia die axis ↑↑

1891S ...................................................................................................45    125    450    1650

**3871D Half-Sovereign.** Jubilee bust 1. No JEB initials on trun. R̶. As last die axis ↑↑

1891S ...................................................................................................45    125    450    1650

**Old Head coinage, 1893-1901, die axis ↑↑**

3872
1893 Five Pounds

**3872\* Five Pounds.** Old veiled bust 1. R̶. St. George and dragon, date and BP in ex.

1893 ...............................................................................................450    800    1200    1750

1893 Proof *FDC* £3250

| 3873 | | 3874 | |
|---|---|---|---|
| 1893 Two Pounds | | 1893 Sovereign | |

|  | EF | UNC |  | F | VF | EF | UNC |
|---|---|---|---|---|---|---|---|
|  | £ | £ |  | £ | £ | £ | £ |

**3873\* Two Pounds.** Old veiled bust 1. R̶. St. George and dragon, date and BP in ex. die axis ↑↑

1893 ...............................................................................................200    325    475    725

1893 Proof *FDC* £900

**3874 Sovereign.** Old veiled bust 1. R̶. St. George, London Mint die axis ↑↑

| 1893 | 80 | 125 | 1898 |  | 75 | 110 |
|---|---|---|---|---|---|---|
| 1893 Proof *FDC* £650 |  |  | 1899 |  | 75 | 110 |
| 1894 | 75 | 110 | 1900 |  | 75 | 110 |
| 1895 | 75 | 110 | 1901 |  | 75 | 110 |
| 1896 | 75 | 110 |  |  |  |  |

**3875 Sovereign.** Similar R̶. St. George. M on ground for Melbourne Mint, Australia die axis ↑↑

| 1893 M | 95 | 200 | 1898 M | 65 | 95 |
|---|---|---|---|---|---|
| 1894 M | 70 | 100 | 1899 M | 65 | 95 |
| 1895 M | 75 | 110 | 1900 M | 65 | 95 |
| 1896 M | 65 | 95 | 1901 M | 65 | 95 |
| 1897 M | 65 | 95 |  |  |  |

*\* beware recent forgeries*

3876
Perth Mint mark

3877
Sydney Mint mark

| | F | VF | EF | UNC | | F | VF | EF | UNC |
|---|---|---|---|---|---|---|---|---|---|
| | £ | £ | £ | £ | | £ | £ | £ | £ |

**3876 Sovereign.** Similar — P on ground for Perth Mint, Australia die axis ↑↑

| | | | | | | | | | |
|---|---|---|---|---|---|---|---|---|---|
| 1899 P | 60 | 125 | 300 | 1150 | 1901 P | | | 80 | 150 |
| 1900 P | | | 80 | 150 | | | | | |

**3877 Sovereign.** Similar — S on ground for Sydney Mint, Australia die axis ↑↑

| | | | | | | | | | |
|---|---|---|---|---|---|---|---|---|---|
| 1893 S | | | 75 | 110 | 1898 S | | | 80 | 150 |
| 1894 S | | | 65 | 95 | 1899 S | | | 65 | 95 |
| 1895 S | | | 75 | 110 | 1900 S | | | 70 | 100 |
| 1896 S | | | 80 | 150 | 1901 S | | | 70 | 100 |
| 1897 S | | | 70 | 100 | | | | | |

3878
1893 Half -Sovereign

**3878 Half-Sovereign.** Old veiled bust 1.R. St. George. Date in ex. London Mint die axis ↑↑

| | | | | | | | | | |
|---|---|---|---|---|---|---|---|---|---|
| 1893 | | | 50 | 100 | 1897 | | | 50 | 100 |
| — Proof *FDC* £475 | | | | | 1898 | | | 50 | 100 |
| 1894 | | | 50 | 100 | 1899 | | | 50 | 100 |
| 1895 | | | 50 | 100 | 1900 | | | 50 | 100 |
| 1896 | | | 50 | 100 | 1901 | | | 50 | 100 |

**3879 Half-Sovereign.** Similar — M on ground for Melbourne Mint, Australia die axis ↑↑

| | | | | | | | | | |
|---|---|---|---|---|---|---|---|---|---|
| 1893 M | | | *Extremely rare* | | 1899 M | 40 | 100 | 325 | 1400 |
| 1896 M | 40 | 100 | 325 | 1350 | 1900 M | 45 | 110 | 325 | 1400 |

**3880 Half-Sovereign.** Similar — P on ground for Perth Mint, Australia die axis ↑↑

| | | | | | | | | | |
|---|---|---|---|---|---|---|---|---|---|
| 1899 P | | | Proof only *unique* | | 1900 P | 65 | 135 | 415 | 1850 |

**3881 Half-Sovereign.** Similar — S on ground for Sydney Mint, Australia die axis ↑↑

| | | | | | | | | | |
|---|---|---|---|---|---|---|---|---|---|
| 1893 S | 40 | 85 | 250 | 1000 | 1900 S | 40 | 75 | 215 | 1000 |
| 1897 S | 40 | 85 | 225 | 1000 | | | | | |

# SILVER

**Young head coinage, die axis ↑↓**

3882
1844 Crown

| | F | VF | EF | UNC | | F | VF | EF | UNC |
|---|---|---|---|---|---|---|---|---|---|
| | £ | £ | £ | £ | | £ | £ | £ | £ |

**3882 Crown.** Young head. l. R. Crowned shield, regnal year on edge in Roman figures (eg 1847 = XI)
1839 Proof only *FDC* £4250

| | F | VF | EF | UNC |
|---|---|---|---|---|
| 1844 Star stops VIII | 30 | 125 | 875 | 2250 |
| 1844 Cinquefoil stops VIII | 30 | 125 | 875 | 2250 |
| 1844 Mistruck edge lettering | 75 | 250 | 1250 | – |
| 1845 Star stops VIII | 30 | 125 | 875 | 2250 |
| 1845 Cinquefoil stops VIII | 30 | 125 | 875 | 2250 |
| 1847 XI | 35 | 175 | 1100 | 2500 |

3883                                    3885
1847 Gothic Crown                Type 'A1' Halfcrown

**3883\*Crown.** 'Gothic' type, bust 1. R. Crowned cruciform Shields, emblems in angles. inscribed edge, mdcccxlvii=1847 Undecimo on edge die axis ↑↓ .................................450   800   1350   2500
1847 Septimo on edge of highest rarity.          1847 Proof, Plain edge die axis ↑↑ *FDC* £3250
1847 Proof in gold plain edge *FDC* of highest rarity     1847 Proof in white metal plain edge *FDC* £5750
*\*Beware of recent forgeries.*

**3884 Crown.** Similar mdcccliii=1853. Septimo on edge die axis ↑↑ Proof *FDC* £5500
1853 plain edge proof *FDC* £7500

**3885 Halfcrown.** Type A¹. Young head l. with one ornate and one plain fillet binding hair. WW in relief on trun. R. Crowned shield of arms, edge milled. Die axis ↑↓
1839 ...................150    450   1250   3750          1839 Proof plain edge *FDC* £1100
1839 Milled edge Proof *FDC Extremely rare*

**3886 Halfcrown.** Type A² Similar, but two ornate fillets binding hair.die axis ↑↓
1839 Proof only *FDC* £2250

**3886A Halfcrown.** Type A²/³ Similar, Two plain fillets, WW relief, die axis ↑↓ plain edge
1839 Proof *FDC* £3500

|  | F | VF | EF | UNC |  | F | VF | EF | UNC |
|---|---|---|---|---|---|---|---|---|---|
|  | £ | £ | £ | £ |  | £ | £ | £ | £ |

**3887 Halfcrown.** Type A³. Similar two plain fillets. WW incuse on trun. die axis ↑↓

| 1839 | 500 | 1650 | 3750 | — | 1839 Milled edge Proof *FDC* £2000 |  |  |  |  |
|---|---|---|---|---|---|---|---|---|---|
| 1839 Plain edge Proof *FDC* £2750 |  |  |  |  | 1840 | 30 | 100 | 475 | 900 |

**3888 Halfcrown.** Type A⁴. Similar but no initials on trun. die axis ↑↓

| 1841 | 125 | 400 | 1400 | 2250 | 1849 large date | 30 | 90 | 500 | 950 |
|---|---|---|---|---|---|---|---|---|---|
| 1842 | 25 | 85 | 475 | 850 | 1849/7 |  | *Extremely rare* |  |  |
| 1843 | 30 | 125 | 600 | 1100 | 1849 small date | 40 | 120 | 600 | 1100 |
| 1844 | 20 | 60 | 400 | 700 | 1850 | 25 | 80 | 550 | 1000 |
| 1844 not in edge collar |  | *Extremely rare* |  |  | 1850 Proof *FDC Extremely rare* |  |  |  |  |
| 1845 | 20 | 60 | 400 | 700 | 1853 Proof *FDC* £1650 |  |  |  |  |
| 1845 5/3 |  | *Extremely rare* |  |  | 1862 Proof *FDC Extremely rare* |  |  |  |  |
| 1846 | 20 | 60 | 400 | 700 | 1862 Plain edge Proof *FDC* £3500 |  |  |  |  |
| 1848/6 | 60 | 175 | 700 | 1650 | 1864 Proof *FDC* £3750 |  |  |  |  |
| 1848 | 25 | 275 | 975 | 1900 | 1864 Plain edge Proof *FDC* £3500 |  |  |  |  |

|  | 3889 |  |  |  | 3890 |
|---|---|---|---|---|---|
|  | Type A5 Halfcrown |  |  |  | 1849 'Godless' Florin |

**3889 Halfcrown.** Similar Type A⁵. As last but design of inferior workmanship R. Crowned cruciform shields, die axis ↑↓

| 1874 | 15 | 40 | 140 | 350 | 1881 | 15 | 40 | 140 | 350 |
|---|---|---|---|---|---|---|---|---|---|
| 1874 Proof *FDC* £3750 |  |  |  |  | 1881 Proof *FDC* £3250 |  |  |  |  |
| 1875 | 15 | 40 | 140 | 350 | 1881 Plain edge proof *FDC* £3750 |  |  |  |  |
| 1875 Proof *FDC* £3750 |  |  |  |  | 1882 | 15 | 45 | 165 | 375 |
| 1876 | 15 | 45 | 165 | 375 | 1883 | 15 | 40 | 140 | 350 |
| 1876/5 | 30 | 55 | 300 | 600 | 1883 Plain edge proof *FDC* £3750 |  |  |  |  |
| 1877 | 15 | 40 | 140 | 350 | 1884 | 15 | 40 | 140 | 350 |
| 1878 | 15 | 40 | 140 | 350 | 1885 | 15 | 40 | 140 | 350 |
| 1878 Proof *FDC* £3250 |  |  |  |  | 1885 Proof *FDC* £3000 |  |  |  |  |
| 1879 | 15 | 45 | 190 | 400 | 1886 | 15 | 40 | 140 | 350 |
| 1879 Proof *FDC* £3750 |  |  |  |  | 1886 Plain edge proof *FDC* £3750 |  |  |  |  |
| 1880 | 15 | 40 | 140 | 350 | 1887 | 20 | 50 | 165 | 350 |
| 1880 Proof *FDC* £3750 |  |  |  |  | 1887 Proof *FDC* £3250 |  |  |  |  |

**3890 Florin.** 'Godless' type A (i.e. without D.G.), WW behind bust within linear circle, die axis ↑↓

| 1848 Plain edge (Pattern) *FDC* £850 |  |  |  |  | 1849 WW obliterated | 35 | 75 | 220 | 375 |
|---|---|---|---|---|---|---|---|---|---|
| 1848 Milled edge ↑↑ or ↑↓ Proof *FDC* £2250 |  |  |  |  | 1849 | 18 | 40 | 140 | 225 |

**3891 Florin.** 'Gothic' type B¹. Reads brit:, WW below bust, date at end of obverse legend in gothic numerals (1851 to 1863) Crowned cruciform Shields, emblems in angles, edge milled. die axis ↑↓

| mdcccli |  | *Extremely rare* |  |  | mdccclvii | 20 | 45 | 140 | 325 |
|---|---|---|---|---|---|---|---|---|---|
| mdccclii | 18 | 40 | 140 | 300 | mdccclvii Proof *FDC* £2400 |  |  |  |  |
| mdccclii Proof *FDC* £1850 |  |  |  |  | mdccclviii | 20 | 45 | 140 | 325 |
| mdccclii, ii/i | 20 | 50 | 165 | 375 | mdccclviii Proof *FDC* £2400 |  |  |  |  |
| mdcccliii | 18 | 40 | 140 | 300 | mdccclix | 20 | 45 | 140 | 325 |
| mdcccliii Proof *FDC* £1600 |  |  |  |  | mdccclx | 25 | 50 | 165 | 350 |
| mdcccliv | 275 | 725 | 2850 | — | mdccclxii | 50 | 150 | 600 | 1350 |
| mdccclv | 25 | 75 | 190 | 400 | mdccclxii Plain edge Proof *FDC* £2600 |  |  |  |  |
| mdccclvi | 25 | 75 | 190 | 400 | mdccclxiii | 100 | 325 | 875 | 1900 |
|  |  |  |  |  | mdccclxiii Plain edge Proof *FDC* £2600 |  |  |  |  |

3891
1853 Florin Type B1

3892
1865 Florin Type B2

| | F | VF | EF | UNC | | F | VF | EF | UNC |
|---|---|---|---|---|---|---|---|---|---|
| | £ | £ | £ | £ | | £ | £ | £ | £ |

**3892 Florin.** Type B². Similar as last but die number below bust (1864 to 1867) die axis ↑↓

| mdccclxiv | 20 | 45 | 140 | 325 | mdccclxv | 40 | 100 | 275 | 475 |
|---|---|---|---|---|---|---|---|---|---|
| mdccclxiv heavy flan | 250 | 500 | 950 | 1750 | mdccclxvi | 35 | 75 | 225 | 400 |
| mdccclxiv heavy flan Proof | | *FDC* £2850 | | | mdccclxvii | 30 | 70 | 225 | 400 |

**3893 Florin.** Type B³. Similar reads britt:, die number below bust (1868 to 1879) die axis

| mdccclxvii Proof *FDC* £2600 | | | | | mdccclxxiii | 20 | 50 | 165 | 300 |
|---|---|---|---|---|---|---|---|---|---|
| mdccclxviii | 30 | 85 | 250 | 525 | mdccclxxiii Proof *FDC* £2500 | | | | |
| mdccclxix | 25 | 75 | 250 | 475 | mdccclxxiv | 25 | 55 | 190 | 375 |
| mdccclxix Proof *FDC* £2750 | | | | | mdccclxxiv iv/iii | 35 | 75 | 250 | 475 |
| mdccclxx | 20 | 45 | 140 | 325 | mdccclxxv | 25 | 50 | 165 | 350 |
| mdccclxx Proof *FDC* £2750 | | | | | mdccclxxvi | 20 | 45 | 140 | 325 |
| mdccclxxi | 20 | 50 | 165 | 350 | mdccclxxvii | 25 | 50 | 165 | 350 |
| mdccclxxi Proof *FDC* £2250 | | | | | mdccclxxix | | | £2250 | |
| mdccclxxii | 18 | 40 | 115 | 275 | | | | | |

**3894 Florin.** Type B⁴. Similar as last but with border of 48 arcs and no WW below bust die axis ↑↓

1877 mdccclxxvii .................................................................................................... *Extremely rare*

**3895 Florin.** Type B⁵. Similar but border of 42 arcs (1867, 1877 and 1878) die axis ↑↓

| mdccclxvii | | *Extremely rare* | | | mdccclxxviii | 20 | 45 | 140 | 325 |
|---|---|---|---|---|---|---|---|---|---|
| mdccclxxvii | 25 | 55 | 190 | 425 | mdccclxxviii Proof *FDC* | | *Extremely rare* | | |

**3896 Florin.** Type B⁵/₆. Similar as last but no die number below bust (1877, 1879) die axis ↑↓

| mdccclxxvii | 100 | 225 | 450 | 900 | mdccclxxix | 100 | 225 | 450 | 900 |
|---|---|---|---|---|---|---|---|---|---|

**3897 Florin.** Type B⁶. Similar reads britt:, WW; Border of 48 arcs (1879) die axis ↑↓

mdccclxxix ...............................................................................20 45 140 325

**3898 Florin.** Type B⁷. Similar as last but no WW, Border of 38 arcs (1879) die axis ↑↓

mdccclxxix ...............................................................................20 45 140 325

mdccclxxix Proof *FDC*. .......................................................................... *Extremely rare*

**3899 Florin.** Type B³/₈. Similar as next but younger portrait (1880) die axis ↑↓

mdccclxxx ............................................................................................. *Extremely rare*

**3900 Florin.** Type B⁸. Similar but border of 34 arcs (1880 to 1887) die axis ↑↓

| mdccclxxx | 15 | 40 | 140 | 300 | mdccclxxxiii Proof *FDC* £2250 | | | | |
|---|---|---|---|---|---|---|---|---|---|
| mdccclxxx Proof *FDC* £2250 | | | | | mdccclxxxiv | 18 | 40 | 115 | 300 |
| mdccclxxxi | 18 | 40 | 115 | 300 | mdccclxxxv | 20 | 45 | 140 | 325 |
| mdccclxxxi Proof *FDC* £2250 | | | | | mdccclxxxv Proof *FDC* £2250 | | | | |
| mdccclxxxi/xxri | 30 | 75 | 190 | 400 | mdccclxxxvi | 15 | 35 | 115 | 275 |
| mdccclxxxiii | 18 | 40 | 115 | 300 | mdccclxxxvi Proof *FDC* £2500 | | | | |

**3901 Florin.** Type B⁹. Similar but border of 46 arcs die axis ↑↓

1887 mdccclxxxvii ..........................................................................30 60 225 425

mdccclxxxvii Proof *FDC* ......................................................................... *Extremely rare*

**3902 Shilling**. Type A¹. First head l., WW on trun.R. crowned mark of value within wreath, date below, die axis ↑↓

| 1838 | 15 | 35 | 150 | 300 | 1839 | 10 | 30 | 140 | 275 |
|---|---|---|---|---|---|---|---|---|---|
| 1838 Proof *FDC* £1750 | | | | | 1839 Proof *FDC* £850 | | | | |

**3903 Shilling** Type A². Second head, l. WW on trun. (proof only), 1839 die axis ↑↑ *FDC* £450

3904
Type A3 Shilling

|  | F | VF | EF | UNC |  | F | VF | EF | UNC |
|---|---|---|---|---|---|---|---|---|---|
|  | £ | £ | £ | £ |  | £ | £ | £ | £ |

**3904 Shilling** Type A³. Second head, l. no initials on trun. R. Similar die axis ↑↓

| 1839 ........................10 | 25 | 120 | 275 | 1852 ........................10 | 20 | 90 | 200 |
|---|---|---|---|---|---|---|---|
| 1839 Proof plain edge *FDC* £525 | | | | 1853 ........................10 | 20 | 85 | 200 |
| 1839 Proof milled edge *FDC Extremely rare* | | | | 1853 Proof *FDC* £400 | | | |
| 1840 ........................15 | 50 | 175 | 325 | 1854 ........................50 | 150 | 550 | 1500 |
| 1840 Proof *FDC* £2250 | | | | 1854/1 ....................150 | 550 | 1650 | — |
| 1841 ........................15 | 50 | 175 | 325 | 1855 ........................10 | 20 | 85 | 200 |
| 1842 ........................10 | 20 | 100 | 225 | 1856 ........................10 | 20 | 85 | 200 |
| 1842 Proof *FDC* £2250 | | | | 1857 ........................10 | 20 | 85 | 200 |
| 1843 ........................15 | 30 | 150 | 325 | 1857 REG F:Ꝺ:error 125 | 325 | 900 | — |
| 1844 ........................10 | 20 | 100 | 225 | 1858 ........................10 | 20 | 85 | 200 |
| 1845 ........................10 | 20 | 110 | 275 | 1859 ........................10 | 20 | 85 | 200 |
| 1846 ........................10 | 20 | 100 | 225 | 1859 Proof *FDC* £2650 | | | |
| 1848 over 6.............45 | 100 | 550 | 900 | 1860 ........................15 | 25 | 120 | 275 |
| 1849 ........................15 | 25 | 110 | 275 | 1861 ........................15 | 25 | 120 | 275 |
| 1850 ....................120 | 825 | 1650 | — | 1861 D/B in FD ........... | | *Extremely rare* | |
| 1851/49.................150 | 625 | 1800 | — | 1862 ........................20 | 40 | 175 | 325 |
| 1851 ........................30 | 85 | 325 | 725 | 1863 ........................25 | 60 | 275 | 600 |
| 1851 Proof *FDC* £2750 | | | | 1863/1 ....................75 | 175 | 500 | — |

**3905 Shilling** Type A⁴. Similar as last, R. Die number above date die axis ↑↑

| 1864 ........................10 | 20 | 85 | 200 | 1866 BBITANNIAR ..50 | 150 | 450 | — |
|---|---|---|---|---|---|---|---|
| 1865 ........................10 | 20 | 85 | 200 | 1867 ........................10 | 20 | 90 | 200 |
| 1866 ........................10 | 20 | 85 | 200 | | | | |

**3906 Shilling** Type A⁵. Third head, l. R. Similar no die number above date die axis ↑↓

| 1867 Proof £2000 | 1867 Proof plain edge £2500 |
|---|---|

| 3906A | Die number location |
|---|---|
| Type A6 Shilling | above date |

**3906A Shilling** Type A⁶. Third head, l. R. Similar die number above date die axis ↑↓

| 1867 ........................45 | 120 | 600 | — | 1874 ........................10 | 20 | 85 | 200 |
|---|---|---|---|---|---|---|---|
| 1868 ........................10 | 25 | 85 | 200 | 1875 ........................10 | 20 | 85 | 200 |
| 1869 ........................20 | 35 | 110 | 225 | 1876 ........................15 | 30 | 90 | 220 |
| 1870 ........................20 | 35 | 110 | 225 | 1877 ........................10 | 20 | 85 | 200 |
| 1871 ........................10 | 20 | 85 | 200 | 1878 ........................10 | 20 | 85 | 200 |
| 1871 Plain edge proof *FDC* £2250 | | | | 1878 Proof *FDC* £2250 | | | |
| 1871 Milled edge proof *FDC* £2000 | | | | 1879 ........................25 | 65 | 225 | 450 |
| 1872 ........................10 | 20 | 85 | 200 | 1879 Proof *FDC* £1500 | | | |
| 1873 ........................10 | 20 | 85 | 200 | | | | |

| | F | VF | EF | UNC | | F | VF | EF | UNC |
|---|---|---|---|---|---|---|---|---|---|
| | £ | £ | £ | £ | | £ | £ | £ | £ |

**3907 Shilling** Type A⁷. Fourth head, l. R. Similar no die number above date die axis ↑↓

| | F | VF | EF | UNC | | F | VF | EF | UNC |
|---|---|---|---|---|---|---|---|---|---|
| 1879 | 10 | 20 | 80 | 175 | 1883 plain edge Proof *FDC* £3650 | | | | |
| 1879 Proof *FDC* £2250 | | | | | 1884 | 10 | 20 | 70 | 150 |
| 1880 | 10 | 20 | 70 | 150 | 1884 Proof *FDC* £2000 | | | | |
| 1880 Proof plain edge £2000 | | | | | 1885 | 10 | 15 | 60 | 125 |
| 1880 Proof milled edge £1500 | | | | | 1885 Proof *FDC* £2000 | | | | |
| 1881 | 10 | 20 | 70 | 150 | 1886 | 10 | 15 | 60 | 125 |
| 1881 Proof plain edge £2650 | | | | | 1886 Proof *FDC* £2000 | | | | |
| 1881 Proof milled edge £1750 | | | | | 1887 | 15 | 30 | 90 | 225 |
| 1882 | 15 | 40 | 110 | 225 | 1887 Proof *FDC* £1750 | | | | |
| 1883 | 10 | 20 | 70 | 150 | | | | | |

**3907A Shilling.** Type A7. Fourth head, R. Similar die number above date die axis ↑↓

| | | | | | | |
|---|---|---|---|---|---|---|
| 1878 | *Extremely rare* | 1879 | *Extremely rare* |

3908
Type A1 Sixpence

**3908 Sixpence.** Type A¹. First head l. R. Crowned mark of value within wreath, date below die axis ↑↓

| | F | VF | EF | UNC | | F | VF | EF | UNC |
|---|---|---|---|---|---|---|---|---|---|
| 1838 | 8 | 15 | 75 | 150 | 1852 | 4 | 12 | 75 | 120 |
| 1838 Proof *FDC* £950 | | | | | 1853 | 6 | 14 | 70 | 110 |
| 1839 | 8 | 15 | 75 | 150 | 1853 Proof *FDC* £425 | | | | |
| 1839 Proof *FDC* £400 | | | | | 1854 | 50 | 140 | 500 | 1000 |
| 1840 | 8 | 15 | 80 | 185 | 1855 | 6 | 14 | 70 | 165 |
| 1841 | 8 | 18 | 85 | 200 | 1855/3 | 12 | 25 | 85 | 200 |
| 1842 | 8 | 15 | 75 | 175 | 1855 Proof *FDC* | *Extremely rare* | | | |
| 1843 | 8 | 15 | 75 | 175 | 1856 | 7 | 15 | 75 | 175 |
| 1844 Small 44 | 6 | 14 | 70 | 165 | 1857 | 7 | 15 | 75 | 175 |
| 1844 Large 44 | 10 | 25 | 85 | 200 | 1858 | 7 | 15 | 75 | 175 |
| 1845 | 7 | 15 | 75 | 175 | 1858 Proof *FDC* | *Extremely rare* | | | |
| 1846 | 6 | 14 | 70 | 165 | 1859 | 6 | 14 | 70 | 165 |
| 1848 | 30 | 85 | 325 | 725 | 1859/8 | 10 | 20 | 75 | 185 |
| 1848/6 or 7 | 40 | 100 | 375 | 775 | 1860 | 7 | 15 | 75 | 175 |
| 1850 | 7 | 15 | 75 | 175 | 1862 | 30 | 100 | 350 | 725 |
| 1850/3 | 15 | 30 | 115 | 250 | 1863 | 18 | 65 | 225 | 600 |
| 1851 | 7 | 15 | 75 | 175 | 1866 | *Extremely rare* | | | |

3909
Die number location above date

3912
Type 'A5' Sixpence

**3909 Sixpence.** Type A². First head, R. Similar die number above date die axis ↑↓

| | F | VF | EF | UNC | | F | VF | EF | UNC |
|---|---|---|---|---|---|---|---|---|---|
| 1864 | 7 | 15 | 75 | 175 | 1866 | 7 | 15 | 75 | 175 |
| 1865 | 8 | 18 | 85 | 200 | | | | | |

|  | F £ | VF £ | EF £ | UNC £ |  | F £ | VF £ | EF £ | UNC £ |
|---|---|---|---|---|---|---|---|---|---|

**3910 Sixpence.** Type A³. Second head, l. R. Similar die number above date die axis ↑↓

| 1867 | 10 | 18 | 80 | 200 | 1873 | 5 | 12 | 60 | 165 |
|---|---|---|---|---|---|---|---|---|---|
| 1867 Proof *FDC* £1250 | | | | | 1874 | 5 | 12 | 60 | 165 |
| 1868 | 10 | 18 | 80 | 200 | 1875 | 5 | 12 | 60 | 165 |
| 1869 | 10 | 20 | 110 | 250 | 1876 | 10 | 18 | 85 | 225 |
| 1869 Proof *FDC* £1500 | | | | | 1877 | 5 | 12 | 60 | 165 |
| 1870 | 10 | 20 | 110 | 250 | 1878 | 5 | 12 | 60 | 165 |
| 1870 plain edge Proof *FDC* £1500 | | | | | 1878 DRITANNIAR | 30 | 80 | 450 | — |
| 1871 | 7 | 15 | 65 | 175 | 1878 Proof *FDC* £1250 | | | | |
| 1871 plain edge Proof *FDC* £1250 | | | | | 1878/7 | 35 | 100 | 400 | — |
| 1872 | 7 | 15 | 65 | 175 | 1879 | 10 | 18 | 85 | 225 |

**3911 Sixpence.** Type A⁴. Second head, l. R. Similar No die number die axis ↑↓

| 1871 | 8 | 16 | 75 | 185 | 1879 milled edge Proof *FDC* £1250 | | | | |
|---|---|---|---|---|---|---|---|---|---|
| 1871 Proof *FDC* £1250 | | | | | 1879 plain edge Proof *FDC* £1500 | | | | |
| 1877 | 7 | 15 | 65 | 165 | 1880 | 8 | 16 | 75 | 175 |
| 1879 | 7 | 15 | 65 | 165 | | | | | |

**3912 Sixpence.** Type A⁵. Third head l. R. Similar die axis ↑↓

| 1880 | 5 | 10 | 50 | 100 | 1883 plain edge Proof *FDC* *Extremely rare* | | | | |
|---|---|---|---|---|---|---|---|---|---|
| 1880 Proof *FDC* £1500 | | | | | 1884 | 5 | 10 | 45 | 95 |
| 1881 | 5 | 10 | 45 | 95 | 1885 | 5 | 10 | 45 | 95 |
| 1881 plain edge Proof *FDC* *Extremely rare* | | | | | 1885 Proof *FDC* £1250 | | | | |
| 1881 milled edge Proof *FDC* *Extremely rare* | | | | | 1886 | 5 | 10 | 45 | 95 |
| 1882 | 10 | 30 | 80 | 200 | 1886 Proof *FDC* £1250 | | | | |
| 1883 | 5 | 10 | 45 | 95 | 1887 | 4 | 8 | 40 | 90 |
| 1883 Small R legend | 15 | 35 | 95 | 225 | 1887 Proof *FDC* £750 | | | | |

3913

1842 Groat

**3913 Groat** (4d.). Young head l. R. Britannia seated r. date in ex, edge milled, die axis ↑↓

| 1837 Proof only *FDC* of highest rarity | | | | | 1846 | 4 | 14 | 45 | 110 |
|---|---|---|---|---|---|---|---|---|---|
| 1838 | 2 | 10 | 40 | 95 | 1847/6 (or 8) | 25 | 80 | 350 | — |
| 1838 plain edge Proof *FDC* £750 | | | | | 1848/6 | 25 | 120 | 350 | — |
| 1838/ ∞ | 3 | 20 | 50 | 150 | 1848 | 3 | 12 | 40 | 95 |
| 1839 | 3 | 12 | 40 | 100 | 1848/7 | 10 | 28 | 90 | 225 |
| 1839 die axis ↑↑ Proof *FDC* £275 | | | | | 1849 | 3 | 12 | 40 | 100 |
| 1839 die axis ↑↓ Proof *FDC* £350 | | | | | 1849/8 | 5 | 14 | 45 | 110 |
| 1840 | 3 | 12 | 40 | 100 | 1851 | 20 | 70 | 200 | 500 |
| 1840 small round o | 5 | 18 | 45 | 120 | 1852 | 35 | 100 | 275 | 600 |
| 1841 | 4 | 14 | 50 | 110 | 1853 | 40 | 120 | 325 | 700 |
| 1842 | 4 | 14 | 45 | 110 | 1853 Proof *FDC* milled edge £450 | | | | |
| 1842 Proof *FDC* £700 | | | | | 1853 Proof *FDC* plain edge *Extremely rare* | | | | |
| 1842/1 | 5 | 18 | 50 | 150 | 1854 | 3 | 12 | 35 | 85 |
| 1843 | 4 | 14 | 45 | 110 | 1855 | 3 | 12 | 35 | 85 |
| 1843 4 over 5 | 8 | 22 | 55 | 165 | 1857 Proof only *FDC* £1000 | | | | |
| 1844 | 4 | 14 | 45 | 110 | 1862 Proof only *FDC*. *Extremely rare* | | | | |
| 1845 | 4 | 14 | 45 | 110 | | | | | |

**Threepence.** R. Crowned 3; as Maundy threepence but with a less prooflike surface

3914
Type A1 Threepence

| | F | VF | EF | UNC | | F | VF | EF | UNC |
|---|---|---|---|---|---|---|---|---|---|
| | £ | £ | £ | £ | | £ | £ | £ | £ |

**3914 Threepence.** Type A$^1$. First bust, young head, high relief, ear fully visible. Dei axis ↑↓
℞ Tie ribbon closer to tooth border, cross on crown further from tooth border, figure 3

| | F | VF | EF | UNC | | F | VF | EF | UNC |
|---|---|---|---|---|---|---|---|---|---|
| 1838*..........................5 | 10 | 60 | 125 | 1851..........................5 | 10 | 60 | 135 |
| 1838 BRITANNIAB.... | | *Extremely rare* | | 1851 5 over 8..........10 | 30 | 110 | — |
| 1839*..........................5 | 18 | 75 | 175 | 1852*......................60 | 175 | 500 | — |
| 1839 Proof (see Maundy) | | | | 1853........................10 | 25 | 85 | 200 |
| 1840*..........................5 | 14 | 70 | 150 | 1854..........................5 | 10 | 60 | 125 |
| 1841*..........................5 | 18 | 75 | 175 | 1855..........................5 | 18 | 75 | 175 |
| 1842*..........................5 | 18 | 75 | 175 | 1856..........................5 | 10 | 55 | 120 |
| 1843*..........................5 | 12 | 60 | 125 | 1857..........................5 | 18 | 75 | 175 |
| 1844*..........................5 | 18 | 75 | 175 | 1858..........................5 | 10 | 55 | 120 |
| 1845..........................3 | 8 | 45 | 100 | 1858 BRITANNIAB .. | | *Extremely rare* | |
| 1846........................10 | 20 | 85 | 200 | 1858/6....................10 | 20 | 110 | — |
| 1847*........................50 | 150 | 350 | 750 | 1858/5......................8 | 18 | 90 | — |
| 1848*........................40 | 125 | 325 | 700 | 1859..........................5 | 10 | 55 | 120 |
| 1849..........................5 | 18 | 75 | 175 | 1860..........................5 | 18 | 75 | 175 |
| 1850..........................3 | 8 | 50 | 90 | 1861..........................5 | 10 | 55 | 120 |

*\*Issued for Colonial use only.*

| 3914A | 3914C | 3914D |
|---|---|---|
| Type A2 | Type A4 | Type A5 |

**3914A Threepence.** Type A$^2$. First bust variety, slightly older portrait with aquiline nose ↑↓

| | F | VF | EF | UNC | | F | VF | EF | UNC |
|---|---|---|---|---|---|---|---|---|---|
| 1859..........................5 | 10 | 55 | 110 | 1865..........................5 | 18 | 75 | 150 |
| 1860..........................5 | 10 | 55 | 110 | 1866..........................5 | 10 | 55 | 110 |
| 1861..........................5 | 10 | 55 | 110 | 1867..........................5 | 10 | 55 | 110 |
| 1862..........................5 | 10 | 55 | 110 | 1868..........................5 | 10 | 55 | 110 |
| 1863..........................5 | 18 | 75 | 150 | 1868 RRITANNIAR .. | | *Extremely rare* | |
| 1864..........................5 | 10 | 55 | 110 | | | | |

**3914B Threepence.** Type A$^3$. Second Bust, slightly larger, lower relief, mouth fuller,
nose more pronounced, rounded truncation die axis ↑↓

| | F | VF | EF | UNC |
|---|---|---|---|---|
| 1867................................................................................................5 | 18 | 75 | 150 |

**3914C Threepence.** Type A$^4$. Obv. as last. ℞. Tie ribbon further from tooth border, cross on
crown nearer to tooth border die axis ↑↓

| | F | VF | EF | UNC | | F | VF | EF | UNC |
|---|---|---|---|---|---|---|---|---|---|
| 1867..........................5 | 18 | 75 | 150 | 1875..........................3 | 8 | 40 | 70 |
| 1868..........................5 | 18 | 75 | 150 | 1876..........................3 | 8 | 40 | 70 |
| 1869........................10 | 20 | 85 | 175 | 1877..........................4 | 10 | 50 | 80 |
| 1870..........................4 | 12 | 60 | 100 | 1878..........................4 | 10 | 50 | 80 |
| 1871..........................5 | 14 | 65 | 125 | 1879..........................4 | 10 | 50 | 80 |
| 1872..........................5 | 14 | 65 | 125 | 1879 Proof *FDC* ........ | | *Extremely rare* | |
| 1873..........................3 | 8 | 40 | 70 | 1884..........................3 | 6 | 35 | 60 |
| 1874..........................3 | 8 | 40 | 70 | | | | |

| | F | VF | EF | UNC | | F | VF | EF | UNC |
|---|---|---|---|---|---|---|---|---|---|
| | £ | £ | £ | £ | | £ | £ | £ | £ |

**3914D Threepence.** Type A$^5$. Third bust, older features, mouth closed, hair strands leading from 'bun' vary, die axis ↑↓

| 1880 | 4 | 10 | 45 | 75 | 1885 | 3 | 6 | 30 | 60 |
|---|---|---|---|---|---|---|---|---|---|
| 1881 | 3 | 6 | 30 | 60 | 1885 Proof *FDC* | | *Extremely rare* | | |
| 1882 | 5 | 10 | 55 | 110 | 1886 | 3 | 6 | 30 | 60 |
| 1883 | 3 | 6 | 30 | 60 | 1887 | 4 | 10 | 45 | 75 |

**3914E Twopence.** Young head 1. ℞ Date divided by a crowned 2 within a wreath, die axis ↑↓

| 1838 | 3 | 7 | 20 | 50 | 1848 | 5 | 10 | 25 | 60 |
|---|---|---|---|---|---|---|---|---|---|

3915 - Three-Halfpence

**3915 Three-Halfpence.** (for Colonial use).Young head 1. ℞ Crowned value and date, die axis ↑↓

| 1838 | 5 | 12 | 35 | 75 | 1843 Proof *FDC* | | *Extremely rare* | | |
|---|---|---|---|---|---|---|---|---|---|
| 1838 Proof *FDC* £500 | | | | | 1843/34 | 8 | 20 | 80 | 175 |
| 1839 | 4 | 10 | 30 | 70 | 1843/34 Proof *FDC* | | *Extremely rare* | | |
| 1840 | 8 | 22 | 75 | 150 | 1860 | 6 | 18 | 60 | 125 |
| 1841 | 5 | 14 | 40 | 90 | 1862 | 6 | 18 | 60 | 125 |
| 1842 | 5 | 14 | 40 | 90 | 1862 Proof *FDC* £650 | | | | |
| 1843 | 3 | 6 | 25 | 65 | 1870 Proof only £650 | | | | |

3916 - 1880 Maundy Set

| | EF | FDC | | EF | FDC |
|---|---|---|---|---|---|
| | £ | £ | | £ | £ |

**3916 Maundy Set.** (4d., 3d., 2d. and 1.) Young head 1., die axis ↑↓

| 1838 | 85 | 160 | 1864 | 75 | 120 |
|---|---|---|---|---|---|
| 1838 Proof *FDC* £800 | | | 1865 | 75 | 120 |
| 1838 Proof in gold *FDC* £12500 | | | 1866 | 75 | 120 |
| 1839 | 95 | 185 | 1867 | 75 | 120 |
| 1839 Proof die axis ↑↑ *FDC* £400 | | | 1867 Proof set *FDC* £600 | | |
| 1840 | 95 | 185 | 1868 | 75 | 120 |
| 1841 | 100 | 220 | 1869 | 80 | 135 |
| 1842 | 95 | 185 | 1870 | 70 | 110 |
| 1843 | 95 | 185 | 1871 | 70 | 110 |
| 1844 | 95 | 185 | 1871 Proof set *FDC* £600 | | |
| 1845 | 85 | 160 | 1872 | 70 | 110 |
| 1846 | 100 | 220 | 1873 | 70 | 110 |
| 1847 | 95 | 185 | 1874 | 70 | 110 |
| 1848 | 95 | 185 | 1875 | 70 | 110 |
| 1849 | 100 | 220 | 1876 | 70 | 110 |
| 1850 | 75 | 135 | 1877 | 70 | 110 |
| 1851 | 75 | 135 | 1878 | 70 | 110 |
| 1852 | 85 | 160 | 1878 Proof set *FDC* £600 | | |
| 1853 | 85 | 160 | 1879 | 70 | 110 |
| 1853 Proof *FDC* £475 | | | 1880 | 70 | 110 |
| 1854 | 85 | 160 | 1881 | 70 | 110 |
| 1855 | 85 | 160 | 1881 Proof set *FDC* £600 | | |
| 1856 | 80 | 135 | 1882 | 70 | 110 |
| 1857 | 80 | 135 | 1882 Proof set *FDC* £600 | | |
| 1858 | 80 | 135 | 1883 | 70 | 110 |
| 1859 | 80 | 135 | 1884 | 70 | 110 |
| 1860 | 75 | 120 | 1885 | 70 | 110 |
| 1861 | 75 | 120 | 1886 | 70 | 110 |
| 1861E | 75 | 120 | 1887 | 75 | 135 |
| 1862 | 75 | 120 | | | |
| 1863 | 75 | 120 | | | |

| | | EF | FDC |
|---|---|---|---|
| **3917 — Fourpence**, 1838-87 | *from* | 10 | 25 |
| **3918 — Threepence**, 1838-87 | *from* | 15 | 40 |
| **3919 — Twopence**, 1838-87 | *from* | 8 | 20 |
| **3920 — Penny**, 1838-87 | *from* | 7 | 15 |

*Maundy Sets in the original dated cases are worth approximately £10, and £5 for undated cases more than the prices quoted.*

**Jubilee Coinage 1887-93, die axis ↑↑**

3921
1887 Crown

| | F | VF | EF | UNC | | F | VF | EF | UNC |
|---|---|---|---|---|---|---|---|---|---|
| | £ | £ | £ | £ | | £ | £ | £ | £ |

**3921 Crown.** Jubilee bust 1. ℞. St. George and dragon, date in ex, edge milled, die axis ↑↑

| | F | VF | EF | UNC | | F | VF | EF | UNC |
|---|---|---|---|---|---|---|---|---|---|
| 1887........................15 | 25 | 65 | 140 | | 1889........................15 | 30 | 70 | 175 |
| 1887 Proof *FDC* £425 | | | | | 1890........................15 | 35 | 95 | 200 |
| 1888 narrow date.....15 | 35 | 95 | 200 | | 1891........................15 | 40 | 110 | 225 |
| 1888 wide date ........60 | 175 | 450 | — | | 1892........................20 | 45 | 125 | 250 |

3922
1887 Double-Florin - Roman I in date

**3922 Double-Florin** (4s.).Jubilee bust 1. ℞. Crowned cruciform shields. Septre in angles. Roman I in date, die axis ↑↑

| | F | VF | EF | UNC |
|---|---|---|---|---|
| 1887.........................................................................................................12 | 20 | 45 | 90 |
| 1887 Proof *FDC* £325 | | | |

**3923 Double-Florin** Jubilee bust l. ℞. Similar but Arabic 1 in date, die axis ↑↑

| | F | VF | EF | UNC | | F | VF | EF | UNC |
|---|---|---|---|---|---|---|---|---|---|
| 1887........................12 | 20 | 45 | 90 | | 1889........................12 | 20 | 55 | 100 |
| 1887 Proof *FDC* £225 | | | | | 1889 inverted 1 for I in | | | |
| 1888........................12 | 20 | 60 | 120 | |    VICTORIA....25 | 60 | 175 | 375 |
| 1888 inverted 1 for I in | | | | | 1890........................12 | 20 | 60 | 110 |
|    VICTORIA......25 | 60 | 175 | 375 | | | | | |

3924
1887 Halfcrown

3925
1887 Florin

| | F £ | VF £ | EF £ | UNC £ | | F £ | VF £ | EF £ | UNC £ |
|---|---|---|---|---|---|---|---|---|---|

**3924 Halfcrown.** Jubilee bust 1. R. Crowned shield in garter and collar, die axis ↑↑

| | F | VF | EF | UNC | | F | VF | EF | UNC |
|---|---|---|---|---|---|---|---|---|---|
| 1887 | 7 | 12 | 25 | 70 | 1890 | 10 | 20 | 60 | 135 |
| 1887 Proof *FDC* £110 | | | | | 1891 | 10 | 20 | 60 | 135 |
| 1888 | 10 | 15 | 45 | 120 | 1892 | 10 | 20 | 60 | 135 |
| 1889 | 10 | 20 | 60 | 135 | | | | | |

**3925 Florin.** Jubilee bust 1. R. Crowned cruciform shields, sceptres in angles, die axis ↑↑

| | F | VF | EF | UNC | | F | VF | EF | UNC |
|---|---|---|---|---|---|---|---|---|---|
| 1887 | 5 | 10 | 20 | 50 | 1890 | 10 | 30 | 85 | 250 |
| 1887 Proof *FDC* £85 | | | | | 1891 | 20 | 55 | 175 | 450 |
| 1888 | 6 | 15 | 35 | 75 | 1892 | 20 | 50 | 140 | 375 |
| 1889 | 8 | 20 | 40 | 85 | 1892 Proof *FDC* | | | *Extremely rare* | |

3926
1887 small head Shilling

3927
large Jubilee head

**3926 Shilling.** Small Jubilee head. R. Crowned shield in Garter, die axis ↑↑

| | F | VF | EF | UNC | | F | VF | EF | UNC |
|---|---|---|---|---|---|---|---|---|---|
| 1887 | 3 | 8 | 14 | 35 | 1888/7 | 5 | 10 | 25 | 65 |
| 1887 Proof *FDC* £70 | | | | | 1889 | 35 | 90 | 300 | 475 |

**3927 Shilling.** Large Jubilee head. R. Similar as before, die axis ↑↑

| | F | VF | EF | UNC | | F | VF | EF | UNC |
|---|---|---|---|---|---|---|---|---|---|
| 1889 | 5 | 9 | 30 | 70 | 1891 | 5 | 15 | 40 | 80 |
| 1889 Proof *FDC* £850. | | | | | 1891 Proof *FDC* £1500 | | | | |
| 1890 | 5 | 10 | 35 | 75 | 1892 | 5 | 15 | 40 | 80 |

3928
1887 'withdrawn type' Sixpence

3929
1889 Sixpence

3930
1888 Groat

| | F £ | VF £ | EF £ | UNC £ | | F £ | VF £ | EF £ | UNC £ |
|---|---|---|---|---|---|---|---|---|---|

**3928 Sixpence.** JEB designer's initials below trun. R. Shield in Garter (withdrawn type), die axis ↑↑

| | F | VF | EF | UNC | | F | VF | EF | UNC |
|---|---|---|---|---|---|---|---|---|---|
| 1887 | 2 | 6 | 12 | 30 | 1887 JEB on trun. | 15 | 45 | 100 | 200 |
| 1887 R/V in | | | | | 1887 Proof *FDC* £60 | | | | |
| VICTORIA | 10 | 35 | 80 | 175 | | | | | |

**3929 Sixpence**. R. Jubilee bust 1. Crowned, value in wreath, die axis ↑↑

| | | | | | | | | |
|---|---|---|---|---|---|---|---|---|
| 1887.............................2 | 6 | 12 | 30 | 1890.............................4 | 10 | 20 | 55 |
| 1887 Proof *FDC* £650 | | | | 1890 Proof *FDC* ......... | | *Extremely rare* | |
| 1888.............................4 | 10 | 20 | 50 | 1891.............................6 | 15 | 25 | 60 |
| 1888 Proof *FDC* £1250 | | | | 1892.............................8 | 20 | 30 | 90 |
| 1889.............................4 | 10 | 20 | 50 | 1893.......................250 | 650 | 2250 | — |

**3930 Groat** (for use in British Guiana). Jubilee Bust 1. R. Britannia seated r. date in axis, die axis ↑↑

| | | | | |
|---|---|---|---|---|
| 1888 Proof *FDC* £750 | | 1888.........................10 | 25 | 50 | 95 |

**3931 Threepence**. As Maundy but less prooflike surface, die axis ↑↑

| | | | | | | | | |
|---|---|---|---|---|---|---|---|---|
| 1887.........................— | 1 | 5 | 12 | 1890.............................1 | 3 | 10 | 20 |
| 1887 Proof *FDC* £35 | | | | 1891.............................1 | 3 | 10 | 20 |
| 1888.............................2 | 5 | 15 | 30 | 1892.............................2 | 5 | 15 | 30 |
| 1889.............................1 | 3 | 10 | 20 | 1893...........................15 | 40 | 100 | 250 |

3932
1888 Maundy Set

|  | EF £ | FDC £ |  | EF £ | FDC £ |
|---|---|---|---|---|---|
| **3932 Maundy Set.** (4d., 3d., 2d. and 1d.) Jubilee bust 1.die axis ↑↑ | | | | | |
| 1888......................................... | 75 | 110 | 1890 ...................................... | 75 | 110 |
| 1888 Proof set *FDC* ................*Extremely rare* | | | 1891 ...................................... | 75 | 110 |
| 1889......................................... | 75 | 110 | 1892 ...................................... | 75 | 110 |
| **3933 — Fourpence**, 1888-92.................................................................*from* | | | | 10 | 20 |
| **3934 — Threepence**, 1888-92 ............................................................*from* | | | | 15 | 25 |
| **3935 — Twopence**, 1888-92...............................................................*from* | | | | 8 | 15 |
| **3936 — Penny**, 1888-92..................................................................*from* | | | | 8 | 15 |

*Maundy Sets in the original dated cases are worth approximately £10 and £5 for undated cases more than the prices quoted.*

**Old Head Coinage 1893-1901, die axis ↑↑**

3937
1893 Old Head Crown

| | F | VF | EF | UNC |
|---|---|---|---|---|
| | £ | £ | £ | £ |

**3937 Crown.** Old veiled bust l. R. St. George. date in ex. Regnal date on edge, die axis ↑↑

| | F | VF | EF | UNC |
|---|---|---|---|---|
| 1893 edge LVI | 15 | 30 | 140 | 325 |
| 1893 Proof *FDC* £500 | | | | |
| 1893 LVII | 25 | 60 | 225 | 475 |
| 1894 LVII | 15 | 40 | 165 | 400 |
| 1894 LVIII | 15 | 40 | 165 | 400 |
| 1895 LVIII | 15 | 35 | 140 | 375 |
| 1895 LIX | 15 | 35 | 140 | 375 |
| 1896 LIX | 18 | 50 | 190 | 425 |
| 1896 LX | 15 | 35 | 140 | 375 |
| 1897 LX | 15 | 35 | 140 | 375 |
| 1897 LXI | 15 | 35 | 140 | 375 |
| 1898 LXI | 25 | 60 | 225 | 475 |
| 1898 LXII | 15 | 40 | 165 | 400 |
| 1899 LXII | 15 | 40 | 165 | 400 |
| 1899 LXIII | 15 | 40 | 165 | 400 |
| 1900 LXIII | 20 | 50 | 225 | 450 |
| 1900 LXIV | 20 | 50 | 200 | 400 |

3938
1893 Halfcrown

| | F | VF | EF | UNC | | F | VF | EF | UNC |
|---|---|---|---|---|---|---|---|---|---|
| | £ | £ | £ | £ | | £ | £ | £ | £ |

**3938 Halfcrown.** Old veiled bust l. R. Shield in collar, edge milled, die axis ↑↑

| | F | VF | EF | UNC | | F | VF | EF | UNC |
|---|---|---|---|---|---|---|---|---|---|
| 1893 | 8 | 15 | 40 | 85 | 1897 | 8 | 15 | 40 | 85 |
| 1893 Proof *FDC* £135 | | | | | 1898 | 10 | 16 | 45 | 100 |
| 1894 | 10 | 18 | 60 | 125 | 1899 | 10 | 16 | 45 | 100 |
| 1895 | 9 | 16 | 45 | 100 | 1900 | 10 | 16 | 45 | 100 |
| 1896 | 9 | 16 | 45 | 100 | 1901 | 10 | 16 | 45 | 100 |

3939
Old Head Florin

| | F | VF | EF | UNC | | F | VF | EF | UNC |
|---|---|---|---|---|---|---|---|---|---|
| | £ | £ | £ | £ | | £ | £ | £ | £ |

**3939 Florin.** Old veiled bust l. R. Three shields within garter, die axis ↑↑

| | F | VF | EF | UNC | | F | VF | EF | UNC |
|---|---|---|---|---|---|---|---|---|---|
| 1893 | 5 | 10 | 40 | 70 | 1897 | 6 | 12 | 40 | 75 |
| 1893 Proof *FDC* £100 | | | | | 1898 | 6 | 15 | 45 | 85 |
| 1894 | 8 | 16 | 60 | 110 | 1899 | 6 | 12 | 40 | 75 |
| 1895 | 7 | 18 | 50 | 85 | 1900 | 6 | 12 | 40 | 75 |
| 1896 | 6 | 12 | 40 | 75 | 1901 | 6 | 12 | 40 | 75 |

**3940 Shilling**. Old veiled bust l. R. Three shields within Garter, small rose, die axis ↑↑

| | | | | | | | | |
|---|---|---|---|---|---|---|---|---|
| 1893 | .........................4 | 8 | 25 | 55 | 1894 | .........................5 | 10 | 30 | 70 |
| 1893 small lettering | 6 | 15 | 40 | 70 | 1895 | .......................10 | 20 | 50 | 100 |
| 1893 Proof *FDC* £85 | | | | | | | | |

3940

1901 Shilling

3941

1893 Sixpence

**3940A Shilling**. Old veiled bust l. R. Second reverse, larger rose, die axis ↑↑

| | | | | | | | | |
|---|---|---|---|---|---|---|---|---|
| 1895 | .........................4 | 10 | 30 | 65 | 1899 | .........................4 | 10 | 30 | 65 |
| 1896 | .........................4 | 10 | 25 | 60 | 1900 | .........................4 | 10 | 30 | 65 |
| 1897 | .........................4 | 10 | 25 | 60 | 1901 | .........................4 | 10 | 25 | 60 |
| 1898 | .........................4 | 10 | 25 | 60 | | | | | |

**3941 Sixpence.** Old veiled bust l. R. Value in wreath, die axis ↑↑

| | | | | | | | | |
|---|---|---|---|---|---|---|---|---|
| 1893 | .........................3 | 8 | 18 | 45 | 1897 | .........................4 | 10 | 20 | 45 |
| 1893 Proof *FDC* £65 | | | | | 1898 | .........................4 | 10 | 20 | 45 |
| 1894 | .........................5 | 12 | 25 | 50 | 1899 | .........................4 | 10 | 20 | 45 |
| 1895 | .........................4 | 10 | 20 | 45 | 1900 | .........................4 | 10 | 20 | 45 |
| 1896 | .........................4 | 10 | 20 | 45 | 1901 | .........................4 | 8 | 15 | 40 |

**3942 Threepence.** Old veiled bust l. R. Crowned 3. As Maundy but less prooflike surface, die axis ↑↑

| | | | | | | | | |
|---|---|---|---|---|---|---|---|---|
| 1893 | .........................1 | 2 | 5 | 15 | 1897 | .........................1 | 2 | 6 | 18 |
| 1893 Proof *FDC* £40 | | | | | 1898 | .........................1 | 2 | 6 | 18 |
| 1894 | .........................1 | 3 | 7 | 20 | 1899 | .........................1 | 2 | 5 | 15 |
| 1895 | .........................1 | 3 | 7 | 20 | 1900 | .........................1 | 2 | 5 | 15 |
| 1896 | .........................1 | 2 | 6 | 18 | 1901 | .........................1 | 2 | 6 | 18 |

3943

1899 Maundy Set

| | EF £ | FDC £ | | EF £ | FDC £ |
|---|---|---|---|---|---|
| **3943 Maundy Set.** (4d., 3d., 2d. and 1d.) Old veiled bust l., die axis ↑↑ | | | | | |
| 1893 | 60 | 85 | 1897 | 60 | 85 |
| 1893 Proof from 1893 proof set FDC £85 | | | 1898 | 60 | 85 |
| 1894 | 65 | 90 | 1899 | 70 | 90 |
| 1895 | 60 | 85 | 1900 | 70 | 90 |
| 1896 | 60 | 85 | 1901 | 60 | 85 |
| **3944 — Fourpence.** 1893-1901 .................................................*from* | 6 | 12 | | | |
| **3945 — Threepence.** 1893-1901 ............................................*from* | 12 | 22 | | | |
| **3946 — Twopence.** 1893-1901 ..............................................*from* | 6 | 12 | | | |
| **3947 — Penny.** 1893-1901..................................................*from* | 6 | 18 | | | |

*Maundy Sets in the original dated cases are worth approximately £5 more than the prices quoted.*

# COPPER AND BRONZE

3948
1843 Penny
Rev. with ornamental trident prongs (OT)

## Young Head Copper Coinage, 1838-60, die axis ↑↑

| | F | VF | EF | UNC | | F | VF | EF | UNC |
|---|---|---|---|---|---|---|---|---|---|
| | £ | £ | £ | £ | | £ | £ | £ | £ |

**3948 Penny.** Young head l. date below ℞. Britannia seated r.

| | F | VF | EF | UNC | | F | VF | EF | UNC |
|---|---|---|---|---|---|---|---|---|---|
| 1839 Bronzed proof *FDC* £850 | | | | | 1851 OT DEF: ........10 | 20 | 110 | 300 |
| 1841 Rev. OT ..........5 | 10 | 75 | 250 | 1853 OT DEF—: ......5 | 12 | 75 | 150 |
| 1841 Proof *FDC* £1250 | | | | | 1853 Proof *FDC* £450 | | | |
| 1841 Silver Proof *FDC* £3500 | | | | | 1853 Plain trident, (PT) | | | |
| 1841 OT. no colon | | | | | DEF:...............10 | 20 | 95 | 275 |
| after REG..........5 | 10 | 75 | 325 | 1854 PT ..................5 | 12 | 75 | 150 |
| 1843 OT. —.............65 | 250 | 1100 | 2500 | 1854/3 PT ...............12 | 25 | 110 | 300 |
| 1843 OT REG: ........35 | 125 | 925 | 2000 | 1854 OT DEF—: ......8 | 15 | 80 | 175 |
| 1844 OT...................10 | 15 | 85 | 185 | 1855 OT —..............5 | 12 | 75 | 150 |
| 1844 Proof *FDC* £1500 | | | | | 1855 PT DEF:..........5 | 12 | 75 | 150 |
| 1845 OT...................15 | 25 | 135 | 350 | 1856 PT DEF:.........65 | 175 | 450 | 1200 |
| 1846 OT...................10 | 20 | 110 | 300 | 1856 Proof *FDC* £1000 | | | |
| 1846 OT colon close | | | | | 1856 OT DEF—: ....25 | 50 | 185 | 950 |
| to DEF ............15 | 25 | 120 | 350 | 1857 OT DEF—: ......8 | 15 | 80 | 175 |
| 1847 — — ...............8 | 15 | 85 | 185 | 1857 PT DEF:..........5 | 10 | 75 | 150 |
| 1847 OT DEF—: ......8 | 15 | 85 | 185 | 1858 OT DEF—: ......5 | 10 | 75 | 150 |
| 1848/7 OT ...............5 | 15 | 80 | 165 | 1858/7 — — ...........5 | 10 | 75 | 150 |
| 1848 OT ..................5 | 15 | 80 | 165 | 1858/3 .....................25 | 75 | 350 | — |
| 1848/6 OT .............20 | 75 | 350 | — | 1858 no ww on trun..5 | 15 | 85 | 200 |
| 1849 OT .................50 | 125 | 950 | — | 1859 .........................5 | 10 | 75 | 185 |
| 1851 OT .................10 | 20 | 110 | 350 | 1859 Proof *FDC* £1850 | | | |
| | | | | | 1860/59.................200 | 650 | 2000 | — |

*The 1860 large copper pieces are not to be confused with the smaller and commoner bronze issue with date on reverse (nos. 3954, 3956 and 3958).*

3949

1854 Halfpenny, dots on shield

**3949 Halfpenny.** Young head l. date below R. Britannia seated r., die axis ↑↑   1853 Rev. incuse dots

| | F £ | VF £ | EF £ | UNC £ | | F £ | VF £ | EF £ | UNC £ |
|---|---|---|---|---|---|---|---|---|---|
| 1838 ...........................5 | 12 | 40 | 120 | | 1852 Rev. normal shield 8 | 18 | 50 | 150 | |
| 1839 Bronzed proof FDC £275 | | | | | 1853 dots on shield......3 | 8 | 25 | 95 | |
| 1841 ...........................4 | 10 | 35 | 110 | | 1853 — Proof FDC £200 | | | | |
| 1841 — Proof FDC £750 | | | | | 1853/2 — ..................15 | 35 | 100 | 275 | |
| 1841 Silver proof FDC | *Extremely rare* | | | | 1854 — .........................3 | 8 | 25 | 95 | |
| 1843 .........................25 | 45 | 110 | 375 | | 1855 — .........................3 | 8 | 25 | 95 | |
| 1844 ...........................6 | 15 | 45 | 130 | | 1856 — .........................5 | 15 | 45 | 130 | |
| 1845 .........................50 | 125 | 650 | — | | 1857 — .........................4 | 10 | 35 | 100 | |
| 1846 ...........................8 | 18 | 50 | 140 | | 1857 Rev. normal | | | | |
| 1847 ...........................8 | 18 | 50 | 140 | |    shield .................4 | 10 | 35 | 100 | |
| 1848 .........................10 | 20 | 55 | 175 | | 1858 — .........................5 | 10 | 40 | 120 | |
| 1848/7 .......................8 | 18 | 50 | 140 | | 1858/7 — ....................5 | 10 | 40 | 120 | |
| 1851 ...........................5 | 15 | 45 | 130 | | 1858/6 — ....................5 | 10 | 40 | 120 | |
| 1851 Rev. incuse dots | | | | | 1859 — .........................5 | 10 | 40 | 120 | |
|    on shield ..........5 | 15 | 45 | 130 | | 1859/8 — ..................10 | 20 | 65 | 200 | |
| 1852 Similar ..............8 | 18 | 50 | 150 | | 1860 — ...................650 | 2000 | 4000 | — | |

*Overstruck dates are listed only if commoner than normal date, or if no normal date is known.*

3950

1847 Farthing

**3950 Farthing.** Young head l. date below R. Britannia seated r. die axis ↑↑

| | F £ | VF £ | EF £ | UNC £ | | F £ | VF £ | EF £ | UNC £ |
|---|---|---|---|---|---|---|---|---|---|
| 1838 WW raised on trun.5 | 10 | 35 | 100 | | 1851 ...........................10 | 20 | 60 | 165 | |
| 1839 ...........................4 | 8 | 35 | 85 | | 1851 D/Ɔ in DEI ......25 | 50 | 200 | — | |
| 1839 Bronzed Proof *FDC* £250 | | | | | 1852 ...........................10 | 20 | 60 | 165 | |
| 1839 Silver Proof *FDC* | *Extremely rare* | | | | 1853 .............................5 | 10 | 40 | 100 | |
| 1840 ...........................4 | 8 | 35 | 85 | | 1853 WW incuse | | | | |
| 1841 ...........................4 | 8 | 35 | 85 | |    on trun ..............10 | 30 | 90 | 275 | |
| 1841 Proof *FDC* | *Extremely rare* | | | | 1853 Proof *FDC* £400 | | | | |
| 1842 .........................15 | 35 | 110 | 275 | | 1854 .............................5 | 10 | 35 | 80 | |
| 1843/2 .......................10 | 30 | 80 | 225 | | 1855 .............................5 | 10 | 45 | 110 | |
| 1843 ...........................4 | 8 | 35 | 90 | | 1855 WW raised.........8 | 15 | 50 | 120 | |
| 1843 I for 1 in date ..50 | 250 | — | — | | 1856 WW incuse .......8 | 20 | 55 | 165 | |
| 1844 .........................45 | 100 | 450 | — | | 1856 R/E in | | | | |
| 1845 ...........................8 | 10 | 40 | 100 | |    VICTORIA ......15 | 40 | 140 | — | |
| 1846 ...........................8 | 15 | 55 | 140 | | 1857 .............................5 | 10 | 40 | 100 | |
| 1847 ...........................5 | 10 | 40 | 100 | | 1858 .............................5 | 10 | 35 | 100 | |
| 1848 ...........................5 | 10 | 40 | 100 | | 1859 ...........................10 | 20 | 60 | 165 | |
| 1849 .........................30 | 60 | 275 | — | | 1860 .........................825 | 2000 | 4000 | | |
| 1850 ...........................5 | 10 | 40 | 100 | | 1864 IWW on truncation | *Extremely rare* | | | |
| 1850 5/4 .................10 | 30 | 80 | 250 | | | | | | |

*These 1860 large copper pieces are not to be confused with the smaller and commoner bronze issue with date on reverse (nos. 3954, 3956 and 3958).*

| | F | VF | EF | UNC | | F | VF | EF | UNC |
|---|---|---|---|---|---|---|---|---|---|
| | £ | £ | £ | £ | | £ | £ | £ | £ |

**3951 Half-Farthing.** Young head l. R. Crowned Value and date, die axis ↑↑

| | F | VF | EF | UNC | | F | VF | EF | UNC |
|---|---|---|---|---|---|---|---|---|---|
| 1839 ............................5 | 10 | 40 | 100 | | 1852 ..........................4 | 10 | 45 | 95 |
| 1839 Bronzed proof *FDC* £350 | | | | | 1853 ..........................5 | 15 | 50 | 135 |
| 1842 ............................5 | 10 | 40 | 100 | | 1853 Proof *FDC* £350 | | | |
| 1843 ............................. | 5 | 30 | 70 | | 1854 ..........................8 | 25 | 75 | 160 |
| 1844 ............................. | 3 | 25 | 60 | | 1856 ..........................8 | 25 | 75 | 160 |
| 1844 E/N in REGINA10 | 20 | 75 | 200 | | 1856 Large date ......50 | 110 | 275 | 600 |
| 1847 ............................4 | 8 | 30 | 85 | | 1868 Proof *FDC* £450 | | | |
| 1851 5/0 ....................10 | 20 | 85 | 185 | | 1868 Cupro nickel Proof *FDC* £600 | | | |
| 1851 ............................5 | 10 | 45 | 95 | | | | | |

| 3951 | 3952 | 3953 |
|---|---|---|
| 1839 Half-Farthing | 1844 Third-Farthing | 1853 Quarter-Farthing |

**3952 Third-Farthing** (for use in Malta). Young head l. date below R. Britannia seated r. die axis ↑↑

| | | | | | | | | | |
|---|---|---|---|---|---|---|---|---|---|
| 1844 ..........................20 | 35 | 95 | 225 | | 1844 RE for REG ....30 | 65 | 325 | 700 |

**3953 Quarter-Farthing** (for use in Ceylon). Young head l. R. Crowned Value and date, die axis ↑↑

| | | | | | | | | | |
|---|---|---|---|---|---|---|---|---|---|
| 1839 ..........................10 | 18 | 45 | 100 | | 1853 ......................10 | 20 | 55 | 120 |
| 1851 ..........................10 | 20 | 50 | 120 | | 1853 Proof *FDC* £700 | | | |
| 1852 ..........................10 | 18 | 45 | 100 | | 1868 Proof *FDC* £500 | | | |
| 1852 Proof *FDC* £500 | | | | | 1868 Cupro-nickel Proof *FDC* £600 | | | |

*Copper coins graded in this catalogue as UNC have full mint lustre.*

### Bronze Coinage, 'Bun Head' Issue, 1860-95, die axis ↑↑

When studying an example of the bronze coinage if the minutiae of the variety is not evident due to wear from circulation, then the coin will not be of any individual significance. Proofs exist of most years and are generally extremely rare for all denominations.

| 3954 | H Mint mark location |
|---|---|
| 1860 Beaded Border Penny | 3955 |

## Bronze Coinage, "Bun Head" Issue, 1860-95, die axis ↑↑

When studying an example of the bronze coinage, if the minutiae of the variety is not evident due to wear from circulation, then the coin will not be of any individual significance. Proofs exist of most years and are generally extremely rare for all denominations.

**3954 The Bronze Penny.** The bronze coinage is the most complicated of the milled series from the point of view of the large number of different varieties of obverse and reverse and their combinations. Below are set out good illustrations with explanations of all the varieties. The obverse and reverse types listed below reflect those as listed originally by C W Peck in his British Museum Catalogue of Copper, Tin and Bronze Coinage 1558-1958, and later in "the Bronze Coinage of the United Kingdom" by Michael J Freeman which gives much fuller and detailed explanations of the types. Reference can also be compared to "The British Bronze Penny" by Michael Gooby.

**OBVERSES**

**Obverse 1 (1860)** - laureate and draped bust facing left, hair tied in bun, wreath of 15 leaves and 4 berries, L C WYON raised on base of bust, beaded border and thin linear circle.

**Obverse 2 (1860-62)** - laureate and draped bust facing left, hair tied in bun, wreath of 15 leaves and 4 berries, L C WYON raised lower on base of bust and clear of border, toothed border and thin linear circle both sides,

**Obverse 1\* (1860)** - laureate and draped bust facing left, hair tied in bun, more bulging lowered eye with more rounded forehead, wreath of 15 leaves and 4 berries, which are weaker in part, L C WYON raised on base of bust, beaded border and thin linear circle.

**Obverse 3 (1860-61)** - laureate and draped bust facing left, hair tied in bun, complete rose to drapery, wreath of 15 leaves and 4 berries, two leaves have incuse outlines, L C WYON raised on base of bust nearly touches border, toothed border and thin linear circle both sides,

**Obverse 4 (1860-61)** - laureate and draped bust facing left, hair tied in bun, finer hair strands at nape of neck, wreath of 15 leaves and 4 berries, two leaves have incuse outlines, L C WYON below bust, nearly touches border, toothed border of shorter teeth, and thin linear circle both sides,

**Obverse 6 (1860-74)** - laureate and draped bust facing left, hair tied in bun, finer hair strands at nape of neck, wreath of 16 leaves, leaf veins raised, no signature, toothed border and thin linear circle both sides,

**Obverse 5 (1860-61)** - laureate and draped bust facing left, hair tied in bun, finer hair strands at nape of neck, wreath of 15 leaves and 4 berries, leaf veins incuse, two leaves have incuse outlines, no signature below bust, toothed border and thin linear circle both sides,

**Obverse 7 (1874)** - laureate and draped bust facing left, hair tied in bun, finer hair strands at nape of neck, wreath of 17 leaves, leaf veins raised, 6 berries, no signature, toothed border and thin linear circle both sides.

**Obverse 8 (1874-79)** - laureate and draped bust facing left, hair tied in bun, with close thicker ties to ribbons, wreath of 17 leaves, leaf veins raised, 6 berries, no signature, toothed border and thin linear circle both sides,

**Obverse 10 (1880-81)** - laureate and draped bust facing left, hair tied in bun, with close thicker ties, wreath of 15 leaves, leaf veins raised and recessed, 4 berries, no signature, toothed border and thin linear circle both sides,

**Obverse 9 (1879-81)** - laureate and draped bust facing left, hair tied in bun, with close thicker ties, wreath of 17 leaves, double leaf veins incuse, 6 berries, no signature, toothed border and thin linear circle both sides,

**Obverse 11 (1881-83)** - laureate and draped bust facing left, more hooked nose, hair tied in bun, with close thicker ties, nose more hooked, wreath of 15 leaves, leaf veins raised, 4 berries, no signature, toothed border and thin linear circle both sides, weak circle on obverse,

**REVERSES**

**Obverse 12 (1881-94)** - laureate and draped bust facing left, hair tied in bun, with close thicker ties, no curls at nape of neck, nose more hooked, wreath of 15 leaves, leaf veins raised, 4 berries, no signature, toothed border, more numerous teeth, and thin linear circle both sides, weak on obverse, larger lettering.

**Reverse A (1860)** - Britannia seated right on rocks with shield and trident, crosses on shield outlined with double raised lines, L.C.W. incuse below shield, date below in exergue, lighthouse with 4 windows to left, ship sailing to right, beaded border and linear circle.

**Obverse 13 (1889)** - laureate and draped bust facing left, hair tied in bun, with close thicker ties, no curls at nape of neck, nose more hooked, wreath of 14 leaves, leaf veins raised, no signature, toothed border and thin linear circle both sides, larger lettering.

**Reverse B (1860)** - Britannia with one incuse hemline, seated right on rocks with shield and trident, crosses on shield outlined with treble incuse lines, L.C.W. incuse below shield, date below in exergue, lighthouse with 4 windows to left, ship sailing to right, beaded border and linear circle.

**Reverse C (1860)** - Britannia seated right on rocks with shield and trident, crosses on shield outlined with wider spaced thinner double raised lines, thumb touches St. George Cross, L.C.W. incuse below shield, date below in exergue, lighthouse with 4 windows to left, rocks touch linear circle, ship sailing to right, beaded border and linear circle.

**Reverse E (1860)** - Britannia seated right on rocks with thick rimmed shield and trident, crosses on shield outlined with wider spaced thinner double raised lines, thumb touches St. George Cross, L.C.W. incuse below foot, date below in exergue, lighthouse with sharper masonry to left, rocks touch linear circle, ship sailing to right, toothed border.

**Reverse D (1860-61)** - Britannia seated right on rocks with shield and trident, crosses on shield outlined with wider spaced thinner double raised lines, thumb touches St. George Cross, L.C.W. incuse below shield, date below in exergue, lighthouse with 4 windows to left, rocks touch linear circle, ship sailing to right, toothed border.

**Reverse F (1861)** - Britannia seated right on rocks with thick rimmed shield and trident, incuse lines on breastplate, crosses on shield outlined with wider spaced thinner double raised lines, thumb touches St. George Cross, no L.C.W. extra rocks, date below in exergue, lighthouse with rounded top and sharp masonry, three horizontal lines between masonry and top, rocks touch linear circle, ship sailing to right, toothed border.

**Reverse G (1861-75)** - Britannia seated right on rocks with convex shield and trident, no signature, date below in exergue, bell-topped lighthouse to left, lamp area depicted with five vertical lines, no rocks to left, sea crosses linear circle, ship sailing to right, toothed border.

**Reverse I (1874)** - Britannia seated right on rocks with convex shield and trident, thick trident shaft, no signature, narrow date below in exergue, thicker lighthouse to left with 4 windows, lamp area of four vertical lines, close date numerals, tiny rock to left, sea touches linear circle, ship sailing to right, toothed border.

**Reverse H (1874-75, 1877)** - Britannia seated right on rocks, smaller head, thinner neck, with convex shield and trident, no signature, narrow date below in exergue, tall thin lighthouse to left with 6 windows, lamp area of four vertical lines, close date numerals, tiny rock to left, sea touches linear circle, ship sailing to right, toothed border.

**Reverse J (1875-81)** - larger Britannia seated right on rocks with shield and trident, left leg more visible, wider date below in deeper exergue, lighthouse to left, ship sailing to right, sea does not meet linear circle either side, toothed border.

**Reverse K (1876, 1879)** - Britannia with larger head seated right on rocks with convex shield and trident, thicker helmet, no signature, narrow date and in exergue, tall thin lighthouse to left, tiny rock to left, sea touches linear circle, ship sailing to right, toothed border.

**Reverse M (1881-82)** - larger Britannia seated right on rocks with shield and trident, flatter shield heraldically coloured, date and H below in exergue, lighthouse to left with faint masonry, ship sailing to right, sea does not meet linear circle, toothed border.

**Reverse L (1880)** - Britannia seated right on rocks with shield and trident, extra feather to helmet plume, trident with three rings above hand, date below in exergue, lighthouse with cluster of rocks to left, ship sailing to right, toothed border.

**Reverse N (1881-94)** - thinner Britannia seated right on rocks with shield and thinner trident, helmet plume ends in a single strand, shield heraldically coloured with different thickness crosses, date in exergue, thinner lighthouse to left, ship sailing to right, sea meets linear circle, toothed border with more teeth.

**Reverse O (1882 - proof only)** – larger Britannia seated right on rocks withshield and trident, flatter shield heraldically coloured, date and H in exergue, lighthouse to left with faint masonry, ship sailing to right, sea meets linear circle, toothed border with more teeth.

|  | F £ | VF £ | EF £ | UNC £ |
|---|---|---|---|---|

**3954 Penny.** Laur. bust l. R. Britannia seated r. date in ex. lighthouse l. ship to r., die axis ↑↑

| | F | VF | EF | UNC | | F | VF | EF | UNC |
|---|---|---|---|---|---|---|---|---|---|
| 1860 obv 1, rev A ........40 | 90 | 220 | 675 | 1867 obv 6, rev G .........8 | 25 | 90 | 500 |
| 1860 obv 1, rev B ........10 | 25 | 70 | 450 | 1868 obv 6, rev G ........15 | 35 | 140 | 675 |
| 1860 obv 1*, rev A ......50 | 110 | 350 | 875 | 1869 obv 6, rev G ........55 | 200 | 550 | 1650 |
| 1860 obv 1, rev C ......30 | 60 | 220 | 725 | 1870 obv 6, rev G .........8 | 25 | 110 | 450 |
| 1860 obv 1*, rev C ........8 | 40 | 140 | 550 | 1871 obv 6, rev G ........30 | 85 | 350 | 825 |
| 1860 obv 1, rev D ....110 | 375 | 1000 | 2000 | 1871 wide date - rev H .... | *Extremely rare* | | |
| 1860 obv 2, rev A ....110 | 375 | 1000 | 2000 | 1872 obv 6, rev G .........5 | 15 | 55 | 275 |
| 1860 obv 2, rev D ..........5 | 15 | 45 | 225 | 1873 obv 6, rev G .........5 | 15 | 55 | 275 |
| 1860 — heavy flan .......... | *Extremely rare* | | | 1874 obv 6, rev G .........5 | 15 | 75 | 450 |
| 1860 N/Z in ONE, 2+D .. | *Extremely rare* | | | 1874 obv 7, rev G ........10 | 35 | 90 | 350 |
| 1860 obv 3, rev D ..........5 | 15 | 50 | 225 | 1874 obv 8, rev G ........25 | 55 | 140 | 600 |
| 1860 obv 3, rev E ......75 | 165 | 450 | 1000 | 1874 obv 8 rev H..........20 | 50 | 110 | 550 |
| 1860 obv 4, rev D ........2 | 10 | 50 | 275 | 1874 obv 6, rev H ........30 | 80 | 275 | 600 |
| 1860 obv 5, rev D .......10 | 40 | 135 | 450 | 1874 obv 7, rev H ........10 | 35 | 85 | 350 |
| 1860 obv 6, rev D .......30 | 110 | 275 | 650 | 1875 obv 8, rev G .........2 | 10 | 50 | 250 |
| 1861 obv 2, rev D ........25 | 80 | 165 | 600 | 1875 obv 8, rev H .........3 | 10 | 40 | 140 |
| 1861 obv 2, rev F ........25 | 85 | 275 | 825 | 1875 obv 8, rev J............5 | 15 | 55 | 275 |
| 1861 obv 2, rev G ........30 | 110 | 275 | 650 | 1877 obv 8, rev J............2 | 10 | 50 | 250 |
| 1861 obv 3, rev D ......90 | 275 | 650 | 1100 | 1877 obv 8, rev H ............ | *Extremely rare* | | |
| 1861 obv 4, rev D ..........3 | 15 | 55 | 275 | 1878 obv 8, rev J............3 | 15 | 70 | 450 |
| 1861 — — heavy flan .... | *Extremely rare* | | | 1879 obv 8, rev J..........10 | 20 | 95 | 500 |
| 1861 obv 4, rev F ......110 | 275 | 700 | 1650 | 1879 obv 9, rev J ............2 | 7 | 40 | 190 |
| 1861 obv 4, rev G ......30 | 110 | 275 | 825 | 1879 obv 9, rev K ........30 | 95 | 275 | 650 |
| 1861 obv 5, rev D ..........2 | 10 | 50 | 250 | 1880 obv 9, rev J ............3 | 15 | 90 | 350 |
| 1861 obv 5, rev F ............ | *Extremely rare* | | | 1880 obv 9, rev L .........3 | 15 | 90 | 350 |
| 1861 obv 5, rev G ......110 | 225 | 550 | 1350 | 1881 obv 9, rev J............4 | 15 | 70 | 450 |
| 1861 obv 6, rev D ........2 | 10 | 50 | 225 | 1881 obv 10, rev J........30 | 95 | 275 | 650 |
| 1861 — — — 6 over 8 .. | *Extremely rare* | | | 1881 obv 11, rev J........25 | 55 | 140 | 600 |
| 1861 obv 6, rev F ......110 | 350 | 800 | — | 1882* obv 11, rev N ........ | *Extremely rare* | | |
| 1861 obv 6, rev G ..........2 | 10 | 50 | 250 | 1883 obv 12, rev N ........3 | 10 | 50 | 225 |
| 1861 — 8 over 6.............. | *Extremely rare* | | | 1883 obv11, rev N..........3 | 10 | 50 | 225 |
| 1862 obv 2, rev G ............ | *Extremely rare* | | | 1884 obv 12, rev N ........2 | 8 | 40 | 165 |
| 1862 obv 6, rev G ..........2 | 10 | 50 | 225 | 1885 obv 12, rev N ........2 | 8 | 40 | 165 |
| 1862 — 8 over 6.............. | *Extremely rare* | | | 1886 obv 12, rev N ........2 | 10 | 40 | 190 |
| 1862 — Halfpenny numerals | *Extremely rare* | | | 1887 obv 12, rev N ........2 | 8 | 40 | 165 |
| 1863 obv 6, rev G ..........2 | 10 | 50 | 225 | 1888 obv 12, rev N ........2 | 10 | 40 | 190 |
| 1863 Die number below .. | *Extremely rare* | | | 1889 obv 13, rev N ........2 | 8 | 35 | 165 |
| 1863 slender 3.................. | *Extremely rare* | | | 1889 obv 12, rev N ........4 | 15 | 70 | 450 |
| 1864 Upper serif..........20 | 85 | 350 | 1000 | 1890 obv 12, rev N ........2 | 8 | 35 | 165 |
| 1864 Crosslet 4.............25 | 95 | 450 | 1400 | 1891 obv 12, rev N ........2 | 7 | 30 | 140 |
| 1865 obv 6, rev G ..........8 | 20 | 95 | 450 | 1892 obv 12, rev N ........2 | 8 | 35 | 165 |
| 1865/3 obv 6, rev G ....40 | 110 | 275 | 925 | 1893 obv 12, rev N ........2 | 8 | 35 | 165 |
| 1866 obv 6, rev G ..........5 | 15 | 60 | 275 | 1894 obv 12, rev N ........3 | 15 | 55 | 225 |

* not to be confused with Heaton Mint

**3955 Penny.** Similar R. Britannia, H Mint mark below date – (struck by Ralph Heaton & Sons, Birmingham)

| | F | VF | EF | UNC | | F | VF | EF | UNC |
|---|---|---|---|---|---|---|---|---|---|
| 1874 H obv 6, rev G ......5 | 20 | 70 | 300 | 1876 H obv 8, rev J ........10 | 30 | 110 | 400 |
| 1874 H obv 6, rev H ....10 | 30 | 110 | 400 | 1881 H obv 11, rev M ....3 | 15 | 50 | 275 |
| 1874 H obv 7, rev G ....10 | 30 | 90 | 350 | 1881 H obv 9, rev M ...... | *Extremely rare* | | |
| 1874 H obv 7, rev H ......5 | 20 | 70 | 300 | 1882 H obv12,rev M......10 | 25 | 80 | 450 |
| 1874 H obv 7, rev I.......... | *Extremely rare* | | | 1882 H obv 12, rev N ......2 | 10 | 40 | 190 |
| 1875 H obv 8, rev J......35 | 100 | 650 | — | 1882/1 H obv 11, rev M10 | 25 | 80 | 450 | |
| 1876 H obv 8, rev K ......2 | 15 | 50 | 225 | | | | |

3956
1860 Halfpenny Beaded border

**3956 Halfpenny.** Laur. bust l. R. Britannia seated r. date in ex. lighthouse l. ship to r., die axis ↑↑

| | F £ | VF £ | EF £ | UNC £ | | F £ | VF £ | EF £ | UNC £ |
|---|---|---|---|---|---|---|---|---|---|
| 1860 Beaded border ....1 | 5 | 35 | 140 | | 1863 large 3 .............2 | 6 | 50 | 190 | |
| 1860 no tie to wreath ....5 | 15 | 65 | 250 | | 1864 .........................2 | 10 | 55 | 225 | |
| 1860 Toothed border ..2 | 10 | 45 | 190 | | 1865 .........................3 | 15 | 65 | 300 | |
| 1860 round top light house | 15 | 65 | 250 | | 1865/3....................40 | 100 | 275 | 700 | |
| 1860 5 berries in | | | | | 1866 .........................2 | 10 | 55 | 225 | |
| wreath ................4 | 12 | 55 | 225 | | 1867 .........................3 | 15 | 65 | 300 | |
| 1860 — 15 leaves, | | | | | 1868 .........................2 | 10 | 60 | 250 | |
| 4 berries .............3 | 10 | 50 | 165 | | 1869 .........................10 | 40 | 190 | 500 | |
| 1860 — rounded | | | | | 1870........................2 | 8 | 50 | 190 | |
| lighthouse .........4 | 12 | 55 | 225 | | 1871 .......................15 | 50 | 225 | 500 | |
| 1860 — Double incuse | | | | | 1872........................2 | 7 | 45 | 165 | |
| leaf veins ............5 | 15 | 65 | 250 | | 1873 ........................2 | 10 | 55 | 225 | |
| 1860 — 16 leaves | | | | | 1873 R. hemline to | | | | |
| wreath ..............10 | 30 | 100 | 350 | | drapery ............2 | 10 | 55 | 225 | |
| 1860 TB/BBmule .......... | | *Extremely rare* | | | 1874 ........................5 | 25 | 110 | 400 | |
| 1861 5 berries in | | | | | 1874 narrow date ....15 | 50 | 250 | — | |
| wreath ..............10 | 30 | 90 | 300 | | 1874 older features ..5 | 25 | 110 | 400 | |
| 1861 15 leaves in | | | | | 1875........................1 | 6 | 45 | 165 | |
| wreath ................6 | 20 | 65 | 250 | | 1877 ........................1 | 6 | 45 | 165 | |
| 1861 — R. no hemline | | | | | 1878 ........................3 | 15 | 65 | 300 | |
| to drapery..........10 | 30 | 90 | 300 | | 1878 wide date........50 | 100 | 275 | 550 | |
| 1861 — R. Door on | | | | | 1879........................1 | 5 | 35 | 140 | |
| lighthouse ..........5 | 15 | 65 | 250 | | 1880........................2 | 7 | 45 | 165 | |
| 1861 4 leaves double | | | | | 1881 ........................2 | 7 | 45 | 165 | |
| incuse veins ........2 | 10 | 45 | 165 | | 1883 ........................1 | 7 | 45 | 165 | |
| 1861 16 leaves wreath ..5 | 15 | 65 | 250 | | 1883 rose for brooch obv. | | *Extremely rare* | | |
| 1861 — R. LCW incuse | | | | | 1884 ........................1 | 4 | 35 | 140 | |
| on rock..............10 | 30 | 90 | 300 | | 1885 ........................1 | 4 | 35 | 140 | |
| 1861 — R. no hemline | | | | | 1886 ........................1 | 4 | 35 | 140 | |
| to drapery...........3 | 12 | 55 | 225 | | 1887 ........................1 | 4 | 30 | 110 | |
| 1861 — R. door on | | | | | 1888 ........................1 | 4 | 35 | 140 | |
| lighthouse ..........1 | 5 | 35 | 140 | | 1889 ........................1 | 4 | 35 | 140 | |
| 1861 HALP error .......... | | *Extremely rare* | | | 1889/8 ...................10 | 20 | 65 | 250 | |
| 1861 6 over 8 ................ | | *Extremely rare* | | | 1890 ........................1 | 4 | 30 | 110 | |
| 1862 ..........................1 | 4 | 30 | 110 | | 1891 ........................1 | 4 | 30 | 110 | |
| 1862 Die letter A B or C to left of | | | | | 1892 ........................1 | 6 | 45 | 165 | |
| lighthouse | | *Extremely rare* | | | 1893 ........................1 | 4 | 35 | 140 | |
| 1863 small 3 ................2 | 6 | 50 | 190 | | 1894 ........................1 | 7 | 45 | 165 | |

**3957 Halfpenny.** Similar R. Britannia, H Mint mark below date (struck by Ralph Heaton & Sons, Birmingham)

| | F £ | VF £ | EF £ | UNC £ | | F £ | VF £ | EF £ | UNC £ |
|---|---|---|---|---|---|---|---|---|---|
| 1874 H ......................1 | 5 | 45 | 165 | | 1881 H......................1 | 5 | 45 | 165 | |
| 1875 H ......................2 | 6 | 50 | 190 | | 1882 H......................1 | 5 | 45 | 165 | |
| 1876 H ......................1 | 5 | 45 | 165 | | | | | | |

3958
1878 Farthing

3960
1884 Third-Farthing

| | F | VF | EF | UNC | | F | VF | EF | UNC |
|---|---|---|---|---|---|---|---|---|---|
| | £ | £ | £ | £ | | £ | £ | £ | £ |

**3958 Farthing.** Laur. bust l. R. Britannia seated r. date in ex. lighthouse l. ship to r. die axis ↑↑

| | F | VF | EF | UNC | | F | VF | EF | UNC |
|---|---|---|---|---|---|---|---|---|---|
| 1860 Beaded border ........ | 5 | 30 | 90 | | 1875 small date ......10 | 25 | 95 | 300 |
| 1860 Toothed border ...... | 3 | 25 | 75 | | 1875 —older features..8 | 20 | 85 | 250 |
| 1860 — 5 berries ............ | 3 | 28 | 85 | | 1877 Proof only £3250 | | | |
| 1860 TB/BB mule............ | *Extremely rare* | | | | 1878............................ | 2 | 20 | 65 |
| 1861 5 berries ................. | 3 | 28 | 85 | | 1879 large 9 ............... | 5 | 25 | 85 |
| 1861 4 berries ................. | 4 | 30 | 90 | | 1879 normal 9 ........... | 2 | 20 | 70 |
| 1862 ............................... | 3 | 30 | 85 | | 1880............................ | 3 | 30 | 90 |
| 1862 large 8 ................... | *Extremely rare* | | | | 1881............................ | 2 | 20 | 75 |
| 1863 ............................20 | 45 | 175 | 400 | | 1883 .........................2 | 10 | 40 | 110 |
| 1864 4 no serif ............... | 5 | 35 | 100 | | 1884............................ | 1 | 15 | 40 |
| 1864 4 with serif............. | 8 | 40 | 110 | | 1885............................ | 1 | 15 | 40 |
| 1865 ............................... | 3 | 28 | 85 | | 1886............................ | 1 | 15 | 40 |
| 1865/2 ............................ | 10 | 35 | 130 | | 1887............................ | 2 | 25 | 70 |
| 1866 ............................... | 3 | 25 | 75 | | 1888............................ | 2 | 20 | 65 |
| 1867 ............................... | 4 | 30 | 95 | | 1890............................ | 2 | 20 | 65 |
| 1868 ............................... | 4 | 30 | 95 | | 1891............................ | 1 | 15 | 55 |
| 1869 ............................... | 10 | 40 | 130 | | 1892.........................2 | 10 | 40 | 110 |
| 1872 ............................... | 3 | 28 | 85 | | 1893............................ | 1 | 15 | 55 |
| 1873 ............................... | 2 | 28 | 85 | | 1894............................ | 2 | 18 | 65 |
| 1875 large date ..............5 | 10 | 40 | 135 | | 1895 .......................10 | 20 | 65 | 160 |

*Bronze coins graded in this catalogue as UNC have full mint lustre*

**3959 Farthing.** Similar R. Britannia. H Mint mark below date (struck by Ralph Heaton & Sons, Birmingham)

| | F | VF | EF | UNC | | F | VF | EF | UNC |
|---|---|---|---|---|---|---|---|---|---|
| 1874 H older features ....5 | 10 | 35 | 100 | | 1876 H large 6 ........10 | 30 | 75 | 160 |
| 1874 H,◌ over G's obv. .. | *Extremely rare* | | | | 1876 H normal 6 ......5 | 10 | 40 | 110 |
| 1875 H younger features..20 | 50 | 140 | 475 | | 1881 H .....................2 | 5 | 25 | 75 |
| 1875 H older features ...... | 2 | 15 | 65 | | 1882 H .....................2 | 5 | 25 | 75 |

**3960 Third-Farthing** (for use in Malta). Laur. head l. R. Crowned date and Value die axis ↑↑

| | F | VF | EF | UNC | | F | VF | EF | UNC |
|---|---|---|---|---|---|---|---|---|---|
| 1866 ............................1 | 3 | 18 | 55 | | 1881 .........................2 | 4 | 20 | 65 |
| 1868 ............................1 | 3 | 18 | 55 | | 1884 .........................1 | 3 | 18 | 55 |
| 1876 ............................2 | 4 | 20 | 65 | | 1885 .........................1 | 3 | 18 | 55 |
| 1878 ............................1 | 3 | 18 | 55 | | | | | |

**Old Head Issue, 1885-1901, die axis ↑↑**

Proofs exist of most years and are generally extremely rare for all denominations

3961
1897 Penny

| | VF £ | EF £ | UNC £ | | VF £ | EF £ | UNC £ |
|---|---|---|---|---|---|---|---|

**3961 Penny**. Old veiled bust l. R. Britannia seated r. date in ex., die axis ↑↑

| | VF £ | EF £ | UNC £ | | VF £ | EF £ | UNC £ |
|---|---|---|---|---|---|---|---|
| 1895 | 2 | 16 | 55 | 1898 | 4 | 18 | 60 |
| 1896 | 2 | 15 | 50 | 1899 | 2 | 16 | 55 |
| 1897 | 2 | 15 | 50 | 1900 | 3 | 12 | 40 |
| 1897 O'NE flawed | 75 | 250 | 625 | 1901 | 1 | 10 | 20 |
| 1897 High tide | 35 | 125 | 325 | | | | |

3961 'High Tide'
Horizon is level with folds in robe

3961A 'Low Tide'
Horizon is level with hem line of robe

**3961A Penny**. Similar As last but 'Low tide', 1895 ........................................ 50   200   450

**3962 Halfpenny**. Old veiled bust l. R. Britannia seated r. date in ex., die axis ↑↑

| | VF £ | EF £ | UNC £ | | VF £ | EF £ | UNC £ |
|---|---|---|---|---|---|---|---|
| 1895 | 2 | 6 | 25 | 1898 | 2 | 5 | 20 |
| 1896 | 2 | 5 | 20 | 1899 | | 5 | 20 |
| 1897 | 2 | 5 | 20 | 1900 | | 8 | 25 |
| 1897 Higher tide level | 5 | 10 | 30 | 1901 | | 2 | 15 |

**3963 Farthing**. Old veiled bust l. R. Britannia seated r. date in ex. Bright finish, die axis ↑↑

| | VF £ | EF £ | UNC £ | | VF £ | EF £ | UNC £ |
|---|---|---|---|---|---|---|---|
| 1895 | 2 | 5 | 20 | 1897 | 2 | 5 | 25 |
| 1896 | 2 | 5 | 20 | | | | |

3962
Old Head Halfpenny

3964
Old Head Farthing

**3964 Farthing**. Similar Dark finish, die axis ↑↑

| | VF £ | EF £ | UNC £ | | VF £ | EF £ | UNC £ |
|---|---|---|---|---|---|---|---|
| 1897 | 2 | 5 | 20 | 1899 | 2 | 5 | 20 |
| 1897 Higher tide level | 5 | 10 | 30 | 1900 | 3 | 8 | 25 |
| 1898 | 2 | 5 | 20 | 1901 | | 2 | 15 |

## Proof Sets

**PS3**   Young head, **1839**. 'Una and the Lion' Five Pounds, and Sovereign to Farthing
(15 coins) ...............................................................................................*FDC*    £30000

**PS4**   — **1853**. Sovereign to Half-Farthing, including Gothic type Crown
(16 coins) ...............................................................................................*FDC*    £28000

**PS5**   Jubilee head. Golden Jubilee, **1887**. Five pounds to Threepence (11 coins) .*FDC*    £6250

**PS6**   — — **1887**. Crown to Threepence (7 coins)..............................................*FDC*    £1250

**PS7**   Old head, **1893**. Five Pounds to Threepence (10 coins) ...............................*FDC*    £7500

**PS8**   — — **1893**. Crown to Threepence (6 coins)...................................................*FDC*    £1600

## EDWARD VII, 1901-10

'Edward the Peacemaker' was born on 9 November 1841, and married Princess Alexandra of Denmark. He indulged himself in every decadent luxury, while his wife tried to ignore his extramarital activities. Edward travelled extensively and was crucial in negotiating alliances with Russia and France. Edward VII died on 6 May 1910.

Five Pound pieces, Two Pound pieces and Crowns were only issued in 1902. A branch of the Royal Mint was opened in Canada at Ottawa and coined Sovereigns of imperial type from 1908.

Unlike the coins in most other proof sets, the proofs issued for the Coronation in 1902 have a matt surface in place of the more usual brilliant finish.

**Designer's initials:** De S. (G. W. De Saulles 1862-1903)
B. P. (Benedetto Pistrucci, d. 1855)

**Engravers and Designers:** WHJ Blakemore, George WIlliam De Saulles (1862-1903), Benedetto Pistrucci (1784-1855)

**Prime Ministers:–** Earl of Salisbury (1830-1903), Conservative 1895-1902, Arthur James Balfour (1848-1930), Conservative 1902-5, Sir Henry Campbell-Bannerman (1836-1908), Liberal 1905-8, Herbert Henry Asquith (1852-1928), Liberal 1908-16

## GOLD

Die axis: ↑↑

3966
Matt Proof Five Pounds 1902

| | EF | UNC | | F | VF | EF | UNC |
|---|---|---|---|---|---|---|---|
| | £ | £ | | £ | £ | £ | £ |

**3965 Five Pounds.** Bare head r. ℞. St. George and dragon, date in ex.
1902 .....................400 600 725 950

**3966 Five Pounds.** Similar Proof. 1902. *Matt surface FDC £850*

**3966A Five Pounds.** Similar Proof 1902S. S on ground for Sydney Mint, Australia    *Extremely rare*

3967                          3969
1902 Two Pounds              1902 Sovereign

**3967 Two Pounds.** Bare head r. R. St George and dragon, date in ex.
1902.....................175 225 350 450

**3968 Two Pounds.** Similar Proof. 1902. *Matt surface FDC £400*

**3968ATwo Pounds.** Similar Proof 1902S. S on ground for Sydney Mint, Australia    *Extremely rare*

**3969 Sovereign.** Bare head r. ℞ . St. George and dragon, date in ex. London mint, die axis ↑↑

| 1902 Matt proof *FDC £175* | | | 1906 ............................ | | BV | 110 |
|---|---|---|---|---|---|---|
| 1902............................ | BV | 110 | 1907 ............................ | | BV | 110 |
| 1903............................ | BV | 110 | 1908 ............................ | | BV | 110 |
| 1904............................ | BV | 110 | 1909 ............................ | | BV | 110 |
| 1905............................ | BV | 110 | 1910 ............................ | | BV | 110 |

**3970 Sovereign.** Similar R. C on ground for Ottawa Mint, Canada

| 1908 C (Satin proof only) *FDC £2750* | | | 1910 C ......................... | BV | 110 | 200 |
|---|---|---|---|---|---|---|
| 1909 C ......................... | 120 | 225 | | | | |

|  | *UNC*<br>£ |  | *UNC*<br>£ |
|---|---|---|---|

**3971 Sovereign.** Similar R. St. George M on ground for Melbourne Mint, Australia, die axis ↑↑

| 1902 M | 100 | 1907 M | 90 |
|---|---|---|---|
| 1903 M | 90 | 1908 M | 90 |
| 1904 M | 90 | 1909 M | 90 |
| 1905 M | 90 | 1910 M | 90 |
| 1906 M | 90 | | |

**3972 Sovereign.** Similar R. P on ground for Perth Mint, Australia die axis ↑↑

| 1902 P | 100 | 1907 P | 90 |
|---|---|---|---|
| 1903 P | 90 | 1908 P | 90 |
| 1904 P | 90 | 1909 P | 90 |
| 1905 P | 90 | 1910 P | 90 |
| 1906 P | 90 | | |

**3973 Sovereign.** Similar R. S on ground for Sydney Mint, Australia die axis ↑↑

| 1902 S | 100 | 1906 S | 90 |
|---|---|---|---|
| 1902 S Proof | *Extremely rare* | 1907 S | 90 |
| 1903 S | 90 | 1908 S | 90 |
| 1904 S | 110 | 1909 S | 90 |
| 1905 S | 90 | 1910 S | 90 |

3974A
1902 Half-Sovereign, no BP in exergue

|  | *F*<br>£ | *VF*<br>£ | *EF*<br>£ | *UNC*<br>£ |  | *F*<br>£ | *VF*<br>£ | *EF*<br>£ | *UNC*<br>£ |
|---|---|---|---|---|---|---|---|---|---|

**3974 A Half-Sovereign.** Bare head r. R. St. George. London Mint no BP in exergue, die axis ↑↑

| 1902 Matt proof *FDC* £120 | | | | 1903 | BV | 40 | 65 |
|---|---|---|---|---|---|---|---|
| 1902 | BV | 50 | 75 | 1904 | BV | 40 | 65 |

**3974 B Half-Sovereign.** R. Similar with BP in exergue

| 1904 | BV | 40 | 65 | 1909 | BV | 40 | 65 |
|---|---|---|---|---|---|---|---|
| 1905 | BV | 40 | 65 | 1910 | BV | 40 | 65 |
| 1906 | BV | 40 | 65 | | | | |
| 1907 | BV | 40 | 65 | | | | |
| 1908 | BV | 40 | 65 | | | | |

**3975 Half-Sovereign.** Similar R. M on ground  for Melbourne Mint, Australia, die axis ↑↑

| 1906 M | 50 | 100 | 350 | 1300 | 1908 M | BV | | 75 | 375 |
|---|---|---|---|---|---|---|---|---|---|
| 1907 M | BV | 40 | 75 | 375 | 1909 M | 50 | | 75 | 425 |

**3976 A Half-Sovereign.** — P on ground for Perth Mint, Australia R. no BP in exergue,  die axis ↑↑

| 1904 P | 65 | 165 | 580 | 1250 |
|---|---|---|---|---|

**3976 B Half-Sovereign.** Similar R. P on ground for Perth Mint, Australia R. with BP in exergue, die axis ↑↑

| 1904 P | 65 | 165 | 580 | 1250 | 1909 P | 60 | 150 | 415 | 1250 |
|---|---|---|---|---|---|---|---|---|---|
| 1908 P | 65 | 165 | 500 | 1575 | | | | | |

**3977 A Half-Sovereign.** Similar R. S on ground for Sydney Mint, Australia R. No BP in exergue,  die axis ↑↑

| 1902 S | 50 | 95 | 325 | 1903 S | 40 | 100 | 425 |
|---|---|---|---|---|---|---|---|
| 1902 S Proof | *Extremely rare* | | | | | | |

**3977 B Half-Sovereign.** — S on ground for Sydney Mint, Australia R. with BP in exergue, die axis ↑↑

| 1906 S | 40 | 75 | 300 | 1910 S | 40 | 60 | 150 |
|---|---|---|---|---|---|---|---|
| 1908 S | 40 | 60 | 150 | | | | |

# SILVER

3978
1902 Crown

|   | F £ | VF £ | EF £ | UNC £ |
|---|---|---|---|---|

**3978 Crown.** Bare head r. ℞. St. George and dragon date in ex. die axis ↑↑

1902 ..................................................................................................45    70    110    175

**3979 Crown.** Similar Matt proof *FDC* £185

3980
1904 Halfcrown

|   | F £ | VF £ | EF £ | UNC £ |
|---|---|---|---|---|

**3980 Halfcrown.** Bare head r. ℞. Crowned Shield in Garter, die axis ↑↑

| Year | F | VF | EF | UNC | Year | F | VF | EF | UNC |
|---|---|---|---|---|---|---|---|---|---|
| 1902 | 15 | 35 | 60 | 100 | 1906 | 20 | 45 | 175 | 500 |
| 1902 Matt proof *FDC* £120 | | | | | 1907 | 20 | 45 | 175 | 500 |
| 1903 | 65 | 250 | 600 | 1250 | 1908 | 25 | 50 | 300 | 700 |
| 1904 | 50 | 200 | 450 | 1000 | 1909 | 20 | 45 | 250 | 600 |
| 1905* | 195 | 475 | 1000 | 2750 | 1910 | 15 | 35 | 150 | 400 |

**3981 Florin.** Bare head r. ℞. Britannia standing on ship's bow die axis ↑↑

| Year | F | VF | EF | UNC | Year | F | VF | EF | UNC |
|---|---|---|---|---|---|---|---|---|---|
| 1902 | 8 | 20 | 50 | 85 | 1906 | 10 | 25 | 90 | 300 |
| 1902 Matt proof *FDC* £75 | | | | | 1907 | 10 | 30 | 100 | 325 |
| 1903 | 10 | 25 | 90 | 300 | 1908 | 15 | 40 | 175 | 450 |
| 1904 | 12 | 30 | 100 | 325 | 1909 | 15 | 40 | 150 | 400 |
| 1905 | 50 | 125 | 400 | 850 | 1910 | 10 | 20 | 75 | 250 |

*\*Beware of recent forgeries.*

|  |  |
|---|---|
| 3981 | 3983 |
| 1903 Florin | 1902 Sixpence |

3982
1902 Shilling

| | F | VF | EF | UNC | | F | VF | EF | UNC |
|---|---|---|---|---|---|---|---|---|---|
| | £ | £ | £ | £ | | £ | £ | £ | £ |

**3982 Shilling**. Bare head r. ℞. Lion rampant on crown die axis ↑↑

| | F | VF | EF | UNC | | F | VF | EF | UNC |
|---|---|---|---|---|---|---|---|---|---|
| 1902 | 5 | 15 | 45 | 75 | 1906 | 5 | 10 | 45 | 125 |
| 1902 Matt proof *FDC* £70 | | | | | 1907 | 5 | 10 | 50 | 150 |
| 1903 | 8 | 20 | 85 | 250 | 1908 | 10 | 20 | 85 | 275 |
| 1904 | 8 | 15 | 75 | 200 | 1909 | 10 | 20 | 85 | 275 |
| 1905 | 50 | 150 | 500 | 1150 | 1910 | 3 | 10 | 40 | 100 |

**3983 Sixpence**. Bare head r. ℞. Value in wreath die axis ↑↑

| | F | VF | EF | UNC | | F | VF | EF | UNC |
|---|---|---|---|---|---|---|---|---|---|
| 1902 | 5 | 10 | 30 | 50 | 1906 | 4 | 10 | 30 | 70 |
| 1902 Matt proof *FDC* £55 | | | | | 1907 | 5 | 10 | 35 | 75 |
| 1903 | 4 | 10 | 30 | 70 | 1908 | 5 | 12 | 40 | 80 |
| 1904 | 6 | 15 | 45 | 95 | 1909 | 4 | 10 | 35 | 75 |
| 1905 | 5 | 12 | 35 | 80 | 1910 | 3 | 5 | 25 | 45 |

**3984 Threepence**. As Maundy but dull finish die axis ↑↑

| | F | VF | EF | | F | VF | EF |
|---|---|---|---|---|---|---|---|
| 1902 | 4 | 8 | 15 | 1906 | 2 | 7 | 25 | 45 |
| 1902 Matt proof *FDC* £18 | | | | 1907 | 1 | 7 | 25 | 45 |
| 1903 | 1 | 7 | 25 | 45 | 1908 | 1 | 2 | 10 | 25 |
| 1904 | 3 | 7 | 35 | 70 | 1909 | 1 | 7 | 25 | 45 |
| 1905 | 2 | 7 | 25 | 65 | 1910 | | 1 | 10 | 30 |

3985
1902 Maundy Set

| | EF | FDC | | EF | FDC |
|---|---|---|---|---|---|
| | £ | £ | | £ | £ |

**3985 Maundy Set** (4d., 3d., 2d. and 1d.) Bare head r. die axis ↑↑

| | EF | FDC | | EF | FDC |
|---|---|---|---|---|---|
| 1902 | 55 | 75 | 1906 | 55 | 70 |
| 1902 Matt proof *FDC* £70 | | | 1907 | 55 | 70 |
| 1903 | 55 | 70 | 1908 | 55 | 70 |
| 1904 | 55 | 70 | 1909 | 65 | 100 |
| 1905 | 55 | 70 | 1910 | 65 | 100 |

| | EF<br>£ | FDC<br>£ |
|---|---|---|
| **3986 — Fourpence.** 1902-10 ......................................................................*from* | 6 | 12 |
| **3987 — Threepence.** 1902-10 ...................................................................*from* | 6 | 15 |
| **3988 — Twopence.** 1902-10 .......................................................................*from* | 6 | 10 |
| **3989 — Penny.** 1902-10...............................................................................*from* | 7 | 12 |

*Maundy sets in the original dated cases are worth approximately £5 more than the prices quoted.*

## BRONZE

3990A
1902 Penny - 'Low Tide'

3990 'High Tide'                              3990A 'Low Tide'

| | VF<br>£ | EF<br>£ | UNC<br>£ | | F<br>£ | VF<br>£ | EF<br>£ | UNC<br>£ |
|---|---|---|---|---|---|---|---|---|
| 1902....................................1 | | 8 | 35 | 1906....................................3 | | 15 | 55 |
| 1903 Normal 3...................2 | | 12 | 45 | 1907....................................4 | | 20 | 65 |
| 1903 Open 3 ....................35 | | 150 | — | 1908....................................3 | | 15 | 55 |
| 1904....................................5 | | 35 | 110 | 1909....................................4 | | 20 | 65 |
| 1905....................................4 | | 30 | 80 | 1910....................................2 | | 12 | 45 |

**3990A Penny.** Similar R. As last but 'Low tide', 1902 ..............................5    20    80    165

3991
1903 Halfpenny

| | VF | EF | UNC | | | F | VF | EF | UNC |
| | £ | £ | £ | | | £ | £ | £ | £ |

**3991 Halfpenny**. Bare head r. R. Britannia seated r. date in ex. die axis ↑↑

| | | | | | | | | | |
|---|---|---|---|---|---|---|---|---|---|
| 1902 | 1 | 5 | 20 | | 1908 | 1 | 8 | 25 | |
| 1903 | 2 | 10 | 30 | | 1909 | 2 | 10 | 35 | |
| 1904 | 2 | 10 | 35 | | 1910 | 2 | 10 | 30 | |
| 1905 | 2 | 10 | 35 | | | | | | |
| 1906 | 2 | 10 | 30 | | | | | | |
| 1907 | 1 | 8 | 25 | | | | | | |

**3991A Halfpenny**. Similar R. As last but 'Low tide', 1902 ......10    30    60    125

3992                                  3993
1907 Farthing              1902 Third-Farthing

**3992 Farthing**. Bare head r. R. Britannia seated r. date in ex. Dark finish die axis ↑↑

| | | | | | | | | |
|---|---|---|---|---|---|---|---|---|
| 1902 | — | 5 | 20 | 1907 | 1 | 5 | 20 |
| 1903 | 1 | 5 | 20 | 1908 | 1 | 5 | 20 |
| 1904 | 2 | 8 | 25 | 1909 | 1 | 5 | 20 |
| 1905 | 1 | 5 | 20 | 1910 | 2 | 8 | 25 |
| 1906 | 1 | 5 | 20 | | | | |

**3993 Third-Farthing** (for use in Malta) Bare head r. R. Crowned date and value die axis ↑↑.
1902 ..................................................................................................    10    30

*No proofs of the bronze coins were issued in 1902*

## Proof Sets
**PS9**  Coronation, **1902.** Five Pounds to Maundy Penny, matt surface, (13 coins) *FDC*      £1800
**PS10 — 1902.** Sovereign to Maundy Penny, matt surface, (11 coins) ..................*FDC*      £750

## GEORGE V, 1910-36

George V, the second son of Edward VII, was born on 3 June 1865 and married Mary of Teck who bore him five sons and a daughter. He was King through World War I and visited the front on several occassions. He suffered a fall breaking his pelvis on one of these visits, an injury that would pain him for the rest of his life. He watched the Empire divide; Ireland, Canada, Australia, New Zealand and India all went through changes. He died on 20th January 1936 only months after his Silver Jubilee.

Paper money issued by the Treasury during the First World War replaced gold for internal use after 1915 but the branch mints in Australia and South Africa (the main Commonwealth gold producing countries) continued striking Sovereigns until 1930-2. Owing to the steep rise in the price of silver in 1919/20 the issue of standard (.925) silver was discontinued and coins of .500 silver were minted.

In 1912, 1918 and 1919 some Pennies were made under contract by private mints in Birmingham. In 1918, as Half-Sovereigns were no longer being minted, Farthings were again issued with the ordinary bright bronze finish. Crown pieces had not been issued for general circulation but they were struck in small numbers about Christmas time for people to give as presents in the years 1927-36, and in 1935 a special commemorative Crown was issued in celebration of the Silver Jubilee.

As George V died on 20 January, it is likely that all coins dated 1936 were struck during the reign of Edward VIII.

**Engravers and Designers:**– George Kuger Gray (1880-1943), Bertram MacKennal (1863-1931), Benedetto Pistrucci (1784-1855) Percy Metcalfe (1895-1970)
**Prime Ministers:**– Herbert Henry Asquith (1852-1928), Liberal 1908-16, David Lloyd George, (1863-1945) Liberal 1916-22, Andrew Bonor Law (1858-1923), Conservative, 1922-3, Stanley Baldwin, (1867-1947) Conservative, 1923, 1924-1, 1935-7, James Ramsey MacDonald, (1866-1931) Labour 1924-7, 1929-35

**Designer's initials:**
  B. M. (Bertram Mackennal)          P. M. (Percy Metcalfe)
  K. G. (G. Kruger Gray)             B. P. (Benedetto Pistrucci; d. 1855)

Die axis: ↑↑

# GOLD

3994
1911 Proof Five Pounds

FDC
£

**3994 Five Pounds.*** Bare head l. R. St. George and dragon, date in ex., 1911 (Proof only) ..1450
**3995 Two Pounds.*** Bare head l. R. St. George and dragon, date in ex., 1911 (Proof only) ...600

3996

| | UNC | | VF | EF | UNC |
|---|---|---|---|---|---|
| | £ | | £ | £ | £ |

**3996 Sovereign.** Bare head l. R. St. George and dragon. London Mint die axis: ↑↑

| | | | | |
|---|---|---|---|---|
| 1911 | 110 | 1914 | | 110 |
| 1911 Proof *FDC* £325 | | 1915 | | 110 |
| 1911 Matt Proof *FDC of highest rarity* | | 1916 | | 125 |
| 1912 | 110 | 1917* | 1850 4250 | — |
| 1913 | 110 | 1925 | | 95 |

*Forgeries exist of these and of most other dates and mints.*

|     | F | VF | EF | UNC |     | F | VF | EF | UNC |
|-----|---|----|----|-----|-----|---|----|----|-----|
|     | £ | £  | £  | £   |     | £ | £  | £  | £   |

**3997 Sovereign.** Bare head l. R. St George, C on ground for the Ottawa Mint, Canada die axis: ↑↑

| | F | VF | EF | UNC | | F | VF | EF | UNC |
|--|--|--|--|--|--|--|--|--|--|
| 1911 C | BV | 95 | 140 | | 1917 C | BV | 95 | 140 | |
| 1913 C | 100 | 500 | — | | 1918 C | BV | 95 | 140 | |
| 1914 C | 140 | 325 | — | | 1919 C | BV | 95 | 140 | |
| 1916 C* | 3250 | 7500 | — | | | | | | |

*\* Beware of recent forgeries*

| 3997 | 3998 | 4004 |
|------|------|------|
| Canada Mint mark | India Mint mark | South Africa Mint mark |

**3998 Sovereign.** Similar R. I on ground for Bombay Mint, India 1918 ............................... 95

**3999 Sovereign.** Similar R. M on ground for Melbourne Mint, Australia die axis: ↑↑

| | F | VF | EF | UNC | | F | VF | EF | UNC |
|--|--|--|--|--|--|--|--|--|--|
| 1911 M | | | | 85 | 1920 M | 750 | 1750 | 2250 | 3150 |
| 1912 M | | | | 85 | 1921 M | 2000 | 3500 | 5500 | 6850 |
| 1913 M | | | | 85 | 1922 M | 1500 | 2750 | 4250 | 6000 |
| 1914 M | | | | 85 | 1923 M | | | | 85 |
| 1915 M | | | | 85 | 1924 M | | | | 85 |
| 1916 M | | | | 85 | 1925 M | | | | 85 |
| 1917 M | | | | 85 | 1926 M | | | | 85 |
| 1918 M | | | | 85 | 1928 M | 500 | 850 | 500 | 2000 |
| 1919 M | | | 70 | 100 | | | | | |

**4000 Sovereign.** Similar small bare head l. die axis: ↑↑

| | F | VF | EF | UNC | | F | VF | EF | UNC |
|--|--|--|--|--|--|--|--|--|--|
| 1929 M | 500 | 900 | 1400 | 1850 | 1931 M | 110 | 200 | 250 | 375 |
| 1930 M | | 95 | 120 | 165 | | | | | |

| 4000 | 4001 |
|------|------|
| 1931 M Sovereign, small head | Perth Mint Sovereign |

**4001 Sovereign.** Similar R. P on ground for Perth Mint, Australia die axis: ↑↑

| | F | VF | EF | UNC | | F | VF | EF | UNC |
|--|--|--|--|--|--|--|--|--|--|
| 1911 P | | | | 85 | 1920 P | | | | 85 |
| 1912 P | | | | 85 | 1921 P | | | | 85 |
| 1913 P | | | | 85 | 1922 P | | | | 85 |
| 1914 P | | | | 85 | 1923 P | | | | 85 |
| 1915 P | | | | 85 | 1924 P | 65 | 90 | 115 | 150 |
| 1916 P* | | | | 85 | 1925 P | 100 | 150 | 200 | 275 |
| 1917 P | | | | 85 | 1926 P | 500 | 1000 | 1400 | 1750 |
| 1918 P | | | | 85 | 1927 P | 85 | 200 | 300 | 450 |
| 1919 P | | | | 85 | 1928 P | 65 | 100 | 150 | 165 |

|  | VF | EF | UNC |  |  | F | VF | EF | UNC |
|---|---|---|---|---|---|---|---|---|---|
|  | £ | £ | £ |  |  | £ | £ | £ | £ |

**4002 Sovereign.** Similar — small bare head l. die axis: ↑↑

| 1929 P | 85 | 1931 P | 85 |
|---|---|---|---|
| 1930 P | 85 | | |

**4003 Sovereign.** Similar R. S on ground for Sydney Mint, Australia die axis: ↑↑

| 1911 S | 85 | 1919 S | 85 |
|---|---|---|---|
| 1912 S | 85 | 1920 S | *Extremely rare* |
| 1913 S | 85 | 1921 S .........400  650  1000  1500 |
| 1914 S | 85 | 1922 S .......3100  5000  7300  9150 |
| 1915 S | 85 | 1923 S .......2500  4000  6500  7650 |
| 1916 S | 85 | 1924 S .........325  575  850  1250 |
| 1917 S | 85 | 1925 S ...................................  85 |
| 1918 S | 85 | 1926 S .......4100  7750  11500  13000 |

**4004 Sovereign.** Similar R. SA on ground for Pretoria Mint, South Africa die axis: ↑↑

| 1923 SA ....................900  1750  3500 | 1926 SA | 85 |
|---|---|---|
| 1923 SA Proof *FDC* £475 | 1927 SA | 85 |
| 1924 SA .................1500  3000  — | 1928 SA | 85 |
| 1925 SA | 85 | | |

**4005 Sovereign.** Similar — small head die axis: ↑↑

| 1929 SA | 85 | 1931 SA | 85 |
|---|---|---|---|
| 1930 SA | 85 | 1932 SA | 95 |

4002
Small head

4003
1921 Sydney Sovereign

4006
1914 Half-sovereign

**4006 Half-Sovereign.** Bare head l. R. St. George and dragon date in ex. London Mint die axis: ↑↑

| 1911 ...............................BV  35  60 | 1913 ...................................  35  60 |
|---|---|
| 1911 Proof *FDC* £225 | 1914 ...................................  35  60 |
| 1911 Matt Proof *FDC of highest rarity* | 1915 ...................................  35  60 |
| 1912 ...............................BV  35  60 | |

**4007 Half-Sovereign.** Similar R. M on ground for Melbourne Mint, Australia die axis: ↑↑

| 1915 M ...................................................................................BV  45  80 |
|---|

**4008 Half-Sovereign.** Similar R. P on ground for Perth Mint, Australia die axis: ↑↑

| 1911 P ...........................55  100  125 | 1918 P ..........125  250  500  825 |
|---|---|
| 1915 P ...........................55  85  750 | |

**4009 Half-Sovereign.** Similar R. S on ground for Sydney Mint, Australia die axis: ↑↑

| 1911 S ...........................45  60  80 | 1915 S ...........................BV  45  60 |
|---|---|
| 1912 S ...........................40  50  70 | 1916 S ...........................BV  45  60 |
| 1914 S ...........................BV  45  65 | |

**4010 Half-Sovereign.** Similar R. SA on ground for Pretoria Mint, South Africa die axis: ↑↑

| 1923 SA Proof *FDC* £275 | 1926 SA .......................BV  35  55 |
|---|---|
| 1925 SA .......................BV  35  55 | |

# SILVER

**First Coinage.** Sterling silver (.925 fine)

4011
1918 Halfcrown

| | F | VF | EF | UNC | | F | VF | EF | UNC |
|---|---|---|---|---|---|---|---|---|---|
| | £ | £ | £ | £ | | £ | £ | £ | £ |

**4011 Halfcrown.** Bare head l. R. Crowned shield in Garter die axis: ↑↑

| | F | VF | EF | UNC | | F | VF | EF | UNC |
|---|---|---|---|---|---|---|---|---|---|
| 1911 | 5 | 18 | 40 | 95 | 1915 | 4 | 10 | 25 | 65 |
| 1911 Proof *FDC* £85 | | | | | 1916 | 4 | 10 | 25 | 65 |
| 1912 | 6 | 25 | 55 | 110 | 1917 | 5 | 15 | 40 | 75 |
| 1913 | 8 | 30 | 65 | 125 | 1918 | 4 | 10 | 25 | 65 |
| 1914 | 4 | 10 | 25 | 65 | 1919 | 5 | 15 | 40 | 75 |

4012
1911 Florin

**4012 Florin.** Bare head l. R. Crowned Cruciform shields sceptres in angles die axis: ↑↑

| | F | VF | EF | UNC | | F | VF | EF | UNC |
|---|---|---|---|---|---|---|---|---|---|
| 1911 | 5 | 10 | 35 | 80 | 1916 | 4 | 10 | 25 | 60 |
| 1911 Proof *FDC* £75 | | | | | 1917 | 6 | 12 | 30 | 70 |
| 1912 | 5 | 15 | 45 | 85 | 1918 | 4 | 10 | 25 | 60 |
| 1913 | 8 | 25 | 65 | 125 | 1919 | 6 | 12 | 30 | 70 |
| 1914 | 4 | 10 | 25 | 60 | | | | | |
| 1915 | 6 | 20 | 40 | 85 | | | | | |

**4013 Shilling.** Bare head l. R. Lion rampant on crown, within circle die axis: ↑↑

| | F | VF | EF | UNC | | F | VF | EF | UNC |
|---|---|---|---|---|---|---|---|---|---|
| 1911 | 2 | 8 | 20 | 40 | 1915 | | 4 | 20 | 40 |
| 1911 Proof *FDC* £55 | | | | | 1916 | | 4 | 20 | 40 |
| 1912 | 4 | 12 | 30 | 60 | 1917 | | 5 | 25 | 45 |
| 1913 | 8 | 15 | 45 | 80 | 1918 | | 4 | 20 | 40 |
| 1914 | 3 | 10 | 25 | 45 | 1919 | 4 | 10 | 30 | 55 |

4013
1919 Shilling

4014
1913 Sixpence

| | F | VF | EF | UNC | | F | VF | EF | UNC |
|---|---|---|---|---|---|---|---|---|---|
| | £ | £ | £ | £ | | £ | £ | £ | £ |

**4014 Sixpence.** Bare head l. R. Lion rampant on crown, within circle die axis: ↑↑

| | F | VF | EF | UNC | | F | VF | EF | UNC |
|---|---|---|---|---|---|---|---|---|---|
| 1911 | 2 | 8 | 15 | 30 | 1916 | 2 | 8 | 15 | 30 |
| 1911 Proof *FDC* £40 | | | | | 1917 | 5 | 15 | 30 | 60 |
| 1912 | 4 | 10 | 25 | 45 | 1918 | 2 | 8 | 15 | 30 |
| 1913 | 5 | 12 | 30 | 50 | 1919 | 4 | 10 | 20 | 40 |
| 1914 | 2 | 8 | 15 | 30 | 1920 | 4 | 10 | 25 | 45 |
| 1915 | 2 | 8 | 15 | 30 | | | | | |

**4015 Threepence.** As Maundy but dull finish die axis: ↑↑

| | F | VF | EF | | F | VF | EF |
|---|---|---|---|---|---|---|---|
| 1911 | 1 | 5 | 15 | 1916 | 1 | 3 | 10 |
| 1912 | 1 | 5 | 15 | 1917 | 1 | 3 | 10 |
| 1913 | 1 | 5 | 15 | 1918 | 1 | 3 | 10 |
| 1914 | 1 | 5 | 15 | 1919 | 1 | 3 | 10 |
| 1915 | 1 | 5 | 15 | 1920 | 1 | 5 | 15 |

4016
1911 Maundy Set

| | EF | FDC | | EF | FDC |
|---|---|---|---|---|---|
| | £ | £ | | £ | £ |

**4016 Maundy Set** (4d., 3d., 2d. and 1d.) die axis: ↑↑

| | EF | FDC | | EF | FDC |
|---|---|---|---|---|---|
| 1911 | 55 | 85 | 1916 | 55 | 85 |
| 1911 Proof *FDC* £80 | | | 1917 | 55 | 85 |
| 1912 | 55 | 85 | 1918 | 55 | 85 |
| 1913 | 55 | 85 | 1919 | 55 | 85 |
| 1914 | 55 | 85 | 1920 | 55 | 85 |
| 1915 | 55 | 85 | | | |
| **4017 — Fourpence.** 1911-20 ........................................*from* | | | | 8 | 15 |
| **4018 — Threepence.** 1911-20 ....................................*from* | | | | 10 | 18 |
| **4019 — Twopence.** 1911-20 ......................................*from* | | | | 7 | 12 |
| **4020 — Penny.** 1911-20 ............................................*from* | | | | 8 | 15 |

**Second Coinage.** Debased silver (.500 fine). Types as before.

| | F £ | VF £ | EF £ | UNC £ | | F £ | VF £ | EF £ | UNC £ |
|---|---|---|---|---|---|---|---|---|---|

**4021 Halfcrown.** Deeply engraved. Bare head l. R. Crowned shield in garter die axis: ↑↑

| | F | VF | EF | UNC | | | F | VF | EF | UNC |
|---|---|---|---|---|---|---|---|---|---|---|
| 1920......................4 | 8 | 25 | 65 | | | | | | | |

**4021A** — recut shallow portrait

| | | | | | | | | | | |
|---|---|---|---|---|---|---|---|---|---|---|
| 1920......................6 | 12 | 40 | 85 | | 1925...................20 | 50 | 175 | 300 | | |
| 1921......................5 | 10 | 30 | 75 | | 1926.....................5 | 10 | 35 | 80 | | |
| 1922......................4 | 8 | 25 | 65 | | 1926 No colon | | | | | |
| 1923......................3 | 5 | 15 | 40 | |   after OMN ....10 | 25 | 85 | 150 | | |
| 1924......................5 | 10 | 35 | 75 | | | | | | | |

**4022 Florin.** Deeply engraved. Bare head l. R. Crowned cruciform shields, sceptres in angles die axis: ↑↑

| | | | | | | | | | | |
|---|---|---|---|---|---|---|---|---|---|---|
| 1920......................3 | 8 | 30 | 80 | | | | | | | |

**4022A** — recut shallow portrait

| | | | | | | | | | | |
|---|---|---|---|---|---|---|---|---|---|---|
| 1920......................5 | 12 | 40 | 90 | | 1923.....................2 | 5 | 20 | 45 | | |
| 1921......................3 | 8 | 30 | 60 | | 1924.....................4 | 10 | 40 | 75 | | |
| 1922......................3 | 6 | 25 | 50 | | 1925...................25 | 45 | 125 | 200 | | |
| 1922 Proof in gold *FDC of highest rarity* | | | | | 1926.....................3 | 10 | 40 | 75 | | |

**4023 Shilling.** Deeply engraved. Bare head l. R. Lion rampant on crown within circle die axis: ↑↑

| | | | | | | | | | | |
|---|---|---|---|---|---|---|---|---|---|---|
| 1920......................3 | 6 | 25 | 45 | | 1921 nose to S ......4 | 10 | 30 | 65 | | |

**4023A** — recut shallow portrait

| | | | | | | | | | | |
|---|---|---|---|---|---|---|---|---|---|---|
| 1921 nose to SV ...5 | 15 | 40 | 95 | | 1924.....................3 | 8 | 30 | 50 | | |
| 1922......................3 | 6 | 25 | 45 | | 1925.....................5 | 10 | 45 | 80 | | |
| 1923......................2 | 5 | 20 | 40 | | 1926.....................3 | 6 | 20 | 45 | | |

**4024 Sixpence.** Bare head l. R. Lion rampant on crown within circle die axis: ↑↑

| | | | | | | | | | | |
|---|---|---|---|---|---|---|---|---|---|---|
| 1920......................2 | 4 | 12 | 25 | | 1924.....................2 | 4 | 12 | 25 | | |
| 1921......................2 | 4 | 12 | 25 | | 1924 Proof in gold *FDC of highest rarity* | | | | | |
| 1922......................2 | 5 | 15 | 30 | | 1925.....................2 | 4 | 15 | 30 | | |
| 1923......................3 | 6 | 20 | 40 | | | | | | | |

4025
1926 Sixpence

4026
George V Threepence

**4025 Sixpence.** Similar new beading and broader rim die axis: ↑↑

| | | | | | | | | | | |
|---|---|---|---|---|---|---|---|---|---|---|
| 1925......................2 | 4 | 12 | 25 | | 1926.....................2 | 4 | 15 | 25 | | |

**4026 Threepence.** Bare head l. R. Crowned 3 die axis: ↑↑

| | | | | | | | | | | |
|---|---|---|---|---|---|---|---|---|---|---|
| 1920...................... | 1 | 3 | 15 | | 1925...................— | 2 | 14 | 25 | | |
| 1921...................... | 1 | 3 | 15 | | 1926.....................1 | 3 | 15 | 30 | | |
| 1922...................... | 1 | 10 | 20 | | | | | | | |
| 1924 Proof in gold *FDC of highest rarity* | | | | | | | | | | |

| | EF £ | FDC £ | | | EF £ | FDC £ |
|---|---|---|---|---|---|---|

**4027 Maundy Set.** (4d., 3d., 2d. and 1d.) die axis: ↑↑

| | EF | FDC | | | EF | FDC |
|---|---|---|---|---|---|---|
| 1921 ..................................... | 55 | 85 | | 1925 ..................................... | 55 | 85 |
| 1922 ..................................... | 55 | 85 | | 1926 ..................................... | 55 | 85 |
| 1923 ..................................... | 55 | 85 | | 1927 ..................................... | 55 | 85 |
| 1924 ..................................... | 55 | 85 | | | | |

| | | EF | FDC |
|---|---|---|---|
| **4028 — Fourpence.** 1921-7.................................................................*from* | | 10 | 15 |
| **4029 — Threepence.** 1921-7 ...........................................................*from* | | 10 | 18 |
| **4030 — Twopence.** 1921-7 ..............................................................*from* | | 7 | 12 |
| **4031 — Penny.** 1921-7.....................................................................*from* | | 8 | 15 |

2nd coinage
BM more central on tr.

3rd coinage
Modified Effigy
BM to right of tr.

**Third Coinage.** As before but modified effigy, with details of head more clearly defined. The BM on truncation is nearer to the back of the neck and without stops; beading is more pronounced.

| | F | VF | EF | UNC | | F | VF | EF | UNC |
|---|---|---|---|---|---|---|---|---|---|
| | £ | £ | £ | £ | | £ | £ | £ | £ |

**4032 Halfcrown.** Modified effigy l. R. Crowned Shield in Garter die axis: ↑↑

| 1926 | 5 | 10 | 35 | 60 | 1927 Proof in gold *FDC of highest rarity* | | | | |
| 1927 | 4 | 7 | 25 | 40 | | | | | |

**4033 Shilling.** Modified effigy l. R. Lion rampant on crown, within circle die axis: ↑↑

| 1926 | 2 | 4 | 18 | 30 | 1927 | 2 | 6 | 25 | 40 |

**4034 Sixpence.** Modified effigy l. R. Lion rampant on crown, within circle die axis: ↑↑

| 1926 | | 3 | 10 | 20 | 1927 | 2 | 4 | 15 | 25 |

**4035 Threepence.** Modified effigy l. R. Crowned 3 die axis: ↑↑

| 1926 | | | | | | | 1 | 8 | 25 |

**Fourth Coinage. New types, 1927-36**

4036
1932 'Wreath' Crown

**4036 Crown.** Modified Bare head l. R. Crown and date in wreath die axis: ↑↑

| 1927 –15,030 struck Proof only *FDC* £185 | | | | 1931 –4056 struck | 45 | 120 | 225 | 350 |
|---|---|---|---|---|---|---|---|---|
| 1927 Matt Proof *FDC of highest rarity* | | | | 1932 –2395 struck | 95 | 165 | 300 | 475 |
| 1928 –9034 struck | 45 | 110 | 185 | 325 | 1933 –7132 struck | 45 | 110 | 185 | 325 |
| 1929 –4994 struck | 45 | 110 | 185 | 325 | 1934 –932 struck | 300 | 675 | 1250 | 2250 |
| 1930 -4847 struck | 45 | 110 | 185 | 325 | 1936 –2473 struck | 75 | 135 | 275 | 425 |

4037
1930 Halfcrown

4038
1928 Florin

| | F £ | VF £ | EF £ | UNC £ | | F £ | VF £ | EF £ | UNC £ |
|---|---|---|---|---|---|---|---|---|---|

**4037 Halfcrown.** Modified bare head l. R. Shield die axis: ↑↑

| | F | VF | EF | UNC | | F | VF | EF | UNC |
|---|---|---|---|---|---|---|---|---|---|
| 1927 Proof only *FDC* £55 | | | | | 1932 | 4 | 8 | 15 | 35 |
| 1927 Matt Proof *FDC of highest rarity* | | | | | 1933 | 2 | 5 | 10 | 20 |
| 1928 | 2 | 5 | 10 | 20 | 1934 | 4 | 10 | 25 | 50 |
| 1929 | 2 | 5 | 10 | 20 | 1935 | | 5 | 10 | 20 |
| 1930 | 10 | 25 | 100 | 250 | 1936 | | 3 | 8 | 15 |
| 1931 | 2 | 5 | 10 | 25 | | | | | |

**4038 Florin.** Modified bare head l. R. Cruciform shields, sceptre in each angle die axis: ↑↑

| | F | VF | EF | UNC | | F | VF | EF | UNC |
|---|---|---|---|---|---|---|---|---|---|
| 1927 Proof only *FDC* £45 | | | | | 1932 | 20 | 50 | 125 | 275 |
| 1928 | | 3 | 10 | 20 | 1933 | | 3 | 10 | 25 |
| 1929 | | 3 | 10 | 20 | 1935 | | 3 | 10 | 20 |
| 1930 | 2 | 5 | 10 | 25 | 1936 | | 2 | 10 | 20 |
| 1931 | 2 | 5 | 10 | 25 | | | | | |

4039
1928 Shilling

4040
1928 Sixpence

**4039 Shilling.** Modified bare head l. R. Lion rampant on crown, no inner circles die axis: ↑↑

| | F | VF | EF | UNC | | F | VF | EF | UNC |
|---|---|---|---|---|---|---|---|---|---|
| 1927 | 2 | 4 | 15 | 30 | 1931 | 2 | 4 | 10 | 20 |
| 1927 Proof *FDC* £35 | | | | | 1932 | 2 | 4 | 10 | 20 |
| 1927 Matt Proof *FDC Extremely rare* | | | | | 1933 | | 3 | 10 | 20 |
| 1928 | | 3 | 10 | 20 | 1934 | 2 | 5 | 16 | 30 |
| 1929 | | 3 | 10 | 20 | 1935 | | 3 | 10 | 20 |
| 1930 | 3 | 6 | 20 | 40 | 1936 | | 3 | 8 | 20 |

**4040 Sixpence.** Modified bare head l. R. Three oak sprigs with six acorns die axis: ↑↑

| | F | VF | EF | UNC | | F | VF | EF | UNC |
|---|---|---|---|---|---|---|---|---|---|
| 1927 Proof only *FDC* £25 | | | | | 1929 | | 2 | 4 | 15 |
| 1927 Matt Proof *FDC Extremely rare* | | | | | 1930 | | 2 | 4 | 15 |
| 1928 | | 2 | 5 | 15 | | | | | |

**4041 Sixpence.** Similar closer milling die axis: ↑↑

| | F | VF | EF | UNC | | F | VF | EF | UNC |
|---|---|---|---|---|---|---|---|---|---|
| 1931 | 2 | 3 | 8 | 20 | 1934 | 2 | 3 | 10 | 22 |
| 1932 | 2 | 4 | 14 | 25 | 1935 | | 2 | 6 | 16 |
| 1933 | 2 | 3 | 8 | 18 | 1936 | | 2 | 5 | 15 |

<table>
<tr><td>4042</td><td>4043</td></tr>
<tr><td>1934 Threepence</td><td>George V Maundy Set</td></tr>
</table>

| | F | VF | EF | UNC | | F | VF | EF | UNC |
|---|---|---|---|---|---|---|---|---|---|
| | £ | £ | £ | £ | | £ | £ | £ | £ |

**4042 Threepence.** Modified Bare head l. R̩. Three oak sprigs with three acorns die axis: ↑↑

| | F | VF | EF | UNC | | F | VF | EF | UNC |
|---|---|---|---|---|---|---|---|---|---|
| 1927 Proof only *FDC* £40 | | | | | 1932 | | | 1 | 10 |
| 1927 Matt Proof *FDC of highest rarity* | | | | | 1933 | | | 1 | 10 |
| 1928 | 1 | 3 | 14 | 35 | 1934 | | | 1 | 10 |
| 1930 | 1 | 3 | 14 | 35 | 1935 | | | 1 | 10 |
| 1931 | | | 1 | 10 | 1936 | | | 1 | 10 |

| | EF | FDC | | | EF | FDC |
|---|---|---|---|---|---|---|
| | £ | £ | | | £ | £ |

**4043 Maundy Set.** As earlier sets die axis: ↑↑

| | EF | FDC | | EF | FDC |
|---|---|---|---|---|---|
| 1928 | 55 | 85 | 1933 | 55 | 85 |
| 1929 | 55 | 85 | 1934 | 55 | 85 |
| 1930 | 55 | 85 | 1935 | 55 | 85 |
| 1931 | 55 | 85 | 1936 | 55 | 85 |
| 1932 | 55 | 85 | | | |

The 1936 Maundy was distributed by King Edward VIII

| | | EF | FDC |
|---|---|---|---|
| **4044 — Fourpence.** 1928-36 | *from* | 10 | 15 |
| **4045 — Threepence.** 1928-36 | *from* | 10 | 15 |
| **4046 — Twopence.** 1928-36 | *from* | 10 | 15 |
| **4047 — Penny.** 1928-36 | *from* | 12 | 18 |

**Silver Jubilee Commemorative issue,** die axis: ↑↑

4048
1935 'Jubilee' Crown

| | VF | EF | UNC |
|---|---|---|---|
| | £ | £ | £ |
| **4048 Crown.** 1935. R̩. St. George, incuse lettering on edge –714,769 struck | 10 | 15 | 25 |
| 1935 — error edge | | *Extremely rare* | |
| **4049 Crown.** Similar Specimen striking issued in box | | | 50 |

**4050 Crown.** Similar raised lettering on edge 2,500 struck.Proof (.925 Æ) *FDC* £300
— error edge inscription Proof *FDC* £1500
— Proof in gold –28 struck £15000

**BRONZE**

H Mint mark location – 4052

4052
1912 H Penny

KN Mint mark location – 4053

| | F £ | VF £ | EF £ | UNC £ | | F £ | VF £ | EF £ | UNC £ |
|---|---|---|---|---|---|---|---|---|---|

**4051 Penny.** Bare head l. R. Britannia seated right die axis: ↑↑

| | F | VF | EF | UNC | | F | VF | EF | UNC |
|---|---|---|---|---|---|---|---|---|---|
| 1911 | 2 | 10 | 35 | | 1918 | 3 | 15 | 40 |
| 1912 | 3 | 15 | 40 | | 1919 | 3 | 15 | 40 |
| 1913 | 4 | 18 | 45 | | 1920 | 3 | 15 | 40 |
| 1914 | 3 | 15 | 40 | | 1921 | 3 | 15 | 40 |
| 1915 | 3 | 15 | 40 | | 1922 | 5 | 25 | 50 |
| 1916 | 3 | 15 | 40 | | 1922 Rev. of 1927 | | *Extremely rare* | |
| 1917 | 3 | 15 | 40 | | 1926 | 6 | 30 | 60 |

**4052 Penny.** Bare head l. R. Britannia, H (Heaton Mint, Birmingham, Ltd.) to l. of date die axis: ↑↑

| | F | VF | EF | UNC | | F | VF | EF | UNC |
|---|---|---|---|---|---|---|---|---|---|
| 1912 H | 10 | 85 | 200 | | 1919 H | 15 | 220 | 450 |
| 1918 H | 20 | 200 | 425 | | | | | |

**4053 Penny.** Bare head l. R. Britannia KN (King's Norton Metal Co.) to l. of date die axis: ↑↑

| | F | VF | EF | UNC | | F | VF | EF | UNC |
|---|---|---|---|---|---|---|---|---|---|
| 1918 KN | 3 | 30 | 275 | 675 | 1919 KN | 3 | 35 | 325 | 775 |

**4054 Penny.** Modified effigy l. R. Britannia Seated r. shorter index finger date in ex. die axis: ↑↑

| | F | VF | EF | UNC | | F | VF | EF | UNC |
|---|---|---|---|---|---|---|---|---|---|
| 1926 | 20 | 125 | 750 | 1450 | 1927 | 2 | 10 | 30 | |

**4055 Penny.** Small bare head l. R. Britannia Seated r. date in ex. die axis: ↑↑

| | F | VF | EF | UNC | | F | VF | EF | UNC |
|---|---|---|---|---|---|---|---|---|---|
| 1928 | 2 | 10 | 30 | | 1933 | | *Extremely rare* | |
| 1929 | 2 | 10 | 30 | | 1934 | 4 | 20 | 45 |
| 1930 | 3 | 15 | 35 | | 1935 | 1 | 8 | 30 |
| 1931 | 3 | 15 | 35 | | 1936 | 0.50 | 6 | 25 |
| 1932 | 5 | 25 | 50 | | | | | |

**4056 Halfpenny.** Bare head l. R. Britannia Seated r. date in ex. die axis: ↑↑

| | F | VF | EF | UNC | | F | VF | EF | UNC |
|---|---|---|---|---|---|---|---|---|---|
| 1911 | | 5 | 25 | | 1919 | | 6 | 30 |
| 1912 | | 6 | 30 | | 1920 | | 6 | 30 |
| 1913 | | 6 | 30 | | 1921 | | 6 | 30 |
| 1914 | | 6 | 30 | | 1922 | | 8 | 35 |
| 1915 | | 6 | 30 | | 1923 | | 6 | 30 |
| 1916 | | 6 | 30 | | 1924 | | 6 | 30 |
| 1917 | | 6 | 30 | | 1925 | | 6 | 30 |
| 1918 | | 6 | 30 | | | | | |

**4057 Halfpenny.** Modified effigy l. R. Britannia Seated r. date in ex. die axis: ↑↑

| | F | VF | EF | UNC | | F | VF | EF | UNC |
|---|---|---|---|---|---|---|---|---|---|
| 1925 | | 8 | 35 | | 1927 | | 6 | 30 |
| 1926 | | 6 | 30 | | | | | |

4056
1923 Halfpenny

4058
Small head

| | EF<br>£ | UNC<br>£ | | EF<br>£ | UNC<br>£ |
|---|---|---|---|---|---|

**4058 Halfpenny.** Small bare head l. R. Britannia Seated r. date in ex. die axis: ↑↑

| | | | | | |
|---|---|---|---|---|---|
| 1928 | 3 | 20 | 1933 | 3 | 20 |
| 1929 | 3 | 20 | 1934 | 5 | 25 |
| 1930 | 3 | 20 | 1935 | 3 | 20 |
| 1931 | 3 | 20 | 1936 | 2 | 15 |
| 1932 | 3 | 20 | | | |

4059
1917 Farthing

4062
1913 Third-Farthing

**4059 Farthing.** Bare head l. R. Britannia Seated r. date in ex. Dark finish die axis: ↑↑

| | | | | | |
|---|---|---|---|---|---|
| 1911 | 3 | 12 | 1915 | 4 | 15 |
| 1912 | 2 | 10 | 1916 | 2 | 10 |
| 1913 | 2 | 10 | 1917 | 1 | 10 |
| 1914 | 2 | 10 | 1918 | 9 | 25 |

**4060 Farthing.** Similar Bright finish, die axis: ↑↑ 1918-25 ................... 1 10
**4061 Farthing.** Modified effigy l. R. Britannia Seated r. date in ex. die axis: ↑↑

| | | | | | |
|---|---|---|---|---|---|
| 1926 | 1 | 5 | 1932 | 1 | 5 |
| 1927 | 1 | 5 | 1933 | 1 | 5 |
| 1928 | 1 | 5 | 1934 | 2 | 8 |
| 1929 | 1 | 5 | 1935 | 2 | 5 |
| 1930 | 1 | 5 | 1936 | 1 | 5 |
| 1931 | 1 | 5 | | | |

**4062 Third-Farthing** (for use in Malta). Bare head l. R. Crowned date and Value die axis: ↑↑
1913 ................................................................................................... 12 30

**Proof Sets**

**PS11** Coronation, **1911.** Five pounds to Maundy Penny (12 coins) ...............*FDC* £3000
**PS12** — **1911.** Sovereign to Maundy Penny (10 coins) ...............................*FDC* £1000
**PS13** — **1911.** Half crown to Maundy Penny (8 coins) ...............................*FDC* £475
**PS14** New type, **1927.** Wreath type Crown to Threepence (6 coins) ...............*FDC* £350

Succeeded his father on 2 January 1936. Abdicated 10 December.

Edward VIII was born 23 June 1894, and was very popular as Prince of Wales. He ruled only for a short time before announcing his intended marriage to the American divorcee Wallis Simpson; a potential religious and political scandal. Edward was not a traditionalist, as evidenced on the proposed coinage, where he insisted against all advice on having his effigy face the same way as his father's, instead of opposite. He abdicated in favour of his brother, and became Edward, Duke of Windsor, marrying Mrs Simpson in France, where they lived in exile. He governed the Bahamas from 1940-45 and died on 28 May 1972.

No coins of Edward VIII were issued for currency within the United Kingdom bearing his name and portrait. The Mint had commenced work on a new coinage prior to the Abdication, and various patterns were made. No Proof Sets were issued for sale and only a small number of sets were struck.

Coins bearing Edward's name, but not his portrait, were issued for the colonial territories of British East Africa, British West Africa, Fiji and New Guinea. The projected U.K. coins were to include a Shilling of essentially `Scottish' type and a nickel brass Threepence with twelve sides which might supplement and possibly supersede the inconveniently small silver Threepence.

**Engravers and Designers**:– George Kruger Gray (1880-1943), Thomas Humphrey Paget (1893-1974), Benedicto Pistucci (1784-1855) Frances Madge Kitchener, Percy Metcalfe (1895-1970), H Wilson Parker (1896-1980)

**Designer's initials:** H. P. (T. Humphrey Paget)     B.P. (Benedetto Pistrucci, d. 1855)
              K. G. (G. Kruger Gray)        M. K. (Madge Kitchener)
              W. P. (H. Wilson Parker)

**Prime Minister:**– Stanley Baldwin (1867-1947), Conservative 1935-7

**Die axis ↑↑**

4063
Edward VIII Proof Five Pounds

**4063 Proof Set**

Gold, Five Pounds, Two Pounds and Sovereign, 1937............................................ *not issued*

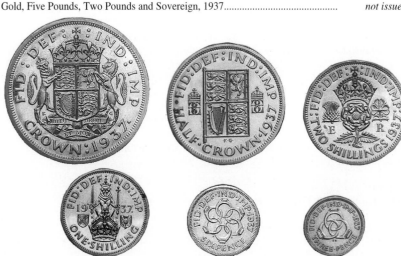

Silver Crown, Halfcrown, Florin, Scottish shilling, sixpence and threepence, 1937    *not issued*

**Sovereign**, Bare head l. R. St George and dragon date in ex............................ *Extremely rare*
**Crown**, Bare head l. R. Crowned Shield of arms and supporters...................... *Extremely rare*
**Halfcrown**, Bare head l. R. Quartered Standard of arms................................. *Extremely rare*
**Florin**, Bare head l. R. Crowned rose and emblems......................................... *Extremely rare*
**Shilling**, Bare head l. R. Lion seated facing on crown .................................... *Extremely rare*
**Sixpence**, Bare head l. R. Six interlinked rings ................................................ *Extremely rare*
**Threepence**, Bare head l. R. three interlinked rings......................................... *Extremely rare*

**4064A** Nickel brass. **Threepence**, 1937 Bare head l. R. Thrift plant below ....... 35000
  Bronze. **Penny. Halfpenny and Farthing,** 1937 .................................... *not issued*

**Pattern**

Edward VIII Brass Threepence

**4064B** Nickel brass dodecagonal **Threepence**, 1937. Bare head l. R. Thrift plant of more
  naturalistic style than the modified proof coin. A small number of these
  coins were produced for experimental purposes and a few did get into  .
  circulation ..................................................................................... 29500

George VI was born on 14 December 1895 and never expected to be King. He suffered ill-health through much of his life and had a stammer. He married Elizabeth Bowes Lyon and together they became very popular especially through the ravages of World War II, when Buckingham Palace was bombed. The war took its toll on George, and ever a heavy smoker he succumbed to lung cancer on 6th February 1952. Elizabeth, known after his death as 'Queen Elizabeth the Queen Mother', lived on to the age of 101 dying on 30 March 2002.

Though they were at first issued concurrently, the twelve-sided nickel-brass Threepence superseded the small silver Threepence in 1942. Those dated 1943-4 were not issued for circulation in the U.K. In addition to the usual English 'lion' Shilling, a Shilling of Scottish type was issued concurrently. This depicts the Scottish lion and crown flanked by the shield of St. Andrew and a thistle. In 1947, as silver was needed to repay the bullion lent by the U.S.A. during the war, silver coins were replaced by coins of the same type and weight made of cupro-nickel. In 1949, after India had attained independence, the title IND:IMP *(Indiae Imperator)* was dropped from the coinage. Commemorative Crown pieces were issued for the Coronation and the 1951 Festival of Britain.

**Engravers and Designers:**– Frances Madge Kitchener, George Kruger Gray (1880-1943), Percy Metcalfe (1895-1970) Thomas Humphrey Paget (1893-1974), H Wilson Parker (1896-1980), Benedetto Pistrucci (1784-1855)

**Designer's initials:**   K. G. (G. Kruger Gray)       B. P. (Benedetto Pistrucci, d. 1855)
                  H. P. (T. Humphrey Paget)     W. P. (Wilson Parker)

**Prime Ministers:**– Stanley Baldwin, (1867-1947) Conservative, 1935-37, Arthur Neville Chamberlain, (1869-1940) Conservative 1937-40, Sir Winston Leonard Spencer Churchill,(1874-1965) Conservative 1940-45. 1951-55, Clement Richard Attlee, (1883-1967) Labour 1945-51

**Die axis ↑↑**

## GOLD

4074
1937 Proof Five Pounds

4076
1937 Proof Sovereign

|  | FDC £ |
|---|---|
| **4074  Five Pounds.** Bare head l. R. St. George, 1937. Proof plain edge only (5001 struck).. | 650 |
| **4074-4077** Proof Struck to Matt finish *FDC of highest rarity* | |
| **4075  Two Pounds.** Similar, 1937. Proof plain edge only (5001 struck)............................... | 375 |
| **4076  Sovereign.** Similar, 1937. Proof plain edge only (5001 struck).................................. | 950 |
| **4077  Half-Sovereign.** Similar, 1937. Proof plain edge only (5001 struck) .......................... | 275 |

## SILVER

**First coinage.** Silver, .500 fine, with title IND:IMP

4078
1937 Crown

| | VF | EF | UNC |
|---|---|---|---|
| | £ | £ | £ |
| **4078 Crown.** Coronation commemorative, 1937. R. Arms and supporters | 10 | 20 | 30 |

**4079 Crown.** Similar 1937 Proof *FDC* £45
　　　　　Similar 1937 Frosted 'VIP' Proof £400
　　　　　— 1937 Matt Proof *FDC of highest rarity*

4080
1937 Halfcrown

4081
1937 Florin

| | EF | UNC | | EF | UNC |
|---|---|---|---|---|---|
| | £ | £ | | £ | £ |

**4080 Halfcrown.** Bare head l. R. Shield die axis: ↑↑

| | EF | UNC | | EF | UNC |
|---|---|---|---|---|---|
| 1937 | 4 | 15 | 1941 | 5 | 15 |
| 1937 Proof *FDC* £20 | | | 1942 | 3 | 10 |
| 1937 Matt Proof *FDC of highest rarity* | | | 1943 | 5 | 15 |
| 1938 | 8 | 30 | 1944 | 3 | 10 |
| 1939 | 5 | 15 | 1945 | 3 | 10 |
| 1940 | 5 | 15 | 1946 | 3 | 10 |

**4081 Florin.** Bare head l. R. Crowned rose, etc. die axis: ↑↑

| | EF | UNC | | EF | UNC |
|---|---|---|---|---|---|
| 1937 | 3 | 10 | 1941 | 4 | 12 |
| 1937 Proof *FDC* £15 | | | 1942 | 3 | 10 |
| 1937 Matt Proof *FDC of highest rarity* | | | 1943 | 3 | 10 |
| 1938 | 8 | 25 | 1944 | 3 | 10 |
| 1939 | 4 | 12 | 1945 | 3 | 10 |
| 1940 | 4 | 12 | 1946 | 3 | 10 |

4082
1945 'English' Shilling

4083
1937 'Scottish' Shilling

**4082 Shilling.** 'English' reverse. Bare head l. R. Lion rampant on large crown die axis: ↑↑

| | EF | UNC | | EF | UNC |
|---|---|---|---|---|---|
| 1937 | 2 | 8 | 1941 | 3 | 12 |
| 1937 Proof *FDC* £15 | | | 1942 | 2 | 10 |
| 1937 Matt Proof *FDC of highest rarity* | | | 1943 | 2 | 10 |
| 1938 | 8 | 25 | 1944 | 2 | 10 |
| 1939 | 3 | 12 | 1945 | 1 | 8 |
| 1940 | 3 | 12 | 1946 | 1 | 8 |

|  | EF | UNC |  |  | VF | EF | UNC |
|---|---|---|---|---|---|---|---|
|  | £ | £ |  |  | £ | £ | £ |

**4083 Shilling.** 'Scottish' reverse. Bare head l. R. Lion seated facing on crown die axis: ↑↑

| 1937 | 1 | 8 |  | 1941 | 3 | 12 |
|---|---|---|---|---|---|---|
| 1937 Proof *FDC* £15 |  |  |  | 1942 | 2 | 10 |
| 1937 Matt Proof *FDC of highest rarity* |  |  |  | 1943 | 2 | 10 |
| 1938 | 8 | 25 |  | 1944 | 2 | 10 |
| 1939 | 3 | 12 |  | 1945 | 1 | 8 |
| 1940 | 3 | 12 |  | 1946 | 1 | 8 |

4084
1937 Sixpence

4085
1937 Threepence

**4084 Sixpence.** Bare head l. R. GRI crowned die axis: ↑↑

| 1937 | 1 | 8 |  | 1941 | 2 | 10 |
|---|---|---|---|---|---|---|
| 1937 Proof *FDC* £10 |  |  |  | 1942 | 1 | 8 |
| 1937 Matt Proof *FDC of highest rarity* |  |  |  | 1943 | 1 | 8 |
| 1938 | 6 | 15 |  | 1944 | 1 | 8 |
| 1939 | 2 | 10 |  | 1945 | 1 | 8 |
| 1940 | 2 | 10 |  | 1946 | 1 | 8 |

**4085 Threepence.** Bare head l. R. Shield on rose die axis: ↑↑

| 1937 | 1 | 8 |  | 1941 | | 6 | 20 |
|---|---|---|---|---|---|---|---|
| 1937 Proof *FDC* £12 |  |  |  | 1942* | 5 | 15 | 50 |
| 1937 Matt Proof *FDC of highest rarity* |  |  |  | 1943* | 5 | 20 | 65 |
| 1938 | 1 | 8 |  | 1944* | 10 | 30 | 95 |
| 1939 | 6 | 15 |  | 1945* | | *Extremely rare* | |
| 1940 | 3 | 12 |  | *\* issued for Colonial use only* | | | |

4086
1937 Maundy Set

|  | FDC |  |  | FDC |
|---|---|---|---|---|
|  | £ |  |  | £ |

**4086 Maundy Set.** Silver, .500 fine. Uniform dates die axis: ↑↑

| 1937 | 65 |  | 1941 | 85 |
|---|---|---|---|---|
| 1937 Proof *FDC* £70 |  |  | 1942 | 85 |
| 1937 Matt Proof *FDC of highest rarity* |  |  | 1943 | 85 |
| 1938 | 85 |  | 1944 | 85 |
| 1939 | 85 |  | 1945 | 85 |
| 1940 | 85 |  | 1946 | 85 |

|  | *FDC*<br>£ |  | *FDC*<br>£ |
|---|---|---|---|
| **4087** — **Fourpence.** 1937-46 ....................................................... *from* | | | 12 |
| **4088** — **Threepence.** 1937-46 .................................................... *from* | | | 12 |
| **4089** — **Twopence.** 1937-46 ....................................................... *from* | | | 12 |
| **4090** — **Penny.** 1937-46 .............................................................. *from* | | | 18 |

**Second coinage.** Silver, .925 fine, with title IND:IMP (Maundy only)
**4091 Maundy Set** (4d., 3d., 2d. and 1d.). Uniform dates die axis: ↑↑

| 1947 ............................................... | 85 | 1948 ................................................ | 85 |
|---|---|---|---|

| **4092** — **Fourpence,** 1947-8 ........................................................... | | | 12 |
|---|---|---|---|
| **4093** — **Threepence,** 1947-8 ........................................................ | | | 12 |
| **4094** — **Twopence,** 1947-8 .......................................................... | | | 12 |
| **4095** — **Penny,** 1947-8 ................................................................ | | | 18 |

**Third coinage.** Silver, .925 fine, but omitting IND:IMP. (Maundy only)
**4096 Maundy Set** (4d., 3d., 2d. and 1d.). Uniform dates die axis: ↑↑

| 1949 ...................................................... | 85 | 1951 ....................................................... | 85 |
|---|---|---|---|
| 1950 ...................................................... | 85 | 1952 ....................................................... | 85 |
| 1951 Matt Proof *FDC Extremely rare* | | 1952 Proof in copper *FDC Extremely rare* | |

*The 1952 Maundy was distributed by Queen Elizabeth II.*

| **4097** — **Fourpence,** 1949-52 ..................................................... *from* | | | 12 |
|---|---|---|---|
| **4098** — **Threepence,** 1949-52 .................................................. *from* | | | 12 |
| **4099** — **Twopence,** 1949-52 .................................................... *from* | | | 12 |
| **4100** — **Penny,** 1949-52 .......................................................... *from* | | | 18 |

## CUPRO-NICKEL

**Second coinage.** Types as first (silver) coinage, IND:IMP.

|  | *EF*<br>£ | *UNC*<br>£ |  | *EF*<br>£ | *UNC*<br>£ |
|---|---|---|---|---|---|
| **4101 Halfcrown.** Bare head l. R. Shield die axis: ↑↑ | | | | | |
| 1947 ............................... | 1 | 8 | 1948 ............................... | 1 | 8 |
| **4102 Florin.** Bare head l. R. Crowned rose die axis: ↑↑ | | | | | |
| 1947 ................................. | 1 | 8 | 1948 ................................ | 1 | 8 |
| **4103 Shilling.** 'English' reverse. Bare head l. die axis: ↑↑ | | | | | |
| 1947 .................................. | 1 | 8 | 1948 ........................................ | | 6 |
| **4104 Shilling.** 'Scottish' reverse. Bare head l. die axis: ↑↑ | | | | | |
| 1947 ................................ | 1 | 8 | 1948 ........................................ | | 6 |
| **4105 Sixpence.** Bare head l. R. GRI crowned die axis: ↑↑ | | | | | |
| 1947 ............................................. | | 6 | 1948 ........................................ | | 5 |

**Third coinage.** Types as before but title IND:IMP. omitted

4106
1951 Halfcrown

|  | EF £ | UNC £ |  | VF £ | EF £ | UNC £ |
|---|---|---|---|---|---|---|

**4106 Halfcrown.** Bare head l. R. Shield die axis: ↑↑

| 1949 ............................... | 3 | 10 | 1951 ............... | 1 | 8 | 20 |
|---|---|---|---|---|---|---|
| 1950 ............................... | 5 | 15 | 1951 Proof *FDC* £25 | | | |
| 1950 Proof *FDC* £20 | | | 1951 Matt Proof *FDC of highest rarity* | | | |
| 1950 Matt Proof *FDC of highest rarity* | | | 1952 ................................. | | *Extremely rare* | |

**4107 Florin.** Bare head l. R. Crowned rose die axis: ↑↑

| 1949 ............................... | 4 | 12 | 1951 ...................... | | 6 | 18 |
|---|---|---|---|---|---|---|
| 1950 ............................... | 5 | 12 | 1951 Proof *FDC* £25 | | | |
| 1950 Proof *FDC* £15 | | | 1951 Matt Proof *FDC of highest rarity* | | | |
| 1950 Matt Proof *FDC of highest rarity* | | | | | | |

**4108 Shilling.** 'English' reverse. Bare head l. die axis: ↑↑

| 1949 ............................... | 4 | 12 | 1951 ............................... | | 6 | 18 |
|---|---|---|---|---|---|---|
| 1950 ............................... | 5 | 15 | 1951 Proof *FDC* £15 | | | |
| 1950 Proof *FDC* £15 | | | 1951 Matt Proof *FDC Extremely rare* | | | |

**4109 Shilling.** 'Scottish' reverse. Bare head l. die axis: ↑↑

| 1949 ............................... | 5 | 15 | 1951 ............................... | | 6 | 18 |
|---|---|---|---|---|---|---|
| 1950 ............................... | 5 | 15 | 1951 Proof *FDC* £15 | | | |
| 1950 Proof *FDC* £15 | | | 1951 Matt Proof *FDC Extremely rare* | | | |
| 1950 Matt Proof *FDC Extremely rare* | | | | | | |

4110
1952 Sixpence

**4110 Sixpence.** Bare head l. R. Crowned cypher die axis: ↑↑

| 1949 ............................... | 1 | 8 | 1951 ............................... | | 5 | 15 |
|---|---|---|---|---|---|---|
| 1950 ............................... | 1 | 8 | 1951 Proof *FDC* £12 | | | |
| 1950 Proof *FDC* £10 | | | 1951 Matt Proof *FDC Extremely rare* | | | |
| 1950 Matt Proof *FDC Extremely rare* | | | 1952 ......................5 | 20 | 60 | |

**Festival of Britain issue** die axis: ↑↑

4111
Festival of Britain Crown

| | EF | UNC |
|---|---|---|
| | £ | £ |

**4111 Crown.** Bare head l. R. St. George and dragon, date in ex, 1951. *Proof-like* 10    20

Similar — 1951 Frosted 'VIP' Proof £350
Similar — 1951 Matt Proof *FDC of highest rarity*
Similar — 1951 Plain edge Proof *FDC* £1000

## NICKEL BRASS

**First issue,** with title IND:IMP.

| 4112 | 4113 |
|---|---|
| 1937 Brass Threepence | Second issue obverse |

| VF | EF | UNC | | VF | EF | UNC |
|---|---|---|---|---|---|---|
| £ | £ | £ | | £ | £ | £ |

**4112 Threepence** (dodecagonal). Bare head l. R. Thrift plant die axis: ↑↑

| | VF | EF | UNC | | VF | EF | UNC |
|---|---|---|---|---|---|---|---|
| 1937 | | 2 | 10 | 1942 | | 3 | 10 |
| 1937 Proof *FDC* £15 | | | | 1943 | | 3 | 10 |
| 1937 Matt Proof *FDC of highest rarity* | | | | 1944 | | 3 | 10 |
| 1938 | | 6 | 20 | 1945 | | 5 | 15 |
| 1939 | | 10 | 40 | 1946 | 15 | 75 | 300 |
| 1940 | | 6 | 20 | 1948 | | 8 | 45 |
| 1941 | | 3 | 10 | | | | |

**Second issue,** omitting IND:IMP.
**4113 Threepence.** Bare head l. R. Similar die axis: ↑↑

| | VF | EF | UNC | | VF | EF | UNC |
|---|---|---|---|---|---|---|---|
| 1949 | 15 | 65 | 275 | 1951 | | 20 | 75 |
| 1950 | | 15 | 50 | 1951 Proof *FDC* £40 | | | |
| 1950 Proof *FDC* £35 | | | | 1951 Matt Proof *FDC of highest rarity* | | | |
| 1950 Matt Proof *FDC of highest rarity* | | | | 1952 | | 5 | 15 |

# BRONZE

**First issue,** with title IND:IMP.

4114
1937 Penny

| | EF £ | UNC £ | | EF £ | UNC £ |
|---|---|---|---|---|---|

**4114 Penny.** Bare head l. R. Britannia Seated r. date in ex die axis: ↑↑

| | EF £ | UNC £ | | EF £ | UNC £ |
|---|---|---|---|---|---|
| 1937 | | 6 | 1944 — | 6 | 18 |
| 1937 Proof *FDC* £15 | | | 1945 — | 5 | 15 |
| 1938 | 1 | 8 | 1946 — | 5 | 15 |
| 1939 | 4 | 12 | 1947 — | | 6 |
| 1940 | 10 | 40 | 1948 — | | 6 |
| 1940 Double exergue line | 4 | 12 | 1946 ONE' die flaw | 35 | — |

| 4115 | 4116 |
|---|---|
| 1937 Halfpenny | 1937 Farthing |

**4115 Halfpenny.** Bare head l. R. Ship sailing l. date below die axis: ↑↑

| | EF £ | UNC £ | | EF £ | UNC £ |
|---|---|---|---|---|---|
| 1937 | | 6 | 1943 | | 6 |
| 1937 Proof *FDC* £10 | | | 1944 | | 6 |
| 1938 | 1 | 8 | 1945 | 1 | 8 |
| 1939 | 2 | 10 | 1946 | 2 | 10 |
| 1940 | 3 | 12 | 1947 | 1 | 8 |
| 1941 | | 6 | 1948 | | 6 |
| 1942 | | 6 | | | |

**4116 Farthing.** Bare head l. R. Wren l. date above die axis: ↑↑

| | £ | | £ |
|---|---|---|---|
| 1937 | 4 | 1943 | 4 |
| 1937 Proof *FDC* £10 | | 1944 | 4 |
| 1938 | 6 | 1945 | 4 |
| 1939 | 4 | 1946 | 4 |
| 1940 | 4 | 1947 | 4 |
| 1941 | 4 | 1948 | 4 |
| 1942 | 4 | | |

**Second issue,** without IND.IMP. Types as before

| | VF | EF | UNC | | VF | EF | UNC |
|---|---|---|---|---|---|---|---|
| | £ | £ | £ | | £ | £ | £ |

**4117 Penny.** Bare head l. R. Britannia Seated r. date in ex. die axis: ↑↑

| | | | | | | | |
|---|---|---|---|---|---|---|---|
| 1949 | | | 6 | 1951 | 10 | 35 | 60 |
| 1950 | 6 | 18 | 40 | 1951 Proof *FDC* £40 | | | |
| 1950 Proof *FDC* £25 | | | | 1952 Proof only ..... | | | *Unique* |

4118
Second issue Halfpenny

4119
Second issue Farthing

**4118 Halfpenny.** Bare head l. R. Ship Sailing l. date below die axis: ↑↑

| | | | | | | |
|---|---|---|---|---|---|---|
| 1949 | 4 | 12 | 1951 | | 5 | 20 |
| 1950 | 3 | 10 | 1951 Proof *FDC* £12 | | | |
| 1950 Proof *FDC* £10 | | | 1952 | | 1 | 8 |

**4119 Farthing.** Bare head l. R. Wren l. date above die axis: ↑↑

| | | | |
|---|---|---|---|
| 1949 | 5 | 1951 | 6 |
| 1950 | 5 | 1951 Proof *FDC* £18 | |
| 1950 Proof *FDC* £10 | | 1952 | 5 |

*The coins dated 1952 were issued during the reign of Elizabeth II.*

## Proof Sets

| | |
|---|---|
| **PS15** Coronation, **1937.** Five pounds to Half-sovereign (4 coins).........................*FDC* | £2500 |
| **PS16 — 1937.** Crown to Farthing, including Maundy Set (15 coins) ...................*FDC* | £300 |
| **PS17** Mid-Century, **1950.** Halfcrown to Farthing (9 coins)...................................*FDC* | £100 |
| **PS18** Festival of Britain, **1951.** Crown to Farthing (10 coins)...............................*FDC* | £125 |

Elizabeth II was born on 21 April 1926. Our current Monarch has lived a long and glorious reign celebrating her Golden Jubilee in 2002. She married Philip a distant cousin in 1947 and has four children, Charles, Anne, Andrew and Edward. Significantly she is the first Monarch to pay taxes and her coinage has been an interesting one with the change to decimal coinage and the numerous bust changes since 1953.

The earliest coins of this reign have the title BRITT:OMN, but in 1954 this was omitted from the Queen's titles owing to the changing status of so many Commonwealth territories. The minting of 'English' and 'Scottish' shillings was continued. A Coronation commemorative crown was issued in 1953, another crown was struck on the occasion of the 1960 British Exhibition in New York and a third was issued in honour of Sir Winston Churchill in 1965. A very small number of proof gold coins were struck in 1953 for the national museum collections, but between 1957 and 1968 gold sovereigns were minted again in quantity for sale in the international bullion market and to counteract the activities of counterfeiters.

Owing to inflation the farthing had now become practically valueless; production of these coins ceased after 1956 and the coins were demonetized at the end of 1960. In 1965 it was decided to change to a decimal system of coinage in the year 1971. As part of the transition to decimal coinage the halfpenny was demonetized in August 1969 and the halfcrown in January 1970. (See also introduction to Decimal Coinage.

**Designer's initials:**

A. V. (Avril Vaughan)
B. P. (Benedetto Pistrucci, 1784-1855)
B. R. (Bruce Rushin)
C. T. (Cecil Thomas)
D. C. (David Cornell)
E. F. (Edgar Fuller)
G. L. (Gilbert Ledward)
I. R. B. (Ian Rank-Broadley)
J. B. (James Butler)
J. M. (Jeffrey Matthews)
J. M. M. (John Mills)
M. B. (Matthew Bonaccorsi)
M. G. (Mary Gillick)
M. M. D. (Mary Milner Dickens)
M. N. (Michael Noakes)
M. R. (Michael Rizzello)
N. S. (Norman Sillman)
P. N. (Philip Nathan)
R. D. (Ron Dutton)
R. D. M. (Raphael David Maklouf)

R. E. (Robert Elderton)
r. e. (Robert Evans)
R. L. (Robert Lowe)
T. N. (Timothy Noad)
W. G. (William Gardner)
W. P. (Wilson Parker 1896-1980)

**Other designers whose initials do not appear on the coins:**
Christopher Ironside (1913-
Arnold Machin (1911-99)
David Wynne
Professor Richard Guyatt
Eric Sewell
Oscar Nemon
Leslie Durbin
Derek Gorringe
Bernard Sindall
Tom Phillips
Edwina Ellis
David Gentleman

## PRE-DECIMAL ISSUES
### Die axis ↑↑
## GOLD

**First coinage,** with title BRITT.OMN, 1953. *Proof only* ................... *of the highest rarity*
**4120 Five Pounds.** Young laur. head r. R. St. George ...................... *None issued for collectors*
**4121 Two Pounds.** Young laur. head r. R. St. George ...................... *None issued for collectors*
**4122 Sovereign.** Young laur. head r. R. St. George .......................... *None issued for collectors*
**4123 Half-Sovereign.** Young laur. head r. R. St. George .................. *None issued for collectors*

**Second issue,** BRITT.OMN omitted

4125
1958 Sovereign

| | EF £ | UNC £ |
|---|---|---|

**4124 Sovereign.** Young laur head r. R. St. George, fine graining on edge
1957 ................................................................................................................ BV 85
1957 Proof *FDC* £3500

|  | *UNC*<br>£ |  | *UNC*<br>£ |
|---|---|---|---|

**4125 Sovereign.** Similar, but coarser graining on edge

| 1958 | 75 | 1963 Proof *FDC* £5000 | |
| 1958 Proof *FDC* £3500 | | 1964 | 75 |
| 1959 | 85 | 1965 | 75 |
| 1959 Proof *FDC* £3500 | | 1966 | 75 |
| 1962 | 85 | 1967 | 75 |
| 1963 | 85 | 1968 | 75 |

## SILVER

The Queen's Maundy are now the only coins struck regularly in silver.
The location of the Maundy ceremony is given for each year.

**First issue,** with title BRITT:OMN:

*FDC*
£

**4126 Maundy Set** (4d., 3d., 2d. and 1d.), 1953. *St Paul's Cathedral* .................................... 400
1953 Proof struck in gold *FDC of highest rarity*
1953 Proof struck in nickel bronze *FDC Extremely rare*
1953 Matt Proof *FDC Extremely rare*
**4127 — Fourpence.** 1953 .................................................................................................. 85
**4128 — Threepence.** 1953 ............................................................................................... 85
**4129 — Twopence.** 1953 ................................................................................................ 85
**4130 — Penny.** 1953 ...................................................................................................... 185

**Second issue,** with BRITT:OMN: omitted

4131
1962 Maundy Set

|  | *FDC*<br>£ |  | *FDC*<br>£ |
|---|---|---|---|

**4131 Maundy Set** (4d., 3d., 2d. and 1d.). Uniform dates

| 1954 *Westminster* | 85 | 1963 *Chelmsford* | 85 |
| 1955 *Southwark* | 85 | 1964 *Westminster* | 85 |
| 1956 *Westminster* | 85 | 1965 *Canterbury* | 85 |
| 1957 *St. Albans* | 85 | 1966 *Westminster* | 85 |
| 1958 *Westminster* | 85 | 1967 *Durham* | 85 |
| 1959 *Windsor* | 85 | 1968 *Westminster* | 85 |
| 1960 *Westminster* | 85 | 1969 *Selby* | 85 |
| 1961 *Rochester* | 85 | 1970 *Westminster* | 85 |
| 1962 *Westminster* | 85 | | |

**4132 — Fourpence.** 1954-70 .................................................................*from* 12
**4133 — Threepence.** 1954-70................................................................*from* 12
**4134 — Twopence.** 1954-70 ..................................................................*from* 12
**4135 — Penny.** 1954-70.........................................................................*from* 18

## CUPRO-NICKEL

**First issue,** 1953, with title BRITT.OMN.

4136
1953 Coronation Crown

|  | EF<br>£ | UNC<br>£ | *PROOF*<br>*FDC*<br>£ |
|---|---|---|---|
| **4136 Crown.** Queen on horseback. R. Crown in centre of emblematical cross, shield of Arms in each angle, 1953 | 6 | 10 | 40 |
| Similar 1953 Frosted 'VIP' proof £400 |  |  |  |
| Similar 1953 Matt Proof *FDC of highest rarity* |  |  |  |

4137                                                    4138
1953 Halfcrown                                  1953 Florin

| | EF | UNC |
|---|---|---|
| **4137 Halfcrown.** with title BRITT:OMN: Young laur. head r. R. Arms, 1953 | 5 | 15 |
| **4138 Florin.** Young laur. head r. R. Double rose, 1953 | 4 | 10 |

4139                            4140                            4141
1953 'English' Shilling      'Scottish' reverse      1953 Sixpence

| | EF | UNC |
|---|---|---|
| **4139 Shilling.** 'English' reverse. Young laur. head r. R. Three lions, 1953 | 2 | 8 |
| **4140 Shilling.** '— 'Scottish' reverse. Young laur. head r. R. Lion rampant in shield, 1953 | 2 | 8 |
| **4141 Sixpence.** Young laur. head r. R. Interlaced rose, thistle, shamrock and leek, 1953 | 1 | 6 |
| **4142 Sixpence.** Set of 9 uncirculated cu-ni, ni-br and Æ coins (2/6 to 1/4d.) in Royal Mint plastic envelope | 30 | |

**Second issue,** similar types but omitting BRITT.OMN.

4143
1960 Crown

4144
1965 Churchill Crown

|  | EF £ | UNC £ |
|---|---|---|
| **4143 Crown,** 1960. Young laur. head r. R. As 4136 | 5 | 10 |
| — — Similar, from polished dies (New York Exhibition issue) | 10 | 30 |
| — — 'VIP' *Proof,* frosted design *FDC* £400 | | |
| **4144 Crown,** Churchill commemorative, 1965. As illustration. R. Bust of Sir Winston Churchill r. | | 2 |
| — — Similar, "Satin-Finish". VIP *Specimen* | | 750 |

**4145 Halfcrown.** Young laur. head r. R. As 4137

| | EF £ | UNC £ | | EF £ | UNC £ | | EF £ | UNC £ |
|---|---|---|---|---|---|---|---|---|
| 1954 | 3 | 20 | 1960 | | 6 | 1965 | | 4 |
| 1955 | | 8 | 1961 | | 4 | 1966 | | 1 |
| 1956 | | 10 | 1961 Polished die | | 10 | 1967 | | 1 |
| 1957 | | 5 | 1962 | | 4 | 1970 Proof *FDC* £5 | | |
| 1958 | 3 | 20 | 1963 | | 4 | | | |
| 1959 | 5 | 30 | 1964 | | 6 | | | |

4146
1955 Florin

**4146 Florin.** Young laur. head r. R. As 4138

| | EF | UNC | | | UNC |
|---|---|---|---|---|---|
| 1954 | 5 | 40 | 1962 | | 4 |
| 1955 | | 6 | 1963 | | 4 |
| 1956 | | 6 | 1964 | | 4 |
| 1957 | 5 | 40 | 1965 | | 4 |
| 1958 | 4 | 20 | 1966 | | 2 |
| 1959 | 5 | 35 | 1967 | | 2 |
| 1960 | | 5 | 1970 Proof *FDC* £5 | | |
| 1961 | | 5 | | | |

|  | *EF* | *UNC* |  | *UNC* |
|---|---|---|---|---|
|  | £ | £ |  | £ |

**4147 Shilling.** 'English' reverse. Young laur. head r. R. As 4139

| | | | | |
|---|---|---|---|---|
| 1954 | | 5 | 1961 | 2 |
| 1955 | | 5 | 1962 | 1 |
| 1956 | | 10 | 1963 | 1 |
| 1957 | | 4 | 1964 | 1 |
| 1958 | 2 | 15 | 1965 | 1 |
| 1959 | | 4 | 1966 | 1 |
| 1960 | | 4 | 1970 Proof *FDC* £3 | |

**4148 Shilling.** 'Scottish' reverse. Young laur. head r. R. As 4140

| | | | | |
|---|---|---|---|---|
| 1954 | | 5 | 1961 | 6 |
| 1955 | | 6 | 1962 | 4 |
| 1956 | | 10 | 1963 | 1 |
| 1957 | 2 | 15 | 1964 | 1 |
| 1958 | | 3 | 1965 | 1 |
| 1959 | 2 | 15 | 1966 | 1 |
| 1960 | | 4 | 1970 Proof *FDC* £2 | |

**4149 Sixpence.** Young laur. head r. R. As 4141

| | | | |
|---|---|---|---|
| 1954 | 6 | 1962 | 1.50 |
| 1955 | 4 | 1963 | 1.50 |
| 1956 | 4 | 1964 | 1.50 |
| 1957 | 3 | 1965 | 1 |
| 1958 | 3 | 1966 | 1 |
| 1959 | 2 | 1967 | 1 |
| 1960 | 3 | 1970 Proof *FDC* £3 | |
| 1961 | 2 | | |

## NICKEL BRASS

**First issue,** with title BRITT.OMN.

4152
1953 Brass Threepence

4153
Second issue

**4152 Threepence** (dodecagonal). Young laur. head r. R. Crowned portcullis, 1953 .................. 5
— Proof *FDC* £10

**Second issue** (omitting BRIT.OMN)
**4153 Threepence** Similar type

| | | | |
|---|---|---|---|
| 1954 | 6 | 1962 | 1 |
| 1955 | 8 | 1963 | 1 |
| 1956 | 8 | 1964 | 1 |
| 1957 | 5 | 1965 | 1 |
| 1958 | 8 | 1966 | 0.50 |
| 1959 | 5 | 1967 | 0.50 |
| 1960 | 5 | 1970 Proof *FDC* £3 | |
| 1961 | 2 | | |

# BRONZE

**First issue,** with title BRITT.OMN.

| 4154 | 4155 |
|------|------|
| 1953 Penny | 1953 Halfpenny |

|  | VF | EF | UNC | *Proof* *FDC* |
|---|---|---|---|---|
|  | £ | £ | £ | £ |
| **4154 Penny.** Young laur. head r. ℞. Britannia (only issued with Royal Mint set in | | | | |
| plastic envelope), 1953 Beaded border ..........................1 | | 5 | 15 | 20 |
| 1953 Toothed border.............................................................. ...................... | | | *Extremely rare* | |
| **4155 Halfpenny.** Young laur. head r. ℞. Ship, 1953 ..................................... | | | 4 | 10 |
| **4156 Farthing.** Young laur. head r. ℞. Wren, 1953 ....................................... | | | 3 | 8 |

**Second issue,** omitting BRITT.OMN.

| | UNC | | UNC |
|---|---|---|---|
| | £ | | £ |

**4157 Penny.** Young laur. head r. ℞. Britannia (1954-60 *not issued*)

| 1954............................................ | *Unique* | 1965 ....................................................... | 0.50 |
|---|---|---|---|
| 1961 ..................................................... | 2 | 1966 ....................................................... | 0.50 |
| 1962 ..................................................... | 1 | 1967 ....................................................... | 0.25 |
| 1963 ..................................................... | 1 | 1970 Proof *FDC* £4 | |
| 1964 ..................................................... | 0.50 | | |

**4158 Halfpenny.** Young laur. head r. ℞. Ship (1961 *not issued*)

| 1954 ..................................................... | 4 | 1960 ....................................................... | 1 |
|---|---|---|---|
| 1954 larger border teeth ..................... | 5 | 1962 ....................................................... | 1 |
| 1955 ..................................................... | 3 | 1963 ....................................................... | 1 |
| 1956 ..................................................... | 3 | 1964 ....................................................... | 1 |
| 1957 ..................................................... | 3 | 1965 ....................................................... | 1 |
| 1957 calm sea ...................................... | 15 | 1966 ....................................................... | 0.50 |
| 1958 ..................................................... | 2 | 1967 ....................................................... | 0.50 |
| 1959 ..................................................... | 1 | 1970 Proof *FDC* £3 | |

| 4156 | 4159 |
|------|------|
| 1953 Farthing | Second issue |

| | EF | UNC |
|---|---|---|
| **4159 Farthing.** Young laur. head r. ℞. Wren | £ | £ |
| 1954...................................................... | 4 | |
| 1955 Rev. with thin rim....................... | 4 | 1956 Rev. with thin rim...   3   6 |

**Proof Sets**

**PS19** Coronation, **1953.** Crown to Farthing (10 coins)...........................................*FDC*   100
**PS20** 'Last Sterling', **1970.** Halfcrown to Halfpenny plus medallion ...................*FDC*   20

All prices quoted assume coins are in their original case. Issued by the Royal Mint in official case from 1887 onwards, but earlier sets were issued privately by the engraver. All pieces have a superior finish to that of the current coins.

| | No. of coins | FDC £ |
|---|---|---|
| **PS1** **George IV, 1826**. New issue, Five Pounds to Farthing ...................(11) | | 20000 |
| **PS1A**—— Similar to above, including Maundy Set ................................(15) | | 21000 |
| **PS2** **William IV, 1831**. Coronation, Two Pounds to Farthing ................(14) | | 19500 |
| **PS3** **Victoria, 1839**. Young head. "Una and the Lion" Five Pounds and Sovereign to Farthing.....................................................(15) | | 30000 |
| **PS4** — **1853**. Sovereign to Half-Farthing, including Gothic type Crown (16) | | 28000 |
| **PS5** — **1887**. Jubilee bust for Golden Jubilee, Five Pounds to Threepence .....................................................................................(11) | | 6250 |
| **PS6** — **1887**. Silver Crown to Threepence ...............................................(7) | | 1250 |
| **PS7** — **1893**. Old bust, Five Pounds to Threepence ..............................(10) | | 7500 |
| **PS8** — **1893**. Silver Crown to Threepence ...............................................(6) | | 1600 |
| **PS9** **Edward VII, 1902**. Coronation, Five Pounds to Maundy Penny. Matt finish to surfaces......................................................................(13) | | 1850 |
| **PS10** — **1902**. Sovereign to Maundy Penny. Matt finish ..........................(11) | | 750 |
| **PS11** **George V, 1911**. Coronation, Five Pounds to Maundy Penny.........(12) | | 3000 |
| **PS12** — **1911**. Sovereign to Maundy Penny.............................................(10) | | 1000 |
| **PS13** — **1911**. Silver Halfcrown to Maundy Penny ...................................(8) | | 475 |
| **PS14** — **1927**. New Coinage. Wreath type Crown to Threepence..............(6) | | 350 |
| **PS15** **George VI, 1937**. Coronation. Five Pounds to Half-Sovereign..........(4) | | 2500 |
| **PS16** — **1937**. Coronation. Crown to Farthing, including Maundy Set .....(15) | | 300 |
| **PS17** — **1950**. Mid-Century, Halfcrown to Farthing................................(9) | | 100 |
| **PS18** — **1951**. Festival of Britain, Crown to Farthing..............................(10) | | 125 |
| **PS19** **Elizabeth II, 1953**. Coronation. Crown to Farthing ........................(10) | | 100 |
| **PS20** — **1970**. "Last Sterling" set. Halfcrown to Halfpenny plus medallion.........................................................................................(8) | | 20 |

A decision to adopt decimal currency was announced in March 1966 following the recommendation of the Halsbury Committee of Enquiry which had been appointed in 1961. The date for the introduction of the new system was 15 February 1971 and it was evident that the Royal Mint facilities which had been located on Tower Hill for more than 150 years would be unable to strike the significant quantities of coins required on that site. The Government therefore decided to build a new mint at Llantrisant in South Wales.

The new system provided for three smaller bronze coins and very large numbers were struck and stock piled for D-Day but the five and ten new pence denominations with the same specifications as the former shilling and florin were introduced in 1968. A further change was the introduction of a 50 new pence coin to replace the ten shilling banknote.

In 1982 and 1983 two more new coins were introduced; the 20 pence which helped to reduce demand for five and ten pence pieces, and the first circulating non-precious metal £1 coin which replaced the bank note of the same value.

Increasing raw material costs, and inflation also play a part in the development of a modern coinage system and a smaller 50 pence was introduced in the autumn of 1997. The bimetallic circulating £2 was also introduced.

For the collector, many of these changes have been accompanied by special issues often in limited editions struck in precious metal. New designs, particularly on the £1 coins, have added interest to the coins that circulate, and may hopefully stimulate new collectors.

In the period since decimalisation there has been a marked increase in the issue of commemorative coins. The crown size pieces, which by virtue of their size allow much scope for interesting designs seem to be reserved for the commemoration of Royal events or anniversaries, and other denominations such as the £2 and the 50 pence have honoured other interesting themes.

The major change in the coinage in 1998 was the new, and fourth, portrait of H. M. The Queen. Designed by Ian Rank-Broadley, a whole new series has started which will stimulate interest among collectors everywhere.

## GOLD

4201

4204

**4201 Five pounds.** As illustration
1980 Proof *FDC* * £500
1981 Proof *FDC* (Issued: 5,400)** £500

1982 Proof *FDC* * £450
1984 Proof *FDC* (Issued: 905) £500

**4202** As 4201 but, 'U' in a circle to left of date
1984 (Issued: 15,104) *Unc* £400

**4203 Two pounds**
1980 Proof *FDC* * £250
1982 Proof *FDC* * £250

1983 Proof *FDC* (Issued: 12,500)** £225

* *Coins marked thus were originally issued in Royal Mint Sets.*
** *Numbers include coins sold in sets.*

**4204 Sovereign.** As illustration

| | | | |
|---|---|---|---|
| 1974 | Unc £75 | 1981 | Unc £80 |
| 1976 | Unc £75 | — Proof *FDC* (Issued: 32,960) £100 | |
| 1978 | Unc £75 | 1982 | Unc £80 |
| 1979 | Unc £75 | — Proof *FDC* (Issued: 20,000) £100 | |
| — Proof *FDC* (Issued: 50,000) £100 | | 1983 Proof *FDC* (Issued: 21,250)** £125 | |
| 1980 | Unc £80 | 1984 Proof *FDC* (Issued: 12,880) £125 | |
| — Proof *FDC* (Issued: 81,200) £85 | | | |

**4205 Half-sovereign**

| | | | |
|---|---|---|---|
| 1980 Proof *FDC* (Issued: 76.700) £60 | | 1983 Proof *FDC* (Issued: 19,710)** £80 | |
| 1982 | Unc £50 | 1984 Proof *FDC* (Issued: 12,410) £80 | |
| — Proof *FDC* (Issued: 19,090) £60 | | | |

## SILVER

| | *FDC* £ | | *FDC* £ |
|---|---|---|---|
| **4211 Maundy Set** (4p, 3p, 2p and 1p). Uniform dates. Types as 4131 | | | |
| 1971 *Tewkesbury Abbey* | 85 | 1989 *Birmingham Cathedral* | 85 |
| 1972 *York Minster* | 85 | 1990 *Newcastle Cathedral* | 85 |
| 1973 *Westminster Abbey* | 85 | 1991 *Westminster Abbey* | 85 |
| 1974 *Salisbury Cathedral* | 85 | 1992 *Chester Cathedral* | 85 |
| 1975 *Peterborough Cathedral* | 85 | 1993 *Wells Cathedral* | 85 |
| 1976 *Hereford Cathedral* | 85 | 1994 *Truro Cathedral* | 85 |
| 1977 *Westminster Abbey* | 85 | 1995 *Coventry Cathedral* | 100 |
| 1978 *Carlisle Cathedral* | 85 | 1996 *Norwich Cathedral* | 100 |
| 1979 *Winchester Cathedral* | 85 | 1997 *Bradford Cathedral* | 100 |
| 1980 *Worcester Cathedral* | 85 | 1998 *Portsmouth Cathedral* | 100 |
| 1981 *Westminster Abbey* | 85 | 1999 *Bristol Cathedral* | 100 |
| 1982 *St. David's Cathedral* | 85 | 2000 *Lincoln Cathedral* | 100 |
| 1983 *Exeter Cathedral* | 85 | 2001 *Westminster Abbey* | 95 |
| 1984 *Southwell Minster* | 85 | 2002 *Canterbury Cathedral* | 120 |
| 1985 *Ripon Cathedral* | 85 | 2002 *Proof in gold from set* | |
| 1986 *Chichester Cathedral* | 85 | *(see PCGS1)* | 1000 |
| 1987 *Ely Cathedral* | 85 | 2003 *Gloucester Cathedral* | 120 |
| 1988 *Lichfield Cathedral* | 85 | 2004 *Liverpool Cathedral* | 120 |

| | | |
|---|---|---|
| **4212 — fourpence**, 1971-96 | *from* | 13 |
| **4213 — threepence**, 1971-96 | *from* | 13 |
| **4214 — twopence**, 1971-96 | *from* | 13 |
| **4215 — penny**, 1971-96 | *from* | 15 |

*The place of distribution is shown after each date.*

*\*Coins marked thus were originally issued in Royal Mint sets*
*\*\* numbers include coins sold in sets*

## NICKEL-BRASS

4221       4222

|  | UNC £ |
|---|---|
| **4221** **One pound** (Royal Arms design). Edge DECUS ET TUTAMEN | |
| 1983...................................................................................................................... | 5 |
| — Specimen in presentation folder (issued: 484,900)............................................ | 5 |
| — Proof *FDC\** £5     — Proof piedfort in silver *FDC* (Issued: 10,000) £125 | |
| — Proof in silver *FDC* (Issued: 50,000) £35 | |
| **4222** **One pound** (Scottish design). Edge NEMO ME IMPUNE LACESSIT | |
| 1984...................................................................................................................... | 5 |
| — Specimen in presentation folder (Issued: 27,960)............................................... | 5 |
| — Proof *FDC\** £5     — Proof piedfort in silver *FDC* (Issued: 15,000) £55 | |
| — Proof in silver *FDC* (Issued: 44,855) £21 | |

## CUPRO-NICKEL

4223       4224

**4223 Fifty new pence** (seven-sided). ℞. Britannia r.

| | UNC £ | | UNC £ | | UNC £ |
|---|---|---|---|---|---|
| 1969 .................. | 2 | 1976.......................... | 2 | 1979.......................... | 2 |
| 1970 .................. | 4 | — Proof *FDC\** £2 | | — Proof *FDC\** £3 | |
| 1971 Proof *FDC\** £4 | | 1977.......................... | 2 | 1980.......................... | 2 |
| 1972 Proof *FDC\** £5 | | — Proof *FDC\** £2 | | — Proof *FDC\** £2 | |
| 1974 Proof *FDC\** £3 | | 1978.......................... | 2 | 1981.......................... | 2 |
| 1975 Proof *FDC\** £3 | | — Proof *FDC\** £3 | | — Proof *FDC\** £2 | |

**4224** Accession to European Economic Community. ℞. Clasped hands, 1973..................... 1.50
—Proof *FDC\*\** £3

**4224A**—Design as 4224 above, but struck in very small numbers in silver on thicker blank. Sometimes referred to as a piedfort but not twice the weight of the regular cupro-nickel currency issue. The pieces were presented to EEC Finance Ministers, and possibly senior officials on the occasion of the United Kingdom joining the European Economic Community............................................................................................................. 1500

*\* Coins marked thus were originally issued in Royal Mint sets as shown on page 492.*
*\*\* Issued as an individual proof coin and in the year set shown on page 492.*

4225

**4225  Fifty (50) pence.** 'New' omitted. As illustration

1982 ..................    2    1983 ...........................    2    1984* ........................    3
— Proof *FDC*\* £2          — Proof *FDC*\* £2          — Proof *FDC*\* £2

4226

**4226  Twenty-five pence.** Silver Wedding Commemorative, 1972 ......................................    2
— Proof *FDC*\* (in 1972 Set, See PS22) £4
— Silver proof in case *FDC*  (Issued: 100,000) £30

4227

|  | UNC |
|---|---|
|  | £ |

**4227  Twenty-five pence** Silver Jubilee Commemorative, 1977 ...........................................    1.50
— Specimen in presentation folder ................................................................................    2
— Proof *FDC*\* (in 1977 Set, See PS27) £4
— Silver proof in case *FDC* (Issued: 377,000) £22
*\* Coins marked thus were originally issued in Royal Mint sets*

4228

**4228 Twenty-Five pence** Queen Mother 80th Birthday Commemorative, 1980 .................. 2
— Specimen in presentation folder............................................................................. 3
— Silver proof in case *FDC* (issued: 83,672) £50

4229

**4229 Twenty-five pence.** Royal Wedding Commemorative, 1981 ..................................... 2
— Specimen in presentation folder............................................................................. 3
— Silver proof in case *FDC* (Issued: 218,142) £30

4230

| | UNC £ | | UNC £ | | UNC £ |
|---|---|---|---|---|---|
| **4230 Twenty (20) pence.** ℞ crowned rose | | | | | |
| 1982 ................ | 0.40 | 1983.......................... | 0.40 | 1984.......................... | 0.40 |
| — Proof *FDC*\* £2 | | — Proof *FDC*\* £1 | | — Proof *FDC*\* £1 | |
| — Proof piedfort | | | | | |
| in silver *FDC* (Issued: 10,000) £50 | | | | | |

\* *Coins marked thus were originally issued in Royal Mint sets*

4231               4232

**4231 Ten new pence.** R. Lion passant guardant.

| | | | |
|---|---|---|---|
| 1968 .................. 0.30 | 1974 .......................... 0.40 | 1978 Proof *FDC*\* £4 | |
| 1969 .................. 0.30 | — Proof *FDC*\* £1 | 1979 .......................... 0.50 | |
| 1970 .................. 0.30 | 1975 .......................... 0.50 | — Proof *FDC*\* £2 | |
| 1971 .................. 0.40 | — Proof *FDC*\* £1 | 1980 .......................... 0.75 | |
| — Proof *FDC*\* £2 | 1976 .......................... 0.50 | — Proof *FDC*\* £1 | |
| 1972 Proof *FDC*\* £3 | — Proof *FDC*\* £1 | 1981 .......................... 0.75 | |
| 1973 .................. 0.40 | 1977 .......................... 0.50 | — Proof *FDC*\* £1 | |
| — Proof *FDC*\* £2 | — Proof *FDC*\* £2 | | |

**4232 Ten (10) pence.** As illustration

| | | |
|---|---|---|
| 1982\* .............. 3 | 1983\* ........................ 3 | 1984\* ........................ 2 |
| — Proof *FDC*\* £1 | — Proof *FDC*\* £2 | — Proof *FDC*\* £1 |

4233               4234

**4233 Five new pence.** R. Crowned thistle

| | | | |
|---|---|---|---|
| 1968 .................. 0.20 | 1974 Proof *FDC*\* £2 | — Proof *FDC*\* £1 | |
| 1969 .................. 0.30 | 1975 .......................... 0.20 | 1979 .......................... 0.20 | |
| 1970 .................. 0.30 | — Proof *FDC*\* £1 | — Proof *FDC*\* £1 | |
| 1971 .................. 0.20 | 1976 Proof *FDC*\* £2 | 1980 .......................... 0.20 | |
| — Proof *FDC*\* £2 | 1977 .......................... 0.20 | — Proof *FDC*\* £1 | |
| 1972 Proof *FDC*\* £2 | — Proof *FDC*\* £1 | 1981 Proof *FDC*\* £1 | |
| 1973 Proof *FDC*\* £2 | 1978 .......................... 0.20 | | |

**4234 Five (5) pence.** As illustration

| | | |
|---|---|---|
| 1982\* .............. 2 | 1983\* ........................ 2 | 1984\* ........................ 2 |
| — Proof *FDC*\* £2 | — Proof *FDC*\* £2 | — Proof *FDC*\* £1 |

*\* Coins marked thus were originally issued in Royal Mint sets.*

# BRONZE

| | 4235 | | | 4236 | |
|---|---|---|---|---|---|

| | *UNC* £ | | *UNC* £ | | *UNC* £ |
|---|---|---|---|---|---|

**4235  Two new pence.** R. Plumes

| 1971 ................. 0.10 | 1976 .......................... 0.20 | — Proof *FDC*\* £1 |
|---|---|---|
| — Proof *FDC*\* £1 | — Proof *FDC*\* £1 | 1980 .......................... 0.15 |
| 1972 Proof *FDC*\* £2 | 1977 .......................... 0.10 | — Proof *FDC*\* £1 |
| 1973 Proof *FDC*\* £2 | — Proof *FDC*\* £1 | 1981 .......................... 0.15 |
| 1974 Proof *FDC*\* £2 | 1978 .......................... 0.30 | — Proof *FDC*\* £1 |
| 1975 ................. 0.20 | — Proof *FDC*\* £1 | |
| — Proof *FDC*\* £1 | 1979 .......................... 0.15 | |

**4236  Two (2) pence.** As illustration

| 1982\* ............... 1 | 1983\* ......................... 1 | £250 ................ 1984\* 1 |
|---|---|---|
| — Proof *FDC*\* £1 | — Proof *FDC*\* £1 | — Proof *FDC*\* £1 |

**4236A** — Error reverse. The word "new" was dropped from the reverse of the currency issues in 1982 but a number of 2 pence coins were struck in 1983 with the incorrect die, similar to coins listed as 4235. Reports suggest that the error coins, or "Mules" were contained in Royal Mint uncirculated sets issued in 1983 ...................... 400

| 4237 | 4238 | 4239 | 4240 |
|---|---|---|---|

**4237  One new penny.** R. Crowned portcullis

| 1971 ................. 0.10 | 1975 .......................... 0.20 | — Proof *FDC*\* £1 |
|---|---|---|
| — Proof *FDC*\* £1 | — Proof *FDC*\* £1 | 1979 .......................... 0.10 |
| 1972 Proof *FDC*\* £2 | 1976 .......................... 0.20 | — Proof *FDC*\* £1 |
| 1973 ................. 0.20 | — Proof *FDC*\* £1 | 1980 .......................... 0.10 |
| — Proof *FDC*\* £1 | 1977 .......................... 0.10 | — Proof *FDC*\* £1 |
| 1974 ................. 0.20 | — Proof *FDC*\* £1 | 1981 .......................... 0.20 |
| — Proof *FDC*\* £1 | 1978 .......................... 0.20 | — Proof *FDC*\* £1 |

**4238  One (1) penny.** As illustration

| 1982 ................. 0.10 | 1983 .......................... 0.20 | 1984\* ......................... 1 |
|---|---|---|
| — Proof *FDC*\* £1 | — *FDC*\* £1 ........... | — Proof *FDC*\* £1 |

**4239  Half new penny.** R. Crown

| 1971 ................. 0.10 | 1975 .......................... 0.25 | — Proof *FDC*\* £1 |
|---|---|---|
| — Proof *FDC*\* £1 | — Proof *FDC*\* £1 .. | 1979 .......................... 0.10 |
| 1972 Proof *FDC*\* £2 | 1976 .......................... 0.20 | — Proof *FDC*\* £1 |
| 1973 ................. 0.20 | — Proof *FDC*\* £1 .. | 1980 .......................... 0.10 |
| — Proof *FDC*\* £1 | 1977 .......................... 0.10 | — Proof *FDC*\* £1 |
| 1974 ................. 0.20 | — Proof *FDC*\* £1 .. | 1981 .......................... 0.20 |
| — Proof *FDC*\* £1 | 1978 .......................... 0.10 | — Proof *FDC*\* £1 |

**4240  Half (1/2) penny.** As illustration

| 1982 ................. 0.10 | 1983 .......................... 0.25 | 1984\* ......................... 2.00 |
|---|---|---|
| — Proof *FDC*\* £1 | — Proof *FDC*\* £1 .. | — Proof *FDC*\* £2 |

\* *Coins marked thus were originally issued in Royal Mint sets.*

The new effigy was designed by Raphael David Maklouf, FRSA. It is the third portrait of the Queen
to be used on UK coinage, the previous change of portrait being in 1968 with the introduction of
decimal coins. The designer's initials R.D.M. appear on the truncation. There is no portrait change
on the Maundy coins (see 4211-4215).

## GOLD

4251                                          4253

**4251**  **Five pounds.** R. St. George
       1985 Proof *FDC* (Issued: 281) £500
       1990 Proof *FDC*\* £525      1993 Proof *FDC*\* £550      1996 Proof *FDC*\* £550
       1991 Proof *FDC*\* £525      1994 Proof *FDC*\* £550      1997 Proof *FDC*\* £550
       1992 Proof *FDC*\* £550      1995 Proof *FDC*\* £550

**4252**  **Five pounds** R. St George, 'U' in a circle to left of date.

|                          | *UNC* |                          | *UNC* |
|--------------------------|-------|--------------------------|-------|
| 1985 (Issued: 13,626)    | £400  | 1993 (Issued: 906)       | £450  |
| 1986 (Issued: 7,723)     | £400  | 1994 (Issued: 1,000)     | £500  |
| 1990 (Issued: 1,226)     | £450  | 1995 (Issued: 1,000)     | £500  |
| 1991 (Issued: 976)       | £450  | 1996 (Issued: 901)       | £500  |
| 1992 (Issued: 797)       | £450  | 1997 (Issued: 802)       | £500  |

**4253**  **Five pounds** Uncouped portrait of Queen Elizabeth II. As illustration. R. St. George, 'U' in a
       circle to left of date.
       1987 (Issued: 5,694)........ £425      1988 (Issued: 3,315)........ £425

**4254**  **Five pounds** 500th Anniversary of Sovereign. As illustration 4277
       1989 (Issued: 2,937)........ £550      — — Proof *FDC*\* £650

**4261**  **Two pounds.** R. St. George
       1985 Proof *FDC*\* £250              1991 Proof *FDC* (Issued: 620) £250
       1987 Proof *FDC* (Issued: 1,801) £225   1992 Proof *FDC* (Issued: 476) £250
       1988 Proof *FDC* (Issued: 1,551) £225   1993 Proof *FDC* (Issued: 414) £250
       1990 Proof *FDC* (Issued: 716)   £250   1996 Proof *FDC*          £250

**4263**  **Two pounds** 500th Anniversary of Sovereign. As illustration 4277
       1989 Proof *FDC*  (Issued: 2,000) £300

The 1986 £2, 1994 £2 and two types of 1995 £2 commemorative coins in gold previously listed as
4262, 4264, 4265 & 4266 respectively are now shown in the section commencing 4311 with their
respective types in other metals.

**4271**  **Sovereign.** R. St. George
       1985 Proof *FDC* (Issued: 11,393) £175   1992 Proof *FDC* (Issued: 4,772)  £250
       1986 Proof *FDC* (Issued: 5,079)  £175   1993 Proof *FDC* (Issued: 4,349)  £250
       1987 Proof *FDC* (Issued: 9,979)  £175   1994 Proof *FDC* (Issued: 4,998)  £250
       1988 Proof *FDC* (Issued: 7,670)  £175   1995 Proof *FDC* (Issued: 7,500)  £250
       1990 Proof *FDC* (Issued: 4,767)  £200   1996 Proof *FDC* (Issued: 7,500)  £250
       1991 Proof *FDC* (Issued: 4,713)  £200   1997 Proof *FDC* (Issued: 7,500)  £250

\* *Coins marked thus were originally issued in Royal Mint sets. Where numbers of coins issued or the
Edition limit is quoted, these refer to individual coins. Additional coins were included in sets which
are listed in the appropriate section.*

**4272** **Sovereign.** 500th Anniversary of Sovereign. As illustration 4277
1989 Proof *FDC* (Issued: 10,535) £400

4277

**4276** **Half-sovereign.** R. St. George

| | |
|---|---|
| 1985 Proof *FDC* (Issued: 9,951) £100 | 1992 Proof *FDC* (Issued: 3,783) £120 |
| 1986 Proof *FDC* (Issued: 4,575) £100 | 1993 Proof *FDC* (Issued: 2,910) £120 |
| 1987 Proof *FDC* (Issued: 8,187) £100 | 1994 Proof *FDC* (Issued: 5,000) £120 |
| 1988 Proof *FDC* (Issued: 7,074) £100 | 1995 Proof *FDC* (Issued: 4,900) £120 |
| 1990 Proof *FDC* (Issued: 4,231) £100 | 1996 Proof *FDC* (Issued: 5,730) £120 |
| 1991 Proof *FDC* (Issued: 3,588) £100 | 1997 Proof *FDC* (Issued: 7,500) £120 |

**4277** **Half-sovereign** 500th Anniversary of Sovereign. As illustration 4277
1989 Proof *FDC* (Issued: 8,888) £175

4281

|   |  *UNC* |   |   *UNC* |
|---|---|---|---|

**4281** **Britannia.** One hundred pounds. (1oz of fine gold) R. Britannia standing.

| | | | |
|---|---|---|---|
| 1987....................................... | £275 | — Proof *FDC* (Issued: 626) £350 | |
| — Proof *FDC* (Issued: 2,486) £350 | | 1989 ......................................... | £275 |
| 1988....................................... | £275 | — Proof *FDC* (Issued: 338)  £350 | |

**4282** **Britannia.** One hundred pounds. (1oz of fine gold alloyed with silver) R. Britannia standing.

| | | | |
|---|---|---|---|
| 1990....................................... | £300 | — Proof *FDC* * £450 | |
| — Proof *FDC* (Issued: 262) £350 | | 1994 ......................................... | £300 |
| 1991....................................... | £300 | — Proof *FDC* * £450 | |
| — Proof *FDC* (Issued: 143) £400 | | 1995 ......................................... | £300 |
| 1992....................................... | £300 | — Proof *FDC* * £500 | |
| — Proof *FDC* * £450.............. | | 1996 ......................................... | £300 |
| 1993....................................... | £300 | — Proof *FDC* * £500 | |

Where numbers of coins are quoted, these refer to individual coins. Additional coins were included in sets which are listed in the appropriate section.

*\* Coins marked thus were originally issued in Royal Mint sets.*

4283

**4283  Britannia. One Hundred pounds.** (1 oz of fine gold, alloyed with silver) R. Standing figure
of Britannia in horse drawn chariot. 10th Anniversary of Britannia issue
1997........................................... £400          1997 Proof *FDC* (Issued: 164) £600

4286

**4286  Britannia. Fifty pounds.** (1/2oz of fine gold). R. Britannia standing.
1987........................................ £150          — Proof *FDC*\* £160
— Proof *FDC* (Issued: 2,485) £160          1989 ......................................... £150
1988........................................ £150          — Proof *FDC*\* £175

**4287  Britannia. Fifty pounds.** (1/2oz of fine gold, alloyed with Silver)
R. Britannia standing.
1990........................................ £175          — Proof *FDC*\* £250
— Proof *FDC*\* £200          1994 ......................................... £175
1991........................................ £175          — Proof *FDC*\* £250
— Proof *FDC*\* £200          1995 ......................................... £175
1992........................................ \*\*          — Proof *FDC*\* £250
— Proof *FDC*\* £250          1996 ......................................... £175
1993........................................ £175          — Proof *FDC*\* £250

4288

**4288  Britannia. Fifty pounds.** (1/2 oz fine gold, alloyed with silver) R. Standing figure of
Britannia in horse drawn chariot 10th Anniversary of Britannia issue
1997 Proof *FDC*\* £300

\* *Coins marked thus were originally issued in Royal Mint sets*
\*\* *Issues of bullion quality coins of these years were modest and should command a premium*

4291 4296

**4291 Britannia. Twenty five pounds.** (1/4oz of fine gold). R. Britannia standing.

| | | | |
|---|---|---|---|
| 1987 | £80 | — Proof *FDC*\* £85 | |
| — Proof *FDC* (Issued: 3,500) £85 | | 1989 | £80 |
| 1988 | £80 | — Proof *FDC*\* £100 | |

**4292 Britannia. Twenty five pounds.** (1/4oz of fine gold alloyed with silver). R. Britannia standing.

| | | | |
|---|---|---|---|
| 1990 | £100 | — Proof *FDC*\* £135 | |
| — Proof *FDC*\* £120 | | 1994 | £80 |
| 1991 | £100 | — Proof *FDC*\* £135 | |
| — Proof *FDC*\* £135 | | 1995 | £80 |
| 1992 | £100 | — Proof *FDC*\* £135 | |
| — Proof *FDC*\* £135 | | 1996 | £80 |
| 1993 | \*\*\* | — Proof *FDC*\* £135 | |

4293

**4293 Britannia. Twenty five pounds.** (1/4 oz fine gold, alloyed with silver) R. Standing figure of Britannia in horse drawn chariot. 10th Anniversary of Britannia issue
1997 Proof *FDC* (Issued: 923) £180

**4296 Britannia. Ten pounds.** (1/10oz of fine gold). R. Britannia standing.

| | | | |
|---|---|---|---|
| 1987 | £40 | — Proof *FDC* (Issued: 2,694) £50 | |
| — Proof *FDC* (Issued: 3,500) £50 | | 1989 | £40 |
| 1988 | £40 | — Proof *FDC* (Issued: 1,609) £55 | |

**4297 Britannia. Ten pounds.** (1/10oz of fine gold alloyed with silver). R. Britannia standing.

| | | | |
|---|---|---|---|
| 1990 | £50 | — Proof *FDC* (Issued: 997) £75 | |
| — Proof *FDC* (Issued: 1,571) £65 | | 1994 | \*\* |
| 1991 | £50 | — Proof *FDC* (Issued: 994) £75 | |
| — Proof *FDC* (Issued: 954) £65 | | 1995 | £50 |
| 1992 | \* | — Proof *FDC* (Issued: 1,500) £65 | |
| — Proof *FDC* (Issued: 1,000) £65 | | 1996 | £50 |
| 1993 | £50 | — Proof *FDC* (Issued: 2,379) £65 | |

*\* Coins marked thus were originally issued in Royal Mint sets.*
*\*\* Issues of bullion quality coins of these years were modest and coins should command a premium*
*\*\*\* Extremely small numbers issued.*

4298

**4298    Britannia. Ten pounds.** (1/10 oz fine gold, alloyed with silver) R̟. Standing figure of
Britannia in horse drawn chariot. 10th Anniversary of Britannia issue
1997 Proof *FDC* (Issued: 1,821) £80

## SILVER

4300

**4300    Britannia. Two pounds.** (1 oz fine silver) R̟. Standing figure of Britannia in horse drawn
chariot. 10th Anniversary of Britannia issue
1997 Proof *FDC* (Issued: 4,173) £50

4300A

**4300A Britannia. One pound.** (1/2 oz of fine silver) R̟. Standing figure of Britannia in horse drawn
chariot. 10th Anniversary of Britannia issue
1997 Proof *FDC\** £25

*\* Coins marked thus were originally issued in Royal Mint Sets.*

4300B

**4300B Britannia. Fifty pence.** (1/4 oz of fine silver) R. Standing figure of Britannia in horse drawn chariot. 10th Anniversary of Britannnia issue
1997 Proof *FDC*\* £20

4300C

**4300C Britannia. Twenty pence.** (1/4 oz of fine silver) R. Standing figure of Britannia in horse drawn chariot. 10th Anniversary of Britannia issue
1997 Proof *FDC* (Issued: 8,686) £15

## CUPRO-NICKEL

4301

|  | UNC |
| --- | --- |
|  | £ |
| **4301 Five pounds (crown).** Queen Mother 90th birthday commemorative. 1990 | 8 |
| — Specimen in presentation folder (Issued: 45,250) | 10 |
| — Proof in silver *FDC* (Issued: 56,102) £60 | |
| — Proof in gold FDC (Issued: 2,500) £650 | |

*\* Coins marked thus were originally issued in Royal Mint Sets.*

4302

**4302   Five pounds (crown).** 40th Anniversary of the Coronation. 1993................................          7
　　　— Specimen in presentation folder...............................................................................          9
　　　— Proof *FDC*  (in 1993 set, see PS51)* £9
　　　— Proof in silver *FDC* (Issued: 58,877) £35
　　　— Proof in gold *FDC* (Issued: 2,500) £600

4303

**4303   Five pounds (crown).** 70th Birthday of Queen Elizabeth II. R. The Queen's personal flag, the
　　　Royal Standard, the Union Flag, two pennants bearing the dates '1926' and '1996' all against
　　　a backdrop of Windsor Castle. Edge: VIVAT REGINA ELIZABETHA.
　　　1996....................................................................................................................................          7
　　　— Specimen in presentation folder (issued: 73,311) ......................................................          9
　　　— Proof *FDC* (in 1996 set, See PS57) * £12
　　　— Proof in silver *FDC*  (Issued: 39,336) £35
　　　— Proof in gold *FDC*  (Issued: 2,127) £600

*\* Coins marked thus were originally issued in Royal Mint Sets.*

4304

**4304  Five pounds (crown).** Golden Wedding of Queen Elizabeth II and Prince Philip. Conjoint portraits of The Queen and Prince Philip. R. Royal Arms and Arms of Prince Philip surmounted by St. Edward's crown which divides the dates 1947 and 1997 20 November, and an anchor below with the denomination.

1997......................................................................................................................... 7
— Specimen in presentation folder............................................................................. 9
— Proof *FDC* (in 1997 set, See PS59)* £12
— Proof in silver *FDC*  (Issued: 33,689) £35
— Proof in gold *FDC*  (Issued: 2,574) £600

## NICKEL-BRASS

4311

|  | *UNC* |  | *UNC* |
|---|---|---|---|
|  | £ |  | £ |

**4311  Two pounds.** R. St. Andrew's cross surmounted by a thistle of Scotland. Edge XIII
COMMONWEALTH GAMES SCOTLAND 1986 ..................................................... 5
— Specimen in presentation folder      5      — Proof in silver *FDC* (Issued: 59,779) £35
— .500 silver (Issued: 58,881)              12      — Proof in gold *FDC* (Issued: 3,277) £225
— Proof *FDC** £6

*\* Coins marked thus were originally issued in Royal Mint Sets.*

4312                                    4313

**4312** **Two pounds** 300th Anniversary of Bill of Rights. ℞ Cypher of William and Mary, House of Commons mace and St. Edward's crown.

1989......................................... 4 — Proof in silver *FDC* (Issued: 25,000) £30
— Specimen in presentation folder 5 — Proof piedfort in silver *FDC*\* £60
— Proof *FDC*\* £6

**4313** **Two pounds** 300th Anniversary of Claim of Right (Scotland). ℞. As 4312, but with crown of Scotland.

1989......................................... 8 — Proof in silver *FDC* (Issued: 24,852) £30
— Specimen in presentation folder 10 — Proof piedfort in silver *FDC*\* £60
— Proof *FDC*\* £10

4314

**4314** **Two pounds** 300th Anniversary of the Bank of England. ℞: Bank's original Corporate Seal, with Crown & Cyphers of William III & Mary II. Edge SIC VOS NON VOBIS.

1994......................................... 5 — Proof piedfort in silver *FDC* (Issued: 9,569) £60
— Specimen in presentation folder 5 — Proof in gold *FDC* (Issued: 1,000) £400
— Proof *FDC*\* £6................... — gold error. Obverse as 4251 (Included in
— Proof in silver *FDC* (Issued: 27, 957) £30      above) £1000

*\* Coins marked thus were originally issued in Royal Mint sets.*

4315

UNC
£

**4315** **Two pounds** 50th Anniversary of the End of World War II. R: A Dove of Peace.
Edge 1945 IN PEACE GOODWILL 1995

1995............................................................................................................................................ 5
— Specimen in presentation folder ............................................................................... 5
— Proof *FDC* \*£6.................... — Proof piedfort in silver *FDC* (Edition: 10,000) £60
— Proof in silver *FDC* (Issued: 35,751) £30 — Proof in gold *FDC* (Issued: 2,500) £350

4316

**4316** **Two pounds** 50th Anniversary of the Establishment of the United Nations. R: 50th
Anniversary symbol and an array of flags. Edge NATIONS UNITED FOR PEACE
1945-1995.

1995............................................................................................................................................ 5
— Specimen in presentation folder............................................................................... 5
— Proof in silver *FDC* (Edition: 175,000) £30    — Proof in gold *FDC* (Edition: 17,500) £350
— Proof piedfort in silver *FDC* (Edition: 10,000) £60

4317

**4317** **Two pounds** European Football Championships. R: A stylised representation of a football.
Edge: TENTH EUROPEAN CHAMPIONSHIP.

1996............................................................................................................................................ 5
— Specimen in presentation folder............................................................................... 5
— Proof *FDC*\*  £6.................. — Proof piedfort in silver *FDC* (Issued: 7,634) £65
— Proof in silver *FDC* (Issued: 25,163) £28    — Proof in gold *FDC* (Issued: 2,098) £350

\* *Coins marked thus were originally issued in Royal Mint Sets.*

4318

|  | UNC | | UNC |
|---|---|---|---|
|  | £ | | £ |

**4318** **Two pounds** Bimetallic currency issue. R. Four concentric circles representing the Iron Age, 18th century industrial development, silicon chip, and Internet. Edge: STANDING ON THE SHOULDERS OF GIANTS

1997.................................................................................................................... 4

— Specimen in presentation folder............................................................. 6

— Proof *FDC*\* £6

— Proof in silver FDC (Issued: 29,910) £29

— Proof piedfort in silver *FDC* (Issued: 10,000) £60

— Proof in gold *FDC* (Issued: 2,482) £325

4331                                                    4332

**4331** **One pound** (Welsh design). Edge PLEIDIOL WYF I'M GWLAD

1985.................................................................................................................... 4

— Specimen in presentation folder (Issued: 24,850)................................. 4

— Proof *FDC*\* £5

— Proof in silver *FDC* (Issued: 50,000) £21

— Proof piedfort in silver *FDC* (Issued: 15,000) £55

1990.................................................................................................................... 5

— Proof *FDC*\* £6

— Proof in silver *FDC* (Issued: 23,277) £24

**4332** **One pound** (Northern Irish design). Edge DECUS ET TUTAMEN

1986.................................................................................................................... 5

— Specimen in presentatioon folder (Issued: 19,908)............................... 5

— Proof *FDC*\* £4

— Proof in silver *FDC* (Issued: 37, 958) £26

— Proof piedfort in silver *FDC* (Issued: 15,000) £60

1991.................................................................................................................... 5

— Proof *FDC*\* £6

— Proof in silver *FDC* (Issued: 22,922) £24

\* *Coins marked thus were originally issued in Royal Mint sets.*

4333                                    4334

**4333  One pound** (English design). Edge DECUS ET TUTAMEN

1987............................................................................................................................ 4

— Specimen in presentation folder (Issued: 72,607)...................................... 4

— Proof *FDC*\* £6

— Proof in silver *FDC* (Issued: 50,000) £30

— Proof piedfort in silver *FDC* (Issued: 15,000) £55

1992............................................................................................................................ 5

— Proof *FDC*\* £6

— Proof in silver *FDC* (Issued: 13,065) £27

**4334  One pound** (Royal Shield). Edge DECUS ET TUTAMEN

1988............................................................................................................................ 5

— Specimen in presentation folder (Issued: 29,550)...................................... 5

— Proof *FDC*\* £6

— Proof in silver *FDC* (Issued: 50,000) £35

— Proof piedfort in silver *FDC* (Issued: 10,000) £55

**4335  One pound** (Scottish design). Edge NEMO ME IMPUNE LACESSIT (Illus. as 4222)

1989........................................ 5    — Proof in silver *FDC* (Issued: 22,275) £21

— Proof FDC\* £6                 — Proof piedfort in silver *FDC* (Issued: 10,000) £55

**4336  One pound** (Royal Arms design). Edge DECUS ET TUTAMEN  (Illus. as 4221)

1993........................................ 5    — Proof in silver *FDC* (Issued: 16,526) £30

— Proof FDC\* £6                 — Proof piedfort in silver *FDC* (Issued: 12,500) £65

4337            4338            4339            4340

**4337  One pound** (Scottish design). R: Lion rampant within a double tressure. Edge NEMO ME
IMPUNE LACESSIT

1994........................................ 4    — Proof in silver *FDC* (Issued: 25,000) £40

— Specimen in presentation folder    5    — Proof piedfort in silver *FDC* (Issued: 11,722) £60

— Proof *FDC*\* £6

**4338  One pound** (Welsh design). R. Heraldic dragon Edge PLEIDIOL WYF I'M GWLAD

1995........................................ 4

— Specimen in presentation folder (Issued: 23,728) £5

— Proof *FDC*\* £5

— Proof in silver *FDC* (Issued: 27,445) £23

— Proof in piedfort in silver *FDC* (Issued: 8,458) £60

\* *Coins marked thus were originally issued in Royal Mint sets.*

**4339  One pound** (Northern Irish design). R. A Celtic cross incorporating a pimpernel at its centre.
Edge DECUS ET TUTAMEN
1996.......................................    4   — Proof in silver *FDC*  (Issued: 25,000) £24
— Specimen in presentation folder    6   — Proof piedfort in silver *FDC* (Issued: 10,000) £55
— Proof *FDC\**  £6

**4340  One pound** (English design) R. Three lions. Edge: DECUS ET TUTAMEN.
1997.........................    4
— Specimen in presentation folder (Issued 56,996) £5
— Proof *FDC\**  £5
— Proof in silver *FDC*  (Issued: 20,137) £25
— Proof piedfort in silver *FDC*  (Issued: 10,000) £55

## CUPRO-NICKEL

4351

**4351  Fifty pence.** R. Britannia r. (4341)

| | | | | | |
|---|---|---|---|---|---|
| 1985 ................. | 5 | — Proof *FDC\** £3.... | | 1995*......................... | 3 |
| — Proof *FDC\** £3 | | 1990*......................... | 4 | — Proof *FDC\** £4 | |
| 1986* ............... | 3 | — Proof *FDC\** £5.... | | 1996*......................... | 3 |
| — Proof *FDC\** £3 | | 1991*......................... | 4 | — Proof *FDC\** £4 | |
| 1987* ............... | 3 | — Proof *FDC\** £5.... | | — Proof in silver *FDC\** £15 | |
| — Proof *FDC\** £3 | | 1992*......................... | 4 | 1997......................... | 3 |
| 1988* ............... | 3 | — Proof *FDC\** £5.... | | — Proof *FDC\** £4 | |
| — Proof *FDC\** £4 | | 1993*......................... | 4 | — Proof in silver *FDC\** £24 | |
| 1989* ............... | 4 | — Proof *FDC\** £4 | | | |

4352

**4352  Fifty pence** Presidency of the Council of European Community Ministers and completion of
the Single Market. R Conference table top and twelve stars
1992-1993 .............................    7   — Proof piedfort in silver *FDC* (Issued: 10,993) £45
— Proof *FDC\**  £10...............      — Proof in gold *FDC* (Issued: 1,864) £400
— Proof in silver *FDC\** (Issued: 26,890) £24

**4352A**— Specimen in presentation folder with 1992 date 4351 ...........................................    10

*\* Coins marked thus were originally issued in Royal Mint sets.*

4353

**4353  Fifty pence** 50th Anniversary of the Normandy Landings on D-Day. R: Allied Invasion Force.
1994.......................................... 2    — Proof in silver *FDC*  (Issued: 40,000) £30
— Specimen in presentation folder  3    — Proof piedfort in silver *FDC*  (Issued: 10,000) £50
— Proof *FDC*\*  £5                           — Proof in gold *FDC* (Issued: 1,877) £425
**4354  Fifty penc**e R. Britannia: diam 27.3mm
1997.......................................... 1    — Proof in silver *FDC*  (Issued: 1,632) £27
— Proof *FDC*\*  £4                           — Proof piedfort in silver *FDC*  (Issued: 7,192) £46

4361

**4361  Twenty pence.** R. Crowned double rose

| 1985 ................ | | — Proof *FDC*\* £3..... | | 1994........................... | |
| — Proof *FDC*\* £2 | | 1990........................... | | — Proof *FDC*\* £3 | |
| 1986\* ............... | 1 | — Proof *FDC*\* £3..... | | 1995........................... | |
| — Proof *FDC*\* £2 | | 1991........................... | | — Proof *FDC*\* £3 | |
| 1987 ................ | | — Proof *FDC*\* £3..... | | 1996........................... | |
| — Proof *FDC*\* £2 | | 1992........................... | | — Proof *FDC*\* £3 | |
| 1988 ................ | | — Proof *FDC*\* £3..... | | — Proof in silver *FDC*\* £15 | |
| — Proof *FDC*  £3 | | 1993........................... | | 1997........................... | |
| 1989 ................ | | — Proof *FDC*\* £3..... | | — Proof *FDC*\* £3 | |

4366

| | *UNC* | | *UNC* | | *UNC* |
| | £ | | £ | | £ |

**4366  Ten pence.** R. Lion passant guardant

| 1985\* ............... | 3 | 1988\*........................ | 3 | 1991\*........................ | 4 |
| — Proof *FDC* \* £2 | | — Proof *FDC*  £3.... | | — Proof *FDC*\* £3 | |
| 1986\* ............... | 2 | 1989\*........................ | 4 | 1992\*........................ | 3 |
| — Proof *FDC*\* £2 | | — Proof *FDC*\* £3..... | | — Proof *FDC*\* £4 | |
| 1987\* ............... | 3 | 1990\*........................ | 4 | — Proof in silver *FDC*\* £14 | |
| — Proof *FDC*\* £3 | | — Proof *FDC*\* £3 | | | |

*\* Coins marked thus were originally issued in Royal Mint sets.*

4367

**4367   Ten pence** R Lion passant guardant: diam. 24.5mm

1992............................

— Proof *FDC*\* £3.................

— Proof in silver *FDC*\* £14..

— Proof piedfort in silver *FDC*\* (Issued: 14,167) £40

1993\*.....................................

— Proof *FDC*\* £2.................

1994\*.....................................

— Proof *FDC*\* £2.................

1995......................

— Proof *FDC*\* £2

1996......................

— Proof *FDC*\* £2

— Proof in silver *FDC*\* £15

1997......................

— Proof *FDC*\* £2

4371

**4371   Five pence.** R. Crowned thistle

1985\* ...............   1       — Proof *FDC*\* £2....

— Proof *FDC*\* £1           1988............................

1986\* ...............   1       — Proof *FDC*\* £2....

— Proof *FDC*\* £1           1989............................

1987 .................           — Proof *FDC*\* £2

1990\* .........................   2

— Proof *FDC*\* £3

— Proof in silver *FDC*\*  £12

4372

**4372   Five pence.** R. Crowned  thistle: diam 18mm

1990 .................

— Proof *FDC*\* £2

— Proof in silver *FDC*\* £12

— Proof piedfort in silver

   *FDC* (Issued: 20,000) £25

1991 .................

— Proof *FDC*\* £2

1992 .........................

— Proof *FDC*\* £2....

1993\*.........................

— Proof *FDC*\* £2....

1994.........................

— Proof *FDC*\* £2....

1995.........................

— Proof *FDC*\* £2

1996.........................

— Proof *FDC*\* £2

— Proof in silver *FDC*\* £15

1997.........................

— Proof *FDC*\* £2

*\* Coins marked thus were originally issued in Royal Mint sets.*

# BRONZE

4376                   4381

**4376   Two pence. R. Plumes**
| | | |
|---|---|---|
| 1985 ................. | 1988 .......................... | 1991 .......................... |
| — Proof *FDC*\* £1 | — Proof *FDC*\* £1.... | — Proof *FDC*\* £1 |
| 1986 ................. | 1989 .......................... | 1992\* ....................... |
| — Proof *FDC*\* £1 | — Proof *FDC*\* £1.... | — Proof *FDC*\* £1 |
| 1987 ................. | 1990 .......................... | |
| — Proof *FDC*\* £1 | — Proof *FDC*\* £1 | |

**4381   One penny. R. Portcullis with chains**
| | | |
|---|---|---|
| 1985 ................. | 1988 .......................... | 1991 .......................... |
| — Proof *FDC*\* £1 | — Proof *FDC*\* £1.... | — Proof *FDC*\* £1 |
| 1986 ................. | 1989 .......................... | 1992\* ....................... |
| — Proof *FDC*\* £1 | — Proof *FDC*\* £1.... | — Proof *FDC*\* £1 |
| 1987 ................. | 1990 .......................... | |
| — Proof *FDC*\* £1 | — Proof *FDC*\* £1 | |

# COPPER PLATED STEEL

**4386   Two pence R. Plumes**
| | | |
|---|---|---|
| 1992 ................. | — Proof *FDC*\* £1.... | — Proof *FDC*\* £1 |
| 1993 ................. | 1995 .......................... | — Proof in silver *FDC*\* £15 |
| — Proof *FDC*\* £1 | — Proof *FDC*\* £1.... | 1997 .......................... |
| 1994 ................. | 1996 .......................... | — Proof *FDC*\* £1 |

**4391   One penny R. Portcullis with chains**
| | | |
|---|---|---|
| 1992 ................. | — Proof *FDC*\* £1.... | — Proof *FDC*\* £1 |
| 1993 ................. | 1995 .......................... | — Proof in silver *FDC*\* £15 |
| — Proof *FDC*\* £1 | — Proof *FDC*\* £1.... | 1997 .......................... |
| 1994 ................. | 1996 .......................... | — Proof *FDC*\* £1 |

*\* Coins marked thus were originally issued in Royal Mint sets.*

GOLD

4400

**4400  Five pounds.** R. St.George
1998 Proof *FDC*\*  £650        1999 Proof *FDC*\*  £650        2004 Proof *FDC*\*  £650
2000 Bullion type  £350        2001 Proof *FDC*\*  £650
— Proof *FDC*\*  £650          2003 Proof *FDC*\*  £650
                               — Unc (Issued: 762)  £500

4401

**4401  Five pounds.** R. Shield, as illustration
2002 Proof *FDC*\*  £600                Unc (Issued: 1,284) £535

**4410  Five pounds.** R. St. George, 'U' in a circle to left of date
1998 (Issued: 825) £500                2000 (Issued: 994) £500
1999 (Issued: 970) £500                2001 (Issued: 1,000) £500

**4420  Two pounds.** R. St. George
1998 Proof *FDC*\* £300                2003 Proof *FDC*\* £300
2000 Proof *FDC*\* £300

**4421  Two pounds.** R. Shield
2002 Proof *FDC*\*  £300

**4430  Sovereign.** R. St. George
1998 Proof *FDC* (Issued: 10,000) £200        2001 Bullion type.......................        £85
1999 Proof *FDC* (Issued: 10,000) £280        — Proof *FDC* (Issued: 8,915)....        £150
2000 Bullion type (Issued: 139,961) £85       2003 Bullion type.......................        £80
— Proof *FDC* (Issued: 9,909) £150            — Proof *FDC* (Issued: 12,166)..        £130

**4431  Sovereign.** R. Shield
2002........................................  £85
- Proof *FDC* (Issued: 12,500)  £220

**4440  Half sovereign.** R. St. George
1998 Proof *FDC* (Issued: 6,147) £120         2001 Bullion type.......................        £50
1999 Proof *FDC* (Issued: 7,500) £150         — Proof *FDC* (Issued: 4,596)....        £80
2000 Bullion type (Issued: 157,101) £50       2003 Bullion type.......................        £43
— Proof *FDC* (Issued: 7,458) £80             — Proof *FDC* (Issued: 4,622)....        £75

*\* Coins marked thus were originally issued in Royal Mint sets.*

**4441 Half Sovereign.** R. Shield
2002.................................£55
- Proof *FDC* (Issued: 10,000) £120

4450

**4450 Britannia. One Hundred pounds.** (1oz fine gold alloyed with silver) R. Standing figure of Britannia

| | |
|---|---|
| 1998 Proof *FDC*\* £500 | 2000 Proof *FDC*\* £500 |
| 1999 .............................£300 | 2002 Proof *FDC* \* £500 |
| 1999 Proof *FDC*\* £500 | 2004 Proof *FDC*\* £500 |
| 2000 ...............................£300 | |

4451

**4451 Britannia. One Hundred pounds.** (1oz fine gold alloyed with silver) R. Helmeted figure of Britannia holding a trident and a shield with a lion in the background
2001 .............................£350          2001 Proof *FDC*\* £500

4452

**4452 Britannia. One Hundred pounds.** (1oz fine gold alloyed with silver) R. Helmeted figure of Britannia with stylised waves
2003 ...............................£350          2003 Proof *FDC*\* £500

*\* Coins marked thus were originally issued in Royal Mint sets.*

4460

**4460** **Britannia. Fifty pounds.** (1/2 oz fine gold alloyed with silver) R. Standing figure of Britannia

| | |
|---|---|
| 1998 Proof *FDC\** £275 | 2000 Proof *FDC\** £275 |
| 1999.....................£160 | 2002 Proof *FDC* \* £275 |
| 1999 Proof *FDC\** £275 | 2004 Proof *FDC* \* £275 |
| 2000.....................£160 | |

**4461** **Britannia. Fifty pounds.** (1/2 oz fine gold alloyed with silver) R. Helmeted figure of Britannia holding a trident and a shield with a lion in the background (see 4451)

2001 .............................£220                     2001 Proof *FDC\** £275

**4462** **Britannia. Fifty pounds.** (1/2 oz fine gold alloyed with silver) R. Helmeted figure of Britannia with stylised waves (see 4452)

2003 Proof *FDC\** £250

4470

**4470** **Britannia. Twenty five pounds**. (1/4 oz fine gold alloyed with silver) R. Standing figure of Britannia

| | |
|---|---|
| 1998 Proof *FDC* (Issued: 560) £125 | 2000 Proof *FDC* (Issued: 500) £125 |
| 1999 ...............................£100 | 2002 Proof *FDC* (Issued: 750) £125 |
| 1999 Proof *FDC* (Issued: 1,000)  £125 | 2004 Proof *FDC*  (Edition: 750) £120 |
| 2000 ...............................£100 | |

**4471** **Britannia. Twenty five pounds.** (1/4 oz fine gold alloyed with silver) R. Helmeted figure of Britannia holding a trident and a shield with a lion in the background (see 4451)

2001................................£100                   2001 Proof *FDC* (Issued: 500) £125

**4472** **Britannia. Twenty five pounds.** (1/4 oz fine gold alloyed with silver) R. Helmeted figure of Britannia with stylised waves (see 4452)

2003 Proof *FDC* (Issued: 604) £115

**4480** **Britannia. Ten pounds.** (1/10 oz fine gold alloyed with silver) R. Standing figure of Britannia

| | |
|---|---|
| 1998 Proof *FDC* (Issued: 392) £60 | 2000 Proof *FDC* (Issued: 659) £60 |
| 1999 .................................£50 | 2002 ...................................£50 |
| 1999 Proof *FDC* (Issued: 1,058)  £60 | 2002 Proof *FDC* (Issued: 1,500) £125 |
| 2000 .................................£50 | 2004 Proof *FDC*  (Edition: 1,500) £70 |

**4481** **Britannia. Ten pounds.** (1/10 oz fine gold alloyed with silver) R. Helmeted figure of Britannia holding a trident and a shield with a lion in the background (see 4451)

2001.................................£50                    2001 Proof *FDC* (Issued: 1,557) £65

**4482** **Britannia. Ten pounds.** (1/10 oz fine gold alloyed with silver) R. Helmeted figure of Britannia with stylised waves (see 4452)

2003 .................................£50                    2003 Proof *FDC* (Issued: 1,351)  £65

*\* Coins marked thus were originally issued in Royal Mint sets.*

## SILVER

4500

**4500** **Britannia. Two pounds.** (1 oz of fine silver) R. Standing figure of Britannia

| | |
|---|---|
| 1998 (Issued: 88,909) £15 | 2002 (Issued: 48,215) £15 |
| - Proof *FDC* (Issued: 2,168) £50 | 2004 (Edition: 100,000) £14 |
| 2000 (Issued: 81,301) £15 | - Proof *FDC* (Edition: 5,000) £40 |

**4501** **Britannia. Two pounds.** (1 oz of fine silver) R. Standing figure of Britannia in horse drawn chariot (Illus. as 4300)
1999 (Issued: 69,394) £12

**4502** **Britannia. Two pounds.** (1 oz of fine silver) R. Helmeted figure of Britannia holding a trident and a shield with a lion in the background (see 4451)
2001 (Issued: 44,816) £13                    — Proof *FDC*  (Issued: 3,047) £45

4503

**4503** **Britannia. Two pounds.** (1oz fine silver) R. Helmeted figure of Britannia with stylised waves
2003 (Issued: 73,271)  £13                    — Proof *FDC* (Issued: 1,833) £37

4510

**4510** **Britannia. One pound.** (1/2 oz of fine silver) R. Standing figure of Britannia
1998 — Proof *FDC*\* £25

**4511** **Britannia. One pound.** (1/2 oz of fine silver) R. Helmeted figure of Britannia holding a trident and a shield with a lion in the background (see 4451)
2001 — Proof *FDC*\* £25

*\* Coins marked thus were originally issued in Royal Mint sets.*

**4512 Britannia. One pound.** (1/2 oz fine silver) R. Helmeted figure of Britannia with stylised wave (see 4503)
2003 — Proof *FDC*\* £25

4520

**4520 Britannia. Fifty pence.** (1/4 oz of fine silver) R̩. Standing figure of Britannia
1998 — Proof *FDC*\* £20
**4521 Britannia. Fifty pence.** (1/4 oz of fine silver) R̩. Helmeted figure of Britannia holding a trident and a shield with a lion in the background (see 4451)
2001 — Proof *FDC*\* £20
**4522 Britannia. Fifty pence.** (1/4 oz fine silver) R. Helmeted figure of Britannia with stylised wave (see 4503)
2003 — Proof *FDC*\* £20

4530

**4530 Britannia. Twenty pence.** (1/10 oz of fine silver) R̩. Standing figure of Britannia
1998 — Proof *FDC* (Issued: 2,724) £15
**4531 Britannia. Twenty pence.** (1/10 oz of fine silver) R̩. Helmeted figure of Britannia holding a trident and a shield with a lion in the background (see 4451)
2001 — Proof *FDC* (Edition: 10,000) £18
**4532 Britannia. Twenty pence.** (1/10 oz fine silver) R. Helmeted figure of Britannia with stylised wave (see 4503)
2003 — Proof *FDC* (Issued: 1,003) £18

## CUPRO-NICKEL

4550

**4550 Five pounds** (crown). Prince of Wales 50th Birthday. R̩. Portrait of The Prince of Wales with the inscriptions 'The Prince's Trust' and 'Helping young people to succeed' on a ribbon at the base of the portrait with the denomination 'Five Pounds' and the dates 1948 and 1998.
1998................................................................................................................... £7
— Specimen in presentation folder £10
— Proof *FDC* (in 1998 set, see PS 61)\* £12
— Proof in silver *FDC* (Issued: 13,379) £50
— Proof in gold *FDC* (Issued: 773) £600

\* *Coins marked thus were originally issued in Royal Mint sets.*

4551

**4551 Five pounds** (crown). Diana, Princess of Wales Memorial. ℞. Portrait of Diana, Princess of
Wales with the inscription 'In memory of Diana, Princess of Wales' with the denomination
'Five Pounds' and the dates 1961 and 1997

1999...................................................................................................................... £7
— Specimen in presentation folder £10
— Proof *FDC* (in 1999 set, see PS63)* £12
— Proof in silver *FDC* (Issued: 49,545) £45
— Proof in gold *FDC* (Issued: 7,500) £650

4552                        4552A

**4552 Five pounds** (crown). Millennium commemorative. ℞. In the centre, on a patterned circle, a
representation of the British Isles with a pair of clock hands emanating from Greenwich, set
at 12 o'clock with the inscription 'Anno Domini' with the denomination 'Five Pounds' and
the dates 1999 and 2000

1999...................................................................................................................... £7
— Specimen in presentation folder £10
— Proof in silver *FDC* (Issued: 49,057) £30
— Proof in gold *FDC* (Issued: 2,500) £600

2000...................................................................................................................... £7
— Specimen in presentation folder £10
— Proof *FDC* (in 2000 set, see PS65)* £12
— Proof in silver *FDC* (Issued: 14,255) £36
— Proof in gold *FDC* (Issued: 1,487) £600

**4552A**
— Specimen in presentation folder with Dome mint mark £15
(See illustration above - the mintmark is located within the shaded area at 3 o'clock).

*\* Coins marked thus were originally issued in Royal Mint sets.*

**4552B**
—Proof in silver *FDC* (Issued: 14,248) £37
(The reverse design is the same as the 1999 issue but with the British Isles coloured with 22 carat gold)

4553

**4553   Five pounds** (crown). Queen Mother commemorative.  R Portrait of the Queen Mother
with Inscription "Queen Elizabeth the Queen Mother" and cheering crowds in 19th
Century and modern day dress with the Queen Mother's signature below and the
denomination 'Five Pounds' and the dates 1900 and 2000.
2000.................................................................................................................................   £7
— Specimen in presentation folder  £10
— Proof in silver *FDC* (Issued: 31,316) £35
— Proof piedfort in silver *FDC* (Issued: 14,850) £50
— Proof in gold *FDC* (Issued: 3,000) £650

4554

**4554   Five pounds** (crown) Victorian anniversary. R. A classic portrait of the young Queen
Victoria based on the Penny Black postage stamp with a V representing Victoria, and taking
the form of railway lines and in the background the iron framework of the Crystal Palace, and
the denomination "Five Pounds" and the dates 1901 and 2001.
2001.................................................................................................................................   £7
— Specimen in presentation folder  £10
— Proof *FDC* (in 2001 set, see PS68)* £10
— Proof in silver *FDC* (Issued: 19,216) £35
— Proof in gold *FDC* (Issued: 2,098) £600
**4554A** — Proof in silver *FDC* with "reverse frosting" giving matt appearance.
(Issued: 596 – issued with sovereigns of 1901 and 2001)* £60
**4554B** — Proof in gold *FDC* with "reverse frosting" giving matt appearance.
(Issued: 733 – issued with four different type sovereigns of Victoria, - Young Head with
shield, and St.George reverse, Jubilee Head and Old Head.)* £750
*\* Coins marked thus were originally issued in Royal Mint sets.*

4555

**4555 Five pounds.** (crown) Golden Jubilee commemorative 2002. O. New portrait of The Queen with the denomination "Five pounds". R. Equestrian portrait of the The Queen with the inscription "Elizabeth II DEI GRA REGINA FID DEF" around the circumference and "AMOR POPULI PRAESIDIUM REG" within, and the date 2002 below separated by the central element of the Royal Arms

2002................................................................................................................ £5

— Specimen in presentation folder £10
— Proof *FDC* (in 2002 set, see PS 72)* £10
— Proof in silver *FDC* (Issued: 60,557) £35
— Proof in gold *FDC* (Issued: 3,500) £650

4556

**4556 Five pounds,** (crown) Queen Mother memorial 2002. R. Three quarter portrait of the Queen Mother within a wreath with the inscription "QUEEN ELIZABETH THE QUEEN MOTHER" and the dates 1900 and 2002, with an edge inscription "STRENGTH, DIGNITY AND LAUGHTER"

2002................................................£5

— Specimen in presentation folder £10
— Proof in silver *FDC* (Issued: 16,117) £35
— Proof in gold *FDC* (Issued: 2,086) £555

*\* Coins marked thus were originally issued in Royal Mint sets.*

4557

**4557** **Five pounds.** (crown) Coronation commemorative 2003. O. Profile portrait of The Queen in linear form facing right with the inscription "Elizabeth II DEI GRA REGINA F D ". R. In the centre the inscription "GOD SAVE THE QUEEN" surrounded by the inscription "CORONATION JUBILEE" the denomination "FIVE POUNDS" and the date 2003.
2003.................................................................................................................................... £5
— Specimen in presentation folder £10
— Proof *FDC* (in 2003 set, see PS 78)* £10
— Proof in silver *FDC* (Issued: 27,350) £35
— Proof in gold *FDC* (Issued: 1,860) £560

4558

**4558** **Five pounds.** (crown) Centenary of Entende Cordiale 2004. R. In the centre the head and shoulders of Britannia and her French counterpart Marianne with the inscription "Entende Cordiale" separated by the dates "1904" and "2004"
2004 ....................................................................................................................................£5
— Specimen in presentation folder £10
— Proof *FDC* (Edition: 50,000) £14
— Proof in silver *FDC* (Edition: 15,000) £35
— Proof Piedfort in silver *FDC* (Issued: 2,500) £90
— Proof in gold *FDC* (Edition: 1,500) £555
— Proof Piedfort in platinum *FDC* (Edition: 501) £2,995

## NICKEL-BRASS

4570

**4570** **Two pounds.** Bimetallic currency issue. R. Four concentric circles, representing the Iron Age, 18th century industrial development, silicon chip and Internet. Edge: STANDING OF THE SHOULDERS OF GIANTS

1998.................................................................................................................... £4
— Proof *FDC*\* £6
— Proof in silver *FDC* (Issued: 19,978) £29
— Proof piedfort in silver *FDC* (Issued: 7,646) £50
1999.................................................................................................................... £4

| | |
|---|---|
| 2000 | 2001 |
| — Proof *FDC*\* £6 | — Proof *FDC*\* £6 |
| — Proof in silver *FDC*\* £30 | |

2002
— Proof *FDC* (in 2002 set, see PS72)\* £6
— Proof in gold *FDC* (in 2002 set, see PGJS1)\* £300

4571

**4571** **Two pounds.** Rugby World Cup. R. In the centre a rugby ball and goal posts surrounded by a stylalised stadium with the denomination 'Two Pounds' and the date 1999

1999.................................................................................................................... £4
— Specimen in presentation folder £6
— Proof *FDC* (in 1999 set, see PS63)\* £6
— Proof in silver *FDC* (Issued: 9,665) £29
— Proof piedfort in silver *FDC* (Issued: 10,000) £150
— Proof in gold *FDC* (Issued: 311) £300

*\* Coins marked thus were originally issued in Royal Mint sets.*

4572

**4572  Two pounds.** Marconi commemorative. ℞. Decorative radio waves emanating from a spark
of electricity linking the zeros of the date to represent the generation of the signal that crossed
the Atlantic with the date 2001 and the denomination "Two Pounds". Edge: WIRELESS
BRIDGES THE ATLANTIC... MARCONI 1901
2001
— Specimen in presentation folder  £7
— Proof *FDC* (in 2001 set, see PS68)*  £10
— Proof in silver *FDC* (Issued: 11,488)  £29
— Proof piedfort in silver *FDC* (Issued: 6,759) £35
— Proof in gold *FDC* (Issued: 1,658)  £300
**4572A**— Proof in silver *FDC*, with reverse frosting. (Issued: 14,803 in a 2-coin set with a Canadian
$5 Marconi silver proof) £29

4573                              4574

**4573  Two pounds.** Commonwealth Games commemorative. England. ℞. A moving figure of an
athlete holding a banner, the top of which being divided into lines to symbolise lanes of a
running track or swimming pool with a cameo of the English flag and the inscription "XVII
Commonwealth Games 2002" and the denomination "£2". Edge inscription SPIRIT OF
FRIENDSHIP. MANCHESTER 2002.
2002..............................................................................................................................
— Specimen (in Presentation set, see US24)*£6
— Proof *FDC* (in set, see PS76)* £8
— Proof in Silver *FDC* (in set, see PSS12)* £30
— Proof in gold *FDC* (in set, see PCGS1)* £350
**4573A** As above but with colour added to the flag and parts of the banner, Proof Piedfort in Silver
*FDC* (in set, see PSS13)* £60
**4574  Two pounds.** Commonwealth Games commemorative. ℞. Northern Ireland. As above but
with a cameo of the Northern Ireland flag. Edge inscription SPIRIT OF FRIENDSHIP.
MANCHESTER 2002.
2002..............................................................................................................................
— Specimen (in Presentation set, see US24)* £6
— Proof *FDC* (in set, see PS76)* £8
— Proof in Silver *FDC* (in set, see PSS12)* £30
— Proof in gold *FDC* (in set, see PCGS1)* £350

* *Coins marked thus were originally issued in Royal Mint sets.*

**4574A** As above but with colour added to the flag and parts of the banner, Proof Piedfort in Silver
*FDC* (in set, see PSS13)* £60

4575       4576

**4575** **Two pounds.** Commonwealth Games commemorative. R. Scotland. As above but with a
cameo of the Scottish flag. Edge inscription SPIRIT OF FRIENDSHIP. MANCHESTER 2002.
2002.................................................................................................................................
  — Specimen (in Presentation set, see US24)* £6
  — Proof *FDC* (in set, see PS76)* £8
  — Proof in Silver *FDC* (in set, see PSS12)* £30
  — Proof in gold *FDC* (in set, see PCGS1)* £350

**4575A** As above but with colour added to the flag and parts of the banner, Proof Piedfort in Silver
*FDC* (in set, see PSS13)* £60

**4576** **Two pounds.** Commonwealth Games commemorative. R. Wales. As above but with a cameo
of the Welsh flag. Edge inscription SPIRIT OF FRIENDSHIP. MANCHESTER 2002.
2002.................................................................................................................................
  — Specimen (in Presentation set, see US24)* £6
  — Proof *FDC* (in set, see PS76)* £8
  — Proof in Silver *FDC* (in set, see PSS12)* £30
  — Proof in gold *FDC* (in set, see PCGS1)* £350

**4576A** As above but with colour added to the flag and parts of the banner, Proof Piedfort in Silver
*FDC* (in set, see PSS13)* £60

4577

**4577** **Two pounds.** Discovery of the structure of DNA. England. R. In the centre the spiraling
double helix structure of DNA with the inscription "DNA DOUBLE HELIX" and the dates
1953 and 2003 separated by the denomination "TWO POUNDS". Edge:
DEOXYRIBONUCLEIC ACID
2003.................................................................................................................................
  — Specimen in presentation folder £7
  — Proof *FDC* (in set, see PS78)*
  — Proof in Silver *FDC* (Issued: 9,974) £30
  — Proof piedfort in silver *FDC* (Issued: 8,632) £50
  — Proof in gold *FDC* (Issued: 1,434) £300

---

*\* Coins marked thus were originally issued in Royal Mint sets.*

4578

**4578  Two pounds. R.**In the centre a depiction of Trevithick's Locomotive Penydarren and the
denomination "Two Pounds" surrounded by a cog representing the Industrial Revolution and
the inscription "R.Trevithick 1804 Invention Industry Progress 2004" Patterned Edge.
2004 ..........................................................................................................................................
— Specimen in presentation folder £7
— Brilliant uncirculated in silver (Edition: 50,000) £15
— Proof *FDC* (in 2004 set, see PS81)*
— Proof in Silver *FDC* (Edition: 25,000) £30
— Proof piedfort in silver *FDC* (Edition: 10,000) £50
— Proof in gold *FDC* (5,000) £345

4590

**4590  One pound** (Royal Arms design). Edge: DECUS ET TUTAMEN (Illus. as 4221)
1998*............................................................................................................................  £10
— Proof *FDC*  £6
— Proof in silver *FDC* (Issued: 13,863) £25
— Proof piedfort in silver *FDC* (Issued: 7,894) £45
2003 ..........................................................................................................................................
— Proof *FDC* (in 2003 set, see PS78)*
— Proof in silver *FDC* (Issued: 14,235) £27
— Proof piedfort in silver *FDC* (Issued: 9,508) £49
**4591  One pound.** (Scottish lion design). Edge: NEMO ME IMPUNE LACESSIT (Illus as 4337)
1999...........................................................................................................................................
— Specimen in presentation folder  £4
— Proof *FDC* (in 1999 set, see PS63)*  £6
— Proof in silver *FDC* (Issued: 16,328) £25
— Proof piedfort in silver *FDC* (Issued: 9,975) £45
**4591A**— Proof in silver *FDC*, with reverse frosting, (Issued: 1,994)*  £40
**4592  One pound.** (Welsh design). Edge: PLEIDIOL WYF I'M GWLAD (Illus. as 4338)
2000...........................................................................................................................................
— Proof *FDC* (in 2000 set, see PS65)*  £6
— Proof in silver *FDC* (Issued: 15,913) £25
— Proof piedfort in silver *FDC* (Issued: 9,994) £47
**4592A**— Proof in silver *FDC*, with reverse frosting,  (Issued: 1,994)*  £40

* *Coins marked thus were originally issued in Royal Mint sets.*

**4593  One pound.** (Northern Irish design). Edge: DECUS ET TUTAMEN (Illus. as 4339)
2001 ........................................................................................................................
— Proof *FDC*\*  £6
— Proof in silver *FDC* (Issued: 11,697)  £22
— Proof piedfort in silver *FDC* (Issued: 8,464) £35
**4593A**— Proof in silver *FDC*, with reverse frosting, (Issued: 1,540)\*  £40
**4594  One pound.** (English design) Edge: DECUS ET TUTAMEN (Illus. as 4340)
2002
— Proof *FDC* (in 2002 set, see PS72)\* £6
— Proof in silver *FDC* (Issued: 17,829)  £27
— Proof piedfort in silver *FDC* (Issued: 6,184) £49
— Proof in gold *FDC* (in 2002 set, see PGJS1)\* £300
**4594A**— Proof in silver *FDC*, with reverse frosting, (Issued: 1,540)\*  £40

4595                               4596A

**4595  One pound.** Scotland R.In the centre a depiction of the Forth Rail Bridge and the
denomination "One Pound" and a border representing a railway track. Patterned Edge.
2004 ......................................................................................................................
— Specimen in presentation folder £6
— Proof FDC (in 2004 set, see PS81)\*  £6
— Proof in silver FDC (Edition: 25,000) £27
— Proof piedfort in silver FDC (Edition: 10,000) £49
— Proof in gold FDC (Edition; 5,000) £345
**4595A One pound pattern.** Scotland. Design as 4595 above but dated 2003 with plain edge and
hallmark
— Proof in silver FDC \*
— Proof in gold FDC \*......................................................................................
**4596A One pound pattern.** Wales. R. Menai Straits Bridge but dated 2003 with plain edge and
hallmark
— Proof in silver FDC \*
— Proof in gold FDC \*

4597A                              4598A

**4597AOne pound pattern.** Northern Ireland. R.MacNeill's Egyptian Arch with plain edge and
hallmark
— Proof in silver *FDC* \*
— Proof in gold *FDC* \*
**4598A One pound pattern.** England. R. Millennium Bridge with plain edge and hallmark
— Proof in silver *FDC* \*
— Proof in gold *FDC* \*

*\* Coins marked thus were originally issued in Royal Mint sets.*

## CUPRO-NICKEL

**4610  Fifty pence.** R. Britannia. (Illus. as 4351)
1998
— Proof *FDC* (in 1998 set, see PS61)* £3
1999
— Proof *FDC* (in 1999 set, see PS63)* £3
2000
— Proof *FDC* (in 2000 set, see PS65)* £3
— Proof in silver *FDC*\* £25
2001
— Proof *FDC* (in 2001 set, see PS68)* £3

2002
— Proof *FDC* (in 2002 set, see PS72)* £3
— Proof in gold *FDC* (see PGJS1)* £250
2003
— Proof *FDC* (in 2003 set, see PS78) * £3
2004
— Proof *FDC* (in 2004 set, see PS81) * £3

4611

**4611  Fifty pence.** R. Celebratory pattern of twelve stars reflecting the European flag with the dates
1973 and 1998 commemorating the 25th Anniversary of the United Kingdom's membership
of the European Union and Presidency of the Council of Ministers.
1998...................................................................................................................................  £2
— Proof *FDC*\* £5
— Proof in silver *FDC* (Issued: 8,859) £25
— Proof piedfort in silver *FDC* (Issued: 8,440) £45
— Proof in gold *FDC* (Issued: 1,177) £250

            4612                                    4613

**4612  Fifty pence.** R. A pair of hands set against a pattern of radiating lines with the words Fiftieth
Anniversary and the value 50 pence with the initials NHS.
1998...................................................................................................................................  £2
— Specimen in presentation folder  £3
— Proof *FDC*\* £5
— Proof in silver *FDC* (Issued: 9,032)  £25
— Proof piedfort in silver *FDC* (Issued: 5,117)  £45
— Proof in gold *FDC* (Issued: 651)  £300

**4613  Fifty pence.** Library commemorative. R. The turning pages of a book above the pediment of
a classical library building which contains the inscription 'Public Libraries' and the
denomination'50 pence' and the dates 1850 and 2000
2000...................................................................................................................................  £2
— Specimen in presentation folder £5
— Proof *FDC*\* £5
— Proof in silver *FDC* (Issued: 7,634) £20
— Proof piedfort in silver *FDC* (Issued: 5,721) £30
— Proof in gold *FDC* (Issued: 710) £300

*\* Coins marked thus were originally issued in Royal Mint sets.*

4614

**4614** **Fifty pence.** Anniversary of the Suffragette Movement commemorative. ℞. A standing figure of a woman holding a banner bearing the initials WSPU with railings in the background and a poster with the words "GIVE WOMEN THE VOTE" the denomination "50 pence" and the dates 1903 and 2003

2003 .....................................................................................................................................

— Specimen in presentation folder £5

— Proof *FDC* (in 2003 set, see PS78)* £5

— Proof in silver *FDC* (Issued: 6,503) £25

— Proof piedfort in silver *FDC* (Issued 5,372) £47

— Proof in gold *FDC* (Issued: 939) £250

4615

**4615** **Fifty pence.** 50th anniversary of the first sub four-minute mile. ℞. The lower half of a running athlete with a stop clock showing the time and the denomination "50 pence"

2004 ..................................................................................................................................

— Specimen in presentation folder £5

— Proof *FDC* (in 2004 set, see PS81)* £5

— Proof in silver *FDC* (Edition: 15,000) £26

— Proof piedfort in silver *FDC* (Edition: 7,500) £47

— Proof in gold *FDC* (Edition: 1,250) £265

**4630** **Twenty pence.** ℞. Crowned double rose. (Illus. as 4230)

| 1998 | 1999 | 2000 |
|---|---|---|
| — Proof *FDC*\* £3 | — Proof *FDC*\* £3 | — Proof *FDC*\* £3 |
| | | — Proof in silver *FDC*\* |

| 2001 | 2002 | |
|---|---|---|
| — Proof *FDC*\* £3 | — Proof *FDC*\* £3 | |
| | — Proof in gold *FDC* (in 2002 set, see PGJS1)\* £200 | |

| 2003 | 2004 | |
|---|---|---|
| — Proof *FDC*\* £3 | — Proof *FDC*\* £3 | |

**4650 Ten pence.** ℞. Lion passant guardant. (Illus. as 4232)

| 1998* | 1999* | 2000 |
|---|---|---|
| — Proof *FDC** £3 | — Proof *FDC** £3 | — Proof *FDC** £3 |
| | | — Proof in silver *FDC** |
| 2001 | 2002 | |
| — Proof *FDC** £3 | — Proof *FDC** £3 | |
| | — Proof in gold *FDC* (in 2002 set, see PGJS1)* £150 | |
| 2003 | 2004 | |
| — Proof *FDC** £3 | — Proof *FDC** £3 | |

**4670 Five pence.** ℞. Crowned thistle. (Illus. as 4234)

| 1998 | 1999 | 2000 |
|---|---|---|
| — Proof *FDC** £3 | — Proof *FDC** £3 | — Proof *FDC** £3 |
| | | — - Proof in silver *FDC** |
| 2001 | 2002 | |
| — Proof *FDC** £3 | — Proof *FDC**£3 | |
| | — Proof in gold *FDC* (in 2002 set, see PGJS1)* £100 | |
| 2003 | 2004 | |
| — Proof *FDC** £3 | — Proof *FDC** £3 | |

## COPPER PLATED STEEL

**4690 Two pence.** ℞. Plumes. (Illus. as 4376)

| 1998 | 1999 | 2000 |
|---|---|---|
| — Proof *FDC** £3 | — Proof *FDC** £3 | — Proof *FDC** £3 |
| | | — Proof in silver *FDC** |
| 2001 | 2002 | |
| — Proof *FDC** £3 | — Proof *FDC** £3 | |
| | — Proof in gold *FDC* (in 2002 set, see PGJS1)* £150 | |
| 2003 | 2004 | |
| — Proof *FDC** £3 | — Proof *FDC** £3 | |

## BRONZE

**4700 Two pence.** ℞. Plumes. (Illus. as 4376)

1998

## COPPER PLATED STEEL

**4710 One pence.** ℞. Portcullis with chains. (Illus. as 4381)

| 1998 | 1999 | 2000 |
|---|---|---|
| — Proof *FDC** £3 | — Proof *FDC** £3 | — Proof *FDC** £3 |
| | | — Proof in silver *FDC** |
| 2001 | 2002 | |
| — Proof *FDC** £3 | — Proof *FDC** £3 | |
| | — Proof in gold *FDC* (in 2002 set, see PGJS1)* £100 | |
| 2003 | 2004 | |
| — Proof *FDC** £3 | — Proof *FDC** £3 | |

*\* Coins marked thus were originally issued in Royal Mint sets*

The practice of issuing annual sets of coins was started by the Royal Mint in 1970 when a set of the £SD coins was issued as a souvenir prior to Decimalisation. There are now regular issues of brilliant uncirculated coin sets as well as proofs in base metal, and issues in gold and silver. In order to simplify the numbering system, and to allow for the continuation of the various issues in the future, the Prefix letters have been changed. The base metal proof sets will continue the series of numbers from the 1970 set, PS20. For ease of reference, where collectors have the 2001 Edition of the Catalogue, the previous numbers are shown in brackets.

In addition to the annual sets of uncirculated and proofs coins sold by the Royal Mint to collectors and dealers, the Mint has produced specially packaged sets and single coins for companies. No details are made available of these issues and therefore no attempt has been made to include them in the listings below. The Mint also sells "Christening" and "Wedding" sets in distinctive packaging but the numbers circulating in the market are relatively modest and of limited appeal after the year of issue.

## Uncirculated Sets

| | | | |
|---|---|---|---|
| US01–**1982** (PS21) | Uncirculated (specimen) set in Royal Mint folder, 50p to ¹/2p, new reverse type, including 20 pence (Issued: 205,000) ........ (7) | | 9 |
| US02–**1983** (PS22) | 'U.K.' £1 (4221) to ¹/2p (Issued: 637,100)...................... (8) | | 15 |
| US03–**1984** (PS23) | 'Scottish' £1 (4222) to ¹/2p (Issued: 158,820) ............ (8) | | 13 |
| US04–**1985** (PS24) | 'Welsh' £1 (4331) to 1p, new portrait of The Queen (Issued: 102,015). (7) | | 13 |
| US05–**1986** (PS25) | Commonwealth Games £2 (4311) plus 'Northern Irish' £1 (4332) to 1p, ((Issued: 167,224) ....................... (8) | | 14 |
| US06–**1987** (PS26) | 'English' £1 (4333) to 1p, (Issued: 172,425)................ (7) | | 12 |
| US07–**1988** (PS27) | 'Arms' £1 (4334) to 1p, (Issued: 134,067)................... (7) | | 15 |
| US08–**1989** (PS28) | 'Scottish' £1 (4335) to 1p, (Issued: 77,569)................ (7) | | 22 |
| US09–**1989** (PS29) | Bill of Rights and Claim of Right £2s (4312 and 4313) in Royal Mint folder (Issued: not known) .................... (2) | | 15 |
| US10–**1990** (PS30) | 'Welsh' £1 (4331) to 1p plus new 5p, (Issued: 102,606) .......... (8) | | 20 |
| US11–**1991** (PS31) | 'Northern Irish' £1 (4332) to 1p, (Issued: 74,975)............... (7) | | 20 |
| US12–**1992** (PS32) | 'English' £1 (4333), 'European Community' 50p (4352) and Britannia 50p, 20p to 1p plus new 10p (Issued: 78,421)............. (9) | | 20 |
| US13–**1993** (PS33) | 'UK' £1 (4336), 'European Community' 50p to 1p ((Issued: 56,945)... (8) | | 25 |
| US14–**1994** (PS34) | 'Bank' £2 (4314), 'Scottish' £1 (4337) and 'D-Day' 50p (4353) to 1p, (Issued: 177,971) .................... (8) | | 15 |
| US15–**1995** (PS35) | 'Peace' £2 (4315) and 'Welsh' £1 (4338) to 1p (Issued: 105, 647)........ (8) | | 15 |
| US16–**1996** (PS36) | 'Football' £2 (4317) and 'Northern Irish' £1 (4339) to 1p (Issued: 86,501) .................... (8) | | 15 |
| US17–**1997** (PS37) | 'Bimetallic' £2 (4318), 'English' £1 (4340) to 1p plus new 50p (Issued: 109,557) .................... (9) | | 15 |
| US18–**1998** (PS38) | 'Bimetallic' £2 (4570), 'UK' £1 (4590) and 'EU' 50 pence (4611) to 1 pence (Issued: 96,192)................. (9) | | 15 |
| US19–**1998** (PS39) | 'EU' and Britannia 50 pence (4611 and 4610) in Royal Mint folder. (2) | | 6 |
| US20–**1999** (PS40) | 'Bimetallic' £2 (4571), 'Scottish' £1 (4591) to 1p (Issued: 136,696) . (8) | | 15 |
| US21–**2000** (PS41) | 'Bimetallic' £2 (4570), 'Welsh' £1 (4592) to 1p plus 'Library' 50 pence (Issued: 117,750)..................... (9) | | 15 |
| US22–**2001** | 'Bimetallic' £2 (4570), 'Bimetallic' £2 (4572), 'Irish' £1 (4594) to 1p (Issued: 57,741) .................... (9) | | 14 |
| US23–**2002** | 'Bimetallic' £2 (4570), 'English' £1 (4594) to 1p......................... (8) | | 14 |
| US24–**2002** | 'Bimetallic' £2 (4573, 4574, 4575 and 4576) Commonwealth Games................... (4) | | 15 |
| US25–**2003** | "Bimetallic" "DNA" £2 (4577), "Bimetallic" £2 (4570), "UK" £1 (4590), "Suffragette" 50 pence (4614) and "Britannia" 50 pence (4610) to 1p. ...................(10) | | 14 |
| US26 – **2004** | "Bimetallic" "Penydarren engine" £2 (4578), "Bimetallic" £2 (4570), "Forth Rail Bridge" £1 (4595),"Sub four-minute mile" 50 pence (4615) and "Britannia"50pence(4610) to1p ...................(10) | | 14 |

| | | | |
|---|---|---|---|
| US27– **2004** | "Bimetallic" "Penydarren engine" £2 (4578), "Forth Rail Bridge" £1 (4595),"Sub four-minute mile" 50 pence (4615)...............................(3) | | 9 |

**Proof Sets**

| | | | |
|---|---|---|---|
| PS21–**1971** (PS47) | Decimal coinage set, 50 new pence ('Britannia' to $1/2$ new pence, plus medallion in sealed plastic case with card wrapper (Issued: 350,000)..................... | (6) | 15 |
| PS22–**1972** (PS48) | Proof 'Silver Wedding' Crown struck in c/n (4226) plus 50p to $1/2$p (Issued: 150,000)..................... | (7) | 20 |
| PS23–**1973** (PS49) | 'EEC' 50p (4224) plus 10p to $1/2$p, (Issued: 100,000)..................... | (6) | 15 |
| PS24–**1974** (PS50) | Britannia 50p to $1/2$p, as 1971 (Issued: 100,000)..................... | (6) | 12 |
| PS25–**1975** (PS51) | 50p to $1/2$p (as 1974), (Issued: 100,000)..................... | (6) | 12 |
| PS26–**1976** (PS52) | 50p to $1/2$p, as 1975, (Issued: 100,000)..................... | (6) | 12 |
| PS27–**1977** (PS53) | Proof 'Silver Jubilee' Crown struck in c/n (4227) plus 50p to $1/2$p, (Issued: 193,000)..................... | (7) | 12 |
| PS28–**1978** (PS54) | 50p to $1/2$p, as 1976, (Issued: 86,100)..................... | (6) | 12 |
| PS29–**1979** (PS55) | 50p to $1/2$p, as 1978, (Issued: 81,000)..................... | (6) | 12 |
| PS30–**1980** (PS56) | 50p to $1/2$p, as 1979, (Issued: 143,000)..................... | (6) | 10 |
| PS31–**1981** (PS57) | 50p to $1/2$p, as 1980, (Issued: 100,300)..................... | (6) | 10 |
| PS32–**1982** (PS58) | 50p to $1/2$p including 20 pence (Issued: 106,800)..................... | (7) | 12 |
| PS33–**1983** (PS59) | 'U.K.' £1 (4221) to $1/2$p in new packaging (Issued: 107,800)......... | (8) | 17 |
| PS34–**1984** (PS60) | 'Scottish' £1 (4222) to $1/2$p, (Issued: 106,520)..................... | (8) | 16 |
| PS35–**1985** (PS61) | 'Welsh' £1 (4331) to 1p, (Issued: 102,015)..................... | (7) | 16 |
| PS36–**1985** (PS62) | As last but packed in deluxe red leather case (Included above)....... | (7) | 20 |
| PS37–**1986** (PS63) | Commonwealth games £2 (4311) plus 'Northern Irish' £1 (4332) to 1p, (Issued: 104,597)..................... | (8) | 20 |
| PS38–**1986** (PS64) | As last but packed in deluxe red leather case (Included above)....... | (8) | 23 |
| PS39–**1987** (PS65) | 'English' £1 (4333) to 1p, (Issued: 88,659)..................... | (7) | 20 |
| PS40–**1987** (PS66) | As last but packed in deluxe leather case (Included above)............ | (7) | 24 |
| PS41–**1988** (PS67) | 'Arms' £1 (4334) to 1p, (Issued: 79,314)..................... | (7) | 25 |
| PS42–**1988** (PS68) | As last but packed in deluxe leather case (Included above)............. | (7) | 29 |
| PS43–**1989** (PS69) | Bill of Rights and Claim of Right £2s (4312 and 4313), 'Scottish' £1 (4335) to 1p, (Issued: 85,704)..................... | (9) | 30 |
| PS44–**1989** (PS70) | As last but packed in red leather case, (Included above)................. | (9) | 35 |
| PS45–**1990** (PS71) | 'Welsh' £1 (4331) to 1p plus new 5p, (Issued: 79,052)................. | (8) | 27 |
| PS46–**1990** (PS72) | As last but packed in red leather case (Included above)................. | (8) | 32 |
| PS47–**1991** (PS73) | 'Northern Irish' £1 (4332) to 1p, (Issued: 55,144)......................... | (7) | 27 |
| PS48–**1991** (PS74) | As last but packed in red leather case (Included above)................. | (7) | 33 |
| PS49–**1992** (PS75) | 'English' £1 (4333), 'European community' 50p (4352) and Britannia 50p, 20p to 1p plus new 10p, (Issued: 44,337)................. | (9) | 28 |
| PS50–**1992** (PS76) | As last but packed in red leather case (Issued: 17,989)................. | (9) | 33 |
| PS51–**1993** (PS77) | 'Coronation Anniversary' £5 struck in c/n (4302), 'U.K.' £1 (4336), 50p to 1p, (Issued: 43,509)..................... | (8) | 30 |
| PS52–**1993** (PS78) | As last but packed in red leather case (Issued: 22,571)................. | (8) | 35 |
| PS53–**1994** (PS79) | 'Bank' £2 (4314), 'Scottish' £1 (4337), 'D-Day' 50p (4353) to 1p, (Issued: 44,643)..................... | (8) | 30 |
| PS54–**1994** (PS80) | As last but packed in red leather case (Issued: 22,078)................. | (8) | 35 |
| PS55–**1995** (PS81) | 'Peace' £2 (4315), 'Welsh' £1 (4338) to 1p, (Issued: 42,842)......... | (8) | 32 |
| PS56–**1995** (PS82) | As last but packed in red leather case (Issued: 17,797)................. | (8) | 35 |
| PS57–**1996** (PS83) | Proof '70th Birthday' £5 struck in c/n (4303), 'Football' £2 (4317), 'Northern Irish' £1 (4339) to 1p, (Issued: 46,295)............. | (9) | 32 |
| PS58–**1996** (PS84) | As last but packed in red leather case (Issued: 21,286)................. | (9) | 37 |
| PS59–**1997** (PS85) | Proof 'Golden Wedding' £5 struck in c/n (4304), 'Bimetallic' £2 (4318), 'English' £1 (4340) to 1p plus new 50p (Issued: 48,761)..................... | (10) | 33 |
| PS60–**1997** (PS86) | As last but packed in red leather case (Issued: 31,987)................. | (10) | 40 |

| | | | |
|---|---|---|---|
| PS61–**1998** (PS87) | Proof £5 'Prince of Wales 50th Birthday', struck in c/n (4550), 'Bimetallic' £2 (4570), 'UK'. £1 (4590), 'EU' 50 pence (4611) to 1 pence. (Issued: 36,907)............... | (10) | 33 |
| PS62–**1998** (PS88) | As last, but packed in red leather case. (Issued: 26,763)................. | (10) | 40 |
| PS63–**1999** (PS89) | Proof £5 'Diana, Princess of Wales', struck in c/n (4551), 'Bimetallic' 'Rugby' £2 (4571), 'Scottish' £1 (4591) to 1p. (Issued: 40,317)............... | (9) | 34 |
| PS64–**1999** (PS90) | As last, but packed in red leather case. (Issued: 39,827)................. | (9) | 40 |
| PS65–**2000** (PS91) | Proof £5 'Millennium', struck in c/n (4552), 'Bimetallic' £2 (4570), 'Welsh' £1 (4592), 'Library' 50 pence (4613) and 'Britannia' 50 pence (4610) to 1p Standard Set, (Issued: 41,379)............... | (10) | £30 |
| PS66–**2000** (PS92) | As last, but Deluxe set (Issued: 21,573 above)............... | (10) | £40 |
| PS67–**2000** (PS93) | As last, but Executive set (Issued: 9,517)............... | (10) | £70 |
| PS68–**2001** | Proof £5 'Victoria', struck in c/n (4554), 'Bimetallic' £2 (4570), 'Bimetallic' £2 (4572), 'Irish' £1 (4594) to 1p. Standard Set. (Issued: 28,244)............... | (10) | 34 |
| PS69–**2001** | As last, but Gift Set (Issued: 1,351)............... | (10) | 43 |
| PS70–**2001** | As last, but packed in red leather case (Isssued: 16,022) ............... | (10) | 48 |
| PS71–**2001** | As last, but Executive Set (Issued: 3,755)............... | (10) | 60 |
| PS72–**2002** | Proof £5 'Golden Jubilee', struck in c/n (4555), 'Bimetallic' £2 (4570), 'English' £1 (4594) to 1p. Standard set. (Issued: 30,997)............... | (9) | 32 |
| PS73–**2002** | As last, but Gift Set ( Issued:1,557)............... | (9) | 40 |
| PS74–**2002** | As last, but packed in red leather case (Issued: 23,160)............... | (9) | 46 |
| PS75–**2002** | As last, but Executive Set (Issued: 5,000)............... | (9) | 70 |
| PS76–**2002** | 'Bimetallic' £2 (4573, 4574, 4575 and 4576) Commonwealth Games.. (Issued: 3,358)............... | (4) | 25 |
| PS77–**2002** | As last, but Display Set (Issued: 673)............... | (4) | 33 |
| PS78–**2003** | Proof £5 "Coronation", struck in c/n (4557), "Bimetallic" "DNA" £2 (4577), "Bimetallic" £2 (4570), "UK" £1 (4590), "Suffragette" 50 pence (4614)and "Britannia" 50 pence (4610) to 1p. Standard set. ( Issued: 23,305) ............... | (11) | 34 |
| PS79–**2003** | As last, but packed in red leather case ( Issued: 14,947)............... | (11) | 47 |
| PS80–**2003** | As last, but Executive Set ( Issued: 5,000)............... | (11) | 70 |
| PS81–**2004** | "Bimetallic" "Penydarren engine" £2 (4578), "Bimetallic" £2 (4570), "Forth Rail Bridge" £1 (4595), "Sub four-minute mile" 50 pence (4615) and "Britannia" 50 pence (4610) to 1p. Standard set. (Edition: 75,000)............... | (10) | 30 |
| PS82–**2004** | As last, but packed in red leather case (Edition: 15,000) ............... | (10) | 40 |
| PS83– **2004** | As last, but Executive Set (Edition: 10,000) ............... | (10) | 65 |

**Silver Sets**

| | | | |
|---|---|---|---|
| PSS01–**1989** (PS96) | Bill of Rights and Claim of Right £2s (4312 and 4313), Silver piedfort proofs (Issued: 10,000) ............... | (2) | 85 |
| PSS02–**1989** (PS97) | As last but Silver proofs (Issue figure not known)............... | (2) | 60 |
| PSS03–**1990** (PS98) | 2 x 5p Silver proofs (4371 and 4372), (Issued: 35,000)............... | (2) | 30 |
| PSS04–**1992** (PS99) | 2 x 10p Silver proofs (4366 and 4367), (Not known) ............... | (2) | 34 |
| PSS05–**1996** (PS100) | 25th Anniversary of Decimal Currency (4339, 4351, 4361, 4367, 4372, 4386, 4391) in Silver proof (Edition: 15,000)............... | (7) | 100 |
| PSS06–**1997** (PS101) | 2 x 50p silver proofs (4351 and 4354) (Issued: 10,304)............... | (2) | 65 |
| PSS07–**1997** (PS102) | Britannia proofs, £2 – 20 pence (4300, 4300A, 4300B, 4300C) (Issued: 11,832) ............... | (4) | 95 |
| PSS08–**1998** (PS103) | Britannia proofs, £2 – 20 pence (4500, 4510, 4520, 4530) (Issued: 3,044) ............... | (4) | 110 |
| PSS09–**1998** (PS104) | 'EU' and 'NHS' Silver proofs (4611 and 4612)............... | (2) | 50 |
| PSS10–**2000** (PS105) | 'Millennium' £5, 'Bimetallic' £2, 'Welsh' £1, 50p to 1p, and Maundy coins, 4p-1p in silver proof (4552, 4570, 4592, 4610, 4630, 4650, 4670, 4212-4215) (Issued: 13,180)............... | (13) | 245 |

| PSS11–**2001** | Britannia proofs, £2–20 pence (4502, 4511, 4521, 4531) (Issued: 4,596) ............................................................................... (4) | 90 |
|---|---|---|
| PSS12–**2002** | Commonwealth Games 'Bimetallic' £2 (4573, 4574, 4575 and 4576) in silver ( Issued: 3,082) ............................................................... (4) | 98 |
| PSS13–**2002** | As above with the addition of colour and piedfort in silver. (4573A, 4574A, 4575A and 4576A) ( Issued: 2,503) ..................... (4) | 195 |
| PSS14–**2003** | Britannia proofs, £2 – 20 pence (4503, 4512, 4522, 4532) (Issued: 3,623) ................................................................................ (4) | 90 |
| PSS15–**MD** | Britannia £2 set of four different designs, 1999 - 2003 (4500, 4501, 4502, 4503)(Edition: 5,000) ...................................................................... (4) | 70 |
| PSS16–**MD** | £5"Golden Jubilee"(4555) and £5 "Coronation" (4557) silver proofs(2) | 69 |
| PSS17–**2003** | £5 "Coronation"(4557), £2 "Britannia"(4503), £2 "DNA"(4577), £1 "UK"(4590) and 50 pence "Suffragette(4614)silver proofs (Edition:    ).................................................................................. (5) | 140 |
| PSS18–**2004** | £5 "Entende Cordial" (4558), £2 "Britannia" (4500), £2 "Penydarren" (4578) £1 "Forth Rail Bridge" (4595) and 50 pence "Sub four-minute mile" (4615) silver proofs (Edition:    )...................................... (5) | 145 |
| PSS19–**2004** | "Bimetallic" "Penydarren engine" £2 (4578), "Forth Rail Bridge" £1 (4595),"Sub four-minute mile" 50 pence (4615) Silver piedfort proofs (3) | 145 |

## Gold Sovereign Proof Sets

| | | | |
|---|---|---|---|
| PGS01–**1980** (PS111) Gold £5 to half-sovereign (4201, 4203-4205) (Issued: 10,000) ....... | (4) | 850 |
| PGS02–**1981** (PS112)U.K. Proof coin Commemorative collection. (Consists of £5, sovereign, 'Royal Wedding' Crown (4229) in silver, plus base metal proofs 50p to 1/2p), (Not known)..................................... | (9) | 650 |
| PGS03–**1982** (PS113) Gold £5 to half-sovereign (Issued: 2,500)...................................... | (4) | 900 |
| PGS04–**1983** (PS114) Gold £2, sovereign and half-sovereign, (Not known) ..................... | (3) | 375 |
| PGS05–**1984** (PS115) Gold £5, sovereign and half-sovereign, (Issued: 7,095)................. | (3) | 675 |
| PGS06–**1985** (PS116) Gold £5 to half-sovereign (4251, 4261, 4271, 4276) (Issued: 5,849) .. | (4) | 900 |
| PGS07–**1986** (PS117) Gold Commonwealth games £2, (4311) sovereign and half-sovereign (Issued: 12,500)............................................................................ | (3) | 425 |
| PGS08–**1987** (PS118) Gold £2 (4261), sovereign and half-sovereign (Issued: 12,500) ...... | (3) | 425 |
| PGS09–**1988** (PS119) Gold £2 to half-sovereign (Issued: 11,192)...................................... | (3) | 425 |
| PGS10–**1989** (PS120) Sovereign Anniversary Gold £5 to half-sovereign (4254, 4263, 4272, 4277), (Issued: 5,000)................................................................. | (4) | 1400 |
| PGS11–**1989** (PS121) Gold £2 to half-sovereign (Issued: 7,936)........................................ | (3) | 750 |
| PGS12–**1990** (PS122) Gold £5 to half-sovereign (as 1985 issue), (Issued: 1,721) ............. | (4) | 900 |
| PGS13–**1990** (PS123) Gold £2 to half-sovereign (as 1988 issue), (Issued: 1,937) ............. | (3) | 500 |
| PGS14–**1991** (PS124) Gold £5 to half-sovereign (Issued: 1,336) ...................................... | (4) | 900 |
| PGS15–**1991** (PS125) Gold £2 to half-sovereign (Issued: 1,152) ...................................... | (3) | 500 |
| PGS16–**1992** (PS126) Gold £5 to half-sovereign (Issued: 1,165) ...................................... | (4) | 900 |
| PGS17–**1992** (PS127) Gold £2 to half-sovereign (Issued: 967) ......................................... | (3) | 500 |
| PGS18–**1993** (PS128) Gold £5 to half-sovereign with silver Pistrucci medal in case (Issued: 1,078) .................................................................................. | (5) | 1000 |
| PGS19–**1993** (PS129) Gold £2 to half-sovereign (Issued: 663) ......................................... | (3) | 500 |
| PGS20–**1994** (PS130) Gold £5, £2 (as 4314), sovereign and half-sovereign (Issued: 918)..... | (4) | 950 |
| PGS21–**1994** (PS131) Gold £2, (as 4314), sovereign and half-sovereign (Issued: 1,249)... | (3) | 550 |
| PGS22–**1995** (PS132) Gold £5, £2 (as 4315), sovereign and half-sovereign (Issued: 718). | (4) | 900 |
| PGS23–**1995** (PS133) Gold £2 (as 4315), sovereign and half-sovereign (Issued: 1,112).... | (3) | 550 |
| PGS24–**1996** (PS134) Gold £5 to half-sovereign (as 1992 issue) (Issued: 742) ................. | (4) | 900 |
| PGS25–**1996** (PS135) Gold £2 to half-sovereign (as 1992 issue) (Issued: 868) ................. | (3) | 500 |
| PGS26–**1997** (PS136) Gold £5, £2 (as 4318), sovereign and half-sovereign (Issued: 860) ................................................................................... | (4) | 900 |
| PGS27–**1997** (PS137) Gold £2 (as 4318) to half-sovereign (Issued: 817) .......................... | (3) | 550 |
| PGS28–**1998** (PS138) Gold £5 to half sovereign (4400, 4420, 4430, 4440) (Issued: 789) ........ | (4) | 1000 |
| PGS29–**1998** (PS139) Gold £2 to half sovereign (4420, 4430, 4440) (Issued: 560)........... | (3) | 550 |
| PGS30–**1999** (PS140) Gold £5, £2 (as 4571), sovereign and half sovereign (Issued: 991) ...... | (4) | 1000 |

PGS31–**1999** (PS141) Gold £2 (as 4571), sovereign and half sovereign (Issued: 912)........ (3)   550
PGS32–**2000** (PS142) Gold £5 to half-sovereign (as 1998 issue) (Issued: 1,000)................ (4) 1000
PGS33–**2000** (PS143) Gold £2 to half-sovereign (as 1998 issue) (Issued: 1,250)................ (3)   550
PGS34–**2001**        Gold £5, £2 (as 4572), sovereign and half sovereign (Issued: 1,000)... (4)   900
PGS35–**2001**        Gold £2 (as 4572), sovereign and half sovereign (Issued: 891)........ (3)   450
PGS36–**2002**        Gold £5 to half sovereign (4401, 4421, 4431, 4441) (Issued: 3,000) . (4) 1100
PGS37–**2002**        Gold £2 to half sovereign (4421, 4431, 4441) (Issued: 3,940)......... (3)   450
PGS38–**2003**        Gold £5 to half sovereign (as 1998 issue) (Issued: 2,250) .............. (4) 1050
PGS39–**2003**        Gold £2 (as 4577) sovereign and half sovereign (Issued: 1,717)..... (3)   425
PGS40–**2004**        Gold £5 to half sovereign (as 1998 issue) (Edition: 2,250).............. (4) 1050
PGS41–**2004**        Gold £2 (as 4578) sovereign and half sovereign (Edition: 2,500).... (3)   425

**Britannia Series**
PBS01–**1987** (PS147) Britannia Gold Proofs £100, £50, £25, £10 (4281, 4286, 4291,
                       4296), (Issued: 10,000) ..................... (4)   650
PBS02–**1987** (PS148) Britannia Gold Proofs £25, £10 (4291 and 4296) (Issued: 11,100) . (2)   125
PBS03–**1988** (PS149) Britannia Proofs £100–£10 (as 1987 issue) (Issued: 3,505)............ (4)   650
PBS04–**1988** (PS150) Britannia Proofs £25, £10 (as 1987 issue) (Issued: 894)................ (2)   125
PBS05–**1989** (PS151) Britannia Proofs £100 – £10 (as 1987) (Issued: 2,268).................... (4)   675
PBS06–**1989** (PS152) Britannia Proofs £25, £10 (as 1987 issue) (Issued: 451)................ (2)   150
PBS07–**1990** (PS153) Britannia Proofs, £100-£10, gold with the addition of silver alloy
                       (4282, 4287, 4292, 4297) (Issued: 527)..................... (4)   775
PBS08–**1991** (PS154) Britannia Proofs, as PS153 (Issued: 509) ............. (4)   775
PBS09–**1992** (PS155) Britannia Proofs, as PS153 (Issued: 500) ............. (4)   900
PBS10–**1993** (PS156) Britannia Proofs, as PS153 (Issued: 462)............. (4)   900
PBS11–**1994** (PS157) Britannia Proofs, as PS153 ((Issued: 435)............. (4)   900
PBS12–**1995** (PS158) Britannia Proofs, as PS153 (Issued: 500) ............. (4)   900
PBS13–**1996** (PS159) Britannia Proofs, as PS153 (Issued: 483) ............. (4)   900
PBS14–**1997** (PS160) Britannia proofs £100, £50, £25, £10 (4283, 4288, 4293, 4298)
                       (Issued: 892) ..................... (4) 1100
PBS15–**1998** (PS161) Britannia proofs £100, £50, £25, £10 (4450, 4460, 4470, 4480)
                       (Issued: 750) ..................... (4)   900
PBS16–**1999** (PS162) Britannia Proofs, as PS161 (Issued: 740) ............. (4)   900
PBS17–**2000** (PS163) Britannia Proofs, as PS161 (Issued: 750) ............. (4)   900
PBS18–**2001**        Britannia Proofs £100, £50, £25, £10 (4451, 4461, 4471, 4481)
                       (Issued: 1,000) ..................... (4)   900
PBS19–**2002**        Britannia Proofs, as PBS17 (Issued: 932) ............. (4)   900
PBS20–**2003**        Britannia Proofs £100, £50, £25, £10 (4452, 4462, 4472, 4482)
                       (Issued: 1,250) ..................... (4)   900
PBS21–**2003**        Britannia Proofs £50, £25, £10 (4462, 4472, 4482) (Issued: 816) ... (3)   400
PBS22–MD              Britannia £100 set of four different designs, 1987, 1997, 2001, 2003
                       (4281,4283,4451,4452) (Edition: 2,500)..................... (4) 1,350
PBS23–**2004**        Britannia Proofs, as PBS15 (Edition: 1,250)................ (4)   900
PBS24–**2004**        Britannia Proofs, £50, £25, £10 (4460,4470, 4480) (Edition: 1,500) (3)   400

**Gold Coin Proof Sets**
PCGS1–**2002**        Commonwealth Games 'Bimetallic' £2 (4573, 4574, 4575 and 4576)
                       in gold (Issued: 312)..................... (4) 1200
PGJS1–**2002**        'Golden Jubilee' £5, 'Bimetallic' £2, 'English' £1, 50p to 1p and Maundy
                       coins, 4p-1p in gold proof (4555, 4570, 4594, 4610, 4630, 4650, 4670,
                       4212-4215) (Issued: 2,002)..................... (13) 3000

**Pattern Proof sets**
PPS1–**2003**         Silver proof set of £1 designs with plain edge and hallmark (4595A,
                       4596A, 4597A, 4598A) (Edition: 7,500)..................... (4)    98
PPS2–**2003**         Gold proof set of £1 designs with plain edge and hallmark (4595A,
                       4596A, 4597A, 4598A) (Edition: 3,000)..................... (4) 1,125

## A SELECT NUMISMATIC BIBLIOGRAPHY

Listed below is a selection of general books on British numismatics and other works that the specialist collector will need to consult.

**General Books:**
BROOKE, G. C. *English Coins.* 3rd ed., 1966.
CHALLIS, C. E. (ed.) *A New History of the Royal Mint.* 1992
GRUEBER, H. A. *Handbook of the Coins of Great Britain and Ireland.* Revised 1970
KENYON, R. Ll. *Gold Coins of England.* 1884
NORTH, J. J. *English Hammered Coinage,* Vol. I, c. 650-1272. 1994; Vol. II, 1272-1662. 1991
SUTHERLAND, C. H. V. *English Coinage, 600-1900.* 1972

**Specialist Works:**
ALLEN, D. *The Origins of Coinage in Britain: A Reappraisal.* Reprint 1978
ALLEN, D. F. *The Coins of the Coritani.* (SCBI no. 3) 1963
ALLEN, D. F. *English Coins in the British Museum: The Cross-and-Crosslets ('Tealby') type of Henry II.* 1951
ARCHIBALD, M. M. and BLUNT, C. E. *British Museum. Anglo-Saxon Coins. Athelstan to the reform of Edgar. 924-c 973.* 1986
ASKEW, G. *The Coinage of Roman Britain.* (1951) Reprinted 1980.
BESLY, E. M. *Coins and Medals of the English Civil War.* 1990
BLACKBURN, M. A. S. *Anglo-Saxon Monetary History.* 1986
BLUNT, C. E. and WHITTON, C. A. *The Coinages of Edward IV and of Henry VI (Restored).*
BLUNT, C. E., STEWART, B.H.I.H. and LYON, C.S.S. *Coinage in Tenth-Century England. From Edward the Elder to Edgar's Reform.* 1989
BRAND, J.D. *The English Coinage 1180-1247: Money, Mints and Exchanges* 1994
BROOKE, G. C. *English Coins in the British Museum: The Norman Kings.* 1916
BROWN, I. D. and DOLLEY, M. *Bibliography of Coin Hoards of Great Britain and Ireland 1500-1967.* 1971
CARSON, R. A. G. *Mints, Dies and Currency. Essays in Memory of Albert Baldwin.* 1971
DE JERSEY, P. *Coinage in Iron Age Armorica.* 1994
DOLLEY, R. H. M. (ed.). *Anglo-Saxon Coins; studies presented to Sir Frank Stenton.* 1964
GRIERSON, P. and BLACKBURN, M. A. S. *Medieval European Coinage, vol. 1, The Early Middle Ages.* 1986
HOBBS, R. *British Iron Age Coins in the British Museum.* 1996
KEARY, C. and GREUBER, H. *English Coins in the British Museum: Anglo-Saxon Series.* 1887, reprinted, 1970, 2 volumes.
LAKER, A. J. *The portrait Groats of Henry VIII.* 1978
LAWRENCE, L. A. *The Coinage of Edward III from 1351.*
LINECAR, H. W. A. *The Crown Pieces of Great Britain and the British Commonwealth.* 1962

— — *English Proof and Pattern Crown-Size Pieces.* 1968

MACK, R. P. *The R. P. Mack Collection, Ancient British, Anglo-Saxon and Norman Coins.* (SCBI no. 20) 1973

MANVILLE, H. E. *Encyclopedia of British Numismatics. Numismatic Guide to British and Irish Periodicals 1731-1991.* 1993

MANVILLE, H. E. and ROBERTSON, T. J. *An Annotated Bibliography of British Numismatic Auction Catalogues from 1710 to the Present.* 1986

MARSH, M. A. *The Gold Half Sovereign.* 2nd Edition, revised 2004

MARSH, M. A. *The Gold Sovereign.* 2nd Edition 1999

MASS, J. P. *The J. P. Mass collection of English Short Cross Coins 1180-1247. (SCBI 56).* 2001

NORTH, J. J. *Edwardian English Silver Coins 1279-1351. (SCBI 39)* 1989

NORTH, J. J. and PRESTON-MORLEY, P. J. *The John G. Brooker Collection: Coins of Charles I. (SCBI 33)* 1984

PECK, C. W. *English Copper, Tin and Bronze Coins in the British Museum, 1558-1958.* 1970

RAYNER, P.A. *The English Silver Coinage from 1649.* 5th ed. 1992

REECE, R. *Coinage in Roman Britain,* 1987.

ROBINSON, Dr. B. *The Royal Maundy.* 1992

RUDING, REV. R. *Annals of the Coinage of Great Britain.* 3rd Edition 1840

SEAR, D. R. *Roman Coins and their Values.* 4th Edition (1999) Reprinted 2000

SEAR, DAVID R. *The History and Coinage of the Roman Imperators 49-27 BC.* 1998

THOMPSON, J. D. A. *Inventory of British Coin Hoards, A.D. 600-1500.* 1956

VAN ARSDELL, R. *Celtic Coinage of Britain.* 1989.

VAN ARSDELL, R. D. *The Coinage of the Dobunni.* 1994

WHITTON, C. A. *The Heavy Coinage of Henry VI.*

WOODHEAD, P. *English Gold Coins 1257-1603. The Herbert Schneider Collection, vol. 1 (SCBI 47)* 1996

— — *English Gold Coins 1603-20th Century. The Herbert Schneider Collection, vol. 2 (SCBI 57)* 2002

WREN, C. R. *The Short-cross coinage 1180-1247. Henry II to Henry III. An illustrated Guide to Identification.* 1992

— — *The Voided Long-Cross Coinage 1247-1279. Henry III and Edward I.* 1993

— — *The English Long-Cross Pennies 1279-1489. Edward I-Henry VII.* 1995

For further references to British hammered coinage see *Sylloge of Coins of the British Isles,* a serial publication now comprising 54 volumes cataloguing collections in private hands and institutions. For full list of the 54 volumes published to date in this series, please contact Spink at the address below.

Other authoritative papers are published in the *Numismatic Chronicle, British Numismatic Journal and Spink's Numismatic Circular.* A complete book list is available from Spink & Son Ltd., 69 Southampton Row, Bloomsbury, London WC1B 4ET. Tel: 020 7563 4046  Fax: 020 7563 4068.

# APPENDIX II

## LATIN OR FOREIGN LEGENDS ON ENGLISH COINS

A DOMINO FACTUM EST ISTUD ET EST MIRABILE IN OCULIS NOSTRIS. (This is the Lord's doing and it is marvellous in our eyes: *Psalm 118.23.*) First used on 'fine' sovereign of Mary.

AMOR POPULI PRAESIDIUM REGIS. (The love of the people is the King's protection.) Reverse legend on angels of Charles I.

ANNO REGNI PRIMO, etc. (In the first year of the reign, etc.) Used around the edge of many of the larger milled denominations.

CHRISTO AUSPICE REGNO. (I reign under the auspice of Christ.) Used extensively in the reign of Charles I.

CIVIUM INDUSTRIA FLORET CIVITAS. (By the industry of its people the State flourishes.) On the 1951 Festival Crown of George VI.

CULTORES SUI DEUS PROTEGIT. (God protects His worshippers.) On gold double crowns and crowns of Charles I.

DECUS ET TUTAMEN. (An ornament and a safeguard: Virgil, *Aenid,* v.262.) This inscription on the edge of all early large milled silver was suggested by Evelyn, he having seen it on the vignette in Cardinal Richelieu's Greek Testament, and of course refers to the device as a means to prevent clipping. This legend also appears on the edge of U.K. and Northern Ireland one pound coins.

DIEU ET MON DROIT. (God and my right.) On halfcrowns of George IV and later monarchs

DIRIGE DEUS GRESSUS MEOS. (May the Lord direct my steps.) On the 'Una' Five pounds of Queen Victoria.

DOMINE NE IN FURORE TUO ARGUAS ME. (O Lord, rebuke me not in Thine anger: *Psalm 6, 1.).* First used on the half-florin of Edward III and then on all half-nobles.

D*omiNus Deus Omnipotens* REX. (Lord God, Almighty King.) Viking coins.

DUM SPIRO SPERO. (Whilst I live, I hope.) On the coins struck at Pontefract Castle during the Civil War after Charles I had been imprisoned.

EXALTABITUR IN GLORIA. (He shall be exalted in glory.) On all quarter-nobles.

EXURGAT DEUS ET DISSIPENTUR INIMICI EIUS. (Let God arise and let His enemies be scattered: *Psalm* 68, 1.) On the Scottish ducat and early English coins of James I (VI) and was chosen by the King himself. Also on Charles I, civil war, and Declaration coins,

FACIAM EOS IN GENTEM UNAM. (I will make them one nation: *Ezekiel, 37, 22.)* On unites and laurels of James I.

FLORENT CONCORDIA REGNA. (Through concord kingdoms flourish.) On gold unite of Charles I and broad of Charles II.

HANC DEUS DEDIT. (God has given this, i.e. the crown .) On siege-pieces of Pontefract struck in the name of Charles II.

HAS NISI PERITURUS MIHI ADIMAT NEMO. (Let no one remove these [letters] from me under penalty of death.) On the edge of crowns and half-crowns of Cromwell.

HENRICUS ROSAS REGNA JACOBUS. (Henry united the roses, James the kingdoms.) On English and Scottish gold coins of James I (VI).

HONI SOIT QUI MAL Y PENSE. (Evil to him who evil thinks.) The Motto of the Order of the Garter, first used on the Hereford (?) halfcrowns of Charles I. It also occurs on the Garter Star in the centre of the reverse of the silver coins of Charles II, but being so small it is usually illegible; it is more prominent on the coinage of George III.

ICH DIEN. (I serve.) Aberystwyth Furnace 2d, and Decimal 2p. The motto of The Prince of Wales.

INIMICOS EJUS INDUAM CONFUSIONE. (As for his enemies I shall clothe them with shame: *Psalm* 132, 18.) On shillings of Edward VI struck at Durham House, Strand.

JESUS AUTEM TRANSIENS PER MEDIUM ILLORUM IBAT. (But Jesus, passing through the midst of them, went His way: *Luke iv. 30.*) The usual reverse legend on English nobles, ryals and hammered sovereigns before James I; also on the very rare Scottish noble of David II of Scotland and the unique Anglo-Gallic noble of Edward the Black Prince.

JUSTITIA THRONUM FIRMAT. (Justice strengthens the throne.) On Charles I half-groats and pennies and Scottish twenty-penny pieces.

LUCERNA PEDIBUS MEIS VERBUM EST. (Thy word is a lamp unto my feet: *Psalm 119, 105.*) Obverse legend on a rare half-sovereign of Edward VI struck at Durham House, Strand.

MIRABILIA FECIT. (He made marvellously.) On the Viking coins of (?) York.

NEMO ME IMPUNE LACESSIT. (No-one provokes me with impunity.) On the 1984 Scottish one pound. Motto of The Order of the Thistle.

NUMMORUM FAMULUS. (The servant of the coinage.) The legend on the edge of the English tin coinage at the end of the seventeenth century.

O CRUX AVE SPES UNICA. (Hail! O Cross, our only hope.) On the reverse of all half-angels.

PAX MISSA PER ORBEM. (Peace sent throughout the world.) The reverse legend of a pattern farthing of Anne.

PAX QUÆRITUR BELLO. (Peace is sought by war.) The reverse legend of the Cromwell broad.

PER CRUCEM TUAM SALVA NOS CHRISTE REDEMPTOR. (By Thy cross, save us, O Christ, our Redeemer.) The normal reverse of English angels.

PLEIDIOL WYF I'M GWLAD. (True am I to my country.) Used on the 1985 Welsh one pound. Taken from the Welsh National Anthem.

POST MORTEM PATRIS PRO FILIO. (After the death of the father for the son.) On siege-pieces struck at Pontefract in 1648 (old style) after the execution of Charles I.

POSUI DEUM ADJUTOREM MEUM. (I have made God my Helper: *comp. Psalm* 54, 4.) Used on many English and Irish silver coins from Edward III until 1603. Altered to POSUIMUS and NOSTRUM on the coins of Philip and Mary.

PROTECTOR LITERIS LITERÆ NUMMIS CORONA ET SALUS. (A protection to the letters [on the face of the coin], the letters [on the edge] are a garland and a safeguard to the coinage.) On the edge of the rare fifty-shilling piece of Cromwell.

QUÆ DEUS CONJUNXIT NEMO SEPARET. (What God hath joined together let no man put asunder: *Matthew 19, 6.*) On the larger silver English and Scottish coins of James I after he succeeded to the English throne.

REDDE CUIQUE QUOD SUUM EST. (Render to each that which is his own.) On a Henry VIII type groat of Edward VI struck by Sir Martin Bowes at Durham House, Strand.

RELIGIO PROTESTANTIVM LEGES ANGLIÆ LIBERTAS PARLIAMENTI. (The religion of the Protestants, the laws of England, the liberty of the Parliament.) This is known as the 'Declaration' and refers to Charles I's declaration to the Privy Council at Wellington, 19 September, 1642; it is found on many of his coins struck at the provincial mints during the Civil War. Usually abbreviated to REL:PROT:LEG: ANG:LIB:PAR: ROSA SINE SPINA. (A rose without a thorn.) Found on some gold and small coins of Henry VIII and later reigns.

RUTILANS ROSA SINE SPINA. (A dazzling rose without a thorn.) As last but on small gold only.

SCUTUM FIDEI PROTEGET EUM or EAM. (The shield of faith shall protect him, or her.) On much of the gold of Edward VI and Elizabeth.

SIC VOS NON VOBIS (Thus we labour but not for ourselves). 1994 £2 Bank of England.

TALI DICATA SIGNO MENS FLUCTUARI NEQUIT. (Consecrated by such a sign the mind cannot waver: from a hymn by Prudentius written in the fourth century, entitled 'Hymnus ante Somnum'.) Only on the gold 'George noble' of Henry VIII.

TIMOR DOMINI FONS VITÆ. (The fear of the Lord is a fountain of life: *Proverbs, 14, 27.*) On many shillings of Edward VI.

TVAETVR VNITA DEVS. (May God guard these united, i.e. kingdoms.) On many English Scottish and Irish coins of James I.

VERITAS TEMPORIS FILIA. (Truth, the daughter of Time.) On English and Irish coins of Mary Tudor.

**Some Royal Titles:**

REX ANGL*orum*—King of the English.

REX SAXONIORVM OCCIDENTALIVM —King of the West Saxons.

DEI GRA*tia* REX *ANGLiae ET FRANCiae DomiNus HYBerniae ET AQVITaniae*—By the Grace of God, King of England and France, Lord of Ireland and Aquitaine.

D*ei GRAtia Magnae Britanniae, FRanciae ET Hiberniae REX Fidei Defensor BRunsviciensis ET Luneburgen-sis Dux, Sacri Romani Imperii Archi-THesaurarius ET ELector*=By the Grace of God, King of Great Britain, France and Ireland, Defender of the Faith, Duke of Brunswick and Luneburg, High Treasurer and Elector of the Holy Roman Empire.

BRITANNIARUM REX —King of the Britains (i.e. Britain and British territories overseas).

BRITT:OMN:REX:FID:DEF:IND:IMP: —King of all the Britains, Defender of the Faith, Emperor of India.

VIVAT REGINA ELIZABETHA — Long live Queen Elizabeth. On the 1996 £5 Queen's 70th birthday £5 crown.

# APPENDIX III

# NUMISMATIC CLUBS AND SOCIETIES

*Coin News, The Searcher* and *Treasure Hunting*, are the major monthly magazines covering numismatics. Spink's *Numismatic Circular* is long established, its first issue appeared in December 1892, and is now published 6 times a year. Many local clubs and societies are affiliated to the British Association of Numismatic Societies, (B.A.N.S) which holds an annual Congress. Details of your nearest numismatic club can be obtained from the Hon. Secretary, Philip Mernick, British Association of Numismatic Societies, c/o General Services, 42 Campbell Road, London E3 4DT email: bans@mernicks.com.

The two principal learned societies are the Royal Numismatic Society, c/o Department of Coins and Medals, the British Museum, Great Russell Street, Bloomsbury, London WC1B 3DG, and the British Numismatic Society, c/o The Secretary, C.R.S. Farthing, c/o Warburg Institute, Woburn Square, London WC1H 0AH Tel: 01329 284 661. Both these societies publish an annual journal.

## MINTMARKS AND OTHER SYMBOLS ON ENGLISH COINS

A Mintmark (*mm.*), is a term borrowed from Roman and Greek numismatics where it showed the place of mintage; it was generally used on English coins to show where the legend began (a religious age preferred a cross for the purpose). Later, this mark, since the dating of coins was not usual, had a periodic significance, changing from time to time. Hence it was of a secret or 'privy' nature; other privy marks on a coin might be the code-mark of a particular workshop or workman. Thus a privy mark (including the *mintmark.*) might show when a coin was made, or who made it. In the use of precious metals this knowledge was necessary to guard against fraud and counterfeiting.

Mintmarks are sometimes termed 'initial marks' as they are normally placed at the commencement of the inscription. Some of the symbols chosen were personal badges of the ruling monarch, such as the rose and sun of York, or the boar's head of Richard III, the dragon of Henry Tudor or the thistle of James I; others are heraldic symbols or may allude to the mint master responsible for the coinage, e.g. the *mm.* bow used on the Durham House coins struck under John Bowes and the WS mark of William Sharrington of Bristol.

A table of mintmarks is given on the next page. Where mintmarks appear in the catalogue they are sometimes referred to only by the reference number, in order to save space, i.e. *mm. 28* (=mintmark Sun), *mm.28/74 (=mm.* Sun on obverse, *mm.* Coronet on reverse), *mm. 28/- (=mm.* Sun on obverse only).

# MINTMARKS AND OTHER SYMBOLS

| | | | | | |
|---|---|---|---|---|---|
| 1 | Edward III, Cross 1 (Class B+C). | 45 | Slipped Trefoil, James I (1). | 91A | Crowned Leopard's Head with collar (Edw. VI). |
| 2 | Edward III, broken Cross 1 (Class D). | 46 | Slipped Trefoil, James I (2). | 92 | Lion. |
| | | 47 | Quatrefoil. | 93 | Lion rampant. |
| 3 | Edward III, Cross 2 (Class E) | 48 | Saltire. | 94 | Martlet. |
| 4 | Edward III, Cross 3 (Class G) | 49 | Pinecone. | 95 | Mascle. |
| 5 | Cross Potent (Edw. III Treaty) | 50 | Leaf (-mascle, Hen. VI). | 96 | Negro's Head. |
| 6 | Cross Pattee (Edw. III Post Treaty Rich. III). | 51 | Leaf (-trefoil, Hen. VI). | 97 | Ostrich's Head. |
| | | 52 | Arrow. | 98 | P in brackets. |
| 7 | (a) Plain of Greek Cross. | 53 | Pheon. | 99 | Pall. |
| | (b) Cross Moline. | 54 | A. | 100 | Pear. |
| 8 | Cross Patonce. | 55 | Annulet. | 101 | Plume. |
| 9 | Cross Fleuree. | 56 | Annulet-with-pellet. | 102 | Plume. Aberystwyth and Bristol. |
| 10 | Cross Calvary (Cross on steps). | 57 | Anchor. | 103 | Plume. Oxford. |
| | | 58 | Anchor & B. | 104 | Plume. Shrewsbury. |
| 11 | Long Cross Fitchee. | 59 | Flower & B. | 105 | Lis. |
| 12 | Short Cross Fitchee. | 60 | Bell. | 106 | Lis. |
| 13 | Restoration Cross (Hen. VI). | 61 | Book. | 107 | Portcullis. |
| 14 | Latin Cross. | 62 | Boar's Head (early Richard III). | 108 | Portcullis, Crowned. |
| 15 | Voided Cross (Henry VI). | | | 109 | Sceptre. |
| 16 | Saltire Cross. | 63 | Boar's Head (later Richard III). | 110 | Sunburst. |
| 17 | Cross and 4 pellets. | | | 111 | Swan. |
| 18 | Pierced Cross. | 64 | Boar's Head, Charles I. | 112 | R in brackets. |
| 19 | Pierced Cross & pellet. | 65 | Acorn    (a) Hen. VIII | 113 | Sword. |
| 20 | Pierced Cross & central pellet. | | (b) Elizabeth. | 114 | T (Henry VIII). |
| | | 66 | Bow. | 115 | TC monogram. |
| 21 | Cross Crosslet. | 67 | Br. (Bristol, Chas. I). | 116 | WS monogram. |
| 22 | Curved Star (rayant). | 68 | Cardinal's Hat. | 117 | y or Y. |
| 23 | Star. | 69 | Castle (Henry VIII). | 118 | Dragon (Henry VII). |
| 24 | Spur Rowel. | 70 | Castle with H. | 119 | (a) Triangle |
| 25 | Mullet. | 71 | Castle (Chas. I). | | (b) Triangle in Circle. |
| 26 | Pierced Mullet. | 72 | Crescent    (a) Henry VIII | 120 | Sun (Parliament). |
| 27 | Eglantine. | | (b) Elizabeth. | 121 | Uncertain mark. |
| 28 | Sun (Edw. IV). | 73 | Pomegranate. (Mary; Henry VIII's is broader). | 122 | Grapple. |
| 29 | Mullet (Henry V). | | | 123 | Tun. |
| 30 | Pansy. | 74 | Coronet. | 124 | Woolpack. |
| 31 | Heraldic Cinquefoil (Edw. IV). | 75 | Crown. | 125 | Thistle. |
| | | 76 | Crozier    (a) Edw. III | 126 | Figure 6 (Edw. VI). |
| 32 | Heraldic Cinquefoil (James I). | | (b) Hen. VIII. | 127 | Floriated cross. |
| | | 77 | Ermine. | 128 | Lozenge. |
| 33 | Rose (Edw. IV). | 78 | Escallop (Hen. VII). | 129 | Billet. |
| 34 | Rosette (Edw. IV). | 79 | Escallop (James I). | 130 | Plume. Bridgnorth or late declaration |
| 35 | Rose (Chas. I). | 80 | Eye (in legend Edw. IV). | | |
| 36 | Catherine Wheel. | 81 | Eye (Parliament). | 131 | Two lions. |
| 37 | Cross in circle. | 82 | Radiate Eye (Hen. VII). | 132 | Clasped book. |
| 38 | Halved Sun (6 rays) & Rose. | 83 | Gerb. | 133 | Cross pomee. |
| 39 | Halved Sun (4 rays) & Rose. | 84 | Grapes. | 134 | Bugle. |
| 40 | Lis-upon-Half-Rose. | 85 | Greyhound's Head. | 135 | Crowned T (Tournai, Hen VIII) |
| 41 | Lis-upon-Sun & Rose. | 86 | Hand. | | |
| 42 | Lis-Rose dimidiated. | 87 | Harp. | 136 | An incurved pierced cross |
| 43 | Lis-issuant-from-Rose. | 88 | Heart. | | |
| 44 | Trefoil. | 89 | Helmet. | | |
| | | 90 | Key. | | |
| | | 91 | Leopard's Head. | | |

*The reign listed after a mintmark indicates that from which the drawing is taken. A similar mm. may have been used in another reign and will be found in the chronological list at the beginning of each reign.*

| | | | | | | | | | |
|---|---|---|---|---|---|---|---|---|---|
| 1 | 2 | 3 | 4 | 5 | 6 | 7a | 7b | 8 | 9 |
| 10 | 11 | 12 | 13 | 14 | 15 | 16 | 17 | 18 | 19 |
| 20 | 21 | 22 | 23 | 24 | 25 | 26 | 27 | 28 | 29 |
| 30 | 31 | 32 | 33 | 34 | 35 | 36 | 37 | 38 | 39 |
| 40 | 41 | 42 | 43 | 44 | 45 | 46 | 47 | 48 | 49 |
| 50 | 51 | 52 | 53 | 54 | 55 | 56 | 57 | 58 | 59 B |
| 60 | 61 | 62 | 63 | 64 | 65a | 65b | 66 | 67 | 68 |
| 69 | 70 | 71 | 72a | 72b | 73 | 74 | 75 | 76 | 77 |
| 78 | 79 | 80 | 81 | 82 | 83 | 84 | 85 | 86 | 87 |
| 88 | 89 | 90a | 90b | 90c | 91 | 92 | 93 | 94 | 95 |
| 96 | 97 | 98 (P) | 99 | 100 | 101 | 102 | 103 | 104 | 105 |
| 106 | 107 | 108 | 109 | 110 | 111 | 112 (R) | 113 | 114 | 115 |
| 116 W | 117a Y | 117b Y | 118 | 119a | 119b | 120 | 121 | 122 | 123 |
| 124 | 125 | 126 | 127 | 128 | 129 | 130 | 131 | 132 | 133 |
| 134 | 135 | 136 | | | | | | | |

# ALPHABETICAL INDEX
# OF RULERS AND COIN ISSUES